# The Doctors Mayo

# THE

# Doctors Mayo

*by*

HELEN CLAPESATTLE

*The University of Minnesota Press · Minneapolis*

*Printed in the United States of America*

FIRST PRINTING BEFORE
PUBLICATION 20,000 COPIES

SECOND PRINTING 20,000 COPIES

HUMPHREY MILFORD
OXFORD UNIVERSITY PRESS, LONDON

PUBLISHED SIMULTANEOUSLY IN CANADA BY
WM. COLLINS SONS & CO. CANADA LTD.
TORONTO, ONTARIO

# Foreword

To recount the genesis of this volume is perhaps unnecessary; the story of the Drs. Mayo would inevitably have been written by someone sometime. The only thing to explain is why it was not written earlier and how, when it was written, the responsibility for its preparation was entrusted by the Drs. Mayo to the university they both had served. My one great regret is that both are gone and the first copies cannot go to them so that they could see how the author and the directors of the University Press have striven to execute the commission to tell the story of their lives and work *wie sie eigentlich gewesen sind,* as they actually were.

If there be a fixed point from which to reckon the origin of this volume and the relation of the University of Minnesota Press to it, it is perhaps the day in 1927 when I suggested to Dr. W. J. Mayo that he write his autobiography and let the Press publish it. Knowing him as I did, I had little hope of getting him to write his own story—if for no other reason than that the idea of anything like personal exploitation was beyond his own and his profession's code. Furthermore, the whole great achievement was so much the work of "my brother and I" that it could never be told in terms of an individual. Had he given my suggestion the slightest consideration the outcome would, I am sure, have been put under seal until he and Dr. Charlie were long beyond any misinterpretation or reasonable criticism of themselves or the institutions, Clinic and Foundation, that they created.

There was nothing novel in my insisting as a historian rather than as chairman of the university committee on the Press that the story must be told. That it would be told whether the Drs. Mayo wished it or not and in terms they could not personally or professionally sanction was borne in upon them over and over again during the last decades of their lives. It was a story that many wanted to hear, many wanted to write, and that publishers would gladly print. The requests for the privilege of preparing and publishing a volume on their lives and on the Clinic were numerous, sometimes insistent, and always embarrassing whether they came from the competent or the incompetent. Even more distressing to the Drs. Mayo and their associates were the unauthorized articles and sketches that appeared with increasing frequency. It was evident to even the most reluctant of the group that some positive and constructive action must be taken.

Such was the setting for a meeting in October 1936 in a cabin on the *North Star,* the yacht owned by the Drs. Mayo. Each fall they took the board of regents and the chief administrative officers of the University of Minnesota as their guests on a two-day cruise on the Mississippi. At some point the party was often joined by members of the staff of the Clinic. On this trip President Coffman and I cornered the Drs. Mayo and their chief advisers in a cabin and put before them the case for the publication of a volume on themselves and their work. A particularly annoying piece of unauthorized writing had put them in a mood to listen to our plea that they should no longer blink the fact that they did not belong to themselves or to their profession alone. They must realize that they belonged to history, which would sooner or later claim them for its own, not as individuals solely but as part of the great story of the development of the American Middle West and of medical science and practice in the United States and in the civilized world. It was not for them to deny their own place in a story to which many historical forces and the worldwide advance of science and medical practice had contributed. They and their father and the development of their contribution to group effort in a highly individualistic profession would be necessarily the central theme, but the whole story when told would reveal an achievement in which the whole profession had shared. It should share likewise in the glories of a century's progress in new and better ways to battle disease and death and in training others to carry on where they left off.

President Coffman and I ended the conference on our part by offering, on behalf of the university, to have prepared and published by the University Press an objective biography that would so far as possible meet the standards of a profession, that of history, whose ethical code is as definite and as high as that of the medical profession. Here at least I was speaking of what I knew, for my professorship was in

# Foreword

history, my father was a country doctor of the old school, and as dean of the graduate school for over twenty years I had been directly and indirectly concerned with doctors and their education.

The Drs. Mayo and their associates were evidently relieved to have the university assume the responsibility involved and stated frankly that on that condition and that alone would they willingly see the volume undertaken. They would do whatever they could in making their records available. Beyond that they wanted no part in it.

This pledge and this commission were embodied a few days later in a brief letter to President Coffman. Its terms have been scrupulously observed by the Drs. Mayo and their families and associates. Although they gave generously of information in the course of the years of patient research reaching far beyond Rochester, Minnesota, neither the Drs. Mayo during their lives nor any member of the staff of the Mayo Clinic has seen a page of the manuscript or ever asked to see it. I am almost certain there are in this volume details of the lives of their father and mother that Dr. Will and Dr. Charlie never knew, and my guess is that among the tens of thousands of readers who will receive the book on its publication date none will be more expectant and eager about its contents than the members of the staff of the Mayo Clinic.

Over a million former patients, millions more to whom the name Mayo is a household word, the residents of Rochester, members of the Physicians and Surgeons Club, fellows of the Foundation, and professional colleagues throughout the world will share this interest in the story of the Drs. Mayo. To it one may truly apply the word unique. Thousands could have contributed some story, some incident, for it was in the very nature of Dr. Will and Dr. Charlie each in his own way to make everyone whose life they touched feel that they had, as they did have, an interest in them. The mass of material, written and oral, at the base of this story is limitless but the author has mastered it, and the Drs. Mayo, father and sons, come alive in the story she has told. It was well that it was done by a trained historian before legend had claimed them for its own.

The author will make her own acknowledgments to those who aided her in her work. I do not want her modesty to obscure for a moment the far-reaching research, the wide reading, the personal interviews that she has so skillfully organized and told with an art that may well set a standard for her seniors in the historical profession when they undertake to write in a field they have long neglected, that of medicine and science. As the only surviving member of the four who took a major part in the decision in the cabin of the *North Star* in October 1936, I have followed with grave solicitude the execution of the commission then entrusted to the university. I cannot deny myself the privilege of saying publicly to the author that I feel she has made possible the execution of that trust in the spirit in which it was given and accepted. If the Drs. Mayo were living, I am sure they would underwrite this well-deserved tribute.

This volume is self-dedicated by its title to a just and impartial appraisal of the great names it bears. In a wider sense, it is dedicated to the profession of medicine, which combines, as does no other in equal measure, the advancement of science and the service of their fellow men. The high obligations of that profession have been stated no better in any code of ethics than by Francis Bacon, and exemplified nowhere more fully than in the story this volume tells:

"I hold every man a debtor to his profession; from the which as men, of course, they do seek to receive countenance and profit, so ought they of duty to endeavor themselves by way of amends to be a help and ornament there unto."

GUY STANTON FORD, *President*
*University of Minnesota*

June 1941

# Table of Contents

# The Doctors Mayo

# List of Illustrations

Will and his pony, little brother Charlie, and the Mayo farmhouse

Pioneer Minnesota physicians: Alexander J. Stone, Charles N. Hewitt, and Franklin R. Staples (portraits courtesy of Minnesota Historical Society)

Mrs. W. W. Mayo, a woman of tolerance, understanding, and equanimity

Dr. W. W. Mayo, "a man of hope and forward-looking mind"

## BETWEEN PAGES 274 AND 275

Early Rochester; Mayo offices, 1883 to 1901; Zumbro Street

The end of medical school was a commencement; Will's and Charlie's graduation classes

Charlie's crowd; toe-in-the-door days

Hattie Damon and Edith Graham as young girls

Minnesota physicians and surgeons who influenced the early careers of the young Drs. Mayo: Amos W. Abbott, Archibald MacLaren, Charles A. Wheaton, Frederick A. Dunsmoor, James H. Dunn, and James E. Moore (MacLaren portrait courtesy of Mrs. Archibald MacLaren; the others courtesy of Minnesota Historical Society)

Young Doctors from the West, Dr. Will and Dr. Charlie

The tornado of 1883 (courtesy of Olmsted County Historical Society)

Mother Alfred, founder of St. Mary's Hospital, with Sister Joseph; St. Mary's in 1894 (courtesy of St. Mary's Hospital)

Dedication of the first addition to St. Mary's

Early hardships at St. Mary's; a private room, 1894 (courtesy of St. Mary's Hospital)

Drs. Will and Charlie in the first operating room at St. Mary's; Sisters Fabian and Constantine (courtesy of St. Mary's Hospital)

The young Drs. Mayo and their wives

Dr. and Mrs. W. W. Mayo

Mayo partners: Christopher Graham and Augustus W. Stinchfield

# List of Illustrations

xiii

# The Doctors Mayo

# The Doctors Mayo

# The Paradox of Rochester

"To Rochester? This way, ma'am. There's a special bus for Rochester." Thus on a midsummer morning a redcap in the Minneapolis bus station directs the traveler, who finds not one special bus but two loading with passengers for Rochester.

You move swiftly southward along the white belt of road for ninety miles, through a countryside of slow rise and fall that is a patchwork quilt in the greens of corn, small grains, clover, and alfalfa. The black and white of grazing cattle and the recurring pattern of hip-roofed barn flanked by the tall pillar of a silo tell you that this is a dairy land.

The towns that interrupt at every ten or fifteen miles are small, some of them just a few stores and houses with a little white church and a one-room schoolhouse grouped around a filling station at a crossroads, others large enough to boast a bank, a hotel above one of the eateries, perhaps a cheese factory or a cannery, and a furniture store that is also the undertaker's establishment. They might all be called as one of them is, Farmington, for they exist solely as market villages, service stations for the farmers.

And then from the crest of a hill you look down upon Rochester. In the saucerlike valley of the Zumbro River it lies, its metropolitan skyline rising to dramatic climax in one tall tower, yellow as ripe wheat against the bright blue sky.

Among cornfields, dairy farms, and market villages you have come upon a little city of great hospitals and crowded hotels; a city with hundreds of acres of parks and playgrounds, with fine stores and specialty shops; a city that is a crossroads of airlines, railroads, and national highways.

Here in the rural calm of southern Minnesota, without a scenic wonder or historic shrine in sight, is a city of twenty-five thousand inhabitants that has an annual transient population of ten times that number. For here, in this river valley town of midwestern America, this "little town on the edge of nowhere," is one of the world's greatest medical centers, to which men come from the ends of the earth for treatment and instruction.

That is the paradox of Rochester.

## 2

It was William James and Charles Horace Mayo who turned a pin point on the charts of commerce into a great starred capital on the map of medicine. In one room of that tall, wheat-colored building, the home of the Mayo Clinic, the walls are hung solid with diplomas, certificates, and medals of honor bestowed upon the Mayo brothers, and in an adjoining corridor two long cases are packed tight with the academic robes they were entitled to wear.

Awards in such number and variety are not made except in recognition of unusual social worth. When the famous brothers died, one of their fellow surgeons in England paid them this tribute: "And now death breaks the David and Jonathan partnership which for forty years has exerted a more profound influence on American medicine, and probably on world medicine, than any other single factor in modern times."*

The Mayos' contribution to medicine began in surgery, but their work there has merged with the general progress of the art and their enduring reputation rests upon the integrated, cooperative form of medical practice and education they developed. There were other great surgeons of their day, some greater than they. What forces then, personal and social, transformed *their* surgical partnership into the Mayo Clinic and the Mayo Foundation? That is an untold story of unique achievement that is part of the proud heritage of all medicine and of every American.

The paradox of Rochester has teased the minds of observers for more than a quarter of a century, but all most of them could find to explain it was the well-worn quotation, "If you . . . build a better mousetrap than your neighbor, the world will make a beaten path to your door, though you dwell in the midst of a forest."

That is an explanation that does not explain. Dr. W. J. Mayo did

---

* Citations of sources and notes of explanation and comment, listed by page number, are given in a separate section following the text.

much better when he said, with perception even above modesty, to a visitor who was exclaiming over the robes and certificates of honor: "Yes, we have them from all over the world. To be frank about it, we have accomplished much, my brother and I. But we *should* have done great things; we were given the opportunity. We were born at the right time and to the right parents. Perhaps no one will ever again have the opportunity to accomplish as much. That day is gone, unless for some genius. We were not geniuses. We were only hard workers. We were reared in medicine as a farmer boy is reared in farming. We learned from our father."

In Mayo Park in Rochester stands the statue of a man whom the inscription identifies as "William Worrall Mayo . . . Pioneer, Physician, Citizen . . . A Man of Hope and Forward-Looking Mind." The sculptor has portrayed him in a lifelike pose. Wearing a long black coat but hatless, he is pausing in the midst of a speech. In one hand he holds the roll of manuscript he has abandoned, in the other the eyeglasses he has just removed in the intensity of his effort. You might think him to be addressing some gathering of his medical fellows, but those who knew him can hear him urging them to some political reform or civic improvement.

That was the father of the Mayo brothers. As an old man he was often congratulated upon the brilliant work of his famous sons. To one well-meaning gentleman he snapped in reply, "Why don't you congratulate *me*? I started all this." That was the irritable answer of an active mind that resented being relegated to the past, but it was the truth. He was the foundation upon which his sons built. He gave them the precepts and principles by which they worked. The phrase "Our father taught us . . ." was forever on their lips.

So with him the story begins.

# The Old Doctor

# CHAPTER ONE

# The Way Westward

When William Worrall Mayo made up his mind to try his luck in America, he straightway journeyed to the nearest seaport and boarded ship. He asked no permissions and said no good-byes. He did not mean to be secretive about his going, nor was there any ill feeling between him and his family. Taking such unceremonious leave was just his impetuous, willfully independent way.

So constantly through life did he turn his face toward the future, so little, even at the age of ninety, was he given to reminiscence, that he left scant knowledge of his parents or his youth. A line of faded writing on the flyleaf of an old family prayer book records his birth "at 1/2 past nine o'clock in the morning" on May 31, 1819 in the English village of Eccles, separated by only a few miles of green countryside from the voraciously spreading industrial city of Manchester. He was the third child and second son of James Mayo and his wife Ann. Ann, christened on February 6, 1785, was the daughter of John Bonselle and his wife Tenneson, whose name had been Worrall. *Tenneson* and *Bonselle* both crossed to England with the Huguenots fleeing France, and the Worralls seem to have been a family of some prominence in Manchester. All else about Ann Mayo is obscure.

James Mayo made his living as a captain of sailing ships. His ancestry is established not by record but by tradition, and William was taught that he belonged to a family whose history goes back to the early sixteenth century, when a group of Flemish Protestants migrated from the Low Countries to escape religious persecution. In southwestern England they multiplied and prospered, making *Mayo,* in all its spellings from *Mao* to *Mayhowe,* a familiar and respected name in the counties of Hereford and Wiltshire.

Some of their number wandered eastward and northward, and according to the tradition one of these wanderers settled in the county of Lancashire, in Eccles, in 1709. From him James Mayo was descended.

Many of these English Mayos were physicians, and several among them achieved distinction in that profession. A full century before Priestley and Lavoisier, John Mayow, a physician chemist, worked out the processes of combustion and respiration so accurately that he was able to postulate the existence of some such agent as oxygen.

Second in magnitude was Dr. Herbert Mayo, who, even while William Worrall was learning to walk and talk, was doing brilliantly original work on the anatomy and physiology of the nervous system and battling for the credit of it with his famous teacher, Sir Charles Bell of London.

2

When William was about seven years old his father died, and the widowed mother shortly thereafter moved her six children to the town of Salford, just across the River Irwell from Manchester.

A tumultuous community was Manchester then, afire with social unrest and political debate. In the year that William Mayo was born its citizens had gathered on St. Peter's Field to hear a plea for parliamentary reform, unarmed and intent on nothing more violent than speechmaking. But the magistrates sent mounted troops to disperse the radicals, and they charged the crowd without warning. Only a few persons were killed and a score more injured, but thousands were deeply embittered by the injustice of the attack, which lingered long in memory as the Peterloo Massacre.

In 1826, shortly after the Mayos moved to Salford, ninety thousand of the county's weavers and spinners were out of work, and during the long months of their distress they rioted often and destructively. In collective fury they smashed the machines and burned the factories to which they attributed their woes. When the rations of pea soup, meal, and bacon at the poor-relief stations were not enough to feed them all, they stormed the bakers' shops and hucksters' stalls to get loaves and cheeses to appease their hunger.

Those were the years that made Old Sarum a classic symbol of political absurdity, the years in which representation in the House of Commons was allowed to a mound of green grass, a length of stone wall, and a plot of land at the bottom of the sea, while it was denied to the new industrial towns inhabited by hundreds of thousands.

The tale of these abuses and the call for reform were the burden of many public meetings in Manchester, of loud words in tavern and newsroom, of galleys of fine print in the newspapers called into being by the political issues. While the Reform Bill of 1832 hung fire in parliament Manchester was a caldron of excitement, alternately simmering with anticipation and boiling with indignation. When the law at last became a fact, the people exploded in a noisy, roistering demonstration that lasted for days.

In such an atmosphere William Mayo's impressionable years were passed. Did it plant in him the seeds of a social and political conscience, nurture an inclination to champion the economic underdog, and set growing a firm conviction that government must be for *all* the people? No direct evidence supports an affirmative answer, but in his maturity William Worrall Mayo possessed those characteristics in full flower.

## 3

Her husband's death had not left Mrs. Mayo in poverty; she was able to give her sons an education when perhaps three quarters of the children in England got no schooling whatever. William studied Latin and Greek with a French tutor, a refugee from the royalist reaction that followed the downfall of Napoleon, and though he may or may not have attended the parochial grammar school in Salford he did finish his general schooling with a course in some college in Manchester.

At that college, whichever of Manchester's several it was, he learned much of Latin and Greek grammar and literature and something of English literature, mathematics, and natural philosophy. At the same time from the famous scientist John Dalton he caught an enthusiasm for chemistry that he never lost. That lonely, morose celebrity was the one person from these early days that he talked of in later life.

John Dalton made original contributions to several fields of science, but his principal achievement was reformulating the ancient atomic theory as a plausible explanation of how chemical elements combine into compounds. His work brought him great honor and visits from many celebrated men of science, who were often astounded to find him teaching elementary arithmetic to some little boy at half a crown an hour. He had neither the classical learning nor the right religion for a professorship at the universities, so he supported himself by private tutoring, performing chemical analyses on order, and giving an occasional course of lectures.

From contemporary descriptions Dalton emerges as a tall, gaunt, awkward figure, repellently uncouth in manner, and sparing of words. He made his pupils learn by doing. Setting them a problem in mathematics or in chemistry, he then went about his own experiments until they had worked it out or had got hopelessly stuck. Young William Mayo was an apt pupil and became Dalton's assistant, helping him to manipulate apparatus and record observations and calculations. Dalton was not skillful in the art of practical chemistry, being self-taught, so his methods were crude and his experiment results rough. But he had the imagination to see meanings where more precise workmen could not.

In one important aspect Dalton's teaching failed. He considered books a snare and a delusion because what he read in them too often misled his thinking. He boasted of the meagerness of his own library, reproved his pupils for buying books, and sought by every means to prevent the Manchester Literary and Philosophical Society, of which he was the president for twenty-seven years, from expending any of its funds on books. But he could not convert William Mayo, who remained an insatiable reader all his life.

4

It may well have been Dalton who set young William on the road to medicine. A good deal of the practical chemistry he taught must have been pharmaceutical in nature, and he even dabbled in prescribing. When he or someone he knew was suffering from a cold, he was wont to mix a medicinal dose of licorice, treacle, and vinegar in a pan over his laboratory fire, discoursing to his students on its virtues while it cooked. He was one of the founders of Manchester's first medical school, though his connection with the enterprise must have been brief, since it has escaped the notice of his biographers.

To study medicine in those days the English boy who could afford it went to Oxford or Cambridge, to a hospital school in London, or to one of the two Scottish universities, which had risen to preeminence, especially in surgery, throughout all Europe. Next to those centers, but considerably below them, stood Manchester. Being one of the first English cities in which poverty and disease were gathered into such a noisome mass that they cried aloud for alleviation, it was also one of the first in which public provision was made for the care of the sick poor.

The establishment of the Manchester Infirmary drew highly trained doctors from the overcrowded capitals who became a dominant influence in the city's intellectual life. As a result a rapidly increasing number of the graduates of the various academies apprenticed themselves to these physicians and surgeons and with them walked the wards of the infirmary, learning medicine by practical experience and clinical observation.

As supplementary instruction for these students courses of medical and scientific lectures were offered, often at the rooms of the Literary and Philosophical Society. In these John Dalton took part and through them he made the acquaintance of the infirmary doctor with whom in 1824 he joined in founding the Pine Street Medical School, the first such school to be opened in the English provinces.

Young William began his study of medicine in Manchester and was among the apprentices who walked the wards of the infirmary, but when, under whose tutelage, and for how long are lost facts. Later he went to study in the hospitals of London and Glasgow, but in neither city did he stay long enough to complete his preparation and receive a license to practice. It took a long time to get such a license, and a longer time, plus rare abilities or the right connections, to secure a hospital appointment, a prospect that would hardly have been inviting to a young man as impatient and independent as William Mayo.

While Mayo was studying in Glasgow he made the acquaintance of a young American physician, Dr. Alfred Stillé of Philadelphia, who was rounding off his medical training with a period of postgraduate study in European clinics. Perhaps that meeting with Stillé and others like him who were to be found in Glasgow and London turned William Mayo's thoughts toward the United States, though such a personal influence was hardly necessary. The call of America was strong in England then, ringing in the ears of any young man adventure-minded or ambitious to better his chances in life. Did one chafe at the competition and lack of elbow room in the struggle for a living? There was

America, wanting men, America rich, vast, with room to spare. Did one fret at the unyielding bonds of established caste? America, without fixed social barriers, offered equality to all.

So William Worrall Mayo joined the exodus from the Old World early in 1845, when he was twenty-five years old.

5

Young Mayo was short and boyishly slight of build, only five feet four inches in height, but he held his head high and his back straight, and the glance of his dark eyes was intense and piercing. His whole manner was decisive and assured. He had no trouble finding work in New York City.

It has been said repeatedly that his position was that of instructor in chemistry at the Bellevue Hospital Medical College, but that college was not organized until some six years later. Nor was enough informal teaching being done in the hospital to call for instruction in chemistry. His connection with Bellevue Hospital was in all likelihood as a pharmacist in the drug department, where the crude drugs were prepared and the prescriptions compounded for use throughout the institution.

Bellevue Hospital was not an inspiring place just then, at its nadir of neglect and political exploitation. Under its roof were housed the charity hospital for the sick poor of New York, the municipal almshouse, and the insane asylum. Until recently it had included the city prison too, and its nursing had been done by prisoners. They had gone elsewhere now, but their rough, unsympathetic care of the sick was continued by the derelicts employed for the service, considered too menial for anyone else.

Positions on the medical staff were political pork, and men were appointed who knew more about political than hospital wards. Among the perquisites that made the position of resident physician a particularly juicy plum were the fees paid to him by the young men he named as his assistants. These were politely called tuition fees, but there the student-teacher aspects of the relationship ended. Although many of the assistants were medical undergraduates, to them was left the care of Bellevue's inmates, while the resident physician was looking after his interests at Tammany Hall.

Hair-raising still are the descriptions of the plight of the sick committed to Bellevue Hospital in those years. Political graft added to poor management made the food bad and insufficient, the supply of fuel inadequate and intermittent, the bed clothing and personal garments provided for the patients so few that they often went unwashed between the death of one patient and the admission of the next.

Infectious diseases were rife, especially typhus, typhoid fever, yellow fever, cholera, jail fever, and ship fever among arriving immigrants. To these ills the staff members were not immune, and in 1847 ten of the thirteen assistant physicians died of typhus. At last the frightful conditions raised a public outcry that would not be stilled, and a thorough reform was undertaken. But months before, William Mayo had had enough and had left Bellevue Hospital and New York City behind him.

## 6

He wandered westward to Buffalo, where he stayed awhile before moving on to newer, more open country. Following the shores of Lake Erie and an inland canal he found himself on the banks of the Wabash in midsummer, 1848, in the town of Lafayette, Indiana, the small but bustling center of trade for a rich agricultural hinterland. Its commercial life throve on a water-borne traffic in farm produce, by way of the river southward to the Ohio and the Mississippi and through the canal eastward to Lake Erie. One of the most promising sites in central Indiana, it was rapidly outgrowing the cocoon of frontier days, lusty, self-consciously proud of itself, and sure of its future.

William Mayo decided to settle there, but not as a chemist. Perhaps his experience at Bellevue Hospital had been too disillusioning, or perhaps he just wanted a fling at something different. At any rate he and a partner, Alphonso W. Roath, rented a room, equipped it with tables and some bolts of worsted, and solicited the custom of all who wanted fashionable garments made to order on short notice and favorable terms.

Where he had learned the tailor's art is a mystery, but he or Roath must have been good at it, for their shop prospered and after only a few months blossomed into the "Hall of Fashion," occupied larger quarters, and took on a third partner, E. B. Schonfeldt, once a cutter in fashionable establishments in New York and Buffalo.

Later they added a department for the ladies, featuring cloth cloaks in a style that would "give additional grace and eloquence to the female form." And for the men who preferred ready-made clothing they kept on hand a full stock of suits which they had cut in the latest New York styles and tailored "with neatness and strength."

This pretentious and successful Hall of Fashion engaged W. W. Mayo's attention until the spring of 1849, when he sold his interest to Schonfeldt and retired, having decided to resume his career in medicine. He had probably been aided to this decision by the man who became his teacher, Dr. Elizur H. Deming, one of Lafayette's leading citizens, and a gentleman possessed of such gifts of eloquence that he was known throughout the state.

He was a man of strong convictions, which he defended persistently and uncompromisingly, sometimes at great inconvenience to himself. He failed of appointment to the presidency of the University of Michigan only because of his ardent abolitionism, and once in Lafayette he faced a mob of river ruffians who so disliked his political principles that they were bent on tearing down his house and rushing him out of town. But his courage and a passionate plea for fair play tamed them and they scattered without doing him harm, though he could not stop them from burning out the negro settlement on the river front.

Dr. Deming was a man of education unusual in Lafayette. He had earned an academic degree, with honor, from Williams College in his native state of Massachusetts before entering upon the study of medicine. He was able and progressive, easily ranking first among the practitioners of Lafayette and well to the fore in the profession of the state, and since 1847 he had been a member of the faculty of the Indiana Medical College at LaPorte.

It is not hard to imagine what such a man's reaction was when he learned, perhaps while trying on a suit, that the young proprietor of the Hall of Fashion was a trained chemist who had actually studied medicine in Europe.

7

The quality of medical education and practice had been good in colonial Boston, New York, and Philadelphia, but as the nation grew and population poured itself thin across the mountains and along the rivers, the demand for doctors outran the supply of well-trained men. Those of the urban centers who had spent years in training and then finished off with a session of European study were not inclined to practice on the frontier, and the frontiersmen had not the money to afford, or the patience to support, long training.

To meet the need, small medical schools arose in the rural areas of the eastern states, offering short courses of a few months a year for two or three years and fitting their fees to the pocketbooks of the farm boys and their schedules to the leisure months between harvest and seedtime. Their graduates went west with the pioneers, and when they were no longer numerous enough, schools of the same kind were opened in the newer communities—a few at first in Kentucky and Ohio, then dozens in Indiana, Illinois, Michigan, and the states west.

These schools were only supplementary, however, for the backbone of medical education then was preceptorship, the American form of Europe's apprentice system. The student kept the doctor's office clean, compounded the powders and salves, and looked after the horses, in return for the use of his preceptor's library and the privilege of watching him at the task of examining and prescribing. When an alert young mind, observant, curious, and full of questions, met with a seasoned practitioner, able and willing to impart the wisdom he had gained from his years of experience, preceptorship was a reasonably satisfactory form of medical education, certainly far superior to classroom lectures alone.

Three years of study and practice with a preceptor and two sessions of lectures at a medical school earned the student his degree of doctor of medicine. He was urged to such an extreme, however, only by his own desire or ambition, for the degree was not required for practice. Anyone at any stage of preparation could dub himself "doctor" and hang out his shingle, for there was no one with either legal or professional authority to stop him.

About 1830 Indiana gave up all pretense of regulating medical practice, as did most of the other states in the Union at about the same time. Democratic Americans, as little appreciating the need for trained men in medicine as in government, insisted upon judging a doctor's qualifications for themselves, nor could medical men agree as to who among them should have a license.

# The Old Doctor

Medical sects and cults were many and acrimonious. The botanic physician battled with the calomel doctor, the allopath ridiculed the homeopath, and all damned the water cure of the hydropathists, the steam bath of the Thomsonians, and the mixed therapy of the eclectics. The doctors of any western community were a motley group, including a generous number of outright charlatans whose knowledge and training were in inverse proportion to their claims.

Amid such confusion the wiser and more profession-minded practitioners earnestly welcomed any newcomer who seemed likely to swell their outnumbered ranks. So Dr. Deming persuaded and William Mayo agreed, resuming his study of medicine with Dr. Deming as his preceptor. It was no accident that his retirement from the Hall of Fashion coincided with Dr. Deming's return from his winter's teaching at LaPorte.

## 8

Young Mayo got his baptism in practice that very summer, combating Asiatic cholera. For two years the people of Lafayette had been reading in the papers of the progress of the dread disease from the court of Persia westward across Europe, noting fearfully that its course was the same it had taken in the early 1830's, when an epidemic had worked frightful havoc in the United States.

And their fear became certainty late in 1848, when the telegraph flashed the news of cholera in New Orleans. Helplessly in the succeeding months they watched it spread up the Mississippi and along the Ohio, steadily nearing the Wabash and Lafayette. Helplessly, because no one knew what caused cholera, or how to prevent it or treat it successfully.

The Lafayette editors gave futile aid by publishing the recipes for a score of supposed remedies and all the bits of advice they could cull from medical literature. They copied emphatic warnings about careful diet, against indulging in fresh fruits and vegetables, especially in such "cholera bombs" as watermelons and cucumbers. They passed on, with all the weight of authority that attached to the name of the "father of medicine in the West," the recommendations that Dr. Daniel Drake had written for the people of Cincinnati. Potatoes, hominy, and rice were the only vegetables that could be eaten safely, said he, and salt meats and fish were better than fresh. He warned the people against exposing themselves to night air and advised them to keep on their winter flannels until the epidemic had passed. And fleeing from the city would be quite useless, he was sure: "In whatever unknown manner the disorder travels from country to country, it is not, like smallpox, a catching disease. . . . The true and safest course is for families and friends to draw closer together than common, and watch over and assist each other."

In the confusion of misinformation and mistaken opinion, the suggestions offered by Lafayette's own board of health, of which Dr. Deming was chairman, were uncommonly wise: Concentrate upon keeping general health and strength at the maximum, remove all accumulated filth from the premises at once, and treat cellars, privies, and stables thoroughly and frequently with lime. And the city officials ought to prepare large and airy quarters in which patients can be isolated and given special care.

The cholera arrived on July 3, 1849, and with it came absolute panic. For two miserable months the normal activities of life were suspended while sickness, death, and terror ruled. All who could manage it fled to the country, while those who remained snatched at straws, even unto the magic of ceremonial bonfires and cannonades to drive away the evil spirit. Rumor said that fifteen persons a day were dying in and around Lafayette. The city newspaper called that a gross exaggeration, but one of the physicians later admitted a total of three hundred local deaths.

In such an emergency the community needed more doctors than it had, and everyone with even a pretense to medical training was pressed into full-fledged service, Mayo with the rest. He probably adopted the treatment used by his preceptor, Dr. Deming, whatever it was, but it is interesting to discover from the testimony of a newspaperman living in Lafayette at the time that young William Mayo was "fortunate" in the number of recoveries among his patients. Interesting, and perhaps even a little prophetic.

## 9

When the scourge passed and Lafayette was calling the country folk to resume their trading in the town, William Mayo rode northward with Dr. Deming, through the valley of the Tippecanoe and across the Kankakee marshes to the little city of LaPorte, whose five thousand citizens were just beginning to admit reluctantly that their townsite could not compete with Chicago, though a few years earlier they had been sure that LaPorte was to be the great metropolis of the Middle West.

In that optimistic period some enterprising citizens had secured a charter for LaPorte University, which was to include colleges of literature, law, and medicine. When the first two did not materialize, the medical department called itself the Indiana Medical College and began an independent existence. William Mayo enrolled there for the session of 1849–50.

Like most such establishments, the Indiana Medical College was a proprietary school, owned and managed by its faculty. Under this arrangement the staff was often more interested in pocketing students' fees than in improving the quality of instruction, but the proprietors of Indiana Medical were content to profit only by the increased prestige in private practice their teaching connections gave them, and they invested much more in the improvement of building and equipment than they could possibly have derived from tuition fees. The founders of the school had chosen their colleagues carefully, reaching even into faraway New York to get men of character and professional integrity who were also good teachers.

The student body averaged a hundred a year, drawn from many states, some as distant as Vermont and North Carolina, and the school had such an excellent and widespread reputation that Rush Medical College of Chicago proposed consolidation to rid itself of a dangerous rival. Yet a description makes it sound something less than impressive. There were no stated requirements for admission, the annual session was only four months long, the course was ungraded, and the professors merely repeated their lectures each year to the entire student body. Two years' attendance was required, apparently in the hope that the student would pick up something the second time that he had missed the first.

The teaching consisted entirely of lectures, with little clinical instruction, for LaPorte had no hospital and the college had no ambulatory clinic. So the student's practical bedside experience had to be provided entirely by his preceptor. However, there was some amphitheater demonstration of surgical method, for the reputation of the professors of surgery brought them patients, often from far away, upon whom they operated in the presence of the class. There were lay visitors too on such occasions, because the operations were events of genuine public interest. Often a reporter was present, and then a description of the operation, replete with gory details, would appear in the next issue of the local paper.

Anatomy was learned chiefly from lectures, textbooks, and colored pictures, and the custom still survived from medieval times for the professor to remain aloof and aloft on his platform while the menial task of illustrative dissecting was performed by an assistant. An optional course in dissection was offered, but some students were prevented from taking it by the extra fee charged.

Perhaps that financial hurdle was placed deliberately, for it was then difficult to keep the eager scalpels of the dissecting room supplied with fresh cadavers. No legal provision having yet been made for that necessity, midnight excursions with sack and shovel to some new grave in a nearby churchyard were not an unusual experience for medical students. But woe unto the body-snatchers if any resident of the community caught them prematurely resurrecting the dead. The public was naturally sensitive on the subject of grave-robbing, and more than one pioneer medical school had its career cut short by the violent action taken against such despoilers.

To the half-dozen subjects that made up the usual medical curriculum, the Indiana Medical College added a course in pathology and physiology, and more remarkable still, it provided a microscope, imported from England "at great expense." The microscope was not available to medical students at Harvard until 1869–70, and even twenty years later the refresher classes at the Johns Hopkins Medical School were filled with practicing physicians who had never seen a microscope.

One microscope for a hundred students! Their study of microscopic anatomy could not have been intensive. But it was enough to arouse in William Mayo an early and extraordinary interest in microscopy, which endured and deepened and later played a part in the education of his two sons.

# The Old Doctor

In 1850 medical science was an infant in its cradle. Its mother was a young chemistry, its father a beardless physics, its nurse the scientific method, in discipline severe but in counsel wise. The laboratory had replaced the library, research and investigation had ousted unverified speculation and armchair theorizing on the bold frontiers of medicine, but not yet in the busy settlements behind the front lines. The new science had as yet contributed little to medical practice. Although it had given the *coup de grace* to the old philosophical systems, so far it had accumulated only a small body of scientific fact to take their place.

Few scientific procedures or instruments of precision were yet available to aid in diagnosis. The techniques of the blood count and the test meal had yet to be developed; even the simplest chemical analyses of urine were too new to be in general use. The stethoscope was still novel and the clinical thermometer had not been invented. Few diseases had been sufficiently differentiated to be easily described and recognized, and for fewer still were the causes and the pathologic processes known. General symptomatic designations such as "lung disease," "fever," "liver complaint," "inflammation of the bowels," and "kidney trouble" were still the terms of diagnosis.

Consequently the practitioner face to face with an illness had to proceed empirically as he had always done, treating the symptoms in the hope that he would reach the cause, prescribing a remedy that had *seemed* to work in what had *seemed* to be a similar case. He had to rely upon what William Osler later called "a pop-gun pharmacy, hitting now the malady and again the patient, the doctor himself not knowing which."

With diagnosis and therapy so blind, the doctor working so much by guess and by hope, it was not unreasonable to remark of a patient's recovery "that whether it came about from the lapsing of a sufficient number of days, the remedies employed, the nature of the disease, or the grandmother's prayers, one could hardly say."

And surgery? When William Mayo was in school at LaPorte the use of anesthetics was only four years old, still a matter for wonder, experiment, and heated controversy among doctors and laymen alike. Only the more advanced surgeons used chloroform regularly; only the most courageous patients would submit to it. Most people still preferred to endure the pain unaided, or with the deadening effects of copious draughts of whisky or an emetic of lobelia. Drs. Meeker and Shipman of the Indiana Medical College used chloroform if they could persuade a patient to take it, but they were satisfied when it rendered him "nearly insensible to pain" and pleased when enough had been used to make him shout and sing during the operation.

The distinction between physician and surgeon that historical forces had produced in Europe did not exist in the United States. Every practitioner labeled himself, and was, a "physician and surgeon," though he might be more one than the other, depending upon his special interests. For instance, Drs. Meeker and Shipman, although practicing general medicine, emphasized surgery, had developed a special skill in it, and attracted an unusual proportion of surgical patients. They dared to operate for cataracts, to cut away the decayed portion of a jaw bone, and to attempt the removal of an ovarian tumor, whereas most of their fellows confined surgery to such procedures as the repair of skin lacerations, the occasional removal of a cancerous sore on lip or wrist, and the amputation of crushed or diseased limbs.

Resort to the knife was in all cases an emergency measure, not an accepted therapeutic method but a weapon of dire necessity. Moreover, cutting into the cavities of the body was an unwarrantedly rash procedure when operations even on the surfaces and extremities were so commonly followed by fatal infection. Suppuration of the incision wound was thought to be a natural postoperative development and the "laudable pus" a necessary adjunct of the healing process. One Indiana surgeon blessed the foul ooze as "God's salve."

On the other hand, some pioneers earned the gratitude of their patients by something more than willingness to ride rough, dark miles to a sickbed. Despite meager schooling and scant science these men really learned the ways of sickness and of healing and made original contributions to medical and surgical practice. Their very lack of formal training seemed to free them from accepted notions of what could *not* be done, particularly in surgery.

That no one had ever cut out an ovarian tumor did not prevent Dr. Ephraim McDowell of Danville, Kentucky, from doing it—while his more cautious colleagues stood on a street corner and decided that when his patient died, as she surely would, he should be charged with manslaughter rather than malpractice. That a caesarean section was almost invariably fatal in the hands of the best surgeons in Europe did not keep young Dr. John L. Richmond of Middletown, Ohio, from attempting it—and saving the mother, though the child died. That the gallbladder had never been opened and gallstones removed did not deter Dr. John Bobbs of Indianapolis from a first performance of the operation.

The crudities of frontier life, the lack of convenient aids and tools, demanded great resourcefulness. Often traditional procedures could not be followed and new ways of doing things had to be devised. And that sort of necessity fostered a practical audacity that advanced the practice of medicine.

11

At such a stage in the development of medicine William Worrall Mayo prepared for, and entered upon, the life of a doctor. His year at Indiana Medical College cost him a hundred dollars in fees and another fifty dollars for sixteen weeks' board and room. He was excused from extended preceptorship and the second round of lectures probably because of his previous study in Europe, and having prepared an acceptable thesis and passed an oral examination, he was given his degree on February 14, 1850.

With his fellow graduates he rose to make public assent to the oath required by the school: "You do solemnly promise that you will, to the utmost of your abilities, exert your influence for promoting the welfare and respectability of the Medical Profession; that you will demean yourselves honorably in the practice thereof; that you will not put forth any nostrum or secret method of cure; and that you will not publish any matter or thing derogatory to the Institution."

When he returned to Lafayette as Dr. Mayo, he found an opening ready for him. Ever since his first arrival in the town he had been rooming at the house of Daniel L. Hart and buying such necessities as shaving materials, candles, shoe blacking, and an occasional pint of whisky at Mr. Hart's drug store. Unusual among druggists of that day, Mr. Hart was neither pharmacist nor doctor but was content to manage the miscellany of his stock and employ a proper young physician to serve patrons in need of medicines or medical advice.

The man who held the position when young Mayo returned from LaPorte with his degree suddenly felt an urge to try his luck in the booming California gold fields, so "Dr. W. W. Mayo, Physician and Surgeon" succeeded to his place and the substantial salary of seventy-five dollars a month, together with such fees as might be collected from private patients.

His work as druggist meant a great deal more than the mere filling of prescriptions, for although some drugs could be imported in crude form from the East, he had to make up many of his own tinctures and extracts from such roots and herbs as he could personally gather in the vicinity. Most doctors did the same thing in their own offices, if not in a convenient drug store, so the task was not unusual.

The new doctor had barely begun to settle down to his professional life when a message came from England. His mother was ill, probably fatally so. He began the long journey back to Salford at once, but his mother was dead before he could reach her—in fact, had died even before he left Lafayette. So he did not linger in England, and though he was delayed by a bout of typhoid fever while passing through New York, he was back at work by the end of September.

One day after his return Dr. Mayo chanced to be at the boatlanding when a barge was poled in. Suddenly he exclaimed, "Why, there's Jim!" And a man on the barge called back, "Hello, Will." The man was his only brother, James.

He too had been trained as a chemist, but had preferred to wander at random on the seven seas, and his appearance in Lafayette was a complete surprise to his brother. After a brief visit he went his way again, but thereafter the two kept in touch and met more often.

The winter after his mother's death, when he was about thirty-two, Dr. Mayo's friends discovered one day that he was missing from his office in the drug store, and a few days later they read in the newspaper of his marriage to Miss Louise Abigail Wright at Galene Woods, Michigan, on February 2, 1851. William was being impulsive and independent as always.

When he returned with his bride, his friends found her a buxom young woman, slightly taller than her husband, with energy, determination, and intelligence quite equal to his. She had been born in the village of Jordan, near Syracuse, New York, on December 23, 1825. Her father was a Scotsman, a mechanic with an inventive turn of mind, and her mother was the granddaughter of an English officer named Totten, who is said to have commanded a battleship during the American Revolution.

When she was eighteen, Louise Wright had gone alone, by canal barge and prairie schooner, to the home of relatives in Michigan, later moving with one of them to LaPorte, where she met her future husband during his year in medical school. Her youth had been one of hard work, with little time for formal schooling, but she was an avid reader and remembered well what she read, so that everyone who met her thought her an educated woman of keen intelligence.

## 12

Despite his new obligations as the head of a family, Dr. Mayo gave up his position at the drug store the following May. All was not going well, for Mr. Hart proved to be less generous in payment than he had been in promises. The young doctor filed suit for a thousand dollars, which he said were owed him for "work and labor, care and diligence," and Mr. Hart countered with an itemized statement of merchandise and cash amounting to half that sum, which he claimed the plaintiff had received. The case dragged wearily through the court of common pleas, at least one jury being unable to reach a decision, but after nearly a year of hearings it was "dismissed by agreement at the plaintiff's cost."

That was the end of the little doctor's first lawsuit and the beginning of his disillusionment with legal redress. Other doctors might turn their books over to the justice of the peace and threaten to sue patients who did not settle accounts, but not Dr. Mayo. Nor did he ever change his mind on the matter.

With the druggist job out of the way Dr. Mayo was invited into partnership with his former preceptor, Dr. Deming, a fine testimonial to his ability, and he accepted. When the Indiana State Medical Society held its annual meeting in Lafayette two years later both men were admitted to membership. Dr. Deming was promptly elected president for the ensuing year and at once put his young associate on a committee to make a study of "the pathological indications of the urine."

When he made his report at the next yearly meeting Dr. Mayo stressed the importance of a chemical analysis of the urine as an aid to diagnosis. That the urine could tell a good bit about the health of a patient was an old idea, for the Sumerian word for doctor in ancient Babylon was *asu,* meaning "one who knows water," and diagnosis based on urine inspection was so important a part of medieval medicine that the urinal became the recognized sign of a doctor's office. In later centuries quacks carried "water-casting" to such extremes that it fell into disrepute, so that early and middle nineteenth century doctors made no more than a perfunctory use of it.

Now Dr. Mayo was recommending chemical analysis of this "messenger of intelligence from the seat of disease." He described the deductions that could be made from acid or alkaline urine, from the presence of sugar, urea, albumen, and pus, and discussed at some length the indications, causes, and possible treatment for such disorders as diabetes mellitus.

His ideas were groping and fumbling; they could not then be otherwise. Their significance lies in the attempt to go behind surface symptoms and get at the processes of disease, and in the acceptance of chemical analysis as a routine tool. Among the papers that make up the *Transactions* of the medical society in those years, Dr. Mayo's report is like a breath of fresh air. Other men might occasionally refer to the era of chemical investigation in which they found themselves, but it remained for the young fellow from Lafayette to give them a practical example of its importance in general practice.

## 13

Office use of beaker and burner was only a small part of Dr. Mayo's work, for he had joined the benevolent tribe of doctors on horseback. In good weather the daily rounds might be made comfortably in a carriage, but many a call between times had to be answered on horseback, with medical and surgical supplies stowed in the saddlebags.

For all the youth and hardihood of the pioneers who settled Indiana, there was plenty of sickness among them. To chronic aches and pains, and to the cholera, which continued to plague the community during the early 1850's, though with less virulence than in 1849, were added frightful epidemics of scarlet fever, typhoid, malignant forms of dysentery and malaria, and the mysterious "milk sickness," which killed cattle and men alike, quickly desolating any area in which it took hold.

Malaria was the great scourge. The fertile bottom lands, low-lying, humid, and often flooded, upon which the prosperity of the Wabash Valley depended made that valley one of the worst malarial districts in Indiana. The agent of infection was unrecognized, so the common guess laid the disease at the door of a "marsh miasma," a vaporous substance rising from stagnant water or putrid matter to float in the air, especially at night, like a poisonous gas.

From midsummer to early fall was the annual sickly season. It was usual then for more persons to be sick than well, sallow faces and listless manners were the rule, and spells of the "shakes" were too prevalent to cause remark. People planned for this as for the time of sowing or reaping, and prudently laid in a sizable supply of their favorite remedies.

The work that could not be got out of the way in advance took its chances with the chills. Sessions of court were recessed while the judge lay on a bench in the corner to chatter through his chill, and schoolroom drills were interrupted while teacher and pupils had their shake together. There was nothing very strange in the experience of the farmer who came upon his neighbor sitting on a log with a gun across his knees.

"Hello, John, what are you doing here?" he asked.

Pointing with a jerking finger toward a tree, the neighbor answered, "I'm waiting for this damn shake to go off, so I can shoot that squirrel up there."

Even the doctors sometimes arrived at their patient's home so weakened by the alternating chills and fever that they had to lie down a bit before they could do the work for which they had come. Dr. Mayo himself fell victim to the disease, with important results for posterity.

All this sickness did not mean so much business for the doctors as might be supposed. The laymen chose to act as their own doctors, carried buckeyes or pieces of potato, or wore bags of asafoetida or camomile to ward off illness, and bled themselves every spring to get rid of the bad blood and make room for a purer product. When illness came in spite of them, they dosed themselves with cathartics, emetics, and various home-brewed bitters, resorted again to the family lancet, tried the prescriptions published in the newspapers, and yielded to glowing testimonials of quack nostrums warranted to cure everything from itch to consumption. Only as a last resort did they send for the doctor.

They knew that all too often he would be able only to purge and puke and bleed them a little more, or pull out his spatula and bottles to mix up a powder he hoped might help. In general, public faith in doctors was at low ebb. People had seen too much of the bad practices of poorly trained men and had too little to guide them in distinguishing between the quack and the qualified practitioner. Both were called doctor, and the reputation of the latter suffered from the sins of the former.

On his side the physician was handicapped in applying what knowledge he had by the ignorance and superstitions of his patients and the exigencies of rural practice. When he found a serious wound festering under a coating of dirty goose grease, he had to undermine the mother's faith in her sovereign remedy before he would be permitted to clean the wound and apply his own brand of salve. When he wished to administer an anesthetic in order to reduce a bad hernia or replace a dislocated shoulder, he often had to overcome the determined opposition of frightened relatives, who were positive the sleep-producing stuff would destroy their loved one's reason if it didn't end his life.

Then, too, in the absence of trained nurses and at the distance that often separated him from his patient, the doctor was forced to depend on the neighbor women, who seldom remembered oral instructions accurately and might not be able to read them if they were written— and who preferred their own methods anyhow.

For practice in a community of that sort Dr. Mayo's personality was an asset beyond price. He reached his decisions quickly and stated them positively, with assurance and authority that brooked no argument. His manner did not antagonize patients; it commanded their confidence and secured obedience. Here was a doctor who knew what he was talking about, with no hemming and hawing. He knew right off what was wrong and what ought to be done about it, and he told you straight out. He was a *real* doctor.

The Indiana Medical College was forced to suspend operations at the close of the session of 1850 because of dissension in the faculty ranks, and some of the proprietors, among them Dr. Deming, planned to move the school to Lafayette. Then before the time for the next winter's session had come round they all accepted positions elsewhere, Deming with the new Central Medical College in Indianapolis. But that school too was soon suffering from "internal commotion" and closed down in 1852, leaving the Lafayette doctor without a teaching post.

The Indiana Medical College building, with equipment and records intact, was still standing, part of its rooms being used by a girls' school. But the old faculty had been dispersed. Who should compose a new one?

Dr. Deming and Dr. Mayo had made the acquaintance of an enterprising young physician named William H. Byford, who as a boy kept a Latin grammar on the bench beside him while working as a tailor's apprentice and bade well to fulfill the promise of such determined ambition. He had graduated from the Ohio Medical College in 1844 and was now teaching in a medical school in Evansville, Indiana, where he was also engaged in practice. The Lafayette men liked his ideas as well as they liked him.

The upshot was, according to a plausible tradition in the Mayo family, that the three of them decided to reopen the Indiana Medical College. Enthusiastically they set off in the fall for LaPorte, assembled materials and some students, and began their teaching, Dr. Mayo as the professor of anatomy. But fate was cruel; in the middle of the first term the building and equipment were destroyed by fire. Disheartened, they abandoned the enterprise and returned to their respective homes.

For Dr. and Mrs. Mayo the college venture must have been quite a financial strain. Practice in Lafayette was not remunerative even when it was extensive, for most of the settlers had started with too little to have yet acquired substantial means and money was scarce. Although the doctor's fees were small, payment was slow and uncertain, more often in kind than in cash—a chicken or two, a pail of lard when the butchering was done, or a bushel of potatoes.

Perhaps that explains why the partners next tried their hand at manufacturing medicine, establishing their "Family Medicine Warehouse, At the Sign of the Infant Hercules." The nature of the remedy is anyone's guess, though it was probably some favorite prescription of Dr. Deming's for which they sought wider distribution than their own practice afforded. The renting of quarters pretentious enough to be called a warehouse indicates undue optimism or considerable initial success.

Since the Mayos' first child, a son, had died at the age of six weeks, Mrs. Mayo was free to devote her abundant energies to supplementing her husband's income. She had no false pride whatever about doing so and kept lodgers for a time, among them a young woman who turned her rooms into a private school.

Soon, however, Mrs. Mayo tried something more ambitious. Renting a room in Lafayette's business section, she opened a millinery shop, sending to New York for buckram frames, braids, and plumes, and presently found herself doing a wholesale business with her far less enterprising competitors. The "New York Millinery" flourished, even moving into larger quarters from time to time. When a daughter, Gertrude, was born in July 1853, Mrs. Mayo merely took in a partner to relieve her of the need for personal attendance at the shop. Being a mother did not put an end to her business activity—which was just as well.

## 15

Dr. Deming was elected to the faculty of the Medical Department of the University of Missouri in the spring of 1853, and when he left for St. Louis in the fall Dr. Mayo went with him. He did not enroll as a student but spent the winter working as an unofficial assistant with Dr. John T. Hodgen, the professor of anatomy. Nevertheless, the following spring he applied for, and was granted, an *ad eundem* degree, that is, another M.D.

It is not easy to understand what prompted Dr. Mayo to take this step. The Missouri school was little better than Indiana Medical, although it did possess the greater potential advantages for clinical teaching afforded by the hospitals and dispensaries of St. Louis. It was a proprietary school, affiliated for prestige with the state university at

Columbia, and the flamboyant Dr. Joseph Nash McDowell, first a follower and then a foe of Cincinnati's Dr. Drake, was its founder and dean. It soon declared its independence of the university as the Missouri Medical College, and later became the School of Medicine of Washington University, in which form it still survives.

Of course, in time it would sound better for Dr. Mayo to cite a degree from the University of Missouri than one from a defunct proprietary school, but foreknowledge of that could hardly have been the motive for his action. And besides, if the degree was what he wanted he had only to present written evidence of his qualifications: good moral character, graduation from an acceptable medical school, and a year's experience in practice.

One would be tempted to conclude that he did not go to St. Louis at all, since there is no record of his presence there, if he had not later told his sons about his work with Dr. Hodgen. Perhaps he went on the off-chance that he might find an opening on the faculty, but most likely he just wanted to get away from Indiana.

For he did not stay long among the Hoosiers after his return from St. Louis. He and Mrs. Mayo had both weathered an attack of cholera without undue irritation, but the debilitating chills and fever of malaria every summer were too much for the Doctor's patience. One hour you were so hot you couldn't get cool; the next you were so cold you couldn't get warm. He loathed the recurrent misery and the feeling of languor it left behind. "Hell," he insisted, "is a place where people have malaria."

So one day in the summer of 1854 in the midst of a chill he stamped into the barn, hitched up horse and buggy, and shouted to his startled wife as he drove off westward, "Good-bye, Louise. I'm going to keep on driving until I get well or die."

# CHAPTER TWO

# On the Minnesota Frontier

Minnesota, with a population of less than five thousand persons, was organized as a territory in 1849 and began emerging from obscurity. Most men had known it only vaguely, as a remote wilderness frequented by fur traders, missionaries to the Indians, explorers, and a few adventurous travelers. Now they were learning to spell its name and to know that one did not cross the Isthmus of Panama or sail around Cape Horn to reach it.

They had been told it was a hyperborean region, inhospitable to man, a land that produced only furs, cranberries, and lumber, where fruit would not grow and grain would not ripen, a chill land of ice and snow and interminable winters, where the temperature was often too low for the thermometer to record it. But letters, newspapers, and visitors from Minnesota began to tell a different tale, of a beautiful country with lakes and rivers thick with fish, forests full of game, and fertile acres on which farms would flourish. And always these reports praised the Minnesota climate: It was without an equal in healthfulness—its cold, clear air made the diseased lungs of the consumptive strong and whole again, brought color to sallow cheeks and vigor to weakened bodies. And they chanted like a refrain, "There is no fever and ague here."

"There has not been one case of sickness in the whole of Hennepin County for several weeks past," boasted one writer. "What do you think of that, you who are shaking yourselves to pieces with the ague?"

They thought it too good to be true, and so they wrote letters of inquiry to the Minnesota editors, asking about land and crops, yes, but also and "more especially" about the chances for good health. "Will we have to bring two physicians for each family of four persons?" asked a man from Indiana. "I am going to emigrate west if I can find a region where there is no chills and fever," said one from Kentucky. Strangely indifferent to the possible effects, or perhaps just sympathetic, newspapermen in the malarial states published such letters together with the reassuring, inviting answers that came back.

So Dr. Mayo was not led to Minnesota by a mere turn in the road. Perhaps he set off on impulse, with no more plan than to ride out the shakes, but it is a safe guess that he had chosen his destination before he had been many hours on the way. He had just returned from a winter in St. Louis, neighbor by way of the Mississippi River to the young northern territory and the principal market from which its residents imported their supplies. He must there have heard much talk of Minnesota's progress and prospects.

2

After a month of leisurely driving Dr. Mayo came to Galena, Illinois, on the Mississippi River. It was in late June or July 1854, and the levee was humming with activity and excitement. Immigrants bound for Minnesota had been arriving in such numbers since the opening of navigation that the men of Galena foresaw a rush to the territory, a rush certain to be stimulated by the great excursion with which the Chicago and Rock Island Railroad had just celebrated the completion of its tracks from Chicago to the Mississippi. By invitation some twelve hundred of the nation's notables had joined in a junket over the new line to Rock Island and then up the Mississippi to St. Paul in a flotilla of steamboats. They had been given a gay time, and the reports from the well-known journalists among them served notice to thousands that Minnesota was actually within thirty hours' reach of Chicago. Galena was a-buzz with speculation as to what that might mean.

Leaving his horse and rig in a livery stable, Dr. Mayo took passage on one of the daily packets to St. Paul. It was loaded to the guards with passengers and freight, and hundreds of people were crowded into quarters meant for half the number. Sanitary facilities, none too good at best, were overtaxed, an invitation to the cholera that was again abroad.

And cholera came, filling the boat with fear and the odor of death. The little doctor did all he could to help care for the sick. It was not much under the circumstances—probably dosing them with Perry Davis Pain Killer and spoonsful of red pepper in whisky, favorite

34

remedies among steamboat crews, for whom this was no new experience. When patients died the bodies were covered with canvas till nightfall, then buried in rough coffins on an island in midstream or at some landing where the boat stopped to take on wood for its boilers.

The packet churned a slow, tortuous way northward past the mouths of many rivers and across the broad, beautiful waters of Lake Pepin. All about was the wild grandeur of shores densely, darkly green, of sheer, oak-crowned bluffs, and masses of bare rock, black against the sky like the ruins of gigantic towers. When it reached the mouth of the Minnesota River, the boat whistled its approach and drew in to the wharf at St. Paul, the head of navigation for the regular Mississippi steamers. The passengers disembarked and scrambled up the bank to the town atop the bluff.

3

The population of St. Paul was then approaching four thousand. It was not entirely a typical frontier town. Among its dwellings were some of brick and a number of neat white cottages with green shutters and white picket fences. There were also a "brick capitol with stout white pillars" and in the miscellany of its business places such urban establishments as a bookstore, a bakery, and a crockery shop that sold sets of fine china imported from Europe.

On the other side of the river was Mendota, district headquarters of the American Fur Company, and a little farther upstream stood old Fort Snelling, soon to be abandoned for a time. To the east lay some scattered farms and beyond them the town of Stillwater, the "log and lumber metropolis" for the rich pineries of the St. Croix Valley. Ten miles up the Mississippi was St. Anthony, second to St. Paul in size and growing mightily with its wealth of water power for the milling of lumber and flour. Across from St. Anthony the village of Minneapolis hesitated until the government should relinquish title to its site, and near by was a beauty spot all visitors to the territory rode out to see, Minnehaha Falls, the girlhood home of Laughing Water, gentle wife of Hiawatha.

But to the north and west of that knot of settlement there was only a vast, still wilderness of forest and prairie, sprinkled with lakes and threaded by streams and faint Indian trails. This was the homeland of

35

the Chippewa, and they were its only tenants except for a few traders, trappers, and missionaries, and the colony of *bois brulés,* or half-breeds, at far-off Pembina on the Red River near the Canadian border. From there had come the caravan of oxcarts encamped on the prairie across the river from St. Paul. Each summer the *bois brulés* made the long journey to exchange the winter's accumulation of furs and pemmican for supplies of foodstuffs and ammunition. While they stayed, their camp was a colorful spectacle that all visitors must see, and Dr. Mayo arrived just in time for it.

To the south of St. Paul lay the eastern end of the "Suland," millions of acres of forest and grassland that the Sioux had been persuaded to cede to the white man three years before. The eastern tribes had left their homeland reluctantly and slowly, but they were almost all gone now, gone to the shoestring tract reserved for them along the upper Minnesota River to the west. Into the lands they had vacated the immigrants were pouring, staking out claims, cutting away the timber, spreading a thin network of roads for stagecoach and wagon. Scores of towns on paper and dozens in fact were being platted on sites along the Mississippi and Minnesota rivers and in the fat triangle of land between them.

The prevailing temper of mind was exuberant optimism. The handwriting on the wall foretold a tide of immigration that would swiftly people those unoccupied acres, and an investment of capital that would vein them with railroads and dot them with mills and factories. Land values would rise, markets would expand, fortunes would be made. Already the speculators were many and busy, the frenzied building of more houses and storerooms was under way, and mechanics, artisans, and merchants were all too few. The air was electric with anticipation.

"Fence in a prairie fire! Dam up Niagara! Bail out Lake Superior! Tame a wolf! Civilize Indians! Attempt any practical thing; but not to set metes and bounds to the progress of St. Paul!" That was the spirit, in the words of a St. Paul newspaperman.

Whether it was this infectious enthusiasm that decided Dr. Mayo, or the beauty of the country, or an improvement in his health he never said, but probably it was a combination of the three. At any rate, in August his letters lay unclaimed in the St. Paul post office, while he went back to Indiana to get his wife and daughter.

4

Among the matters to be arranged in Indiana was the disposal of Mrs. Mayo's millinery business. But why dispose of it? Why not just move it to St. Paul? In the boom that was in progress a milliner should do well. So Dr. Mayo took his wife's stock of goods to Chicago, where they were invoiced and packed for shipment. He ordered a quantity of new braids, mourning crapes, linen collars, and bandboxes to be sent with them, and then went all the way to New York to order still more from the dealers there. When he returned to Indiana, the Mayos piled their household effects into a wagon and started for St. Paul.

Arriving in October 1854, Mrs. Mayo established herself in a shop on Third Street and immediately prospered. Spring and fall thereafter she made the long trip to New York to order new supplies and the latest styles in straw or velvet bonnets and trimmings. In time she added dressmaking to her activities, as well as the retailing of fur sets, including "mantle, muff, and wristlets."

But the Doctor was not so easily settled. He seems to have made little or no attempt to practice medicine in St. Paul. Perhaps he thought it was no use; the town was overrun with doctors, some twenty to thirty of them being in residence in the latter months of 1854. Among pioneers who preferably dosed themselves and in a community that was straining every nerve to become known as the most healthful spot in the nation, there was not enough business to support so many. The doctors, like all frontiersmen, had to become jacks-of-all-trades, and they taught school, dabbled in real estate, ran for public office, or managed a drug store.

Dr. L. C. Kinney, for instance, owned and operated the World's Fair Drug Store, which advertised everything from rutabaga seed and fishing tackle to silverware and canes, including in the gamut nostrums like Dr. Green's Oxygenated Bitters, Mexican Mustang Liniment, and Professor Alexander Barry's Tricopherous for preventing baldness and gray hair. In addition the versatile doctor ran a livery stable, sold wood "by the single cord or otherwise," announced "first-rate winter apples for sale cheap," and sold town lots "in lower St. Paul, opposite Pig's-Eye Bar."

One reason why he and his fellows found it necessary to keep so many irons heating may be guessed from the postscript one of them added to his business card in the newspaper: "Dr. H. wishes it to be distinctly understood that when his services are rendered, he expects his pay."

That being the general situation, Dr. Mayo felt free to indulge his desire to see something of Minnesota. "I was perfectly charmed with the new country," he said, "and I was anxious to see it in all its wild beauty and to tread where the foot of man had never trod before, unless it be that of the Indian."

## 5

When the building of the canal around Sault Sainte Marie was begun in 1853, alert men eyed the length of the waterway in the making and found the magnificent natural harbor at the head of Lake Superior. There ought to be a city on those shores, a great city, with all the mineral wealth said to lie in the ranges behind them and all the vast West to be tapped beyond. The influx of capital and of men to the head of the lake began at once.

First to arrive were the townsite promoters from the East and from St. Paul, but close on their heels came mining men from Michigan looking for copper. The north shore of the lake was forbidden ground because it still belonged to the Indians, but the southern shores, within the boundaries of Wisconsin, were already being surveyed. There Superior and Superior City were platted and a knot of settlers gathered, looking longingly at the north shore, where rumor said large masses of pure copper were to be found in rich veins miles long.

Then in September 1854 the Chippewa signed the Treaty of La Pointe, ceding those lands to the white man. The United States government ratified the treaty early in 1855, and that was the signal for a rush from Superior across the bay to stake out claims that could be bought when the land had been surveyed and came on the market.

In the fall of 1854 all St. Paul was discussing this development heatedly, because the machinations of a company organized to build a railroad from Lake Superior to Iowa through St. Paul had just lost to the territory a large land grant which Congress had been disposed to make. Curiosity about what was happening at the head of the lake was enough to move one of the local editors to publish descriptions of the possible routes covering the hundred and thirty miles to Superior.

# On the Minnesota Frontier

None of them promised easy traveling. The two by water were full of portages and dangerous rapids, and each of the three by land included long stretches of travel on foot through dense woods, where the trail would be faint to inexperienced eyes.

Nothing daunted, Dr. Mayo decided to see what everyone was talking about. He thoroughly enjoyed the journey to Lake Superior and repeated it several times in quick succession. He told something of his adventures in a description he wrote later on:

Before this time I had done considerable camping out. I had made my way on foot three times from Saint Paul to Lake Superior. Once I had trod the Indian trail alone for three days without seeing the face of man or beast. Once again in a birch bark canoe I had paddled the length of the Saint Croix from [its] commencement . . . as a small creek, rushing over its sand bars, shooting down its rapids, and again gliding leisurely along past tall pine trees or watching the bright eyes of the deer as they paused for a moment before taking those beautiful bounds for which the animal is noted.

[I made my bed] on the bottom of the canoe, swung to sleep by the light, rippling waves, while the boat was tied to the banks waiting for the morning's light to pursue the journey. . . . [I carried] the canoe around the great falls by the Indian portage and launched it again just above the dalles, passing through the narrow channels, arresting the boat's progress at every short distance to wonder and speculate upon the time taken for the water to cut through that rock dike and at the same time admire the picturesque beauty of the rocks.

Thus three days passed, floating through wild scenes, viewing nature in all her wildness and grandeur of stillness, following the course of the now broad river until it expands into the lake Saint Croix. These scenes had given me a taste for trips in solitude. To notice a small rabbit cross my tracks . . . to be glared at by wolves through the day and to be regaled by their wild concert of howling during the night, had for me a real pleasure.

The first two trips to which Dr. Mayo referred must have been made in the fall of 1854. The third he accomplished in January 1855 with two companions, Edwin H. Hall, a young man who had just come from the East and who later became a prominent businessman in Duluth, and Edmund F. Ely, who had lived in the Minnesota country since 1834 and had learned to know the northern woods through his work as a missionary among the Indians. Traveling on snowshoes, the three men made the journey in six days.

# The Old Doctor

Ely had already staked his claim on the north shore, and Hall and Mayo each chose one near by, probably on the site of the present west end of Duluth. Soon after, Dr. Mayo spent several weeks among the Indians to learn something of their social customs. When he returned to his claim he found it occupied by another man, who refused to yield possession. In his account of the incident, the little doctor "cussed the fellow and let it go," and returned disgruntled to St. Paul.

## 6

Meanwhile, the territorial legislature had recognized the cession of the Chippewa lands by defining the boundaries of two new counties along the lake shore, Doty County to the west and Superior County to the east. Six days later the legislators, for some unknown reason, changed the names, *Doty* to *Newton* and *Superior* to *St. Louis*. But they made the change in a section tacked onto an act granting a franchise for a telegraph line between St. Paul and St. Anthony, so that everyone, including the governor, missed it and went on calling the counties Superior and Doty.

Moreover, in application the names somehow got transposed, so that *Superior* was used for the western county, and *Doty* for the eastern. To top off the blunder, Governor Gorman and the residents of the north shore both assumed that the legislative action authorized the organization of county governments and did not observe that the law merely defined boundaries, attaching the new areas to Chisago and Washington counties for governmental purposes.

Some of the men living at the head of the lake sent letters to the governor recommending appointees for the county offices, and among those suggested as commissioners for Superior County was W. W. Mayo. On May 15, 1855 Governor Gorman appointed him to that position. The legislature had also directed that a census of the territory be taken as a basis for reapportioning representation in the legislature, and the sheriff of Chisago County now named Dr. Mayo as his deputy to take the census in the lake-shore area.

The Doctor set out for Lake Superior once again and this is the story of the trip's beginning as he later wrote it, apparently intending it for publication as a "letter to the editor":

# On the Minnesota Frontier

At the time of year I speak of the only means of communication between Superior City and St. Paul was by foot travel, and this required the pedestrian to carry his provisions in a blanket strapped upon his back; on the outside of the blanket and attached to the straps hung a coffee pot [and] a frying pan; attached to a leathern belt was a tin cup and a camping knife suspended in a leathern case. The provisions consisted of flour and pork, tea and coffee, and a very liberal supply of sugar. Bread of all kinds was too bulky to pack. The amount required for the trip including the blanket was about fifty pounds. My friend, did you ever carry this weight upon your back for a day at a time? If you ever have, you can judge how many hundred [pounds it seems] before the first day is over.

Having made up a party of three for the lake, I induced them to take a new route, a foolhardy one; it was to strike as near as possible a bee line from Saint Paul to the lake. Each equipped as above . . . we left Saint Paul one beautiful May morning in 1855. One of the members was a tall young man of about thirty summers who had just come from Philadelphia. He was by trade a tailor. He was a well-dressed man, had on a suit of fine black cloth and a stove pipe hat and small, neat-fitting boots. The other of the party was of western birth, had from a boy been used to a rough outdoor life. He was thickset, muscular, and very hardy. Your correspondent, [then] aged thirty-five, of the profession of medicine, was small of stature, five feet four, thin of flesh, weighing one hundred twenty pounds, but wiry and active and capable of great endurance and fortitude as my previous experience had proved. . . . [My] dress consisted of a straw hat, red flannel shirt, coarse, thick pants and stockings, with Indian moccasins—and of the last, three pairs.

So equipped we stepped lightly over the sandy roads and through the oak openings and meandered along the shores of the beautiful lakes which abound in the vicinity of Saint Paul. When some miles [have] passed, the steps begin to lag. The long man's pack gets heavy, but he will not own it. His body continues to bend under its increasing weight. There are frequent hitches to give it better position, but of no use. At last to get relief from his bent position he straightens up to his full height. The effort is too great, and like Bunyan's pilgrim his load of fifty pounds has increased to three hundred; he is over balanced, and we look back to find him sprawling upon his back, unable to rise without being relieved of his pack. So passed the first stage of this eventful journey.

Eventful was the word. The attempt to strike out a new trail through the wilderness proved unwise, for the men lost their way. Then one night a sudden change in the wind scattered sparks from their campfire among the dry pine needles, and they awoke to find themselves in the midst of a forest on fire. Taking to their heels, they barely managed to reach safety outside the path of the spreading flames. Later Dr. Mayo tried to set down his memory of the scene:

The hot fire ran along the ground licking up the dried pine needles and vaulting up the tall spruce trees, making beautiful cones of flame and throwing out from the long branches over head volleys of scintillating blaze . . . fire works far excelling the art of pyrotechnica. The great clouds of smoke rolled away dire, black, tremendous. The fire passed us, but we heard its sounds through the dreary woods and saw at times dreadful gleams of light as some tall tree became food to the devouring element. Our imaginations would distort its sounds into dismal screams . . . dying off in sullen moans as falling trees gave out hollow groans like cries of tortured ghosts. The fire still glittered through the now gloomy woods; a deathlike silence began to pervade the scene. . . . My companions stood trembling with a weird and pale look.

Well they might. The fire had destroyed their camp and all their supplies and equipment, and for five days they were without food other than the berries they found. At last they were forced to kill and eat the little spaniel that had been keeping them company. When hope was giving way to despair, they met some friendly Indians who gave them food and set them on the trail again.

## 7

Men naive enough to believe the magnificent maps of Superior that were then hanging in hotel lobbies in all the larger cities of the country were dismayed when they reached the town and found the wide avenues nonexistent, the spacious public square a mat of underbrush, and the handsome hotel a barnlike shed in the middle of an acre of tree stumps.

Superior numbered some fifty buildings and between five and six hundred inhabitants in the summer of 1855. Half the buildings were mere one-room preemption cabins, in which six or eight men, coming back from a day's exploring on the mineral ranges, would bunk on the floor "spoon fashion." Reed's boardinghouse, in which Dr. Mayo found lodgings, was probably little more pretentious. Even the hotel bedded its guests on piles of blankets or shavings, and for such accommodations plus a diet of bread, beans, pork, and prune pie collected two dollars and a half a day. Yet Superior had stores of a sort, some lawyers' offices, and even a newspaper, copies of which were distributed to serve, like the maps, as immigrant bait.

On the Minnesota side of the lake, settlement consisted of a hundred or so whites and half-breeds strung out along one hundred and fifty miles of rough lake shore in isolated clusters of two or three preemption shacks each.

When Dr. Mayo looked over the situation, he felt that he had accepted two impossible jobs. He could not take an accurate census of the Minnesota shore; he could not even get to much of it without spending more for provisions and transportation than he would receive in remuneration. Nor could he organize a county government, unless its headquarters were to be in Superior. He decided to return to St. Paul without attempting either task.

But the men with claims in Minnesota urged him to reconsider, for even a semblance of county government would further the progress of settlement. So would representation in the territorial legislature, and they were anxious to participate in the coming election. They would help with the census. Carlton lived at Fond du Lac; he would count the heads in that area. Elliot would do the same for Grand Portage, Godfrey for Grand Marais (Grand Marie, they all called it), and so on down the shoreline.

At their "earnest solicitation" Dr. Mayo agreed to do the best he could under the circumstances. But when the census lists from his agents came in, he was troubled. On them were the names of men actually living in the boardinghouse with him, and of others he knew to be businessmen or lawyers in Superior. They spent only an occasional day or two on their Minnesota claims and could hardly be said to live there.

The difficulty was that the arbitrary state boundary cut through a geographic unit. It was natural for the men to go back and forth across the lake. The land they wanted, the places where they wished eventually to live, were on the north shore, but all the facilities for making a living were on the Wisconsin shore. So, as one of the men put it later on, "Superior was the abiding place of all Duluth." And of course even the oldest and hardiest of north-shore residents moved to Superior during the long, hard winters.

Dr. Mayo decided that it was not for him to determine whether or not the men were justified in claiming residence in Minnesota. He knew, though, that the law provided a stiff penalty for making false returns, so he compromised by sending the census lists to the sheriff as they came to him, without certifying them by the customary oath. Including whites and half-breeds, they totaled two hundred and thirty-four inhabitants for the two lake counties.

## 8

Meanwhile, the Doctor was preparing to make an expedition along the north shore on private business. The search for mineral deposits was the breath of life for the community at the head of the lake. Everyone talked and dreamed of the wealth to be found in the hills beyond, but the mineral they had in mind was copper; the thought of iron ore left them unmoved. The editor of the *Superior Chronicle* might think there was a rich iron range behind Superior, extending "even to the Minnesota boundary," but the mining men paid him no heed. They were after copper.

Richard B. Godfrey of Detroit had lately come to Superior as the agent for the Northwest Exploring Company, one of the firms competing for possession of the richest copper lands in the vicinity. Godfrey had hired men to explore the north shore, stake claims where they found shows of copper, and build shanties on the claims to hold them. He now employed Dr. Mayo to visit those men, examine the specimens of copper they had gathered, and judge the worth of their claims. And the Doctor could also take a look at the lands held by rival companies.

Foot travel along the length of rocky, heavily wooded shore was impossible, so the journey had to be made by water. Having assembled the necessary camping equipment and food supplies, Dr. Mayo and two companions set out in a Mackinaw boat manned by three French-Canadian *voyageurs*. Their first trip, early in July, was short, just up to Knife River and back, but the second, begun late in the same month, covered the entire shoreline from Minnesota Point to within a mile or two of Pigeon River on the Canadian border.

Sailing when the wind permitted, at other times rowing, the men cruised slowly along the lonely coast. They would land on the shore of a bay or a river's mouth. visit any cabins in sight, and then cut their way into the interior as far as there were any signs of men or claims. Sometimes a few hours would suffice for the inspection; again it would take two or three days. Then after cooking breakfast or dinner on the beach, they would take to the boat again and move on to the next dot of habitation.

Thus for a month Dr. Mayo lived close to the solitary wilds he liked so well. No notes survive to tell what he thought of the moving beauty of Minnesota's now famous North Shore, nothing to tell in what mood he found the lake, in what tone the landscape. And nothing to tell his opinion of the specimens of copper the company's prospectors presented for his judgment.

Late in August he returned to Superior. So far the county commissioners had taken no action. One of the three refused to serve because he had no intention of living in Minnesota, but the Doctor, with Henry S. Burk, took the oath of office on the day he returned, and at once the commissioners held their first and last meeting, Dr. Mayo acting as chairman of the "board." They appointed election precincts for Superior County and probably also named the county seat at the present site of Duluth.

The next day Dr. Mayo left for St. Paul, traveling once again by canoe down the St. Croix waterway, this time with a Chippewa half-breed as guide and canoeman. He reached town in time to join Mrs. Mayo on her fall trip to New York, where he helped her select the seasonal additions to her millinery stock. So easily did he turn from copper to milady's bonnet!

## 9

But he had not done with Lake Superior. On October 9 the voters of Minnesota Territory went to the polls to elect a territorial legislature and a delegate to Congress. Personal factions and local issues cut across party lines, not yet sharply drawn in the territory. For all practical purposes the voters were either pro-Rice or anti-Rice. Henry M. Rice, the incumbent delegate, was a Democrat, a resident of St. Paul, and an active participant in most of the schemes for developing the territory. He was, or had been, one of the proprietors of Superior City, his brother was a bona fide resident of Minnesota Point, and Rice himself was exerting every effort to recover the federal land grant for the company of eastern capitalists who proposed to build a railroad from Lake Superior to the Iowa boundary.

Opposed to Rice were the members of the fledgling Republican party, the personal following of his most influential rival, Henry H. Sibley, and those few who preferred to lose the railroad rather than hand over a million or more of the territory's acres to eastern promoters.

In the election the lake-shore counties polled four hundred and sixty-four votes, almost all for Rice. That mattered little, for he was elected without them, but those same votes were enough to elect two Rice men to the legislature from the first district.

The anti-Rice men scanned these lake-shore returns carefully. On the poll lists they found the names of men whose cards appeared among the business advertisements of the *Superior Chronicle,* and they had no trouble finding witnesses to swear that boatsful of men had gone from Superior to vote in the Minnesota election. The *Daily Minnesotian,* Republican organ in St. Paul, came out with charges of fraud, accusing the Wisconsin townsite promoters of "perpetrating a debauch upon the ballot boxes of Minnesota."

When the Democrats countered by impeaching the veracity of their witnesses, the Republicans looked around for other evidence. The law required that in order to vote a man must have lived in Minnesota for six months. Six months back from October 9 was April 9. Where was the man who had taken that census in July?

Thus they came to Dr. Mayo. He told them that according to the most lenient interpretation of the meaning of residence, fewer than three hundred persons, and not all of them voters, had been living in the lake counties in July. Moreover, because of his subsequent explorations along the shore he could name persons and locations. He was lead on the scales for the Republicans, though he was himself a Democrat.

The officials of Chisago County were persuaded to declare the lake-shore vote invalid and to certify the election of the anti-Rice men. Consequently, when the legislature met the Democrats contested the first district seats. In the lengthy hearings before commitees of both houses Dr. Mayo was the key witness, and over and over he was asked to tell when, where, and how he had gone and whom he had seen.

He was given precinct poll lists and asked to identify the men named and tell where they lived. His testimony that most of them lived in Superior was amply corroborated by the word of other witnesses as well as by the business cards in the *Superior Chronicle*.

In the heat of the fray Dr. Mayo suffered attack from both sides. The Democrats rejected the evidence of his census returns because he had not made the count himself, ignoring the fact that had he done so the total would have been even smaller. When they heard the story of his exploring trips they immediately declared that most of the population lived in the interior and along the stretches of coast he had not traversed on foot. They even charged that he had solicited his appointment as county commissioner, pretending to be a resident of the district, but both the majority and minority committee reports declared that to be untrue.

The Republicans, on the other hand, sought to nullify the whole lake-shore vote by showing that the precincts had been established extralegally. The commissioners had no power to act, they said, since the law had given Governor Gorman no authority to appoint them. Furthermore, Dr. Mayo and Mr. Burk had acted for Superior County, which did not exist and never had existed in the area so named.

It was a hot little scrap. Though the majority of the legislature was pro-Rice, the Republicans won the day, because, said they, the evidence of fraud was too overwhelming to be ignored by even the calloused consciences of the Democrats.

## 10

His first brush with Minnesota politicians at an end, Dr. Mayo did not linger long in St. Paul. "He was a pioneer in the true sense of the word," once said his elder son. "He was never satisfied with things as they were, but always wanted to go further." And *farther* too, in these early years. His was the curiosity of the true wanderer, who cannot resist the enticement of a highway passing his door, stretching away into the unknown distance. "I fain would see what lies beyond," Minnesota's motto, was the Doctor's too.

This time he wandered south along the course of the Minnesota River, which twists and turns from St. Paul for nearly a hundred miles, then rounds a sweeping curve and lengthens on northwestward to its source. Moving from village to village on its banks—Shakopee, Chaska, Belle Plaine, Henderson—he stopped off finally at the home of the Dunhams, a family lately come from Indiana like himself.

Their farm was one of a scattered group that made up the neighborhood known as Cronan's Precinct, after the name of the genial Irishman at whose house the polls were located. It lay just within the wide belt of magnificent hardwood forest the early settlers called the Big Woods. Here and there the deep shade of the trees gave way to patches of open meadowland, bright in spring and summer with wild flowers and berries, yellow and purple and crimson. Not far to the west began the long, rolling, treeless hills of the prairies—a boundless white in snowtime, a gentler vista of rippling green under the summer sun.

There was beauty and wildness enough here to satisfy even Dr. Mayo, but it was less stark than Lake Superior and neighbors were more numerous. Four miles from the Dunhams', across the river and a little downstream, was the nearest town, Le Sueur, cozily settled on one of the largest and fairest woodland meadows. Not far upstream was Traverse des Sioux, grown up at the spot where an old Indian trail crossed the river, and a stone's throw beyond lay the newer and livelier village of St. Peter. Still farther upstream, at the bend of the river, was Mankato, and a few miles around the curve a colony of German immigrants were building New Ulm. Then came the military outpost at Fort Ridgely and the beginning of the Sioux Reservation.

Those were the milestones along the river, and strung between were a score of smaller settlements or single homesteads. Axes were clearing farms and townsites in the Big Woods back from the river, and the immigrant wagons had already begun to strike boldly across the prairies, cutting tracks through the tall grass to unclaimed plots in the interior.

Dr. Mayo could make a home here. Near the Dunham farm was one abandoned by its owner when he left for California, and, according to the memory of a neighbor lad who later worked for Dr. Mayo, foreclosure of a mortgage had given possession of the place to an uncle of Mrs. Mayo's who was living in Mankato. At any rate, Dr. Mayo took over, and a few months later Mrs. Mayo, having sold out her business in St. Paul, came with their daughter Gertrude to join him.

Navigation had opened on the river, and the Minnesota Valley was humming with life. Every steamboat brought new settlers and piles of freight, supplies for them and their fellows in the immigrant caravans crossing the river at St. Peter by the dozens weekly.

Among the arrivals that spring of 1856 was a young man from Indiana, Edward Eggleston by name, who had come to Minnesota in search of healing for sick lungs. In one of the novels he wrote later, *The Mystery of Metropolisville,* he vividly described the dizzy frenzy of speculation in land he witnessed in the Valley. It was a time "when money was worth five and six per cent a month on bond and mortgage, when corner lots doubled in value over night, when everybody was striving frantically to swindle everybody else." Men infected with the fever put every cent they had into the first payment on a piece of land, hoping to sell out at an advance before the second payment became due.

The future on which they gambled did not depend on minerals, at least not on the sort taken from the ground in chunks or scoopsful. Minerals that made land rich for farming were the wealth and fertile acres the attraction—acres that did not exude malarial miasma. To quote Eggleston again:

To the emigrants whose white-top "prairie schooners" wound slowly along the road, these grass-grown hills and those far away meadowy valleys were only so many places where good farms could be opened without the trouble of cutting off the trees. It was not landscape, but simply land, where one might raise thirty or forty bushels of spring wheat to the acre, without any danger of "fever-nager."

Agriculture would make the Valley rich and the settlers knew it. They might be having all they could do to raise enough food for themselves, but give them time to assemble stock and tools, to break more land, and their fields would produce for market. That time was not far off. In another year the first wheat to be exported from Minnesota was grown on Le Sueur Prairie, across the river from Dr. Mayo's farm, and a few years more found the Valley farmers sending livestock, butter, and cheese to the eastern markets.

Of course the Doctor entered heartily into the community's primary interest. On his own farm he had eight head of livestock, oxen it is said, but more likely assorted cattle, mostly cows. When the call went out from St. Peter for the men of Nicollet County to assemble and organize a county agricultural society to discuss farm problems, pool experience, and advertise the Valley's agriculture, Dr. Mayo rode up to attend the meeting. He was elected one of the directors and as such participated in the fitful activity of the new society for three years.

He won none of the premiums at the autumn fairs it staged, however, for he apparently found successful farming impossible as an incidental occupation. Cattle, for instance, were a problem. Not in summer, for then they could roam at random and forage for themselves, but to provide adequate winter food and shelter was beyond the power of most pioneer farmers. They used the prairie grass, marsh hay they called it, for both purposes. Cut with a scythe and pulled to the farmyards in cocks on a sort of *travois,* Indian fashion, it was stacked for food and piled on a rough framework of poles for shelter. When the grass was scant or the winter fiercely cold, the cattle did not survive.

In the latter fifties the settlers were plagued with fires that swept the prairies just when the grass was ready for cutting. The masses and streaks of red flame were beautiful to see on the horizon at night but they were disastrous. Many a farmer found himself forced to kill or sell his cattle in the fall because he had no food to carry them through the winter.

On one such occasion Dr. Mayo arranged with a richer, better equipped neighbor across the river to lodge and board the Mayo stock in his barns for the winter. But later he must have sold them, for the boy who helped him with his chores in 1858–59 remembered that "he had not even a cow." Though still living on a farm he was no longer farming, yet he came to be considered, or at least to consider himself, an authority on the arts of husbandry.

## 12

When he settled in Cronan's Precinct, Dr. Mayo resumed the practice of medicine, but slowly, because the calls for his services were few at first. He faced the competition of doctors already established, as well as that of the midwives, herbalists, and bonesetters who willingly obliged the neighbors unfortunate enough to need their services.

There was no malaria and no annual sickly season in the Minnesota Valley, but there was plenty of sickness nonetheless. Improper food, poorly heated, draughty houses, overexertion, exposure to cold and snow and high waters, lack of adequate sanitation, ignorance, and superstition nourished a bountiful crop of ills. The records that survive dispel the aura of rosy, robust health that later generations have shaped into the halo of romance around the pioneers, for those records are full of chronic aches and pains and serious, acute illnesses.

Stone slabs rose one after another in the churchyard as whole families were wiped out by typhoid fever, scarlet fever, or the increasingly prevalent diphtheria, then commonly called putrid, or malignant, sore throat. Waves of smallpox inspired terror and uncovered ugly depths of inhumanity in men. Children were so cold day after day, in spite of heavy wool-knit clothing, that their little hands were too blue-numb to hold a spoon for eating. And boys not yet in their teens caught croup or pneumonia as they struggled in the chill of a winter's morning to get a fire going in a refractory stove. Sickly babies cried and cried.

Infant mortality was frightful, so usual in fact, that when a child was born its parents only *hoped* that it might live; they did not assume that it would.

There was need enough for doctors. But knowing how to care for the family's fevers and bruises was part of mother's job, and when the illness was too acute for her skill, she called in some community grandmother wiser still in the ways of plasters, teas, and poultices. Calling the doctor was postponed as long as possible.

The habit was encouraged by those who trafficked in patent medicines. "Ask your neighbors, who have used them, and they will say they are *Good Medicines,* and you should try them before going for a physician." "Call and examine our medicines and after satisfying yourself that in nine cases out of ten, at a trifling outlay you can save enormous Doctor's bills, purchase and attend to the wants of your family independent of the aid of any Leech." So ran the advertisements of the manufacturers and the druggists.

A few calls a week made up Dr. Mayo's practice for several years. When he was sent for, he set off with his little medical bag, walking along the narrow trails through the woods, lighting his way at night with a whale-oil lantern, square-shaped, one side a glass door to emit the light and the other three pricked out in stars or crescents.

Sometimes the call was too urgent or the distance too great for walking. Then the little doctor made sure that his saddlebags were full and rode his pony, sometimes taking hours for the trip. He had no carriage; there were no roads for one. To reach a patient across the river he traveled by canoe or ferry boat; there were no bridges.

At the end of the journey, he was as likely as not to find his patient in a one-room log cabin or sod hut, heated by a fireplace and lighted by a lard lamp or homemade candles. Family and friends might be assembled in stifling proximity to the sick person, or he might be alone in the cabin. Sometimes Dr. Mayo stayed a day or two to act as nurse, even on occasion splitting wood to step up the fire and stirring up a nourishing broth or gruel to help restore strength.

This practice did not return much in money. Most of the people were poor, struggling to get a start, probably deep in debt for their land and stock. If they could give the Doctor a dollar for his trouble, he accepted it as graciously as though it were adequate recompense. If they could spare him a side of bacon or a smoked ham to carry home, it was welcome. From many he had not the heart to take even that, for beneath his brusque, even severe, manner lay a quick sympathy and ready emotions that often rose to choke off speech.

To supplement his meager income Dr. Mayo did whatever he could find to do. He practiced veterinary medicine when called upon to do so. He was elected justice of the peace for Cronan's Precinct in 1857 and served in that capacity at least until the area was organized as Lake Prairie Township the following year. And he operated a ferry back and forth across the river to Le Sueur. There is even reason to believe he inaugurated that ferry service. If so, he saw a need and an opportunity; his neighbors had been taking their business ten miles upstream to St. Peter instead of the five miles to Le Sueur because part of the shorter distance was unbridged water.

13

These extramedical activities of Dr. Mayo's have been isolated from their context of circumstances to indicate professional incompetence or improvidence on his part. The Doctor was not a money-maker and never would be; he was too soft-hearted and too unbusinesslike about his collections. But it needs no such personal defects, if that they are, to explain the leanness of the Valley years.

The glow of promise that lighted the Valley in 1856 became dazzlingly bright in the spring of 1857. Minnesota was preparing for statehood, and there seemed to be a good chance that the new boundary would be drawn along a parallel of latitude just north of St. Paul, which would then not be central enough to remain the capital. The St. Peter Company, proprietors of the townsite of St. Peter, smelled cheese. Carefully and quietly they laid their plans, then introduced in the legislature a bill for the removal of the capital from St. Paul to St. Peter. It passed both houses.

The Valley folk were jubilant, St. Peter residents staged a big celebration, the prices of land and lots for miles around rose dizzily. But the owners were reckoning without political ingenuity and lack of scruples. The capital removal bill went to the enrolling committee of the council to be prepared for the governor's signature, but days passed and it did not reappear. When an impatient member finally called for it, he learned that the chairman of the committee had disappeared, taking the bill with him!

His absence deadlocked the council in the midst of a roll call, because the president would not be convinced that nine votes should be considered two thirds of fourteen. The chamber sat in continuous session for more than a week, meals and cots being brought in to accommodate the irate members, while the sergeant-at-arms ostentatiously scoured the byways of St. Paul for the missing councilor, "Jolly Joe" Rolette from faraway Pembina. It was rumored that he had harnessed up his dog sled and started for home.

The legislative session, according to law, expired on March 7. As the clock began to strike the hour of midnight on that day, Joe Rolette walked down the aisle to his seat and began, "Mr. President . . ." But the gavel sounded. "The council is adjourned. The councilor is too late."

During that week Rolette had been living comfortably, and not without companions it is said, in an upper hotel room in St. Paul, while the bill reposed in the safe of a city banker.

# The Old Doctor

A copy of the bill had been prepared, of course, and the governor signed it, despite its "numerous irregularities." The St. Peter Company, sure that it would be considered valid, fullfilled its contract by building a handsome new capitol to house the state government. Then the courts ruled that the bill had not been properly passed, and the company was forced to content itself with maneuvering the removal of the county seat from Traverse des Sioux to St. Peter.

That was the popping of one little local balloon, but a bigger one burst when a New York life insurance company failed in August 1857, precipitating a nationwide panic. Eastern creditors called in their loans, draining the western territory of cash, and the boom collapsed. The zip went out of life in Minnesota.

Commodity prices fell, business came almost to a standstill, and men who had thought they possessed a fortune found themselves virtually penniless overnight. Lots once quoted at hundreds of dollars could not be given away, towns that had been zooming toward city size, on paper, relapsed into wilderness, speculators quietly folded their maps and stole away, while loafers suddenly yielded to the lure of gold and set out in companies for the diggings in California.

Awakening gradually from the daze induced by the sudden and complete collapse, the men and women who had gone to the territory to make homes on the land pulled in their belts and settled down to work their way out of the hard times. Pioneers though they were, they were not too individualistic to ask the government for relief legislation to mitigate the stringency. The Republicans, then the nation's radical third party, urged the adoption of moratoriums on mortgages and taxes, "stay measures" they called them, that would "tie up the boat until the hands can cut wood enough to run it." When the Republicans got control of the state legislature in 1860 they put such measures through, defending themselves against the charge of radicalism by pointing to precedents in Bible times and in the laws of older states.

The most urgent need was for cash. To get it the settlers in the Minnesota Valley trapped prairie chickens and shipped them east at two to four dollars a dozen. In the spring they took to the woods to make sugar, some on a small scale for the home supply they could not afford to buy, others to earn cash by tending the troughs and kettles in the big sugar camps that tapped thousands of trees.

# On the Minnesota Frontier

When some alert St. Peter man discovered that there was a ready market for the man-shaped, fiery-tasting ginseng root that grew in profusion throughout the Big Woods, the community went wild; here was a cash crop that could be picked from the ground without capital outlay! Carpenters left the houses they were building, barkeeps closed their saloons, and merchants quit their counters to set out for the woods with sack and hoe. The trade in ginseng grew to amazing proportions. In 1859 the town of Henderson listed in its business directory one doctor, one butcher, one baker, and *seven* ginseng dealers.

That eased things a little, but it did not dispel "the blue haze of hard times." Newspaper editors pleaded with their subscribers to pay up—in wood, pumpkins, potatoes, anything useful. Ministers were kept going by "donation festivals," parties to which their parishioners brought what clothing and foodstuffs they could spare. Edward Eggleston, then serving as the pastor of churches in Traverse des Sioux and St. Peter, supplemented such uncertain bounty by working as a surveyor, by pasturing sheep, and by peddling a recipe for soap from door to door.

The doctors were hard hit. Although they were willing to accept any kind of produce in payment of their accounts, they could not get enough of it for their needs, and at last some of them, worthy men all, announced that their services must be paid for in advance. They apologized for making such a stipulation but said that justice to their families demanded it.

Against such a background it is no cause for wonder that Dr. Mayo could not support his family by the practice of his profession alone. He seems to have done as well as most, and he could afford to hire help with the chores on the farm, even though it was only a boy who worked for a pittance.

## 14

Life was not easy for Mrs. Mayo either. She was not cut to the pattern of a pioneer Martha and did not wear the role happily. With the education, opportunities, and social sanction of a later day she would have been a career woman, devoting her mind and talents to a business or a profession and relegating the dusting, sweeping, and cooking to someone more suited to it. Housekeeping was not her forte.

But she buckled down to it. She had two children now and for a time three. In June 1856, shortly after she moved to the farm, a second daughter, Phoebe Louise, was born, and in March 1859 came a third, Sarah Frances, who lived for little more than a year. Keeping her family clothed and fed and the house furnished and respectably clean was a hard, full-time job. She had to bake the bread, cure the meat, dry the beans, corn, and peas, spin, weave, knit, mold the candles, and make the soap by leaching lye from the winter's ashes and adding cracklings or lard.

One day as she bent over a kettle of soap on the stove, she suffered a severe hemorrhage from the lungs. Little Gertrude, badly frightened by the blood, ran screaming for her father. Mrs. Mayo recovered fully after a brief spell of rest, and her family never knew that she feared a recurrence. But thereafter she kept out of doors as much as possible. Perhaps it was that which directed her reading to the woods and the sky and made her a good amateur botanist and astronomer.

She had need of great courage. She and the children were often alone on the farm, and she must have been mindful of the possible presence of wolves, wildcats, and bears. There were always Indians around too. She never knew when she might look up to see one flattening his nose against the windowpane to peer inside, or when several of them might appear at the door to beg for food and liquor. They did not seem unfriendly, but she knew they could turn nasty if they were crossed.

Dr. Mayo had one unpleasant experience with Indians while making a sick call on horseback. As he was fording one of the tributaries of the Minnesota, three drunken braves waded out from the brush on the bank and demanded his horse. The peppery little doctor refused to yield it, and apparently by the sheer force of his anger he drove them away. One of those three Dr. Mayo was to encounter again, the huge, hideously ugly Cut Nose, so called because one of his nostrils was missing, having been bitten off in one of his numerous fights.

Trachoma was prevalent among the Indians at that time, and it spread to the whites of the Valley. Mrs. Mayo caught it. For several years she was almost blind, and she suffered from wild hairs on her eyelids, which her children often helped her to pull out. Eventually her sight was restored, but her eyelids were left lashless.

# On the Minnesota Frontier

One winter day in 1859 Mrs. Mayo found time to write a letter, but she was out of writing paper. Remembering the unused sheets in her old millinery account book, she began her letter crosswise on one of them:

My dear Mrs. Lucans,

Will you accept a leaf from my account book? Tis all I have and I have time to write now. It looks very shiftless, we live so near town, but I do not improve every opportunity or I should have written to you long ago. I have had many ups and downs since you wrote me and still I keep about on a level. . . . I'll direct this to your old place hoping it may find you well. Well'er than it leaves me. The stove smokes and my expressive eyes are red and angry. We have had very cold weather for a few days but today it is very pleasant, but too bright, too light, for my eyes.

These are the only written words surviving from her own hand, and they give but little hint of the experiences that in remembrance made her say of the Minnesota Valley, "It was a hard country."

## 15

The Minnesota River and its tributaries were then given to frequent and heavy floods. On a sudden would come a freshet and the waters would swirl over the banks and across the prairies, sweeping along anything lying loose or lightly anchored—haystacks, fences, even livestock.

One such flood, unusually widespread and protracted, occurred in the spring of 1859. For weeks the river communities above Henderson were almost entirely cut off from the towns downstream and from communication with each other. The residents of Cronan's Precinct (they still called it that, though legally it had become Lake Prairie Township) were virtually marooned in their homes. The trails they used were mostly under water, and the ferries were all out of order.

Some of the men, including Dr. Mayo, were irritated by this constriction. Why could they not have a road independent of high waters and fickle ferries? They knew the route for it, and they called upon the "west side men" to bestir themselves and see that it was built.

Dr. Mayo did not wait for the road. Apparently he did not choose to risk another such experience and decided to move across the river to Le Sueur. He bought a lot and he and his brother James (the one

who had appeared so unexpectedly on the canal barge in Lafayette)
spent the following summer building a house and barn on it. When
the house was ready the Mayos moved to town.

It was not pretentious, just a small, two-story, gabled cottage. The
largest room was the kitchen, which served also as a dining room, and
upstairs under the gables, in a room so low ceiled as to give away the
small stature of its builder, Dr. Mayo arranged his medical books, his
massive rolltop desk, overlarge for the space, and his equipment for
mixing medicines. That was his office.

In that house on June 29, 1861 a son was born to the Mayos. They
named him William James, after the father and his brother. With an
Englishman's feeling for family, Dr. Mayo rejoiced in his first-born
son, but he could not foresee what cause the world would have to
rejoice with him.

## 16

The removal to Le Sueur did not mean that the Doctor would have
to build up a new practice. He remained within frontier reach of his
former patients and had merely enlarged the circle of possible new
ones. The first call came quickly. While he was still roofing the cottage,
a man rode up and introduced himself as J. L. Drake, a farmer living
near town. Neither he nor any member of his family was in need of a
doctor, he said, but he had a pretty sick horse that wanted attention.
Would the Doctor come and look at him?

Dr. Mayo's reply was unequivocal. "Sure I'll come. I'll look at a
horse or any other damn thing you've got." According to the story,
a legend in Le Sueur, he treated the horse successfully and made a
favorable impression on his new neighbors.

His coming apparently caused some uneasiness in the mind of Dr.
Otis Ayer, Le Sueur's other practitioner, a man of Dr. Mayo's own
age, but dour and difficult. When Dr. Mayo did him the professional
courtesy of calling on him, Ayer bluntly observed that Le Sueur was
not big enough to support two physicians. Dr. Mayo was innocently
surprised. "Why, Doctor, were you thinking of leaving?"

He knew that Dr. Ayer was right, however, and that he still had
to find other work to supplement his income, so during the spring and
summer of 1860 he tried his hand at steamboating.

# On the Minnesota Frontier

The traffic on the river was growing mightily. There were the government supplies, hundreds of barrels of pork and flour and sugar, to be carried to Fort Ridgely and the Indian agencies, and there were people and goods to be transported to the river towns as *entrepôts* for the developing interior country. And from that interior there was now a swelling stream of farm produce to be carried down the river to St. Paul, thousands of bushels of wheat and oats, barrels of butter, baskets of eggs, poultry, and vegetables.

For all of this the steamboats were the cheapest carriers. When the river froze over in winter and goods had to be hauled up from St. Paul by team and wagon, commodity prices in the Valley towns leaped upward.

The fleet plying the river was increasing with the traffic. In the 1860 season two rival lines of four or five boats each operated out of St. Paul on a regular schedule, or as regular as the state of the river and the boats permitted. The Minnesota was a tricky stream to navigate, one of the most tortuous in the West. It fairly squirmed its way through the Valley, and its channel was full of growing sandbars.

In the spring floodtime these were not serious obstacles, but when the freshet was over, the waters subsided fast, so that usually by summer's coming it was more than the larger boats could do to scrape their bottoms over the bars. Then it was necessary to end the trip at Belle Plaine or St. Peter and transfer passengers and freight to smaller vessels of shallower draft for the rest of the journey upstream. In that upper river traffic small, independently owned steamers did a thriving business.

It was on one of those small vessels that Dr. Mayo served. By some accounts he was the captain, by others a clerk or purser. In the latter event the boat was probably the trim little *Albany,* built at Ottawa, near Le Sueur, in the winter of 1859–60. Needing "only a heavy dew to run in," it was one of the mainstays of the river trade throughout the season of 1860. The merchants of St. Peter had subscribed capital for the outfitting of the *Albany,* and they were proud of her success because her builders and her officers were all local men.

But if Dr. Mayo was in charge of the boat he worked on, it may have been the *Little Dorritt,* the names of whose officers have been lost. That little steamer made two trips a week to and from Fort

59

Ridgely, often towing a barge or two loaded with lumber, hides, and grain, in addition to the cargo in the hold and the passengers on deck. *Little Dorritt* is just the literary sort of name Dr. Mayo would have chosen, and he had a passionate admiration for the works of Dickens.

Whichever the boat, Dr. Mayo had a good time that summer, for he loved the rough life on the river and the bustle and excitement that greeted the boat at every stop. One acquaintance he made was a young man by the name of James J. Hill, who was a clerk on one of the lower river boats. Many years afterward, when Dr. Mayo was the famous father of his famous sons and Hill was one of the great railroad men of the nation, Dr. Mayo attended a reception at the Hill home in St. Paul. When he arrived he exclaimed jovially, "Why, it's Jim Hill, coming up the river!"

Whereupon his host returned, "And you're the little doctor coming down the river!" After which the two excused themselves and went off to Hill's study for a long talk about old times.

## 17

Dr. Mayo's season on the river was brought to an end early in September by a summons to appear in court. A Mrs. Wirt of Le Sueur had been troubled with an abscess on her wrist, and Dr. Ayer lanced it. When the wrist healed it was stiff and useless. Claiming that in lancing the abscess Dr. Ayer had cut into the wrist joint and let out the synovial fluid, thus causing the wrist's stiffness, Mrs. Wirt filed suit against Dr. Ayer, charging him with malpractice and asking ten thousand dollars damages.

When the plaintiff's lawyer asked Dr. Mayo's opinion of the case, he stated promptly and positively that in his opinion if Dr. Ayer had cut into the wrist joint he was guilty of malpractice. But in court Dr. Mayo found himself standing alone against some six of his professional brethren. Called for the defense, they testified that from the evidence they believed the stiffness had developed before the lancing was done and so could not be charged to Dr. Ayer's treatment.

Coached by Dr. Mayo no doubt, the counsel for the plaintiff put the medical gentlemen through their paces. Gleefully the spectators observed that not since medical school days, if then, had the doctors suffered so grueling an examination of their knowledge of physic and that some of them came out of it sweating. Not so old Dr. Hiram Catlin of St. Peter. Gruff and crusty, he refused to dodge the issue as his colleagues for the defense were doing. He said that in cutting into the joint and letting out its fluid, Dr. Ayer had done exactly what he should do; that wasn't malpractice, but the best sort of practice.

The prosecution pounced. According to Dr. Mayo and to the best authorities in print it was a dangerous and unwarranted procedure. "Your medical books don't say that, do they?" asked the plaintiff's lawyer.

"No," growled Catlin. "But twenty years from now they will." And in some forty years they did.

For four and a half days the trial was the absorbing interest of all Le Sueur County. In the minds of the laymen the battle was one between Dr. Ayer and Dr. Mayo, and the community was about evenly split. After twenty-four hours' deliberation the jury decided for the plaintiff, but awarded her only fifty-seven dollars.

That case was Dr. Mayo's second experience in the courts, and more important, it was his first experience with a malpractice suit. He had testified according to the best of his knowledge, telling the truth as he saw it without thought of compromising his convictions for the sake of his profession.

## 18

In December 1860 the Baptists of Le Sueur gave a supper to raise money for painting the church they had just finished building. The Mayos attended, and so did Harry H. Young, the editor of the *Henderson Democrat* from across the river. When the laden tables had been cleared of the cold beef, pickles, and pie and the time for speeches had come, Mr. Young was chosen to act as toastmaster. He promptly embarrassed Dr. Mayo by calling on him to respond to a toast, but the Doctor was unprepared and begged to be excused.

Mr. Young and he had met before, when one was a journalist and the other a tailor and student doctor in Lafayette. The result of their renewed acquaintance was a newspaper, the *Le Sueur Courier,* published by Dr. Mayo and edited by Young. The first issue appeared early in January 1861 and the last about three months later.

The life expectancy of newspapers was short in those days, because it was hard to make them pay despite their importance to the community. Consequently the turnover in editors and owners was rapid. Unless one had some ulterior motive, such as boosting a townsite or advancing some political cause, publishing a newspaper was an unprofitable enterprise.

The editors' wail about their unfortunate lot was constant and general, so Dr. Mayo cannot have undertaken the venture in the expectation of making money. It may have been civic spirit that impelled him. Le Sueur had one of the best sites on the Minnesota River, but it had lost out in the race for settlers because of a long litigation between rival claimants to the land. Now that had been settled, and the title to town lots was clear. All Le Sueur needed was advertising, and the citizens had been clamoring for a newspaper of their own for some time. It would have been quite in character for Dr. Mayo to start his *Courier* in response to that demand.

The agricultural department Dr. Mayo kept for himself, leaving the news and politics to editor Young. He prepared a weekly article on some phase of the theory and practice of agriculture or of farm homemaking, nor did the briefness of his experience and its indifferent success deter him from telling the farmers and their wives how to shear sheep, tend apple trees, make good butter, and concoct substitutes for coffee out of rye, carrots, or peas.

## 19

It is a likely guess that the *Courier* went down on the rock of politics. It was 1861 and political passions were rising high, with the line drawn sharply between "Black Republicans" and "Slavery Democrats." Neither side admitted shades of moderation in the other, and both gave short shrift to nonpartisanship.

The *Le Sueur Courier* was unmistakably Democratic. Harry H. Young was a stanch spokesman for the Democrats and Dr. Mayo had been elected justice of the peace for Cronan's Precinct on the Democratic ticket. But "it was a time for the searching of hearts in politics," and newspapers, editors, and plain men were shifting their allegiance to the Republican party in great numbers, principally because of its stand on the Union question but also because of local opposition to the well-oiled Democratic machine with headquarters in St. Paul.

# On the Minnesota Frontier

Dr. Mayo had apparently given his friends reason to believe that he was among those who had turned their political coats, for they were greatly puzzled by *his* publishing a Democratic paper. He and Mr. Young did not see eye to eye. In one case the Doctor invited a Mr. Hathaway of Belle Plaine to contribute to the editorial columns, but when he obliged the essay was published under a prefatory statement saying that the editor did not approve the sentiments and was only publishing the article at the writer's request.

In righteous indignation at such treatment, Mr. Hathaway wrote a letter to the *Mankato Independent,* giving it as his opinion that such an "unfounded lie" could have been written only by someone "mean and dirty enough to conduct a newspaper which will advocate the cause of the secessionists at the north." He hastened to add, however, that in so saying he "did not reflect in the least upon Dr. Mayo."

At last the inquiries were so many that Dr. Mayo was impelled to make a public confession of his political faith. He denied all responsibility for the political tone of the *Courier*; that was the business of its editor. He had good reasons, he said, for acting as publisher of a paper that took a position "diametrically opposed" to his own and probably to that of most of its readers, but he did not feel called upon to make those reasons public.

On the question of slavery Dr. Mayo was clearly for peace and compromise:

There are very few religiously rabid abolitionists who allow themselves to think for a moment that if they had been brought up under slave institutions, and had slavery surrounding them from their earliest infancy, they would themselves be slavery propagandists, and as violently so as any Southern fire eater. . . . Yea, we believe that Wendell Phillips himself, had his lot been cast in a Southern clime, would have out-Yancied Yancy; for such turbulent spirits will have vent, and the difference in the violent and abstract principles they announce is owing to the difference in their chance of birth. . . . We look upon the man who would sacrifice the immutable obligations of truth, justice, and the charities of social life, for the sake of an abstract principle about which one-half of our nation differ from the other half, as one of the most dangerous of citizens.

For his part, he continued, he hoped Mr. Lincoln as President would champion neither the abstract right of the negro nor the real right of the slave-owners, but would arrange a compromise, even allowing the

South a portion of the public domain, if necessary, in which to spread its peculiar institution. Give time a chance and within another generation the South would see and acknowledge "the right of human freedom from servile bondage."

More Democrats than Republicans would have said amen to those views, but the tone of Dr. Mayo's communication, which was columns long, leaves no doubt that he considered himself a Republican, one of those who had joined the new party more for the purpose of breaking up the graft of the Democrats than from acceptance of Republican doctrines.

At any rate, within a year Dr. Mayo was actively and whole-heartedly at work in Republican ranks. He served as the chairman of the Republican district convention in 1862 and was elected to the district committee of the party for the succeeding year. His career in politics had begun.

## 20

The divergent activities in which the little doctor engaged were not such deviations from his professional path as they might appear; they were merely detours, though he did not know them as such when he began them. They spread his name and acquaintance up and down the Minnesota Valley.

The term *Minnesota Valley* is not merely a verbal abstraction used for convenience; the Valley was a geographic unit and in a very real sense a social unit too. Dependence on "the river" for transportation and communication made close neighbors of the families and towns scattered along its banks. Although Henderson, Le Sueur, St. Peter, and the rest were often bitter rivals, jealous and outwardly contemptuous of each other, they nevertheless formed a single community within which persons and news moved easily.

When Mr. Hathaway of Belle Plaine wished to complain of the injustice of a Le Sueur editor, it was quite natural for him to do so in a Mankato newspaper. A ball at St. Peter, a dramatic performance by the Thespian Club of Mankato, an Independence Day picnic on Le Sueur Prairie, were all social occasions that drew attendance from the full length of the Valley.

To extend his acquaintance throughout that neighborhood Dr.

Mayo could not have chosen his activities better. At his ferry converged the folk of two counties who wished to cross the river to do business in Le Sueur or to catch the stage for St. Paul. When the river was highway, railroad, telephone, and telegraph all in one, when "every farmhouse on the bank was a steamboat landing," and when the day's main event was the boat's arrival, no one was better loved or more widely known than the boat's kindly captain or clerk.

The *Le Sueur Courier,* shortlived as it was, and the Doctor's subsequent political activity brought him into contact with the editors, lawyers, and businessmen who were the leaders in Valley life and would shortly become leaders in the state at large. These men found Dr. Mayo an educated, intelligent gentleman, a good talker, serious, energetic, forthrightly honest, and they said so. When they became his patients, as numbers of them did, they also found him professionally able.

They were as likely as lesser men to be impressed by Dr. Mayo's manner with a patient. He was called to see old Thomas Lang, who lived in Sibley County some ten or fifteen miles from Le Sueur. Lang had a bad case of pleurisy. The Doctor pulled him through it but warned him when leaving, "Lang, if you get sick like this again, there won't be anything I can do for you; so don't send for me." Sure enough, in a few months Mr. Lang had another attack and died in it. The accuracy of Dr. Mayo's prognosis did as much for his reputation among Lang's neighbors as a cure would have done, and being anecdote material perhaps it did more.

In remarkably few years Dr. Mayo had emerged as one of the outstanding citizens of the Valley, well toward the top in its medical profession. His regular practice covered most of three counties, and he was occasionally called farther afield upstream. His professional card was running in the papers of Henderson, Belle Plaine, and St. Peter as well as Le Sueur, and those papers habitually referred to him simply as "Dr. Mayo," with no initials, no place of residence, no identification of any kind. Just "Dr. Mayo," whom the readers might be expected to know. Certainly the practice of medicine alone could not have given him so wide a reputation.

# CHAPTER THREE

# Civil War Days

When Fort Sumter fell on April 12, 1861 Governor Alexander Ramsey of Minnesota was in Washington. Knowing that now the battle must be joined, he went at once to the secretary of war and offered a thousand men from the youngest of the states for the defense of the Union. His offer was accepted, and the call for volunteers was heard in Minnesota.

Community leaders throughout the state recruited companies from among their friends and neighbors, and as the companies were grouped into regiments the scramble for commissions and offices began. Governor Ramsey, with power of appointment, was deluged with applications and recommendations from men claiming favors in return for their Republicanism.

Among the positions to be filled were those of surgeon and assistant surgeon for each regiment. Naturally they seemed financially desirable to men whose profession normally paid them so little, and before the war was over there were few doctors in the state who had not sought an appointment.

Dr. Mayo made his bid early, in the fall of 1861. Men were aglow with the first warm flush of enthusiastic loyalty and recruiting was easy. Many Le Sueur men had gone and others were enrolling in companies of the Third Regiment, now forming. Among them were friends of Dr. Mayo's—the brother of his next-door neighbor was a first lieutenant—and the little doctor wanted to go with them.

On September 22 he sent the governor an application for the appointment as surgeon of the Third Regiment, and with it several letters of recommendation gathered from his friends in the Valley, including a former state senator, two members of the state supreme court, and two prominent lawyers of St. Peter who were afterward governors.

They all wrote warmly of Dr. Mayo's qualifications, his integrity and honor, his liberal education and professional competence. Although he was a stanch Republican, they said, he was "a general favorite amongst men of all parties," "enjoying the unbounded confidence of all who know him." Wrote one, "He is well known as one of the first in his profession in the Valley and you can use your influence for no better man."

They pointed out that Dr. Mayo's experience in practice in the "bilious districts" of Indiana made him peculiarly fitted to care for men fighting in the warm, humid South and that the appointment would give great satisfaction to his "host of friends" in the Minnesota Valley—which, they gently reminded the governor, had not yet been given a share in the war's political spoils.

When a month had passed without an answer, Dr. Mayo collected another batch of letters and set off to present them in person. In St. Paul he talked to Ignatius Donnelly, acting-governor while Ramsey was in Washington, a young man, just beginning his long, turbulent career in politics.

What Donnelly said may be guessed. There was little likelihood of Dr. Mayo's getting the appointment because there were several applicants for the position, among them the popular Dr. Levi Butler of Minneapolis, who was already acting as captain of one of the companies in the Third Regiment. His appointment as surgeon was being demanded in so many letters and petitions from citizens of Hennepin County and the men of the regiment that Ramsey would scarcely dare to name anyone else. Donnelly might have added, but probably did not, that Butler and his friends were too powerful in the Republican party to be ignored.

Thinking the matter over as he started for home, Dr. Mayo stopped at Shakopee and wrote back to Donnelly, saying that he was more desirous of "practical experience in the field" than of a surgeon's wage and had decided to ask Donnelly to present his papers in application for the post of assistant surgeon.

To be named regimental surgeon or assistant, the candidate had to appear before a board of examiners and be recommended by them as qualified. The board appointed for the Third Regiment met in St. Paul early in November 1861, and Dr. Mayo appeared before it, but the examiners did not choose to recommend him. Butler was named surgeon and Dr. Francis Milligan assistant. They may have been competent physicians, but Dr. Butler had not been practicing medicine since he came from Indiana four years before, and Dr. Milligan was the protégé of a Republican friend of Governor Ramsey's in Wabasha.

When Dr. Milligan resigned his commission the following spring, Dr. Mayo again asked for the appointment, but he might as well have saved the paper and ink. Ramsey had already telegraphed his friend in Wabasha to send another candidate up to St. Paul "to pass the examination."

2

By the summer of 1862 the pace of volunteering had slackened. Reverses suffered by the armies in the field and reports of what the war was really like had dulled men's enthusiasm for fighting. Accordingly on August 4 President Lincoln proclaimed a draft of three hundred thousand men. Each state was assigned a quota, which it in turn apportioned among its counties, and if these quotas were not filled by volunteers before September 3, the deficiencies were to be made up by draft.

Although that threat alone promised to be sufficient, in Minnesota preparations for the draft began at once. The methods of enrolment and drafting were prescribed by the War Department, but the administration was left to the state authorities. The governor appointed a commissioner and surgeon in each county to act on applications for exemption, and Dr. Mayo became the examining surgeon for Le Sueur County. At once he and his commissioner set about recording the halt, lame, and blind of the county according to specifications issued from Washington.

But Le Sueur County was determined that it should not incur "the odium of a draft." All the county officials went out recruiting, and three ministers and two lawyers besides. Finding their efforts blocked by the men's unwillingness to leave their fields at harvest time, they wrote to ask the governor whether enlisted men would be permitted to remain at home long enough for the reaping before being sent to the front.

Before their question could be answered it was forgotten, for suddenly they found themselves fighting for their lives on their own doorstep; the Minnesota Sioux had taken the warpath.

# Civil War Days

The outbreak came suddenly, but not without warning. Indeed, warnings had been so many that the first news of the actual uprising was shrugged away—just another of the "Indian scares" that had been exciting the morbid imaginations of alarmists all summer. Only a few men who knew the Sioux and the duplicity and rascality to which they had been subjected for years suspected that those scares were a sign that their tempers were rising, that their smoldering resentment was breaking into open blaze.

In the spring of 1862 the tribes gathered at the agencies to receive their annuity payments in foodstuffs and cash. The winter had been hard, provisions were gone, and they were hungry. But Agent Galbraith told them they must wait a while for their payment; he had got the food but the money had not yet arrived, and he refused to distribute the food until the money came, simply because checking the rolls twice would be too much trouble.

With a sensible incomprehension, the Indians could not see why they had to go hungry while their flour and sugar and pork stayed locked up in the agency warehouses. All through the summer they waited, teased along by occasional doles of just enough food to keep them from starving. On August 15 they came to parley once more with the agent and the traders. Chief Little Crow spoke for them. If the white man did not give them food they would take it. "When men are hungry they help themselves."

Alarmed by that, Galbraith turned to the traders. Would they let the Indians have food on credit until the payment money arrived? One Andrew J. Myrick answered for the group: "As far as I am concerned, if they are hungry let them eat grass."

The interpreter repeated the cruelly insolent words. There was a moment's silence, then with whoops of savage fury the Indians strode away.

That was on Friday. At midday on Sunday a band of four Indians, drunk on anger if not on firewater, killed five whites on a lonely farm in Meeker County. Their escapade, reported to their tribes, was a match to the ready fuse, and early Monday morning a large band of Sioux braves arrayed for war in feathers and paint attacked the Redwood agency, shot all the men they could find, then looted and plundered the stores. Myrick the trader was one of the first to fall, and into his dead mouth the Indians stuffed a handful of the grass he had told them to eat.

Meanwhile, other bands were working havoc in the countryside adjacent to the reservation. Taking the settlers unaware, they killed and pillaged with savage joy. They moved from farm to farm, making captives of the women and some of the children, gorging themselves with food, and setting fire to the barns and haystacks.

Survivors and a few friendly Christian Indians managed to warn some of the settlers, who fled downstream spreading the alarm as they went. In a frenzy of fright the farm families took to the road toward Fort Ridgely and New Ulm, but some of them were overtaken and murdered on the way. Even a detachment of troops sent out from the fort when the news arrived was ambushed and half its number killed.

## 4

The news came to the lower Valley in the night. Some courageous Paul Revere from New Ulm, galloping hard under cover of darkness, brought word of the outbreak and an urgent appeal for help. From house to house he rode, rousing the citizens of St. Peter, then spurring on through the night to spread the alarm in Traverse des Sioux and Le Sueur.

Dr. Mayo was wakened at daybreak and joined his excited neighbors in a discussion of what was to be done. Enlistment had left the town short of men, but it was agreed that every able-bodied man must go to the aid of New Ulm. Hastily the men collected what guns they could find, molded lead into a supply of bullets, and filled their pouches and powder horns. By eleven o'clock they were ready, and set off under the command of the sheriff.

At St. Peter they joined with the company of "Frontier Guards," hurriedly organized and armed that morning like themselves, and the troop, numbering one hundred and twenty-five, began their march to New Ulm at one o'clock. They made a motley, straggly column. A few of them rode in buggies, some were on horseback, but most of them walked. Dr. Ayer of Le Sueur and Dr. Asa W. Daniels of St. Peter took the bags of medical and surgical supplies in one of the buggies, but Dr. Mayo marched with the ranks.

# Civil War Days

Wet to the skin from a rainstorm in the late afternoon, they arrived at the ferry crossing to New Ulm just as night was falling. Two persons in the town had been killed, several wounded, and half a dozen houses on the outskirts had been fired in a skirmish with the Indians that afternoon. The townsfolk were panic-stricken.

A line of guards was immediately posted all around the town, and hospital quarters were appointed for the doctors' use. Dr. Mayo was established in a front room of the Dacotah House with Dr. W. R. McMahon of Mankato, and Drs. Ayer and Daniels in the basement of a drygoods store across the street. They were all busy for several hours ministering to the casualties of the afternoon's battle and to some of the Sioux's victims who had been brought in from the country still alive. The hospital quarters filled rapidly during the next few days, and the presence of good doctors was acclaimed a godsend.

## 5

Thursday night a refugee came in with a story of thirteen women and children who were hiding in a slough near the little settlement of Leavenworth, ten miles to the southwest along the Cottonwood River. About a hundred men volunteered to rescue them the next day, and Drs. Mayo, Ayer, and Daniels went with them.

Starting early in the morning, some again in buggies and wagons, with provisions for a two days' trip, they proceeded slowly, stopping to examine every house and cabin on the route and to bury the dead they found. When they reached the women and children hiding in the tall grass of the slough, the emotions of the rescued may be imagined. They had been living on a diet of flour and water for three days, in constant fear of being discovered by the roving red men.

The object of the expedition accomplished, the men might reasonably have retraced their course as quickly as possible, but the captain proposed to move on, striking across the prairie in the direction of Fort Ridgely. The doctors protested. That would be needlessly dangerous and would necessitate camping out overnight. With so many in the party they ought not to be away from New Ulm any longer than necessary. But the captain had his way.

As they got within earshot of the fort, they heard the sound of artillery fire. A battle was in progress there, and every detonation persuaded more of the party to the doctors' point of view. At last the medical men forced the captain to take a vote on the matter, and the group scurried back to New Ulm.

Early the next morning the sleepy town was startled to attention by shouts from the guards, "The Indians are coming! To arms everybody!"

The defenders prepared swiftly for battle. The women and children were hurried into the cellars of stores and houses within the barricades; the companies were formed and marched out to their appointed positions on a low ridge about half a mile south of town.

The Sioux leaders deployed their forces at the foot of the bluff in the distance, spreading the line thin so as to promise a complete encirclement of the town. As they advanced slowly across the sloping prairie, their red bodies and brilliant feather headgear made a splendid spectacle in the sunlight. Suddenly as they got within rifleshot they raised a terrific yell and "came down like the wind" upon the citizen soldiers, shooting as they came.

The quick change of pace and the chilling, savage screech of the warwhoop were too much for the nerves of the inexperienced settlers. They fled precipitately toward the rear and did not stop until they were inside the barricades. The Indians could have followed them over the barriers in the scramble, but they preferred to seek cover for fighting according to their wont.

From then on the whites fought Indian-fashion too, every man or small group of men on its own. Some adventurous souls crept out to occupy the windmill or the post office or some other structure strategic for defense, while others set fire to the nearer buildings to deprive the Sioux of cover close at hand. The Indians countered by firing a block of houses on the lower side of town, and a brisk south wind carried the smoke and flames toward the barricades.

With the crackling of flames, the Indian yells, the cries of frightened women and children, and all the shooting, the town was a bedlam. Sharp skirmishes were in progress here and there, men were racing back to headquarters near the Dacotah House to replenish their ammunition and receive instructions, and everything was wild confusion. Not all the men were brave enough to take it, and some sought refuge in the cellars with the women. Dr. Mayo went after them, thrust pitchforks into their hands—since there were not enough guns to go around—and stationed them behind the barricades. When the frightened fellows asked what they should do if the Indians came, Dr. Mayo swore. "Run your forks through them, of course."

In one hour and a half of battle ten were killed and fifty wounded. The latter were carried to the hospital rooms on doors ripped from their hinges to serve as stretchers. The doctors had their hands full, but Dr. Mayo kept an eye on what was happening outside. Looking up once when he was engaged in amputating a man's leg, he saw two men who were supposed to be on guard at the barricades (perhaps two of those he had put there) sneaking past the window. In a trice he was out the door, shouting and brandishing his bloody knife. The men returned to their posts in a hurry.

Late in the afternoon a hullabaloo in the street called all the physicians to their doorways. Someone had spied a group of men in whites' clothing approaching from the direction of the river. Thinking they must be reinforcements, the impetuous Captain Dodd, second in command under Judge Flandrau, proposed to drive off the Indians in that section and clear a way for them. It would take only a few minutes and might in the end decide the battle's outcome.

When the men hesitated, both Father Sommereisen, the beloved pastor of half southwestern Minnesota, and Dr. Mayo made brief, impassioned speeches. Then twenty of them offered to go and at once galloped off down the avenue, beyond the barricades.

Watching anxiously, those behind saw Captain Dodd halt suddenly, wheel his horse, and ride back with the entire company following. The "reinforcements" had been a decoy, the Indians fired from ambush, and Dodd and his horse were both hit. He managed to reach the barricades before he fell, and he was carried into an adjoining blacksmith shop, where he died a few hours later.

As twilight came on the pace of the battle slackened, and Judge Flandrau sent men out to burn the buildings still standing outside the barricades. The flames lighted up the area sufficiently throughout the night to prevent the Indians' advancing in a surprise attack.

In the morning the red men, after a few casual shots at long range, gave up the attack and withdrew in the direction from which they had come.

On Sunday afternoon the officers met to discuss the situation. The town was a shambles inside the defenses and smoking ruins without, provisions and ammunition were running low, and two thousand mortals crowded into cellars and storerooms like cattle in a boxcar were an invitation to disease. So they decided to evacuate New Ulm.

Some of the defenders thought abandoning the town a cowardly postscript to the heroic defense of the day before, since they were sure that they would soon be relieved by the large force reportedly moving up from the lower Valley. For some unexplained reason the medical officers were not told of the proposed move and knew nothing of it until women appeared at the hospitals to gather up the bedding. Dr. Daniels at once became one of the most vociferous critics of the evacuation and remained so ever after, but what Dr. Mayo thought of it is not recorded.

In spite of the protests, preparations went forward. The barricades were broken up, and the wagons moved into line to serve as conveyances for the wounded. The dead were hastily buried in the streets or in the garden near the Dacotah House, and people began assembling their belongings, until officers called a halt. The train must not be delayed by lagging footsteps any more than necessary, so all available space in the wagons must be used for the less able women and children and personal baggage must be light. This ruling caused heart-rending scenes, and when the caravan had gone the street in which it formed was littered with odds and ends thrown out of the wagons or dropped at the last minute to lighten the load for team or shoulders already weary.

The merchants threw open their stores and told the defenders to help themselves; it was better that they have the goods than that they be left for the Indians. According to a story current at the time, they left conspicuously open several barrels of whisky, brown sugar, and flour which had been liberally dosed with strychnine, an exterminator they were in the habit of using for all kinds of pests.

Early Monday morning the wagons filed slowly out onto the road for Mankato followed closely by a column of marchers more than two miles long. As Mankato was the home of Dr. McMahon, he was sent ahead to prepare quarters for the injured, and apparently Dr. Mayo went with him. Their news caused a flurry in Mankato. Accommodations were already sorely overtaxed by the refugees who had sought shelter in the town during the past week, but the generous citizens set to work to do their best. They commandeered flour from the bakeries and private kitchens and cattle from the fields, and all day the women baked and cooked. When the head of the fleeing caravan arrived in the early evening, food at least was ready for them.

The wounded were received at the American House, where the doctors and the Ladies Aid Society had fitted up rooms for them, and the rest were bedded down as comfortably as possible in private homes, churches, the school, the public hall, and even in the newspaper office, where the fonts of type got so pied in the crush that the editor complained about it for weeks.

When most of the caravan moved on toward St. Peter the next morning, no doubt wishing to put as great a distance as possible between themselves and the "red devils," Drs. Daniels and Ayer went with them. Dr. Mayo, however, stayed in Mankato for a week longer to help Dr. McMahon with the score or so too seriously wounded to travel farther.

The part he played in the Sioux Outbreak probably did as much as all his previous activities to make Dr. Mayo known to the populace of the Minnesota Valley. Long afterward a man from Montana, returning to his home after a serious operation at the Mayo Clinic, received the felicitations of his friends on his recovery. "Yes," he agreed, "the Mayo brothers are remarkable men, but so was their father. He saved my life in the Sioux Outbreak when I was eleven years old. I was hurt in one of the battles and they took me to the hospital behind the lines, where a kindly little man dressed my wounds and praised me for my courage. He was the Old Doctor Mayo. Everybody on the frontier called him the 'little doctor'."

## 7

In the midst of the turmoil and alarm Mrs. Mayo was alone with her three small children, as were most of the women of Le Sueur. The menfolk had gone to fight, taking the firearms with them. When a rumor spread that Indians were closing in on the town, Mrs. Mayo rose to the occasion. She called the women together and told them to put on men's clothing and arm themselves with hoes, pitchforks, broom handles, anything the general size and shape of a gun. Then to the ends of the handles they tied knives or spoons to reflect the sun and look like the bayonets on army rifles.

Thus garbed and armed the women marched in formation up and down the streets of Le Sueur at stated periods each day, hoping to make the Indians believe the steamboat had landed a defense force from Fort Snelling. Their ruse was successful apparently, for Le Sueur was not attacked.

That is the legendary story as it has been told again and again. The core of truth from which it may have grown appears in Mrs. Mayo's own version of her experiences as phrased by a reporter to whom she told it.

Will was a baby in arms and safe enough, and I scared the other two children into staying indoors. When it was necessary for me to go to the barn or the well, I'd put on a pair of overalls and tuck my hair under one of the Doctor's old hats. . . . With a gun in my hand what a figure I must have cut in those overalls! I often think of it. So brave and manly; and my heart in my mouth!

But she did her part to care for the refugees. Eleven families took shelter in the house and barn, and beds were set up or blankets spread out in every room, Gertrude and Phoebe sleeping on the parlor floor with some of the little girls from the country. Mrs. Mayo and little Gertrude worked hard to feed their guests, and in one day baked an entire barrel of flour into bread for them.

One morning the children discovered the prints of Indian moccasins on the path outside the door, and then Mrs. Mayo's nerve broke. She prepared to pack up and take the children to St. Paul. But while Gertrude and Phoebe wrangled over which kitten they should take along, an older neighbor persuaded Mrs. Mayo to stay at home.

To the fear for her own and her children's safety was added anxiety about her husband. She often went out to stand at the gate, and when refugees straggled by she asked the injured, "Who dressed your wounds?" When some of them answered, "The little doctor," she knew that her husband was still alive.

On Saturday one of the men returned from New Ulm and told the women that all the rest of his party had been killed. Their grief may be imagined. It was a full day or more before they learned the truth, that the man was a deserter who had left New Ulm just as the Indians were approaching for the battle. So sure was he that New Ulm would fall and the defenders be wiped out that he felt safe in telling the story he did. His lot in Le Sueur thereafter was not a happy one.

At last, two hectic weeks after his departure, Dr. Mayo came home again, and his wife relaxed.

### 8

Meanwhile Governor Ramsey had assembled some companies of drafted men and volunteers and sent them to the Minnesota front under the command of Henry H. Sibley, a man well acquainted with the Indians and their ways. After a few skirmishes in which the Indians got the better of the raw troops, Sibley engaged the redskins in battle and put them to rout. Their white prisoners were recovered and some two thousand Sioux were themselves taken captive.

After a trial before a military commission, three hundred and seven warriors were condemned to death. When President Lincoln, feeling the fundamental unfairness of the procedure, as he said, "down to my boots," postponed execution of the sentence, the people of Minnesota threatened to lynch the prisoners if they were pardoned. But he delayed his decision long enough for the hottest passions to cool a little. Then he ordered the hanging of thirty-nine Indians whom the evidence showed to have committed rape and wanton murder; the others Lincoln found guilty only of waging war.

The condemned Sioux were hanged at Mankato on December 26, 1862. When the bodies had been pronounced dead by the regimental surgeons in attendance, they were placed two deep in a long trench dug in the sand of the river bank, but they did not stay there long. When bodies for dissection were hard to get, so many hated and unmourned dead were a windfall. In the crowd of spectators were many medical men, including Dr. Mayo, who had come to the hanging in the hope of getting a body for dissection, and under cover of darkness the grave was hastily opened and the bodies removed and distributed.

To Dr. Mayo's lot fell the body of that same Cut Nose whom he had once bested in a struggle for his horse. By all accounts the giant Sioux had been a fiend incarnate during the outbreak, the ringleader in all the most brutal outrages. Carted to Le Sueur, his body was dissected by Dr. Mayo in the presence of some medical colleagues, and the skeleton was cleaned and articulated for his permanent use.

## 9

The Sioux Outbreak was a local whirlwind that did not disturb the nation's preoccupation with the Civil War. Throughout the winter of 1862–63 the Union leaders were gradually preparing the public mind to accept the idea of conscription, and in March 1863 Congress passed the Conscription, or Enrolment, Act.

Under this law the procedure used in the draft of the preceding fall was retained, but the responsibility for administration was now transferred from the states to the federal government. A provost marshal general was appointed to direct the work of enlistment and conscription, which was to be carried on in each congressional district by an enrolment board consisting of a provost marshal, a commissioner of enrolment, and an examining surgeon.

On April 24, 1863 Dr. Mayo was named the examining surgeon of the enrolment board for the first Minnesota district, which comprised the entire southern half of the state. The appointment was made by the President on the recommendations of three Minnesota congressmen, one of whom, Senator Morton S. Wilkinson, lived in Mankato, in the legislative district of whose central Republican committee Dr. Mayo was now a member.

For its headquarters the board selected Rochester, the seat of government in Olmsted County. Rochester was a good-sized town, located near the center of the most thickly populated part of the district on a good road to St. Paul and Fort Snelling, and it was soon to be reached by the railroad creeping westward from the Mississippi River. In mid-May 1863, Dr. Mayo said good-bye once again to his wife and children and journeyed to Rochester to take up his new duties.

These began with the routine examination of volunteers, who were mustered in, fitted with uniforms, and dispatched to Fort Snelling if they were physically fit for service. Presently, however, the board got down to its special task of registering all males liable to the draft—a dangerous job, literally so. Instead of requiring the men to report themselves for registration, the law ordered the enrolment officers to *take* the names of those within the prescribed age limits. Many opposed conscription and often vented their opposition on the hapless officers. In some parts of the Union they were subjected to physical assault; several lost their lives and others were beaten, had their enrolment sheets destroyed, even their homes burned. Sometimes they went about their task accompanied by a strong guard.

Although nothing so extreme seems to have happened in southern Minnesota, the officers did find it impossible to secure accurate registrations. Men went into hiding when they appeared, and the women either lied shamelessly, giving fictitious names and ages for their menfolk, or refused to answer questions at all. The completed lists were full of errors.

Therefore, when the July draft had been completed, the board, under instructions from Washington, undertook the correction of the rolls. It was announced that any person could appear before the board and have his name stricken from the list by proving alienage, nonresidence, over-age, or physical disability. In effect that meant exemption from the draft, determined before rather than after the drawing of names.

With this the trek to Rochester began, and Dr. Mayo found himself exceedingly busy. The deaf, blind, and crippled—and "the morally weak-kneed"—filled the town's streets and hotels and thronged the office of the enrolment board. Said the newspaper, "Rochester has been turned into a Mecca for a season, and pilgrims from all parts of Southern Minnesota have darkened our streets with their coming."

There it is, the first time that Rochester was called a mecca for the sick. And for sick who came to be examined by Dr. Mayo!

## 10

For more than a year and a half the office of the enrolment board in Rochester was the busiest place in the state. Dr. Mayo worked long hours every day, examining volunteers after each new call, drafted men after each drawing, and between times the "droves" who hoped to have their names taken from the rolls.

It was not an easy job. The provost marshal general's bureau issued detailed specifications of exactly what constituted sufficient physical disability for exemption. In theory these were supposed to be merely a general guide for the surgeon's judgment, but in practice they were ironclad rules. If a surgeon exempted too many drafted men, he was likely to receive an official reprimand, yet if he accepted too many recruits and cluttered the army with men unable to endure the regimen, he was liable to discharge and financial penalties.

To that dilemma were added strong local pressures. The people could not rid themselves of the notion that the need for a draft was a blot on the escutcheon of the community—with reason, since the method of procedure made the draft a penalty for deficiency in enlistments. Consequently they went to extreme lengths to escape the disgrace. Every county and town offered bounties for volunteers, and because of the competition the bounties got bigger and bigger, saddling many small towns with debts they could ill afford.

Naturally then, the citizens did not look with favor upon the surgeon who examined volunteers too carefully. But if he exempted too few drafted men he was courting censure as a hardhearted wretch who sent sick men to death in the army.

Then too, the surgeon had to be on his toes to detect attempts to deceive him. The volunteers tried to conceal their ailments, whereas those claiming exemption often feigned theirs. Some resorted to violent physical exercise just before coming to the surgeon, hoping he would interpret their hard breathing and pounding pulse as signs of a cardiac lesion. Some even chopped off a finger or a toe, and in two cases the men had an unscrupulous doctor puncture the skin of their chests, so they could claim to be suffering from emphysema, a condition of the lungs sometimes treated by puncturing.

Such tricks were so common that the bureau in Washington was soon sending circulars to the surgeons describing elaborate methods by which they could detect fraud. If a man claimed exemption for defective vision, for instance, the doctor was to lead him on a regular steeplechase, a rapid run over a route marked with unexpected stairways, boxes, barrels, and overturned chairs. If the man got over them all without stumbling, his eyesight was good enough for the army, but what was to be done if he could not and suffered injury in the attempt was not set forth. Dr. Mayo found a few whiffs of chloroform the quickest way of discovering whether legs were as permanently stiff or crooked as the applicant claimed.

Some men did not bother with such subterfuges; they merely tried to bribe the surgeon. Dr. Mayo had his share of offers, and one man even came to his home at night to ask his price, but when the Doctor started toward him, wrath in his eye and on his tongue, the fellow, big though he was, backed hastily through the door.

On the whole, Dr. Mayo and his assistant, Dr. Hector Galloway of Rochester, steered a successful path among the pitfalls. Visitors coming to Rochester to watch the enrolment board at work remarked on the order, dispatch, and fairness with which the examinations were conducted. Dr. Mayo was "a very agreeable gentlemen," they said, adding that he was at the same time the most blessed and the most cursed man in southern Minnesota. Certainly he was one of the most widely known.

## 11

Toward the end of 1864 the number of claimants for exemption rose; the people had suddenly awakened to the obvious fact that to clear the lists of the exempt would reduce the draft quotas. As the Rochester paper put it, every six names taken from the roll lessened the quota by one man. Since the city was then paying three hundred dollars for each volunteer, every name struck from the list saved fifty dollars.

A demand arose for the board to leave its berth in Rochester and travel around the district, so that more applicants for exemption could appear before it. When Congress authorized that procedure in districts of wide extent, the Rochester board announced that on certain dates in January and February 1865 it would hold sessions in Preston to the east and in St. Peter and Faribault to the west.

The sitting at Preston passed off without reported incident, though there were more than a thousand candidates for examination. Finding several thousands awaiting it in St. Peter, the board established itself in the office of the judge of probate, and the mill began to grind. Around the door of the office surged the throng, jostling and shoving to be first, and the guard at the door soon collected a tidy sum for expediting the passage of those in a hurry.

On the streets the lawyers and doctors who had assembled to profit from the board's session were doing a land-office business—the lawyers preparing the affidavits required to prove alienage, nonresidence, and over-age, while the doctors filled out certificates of physical disability. Within limits prescribed by the Enrolment Act, these were legitimate activities, but some of the operators ignored those limits, charging what the traffic would bear instead of the five-dollar fee allowed by law and claiming to have special influence with the board which they would use for fifty, a hundred, or two hundred dollars. There were plenty of men willing to believe and to pay.

Inside the office the board, faced with the herculean task of acting on five or six hundred cases a day, was making its examinations and decisions at the rate of one a minute!

After six such frenzied days the board moved on for an unscheduled sitting in Mankato. The outside operators, unwilling to pass up so good a thing, accompanied it, and the St. Peter scene was repeated on only a slightly smaller scale. Then came Faribault. Enlarged by the addition of men from Mankato, the coterie journeyed ahead and were waiting, with signs up and business cards distributed among the crowd, when the board arrived.

## 12

The doings at St. Peter, noised abroad, drew observers to see for themselves. Among these was a farmer from Ottawa in Le Sueur County. The swindle worked by the outsiders made him angry, and when he talked to a man with lung disease who had been refused exemption and to another, able-bodied, who had been granted it, he decided that the government doctor was in collusion with the swindlers. The enrolment board's action was no "examination of fitness or unfitness for the service, but merely a buying and selling of exemption certificates."

To think of such a shameful, disloyal traffic, when brave men were fighting for the Union, baring their breasts to the enemy's bayonets, standing between Minnesota's firesides and the foe! It made his blood boil. He wrote a lengthy letter about it to the *St. Paul Daily Press,* which published it on January 31, 1865 over the signature "Radical Republican."

"Truth" and "Justice" quickly wrote to support "Radical Republican" with more examples of unfair exemptions and apparent corrup-

Outline map of the state of Minnesota, showing the
places associated with the Mayo story

Dr. and Mrs. W. W. Mayo, with Sarah, Phoebe, and Gertrude

Galena, Illinois, on the
Mississippi River, 1852

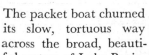

The packet boat churned
its slow, tortuous way
across the broad, beauti-
ful waters of Lake Pepin (from a water color by Edwin Whitefield, May 1859).

The boat whistled its approach and drew in to the wharf at St. Paul, the head of navigation for the regular Mississippi steamers.

The caravan of *bois brulés* camped on the prairie across the river from St. Paul.

From the St. Paul *Daily Minnesota Pioneer,* November 2, 1854

From the St. Paul *Daily Minnesotian,* October 2, 1855

The land route from St. Paul to Superior included long stretches of travel through dense woods (from a pencil sketch by Eastman Johnson).

The *Superior Chronicle* office in 1855

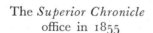

On the Minnesota side of Lake Superior stretched a hundred and fifty miles of rough lake shore.

There was beauty and wilderness enough in the Minnesota Valley to satisfy even Dr. Mayo.

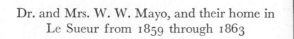

Dr. and Mrs. W. W. Mayo, and their home in
Le Sueur from 1859 through 1863

Everybody on the frontier called him
the "little doctor."

The Minnesota Sioux took the warpath (from a painting of New Ulm by Anton Gág).

Minnesota House    Post Office    Turn Hale    Bialzs Residence    Dacotah House

Dr. Mayo helped to defend New Ulm against the "red devils."

Cut Nose, the giant Sioux. From his skeleton the Mayo boys learned their first lessons in anatomy.

Execution of the thirty-nine Sioux, Mankato, December 26, 1862

Plat of Rochester, political, economic, and social capital of a rich farming area

Rochester in 1868

A wise woman, Mrs. W. W. Mayo,
enterprising and courageous

Friend and physician, ever true to a
trust and ever equal to the occasion

Will and his pony, little brother Charlie,
and the Mayo farmhouse

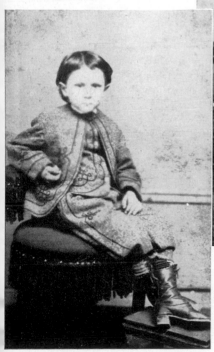

*Pioneer Minnesota physicians*
Alexander J. Stone, Charles N. Hewitt,
and Franklin R. Staples

A woman of tolerance, understanding, and equanimity

"A man of hope and forward-looking mind"

tion on the part of the officials. Then several others came hotly to the defense of the board, among them a lawyer and a newspaperman of eminence in the Minnesota Valley.

They admitted the activities of the outsiders but denied emphatically that the officials had any part in them. Could the board help it if unscrupulous practitioners charged illegal fees and insinuated that it was influence which made their papers effective? Eminent citizens of St. Peter who had been invited to be present at the board's sitting could testify that Dr. Mayo examined every candidate impartially, regardless of the certificate presented. His examinations were hurried and perhaps he made mistakes, but what on earth was the poor man to do with such a horde waiting outside the door? Besides, how did "Radical Republican" know whether a man was physically fit or not? Had he seen him stripped? Surely Dr. Mayo's opinion was worth more than that of an Ottawa farmer!

This discussion was in progress when the enrolment board began its session in Faribault. The editor of the Faribault newspaper had warned his readers not to be taken in by the promises of the outsiders. Their guarantees of exemption could not be worth a continental except in collusion with Dr. Mayo, and, he added, although we have no personal acquaintance with the Doctor, "from what we have heard of him we would not believe him a man guilty of any such baseness."

In his next issue the editor, well-known for his acid-tipped pen, fairly sputtered for lack of names vile enough to call the shylocks, shysters, and sharks who had come to prey upon the credulity of the people.

Considering the question of connivance by the enrolment board, he was calmer. He admitted that in the several hours each day that he had spent in the examining rooms he had seen no evidence of corruption, nothing but the most impartial examinations and consideration of claims. But his suspicion was aroused by the fact that Dr. Mayo gave private examinations in his rooms after hours and charged five-dollar fees for them, and then exempted most of the men he had examined when they appeared before the board.

By that time, if the uproar in the newspapers was a reliable sign, the entire state was talking about the scandal, and the question most hotly argued was whether or not Dr. Mayo was involved. The *St. Paul*

*Pioneer* informed its readers editorially that "In the Minnesota Valley, where Dr. Mayo has been known for years, no charge of official corruption would for a moment be entertained by the people." The *Daily Press,* more cautious, regretted that anything should "seem to impeach the integrity" of Dr. Mayo, who "has heretofore stood so high in the community."

## 13

Colonel John T. Averill, then acting as assistant provost marshal general for Minnesota, was moved to investigate the charges. He put a summary end to the session at Faribault, ordered the provost marshal of the board and Dr. Mayo to report to St. Paul, and authorized the arrest of the attendant doctors and lawyers who had been collecting illegal fees. Among the doctors so arrested were two army surgeons and the highly respected Dr. W. R. McMahon of Mankato, the president of the newly organized Minnesota Valley Medical Society.

In his hearing before Colonel Averill, Dr. Mayo frankly acknowledged that he had made private examinations. Some men could ill afford, or did not wish, to spend several days needlessly waiting in line. These he examined at night to inform them whether or not they were entitled to exemption. If he thought they were, they stayed for the examination in the presence of the board. If he thought not, they went home without waiting longer. What was dishonest about that? There was nothing at all like a bribe in the fees he collected. He had a right to charge something for his extra trouble and time, and the law permitted doctors to collect a five-dollar fee for such examinations.

But Colonel Averill did not agree. He ordered Dr. Mayo to report at Rochester under arrest and sent an account of the affair to the authorities in Washington. When the deputies sent to collect evidence at St. Peter and Faribault could find nothing more substantial than rumors, Colonel Averill decided to test the charges by a reexamination of those declared exempt at Faribault. He sent Dr. J. D. Wheelock, assistant surgeon of the second district enrolment board, to make the examinations and Captain W. H. Rossell, the mustering officer at Fort Snelling, to supervise them.

Their reports were written on February 20 and published two days later. Dr. Wheelock had approved one hundred and five of the one hundred and fifty-three exemptions granted by Dr. Mayo. In the other forty-eight cases he did not consider the disability sufficient to warrant exemption "under a *strict* construction" of the regulations issued by the provost marshal general. In most of these cases the certificates had been issued for loss of teeth, varicose veins, and heart disease.

Captain Rossell reported that he had found some persons in Rice County who believed that Dr. Mayo had received bribes, either directly or indirectly, but that as many others averred their complete confidence in the Doctor's integrity. Although he had made "full and free inquiry," he discovered no evidence of improper transactions on the part of the board, other than Dr. Mayo's private examinations.

Without waiting to receive those reports, however, the War Department dismissed Dr. Mayo from the army service "for receiving fees for private examinations," and a week later revoked the appointments of the provost marshal and the commissioner. A new board was immediately appointed, with Dr. Edwin C. Cross of Rochester as the examining surgeon, and in less than a month the newspapers were printing sensational stories of Dr. Cross's venality and incompetence.

14

When allowance has been made for rumor and suspicion exaggerated by indignation, it seems clear that the worst to be said of Dr. Mayo is that he was unwise. It is easy to understand his position in the matter of the private examinations, though it was injudicious to continue the practice when swindling was in progress all around and he himself was under suspicion. But as one of his defenders pointed out, the very smallness of the sum involved makes the idea of bribery absurd. If the Doctor wished to prostitute his office, there was no need to stop at five dollars; he could have had hundreds.

Nor is the charge that he granted unjustified exemptions sustained by Dr. Wheelock's findings in the reexamination at Faribault. There could easily be an honest difference of opinion between able doctors as to when loss of teeth had progressed to the point of hindering mastication, or when varicose veins were swollen and painful enough to interfere with marching—particularly if one man relied on a *strict* construction of a set of rules and the other was independent enough to use his own judgment.

# The Old Doctor

If Dr. Mayo was culpable, it was for allowing himself to be stampeded into such farcical examinations. In the opinion of other enrolment board surgeons not more than fifty men could be properly examined in one day, and to attempt doing several hundred was absurd.

The public verdict at the time, as expressed in the newspapers, is an impressive testimonial to the reputation Dr. Mayo had established. The overwhelming majority refused to believe that he could be deliberately guilty of anything dishonorable, and the *Mankato Union* was sure that

No one who is acquainted with Dr. Mayo will for a moment question his honesty and good intentions. He supposed from a reading of the law that he had a perfect right to give a private examination and charge a fee of five dollars. The authorities at Washington construed the law differently, and his official head has paid the forfeit.

The Republican journals were on his side, of course, but few even of the Democratic organs would go further than to approve his dismissal on the grounds that a public official ought to be, like Caesar's wife, above suspicion. The *Winona Democrat,* forswearing political partisanship, concluded an account of the affair by saying, "We have too much confidence in the character which [Dr. Mayo] has established, to yield our judgment till convinced by far more damning proof than has yet come to light."

# CHAPTER FOUR

# Rochester Then

"O Moses, how we would like to live in Rochester!" was the heartfelt wish of a Chatfield journalist after a visit to the Olmsted county seat early in 1865. He found everybody busy, in good spirits, full of ambitious plans, and magnificently sure of his own and the town's great future.

What Rochester was then is an essential factor in the story of what it has become. Although it was only ten years old, with fewer than three thousand residents, it was already the political, economic, and social capital of a rich agricultural district several hundred miles square and was rapidly developing into one of the largest primary wheat markets in the world.

In the fall of 1864 the railroad that had been moving slowly westward from Winona on the Mississippi finally reached Rochester. An elevator was built alongside the tracks, and the inland city became the grain depot for most of south central Minnesota, the funnel into which hundreds of thousands of bushels of wheat poured from all sides each year, and then poured out again along the railroad eastward. In harvest time the roads were lined with farmers on the way to dump their loads of grain into the wide-mouthed hoppers of the elevator. Wheat buyers, many of them agents for dealers in Milwaukee and Chicago, gathered at every entrance to town and as the wagons passed them called out their bids. Competition among them and between them and the local flour mills raised the price and the farmers' profits.

The farmers went wheat mad. They claimed more land, bought more machines, planted more wheat, more, and more. Never mind that being without capital they must finance the expansion on credit. If nature was kind a few good crops would pay off the debts. Here and there a wise man warned of danger in "this eternal wheat-raising," but his warning went unheeded. Wheat production spiraled dizzily upward.

# The Old Doctor

Where the farmers sold they bought. When father took the wheat to market mother and daughter went along "to trade a little" at the stores. Business boomed, and Rochester soon became a thriving distribution center for furniture, clothing, "Yankee notions," hardware, and farm machinery.

It became also a center of social life. When men made a trip to the county seat to appear in district court or to pay their taxes, they took time for conviviality in the saloons, billiard rooms, or "ball alleys." On holidays the population of the countryside drained into town for the mass entertainments arranged by the merchants—a parade, band concert, speeches, and fireworks on the Fourth of July, balls and banquets on Christmas and New Year's Day. Not content with the drawing power of their annual county fair, the Rochester men provided grounds, buildings, and arguments enough to win the state fair away from the Twin Cities several times. On such occasions the crowds numbered thousands, and visitors paid well for the privilege of sleeping on pallets of straw in churches or barns.

Word soon spread that Rochester was a paradise for showmen, and all sorts of troupers added it to their circuit—musicians and magicians, circuses and minstrel shows. People came from as far away as Winona to hear concerts by the Black Swan, a popular negro contralto, and Ole Bull, the celebrated Norwegian violinist.

Rochester was also a favorite rendezvous for the horse-racing fraternity, for it possessed the best race track in the state. A wealthy local businessman established a brood farm and racing stables, and raised and trained thoroughbreds that made creditable records in regional and national turf events. His horses, especially the oft-winning stallion Star of the West, became one of the prides of Rochester, and interest in the breeding and racing of fine horses spread among the people. The racing crowd was often rough and rowdy, but many of them had money and spent it freely, so Rochester did not complain but made them welcome.

2

It took only a few months' acquaintance with the busy, happy little town to make Dr. Mayo, like the Chatfield journalist, wish to live there, and with him the wish was father to the deed. He bought two lots on Franklin Street, built a cottage on one of them, and moved his family down from Le Sueur early in January 1864.

In the bedroom of that cottage, approximately where the fountain bubbles in the lobby of the present Clinic building, the Mayos' second son was born on July 19, 1865. They named him Charles Horace, Charles because that was a favorite name in the family from which Dr. Mayo was descended, and Horace because it was the name they had given to the son who died.

When Dr. Mayo was dismissed from his post as examining surgeon, he bought a small piece of ground on downtown Third Street, built a snug little office room, decorated it with a plaster bust of President Lincoln, and invited patronage with a newspaper card that was bold and defiant by virtue of its uncommonly few words and big type. No one could miss it, it stood out so among its fine-print fellows:

DR. MAYO

Office on Third Street
Rochester, Minn.

With characteristic energy and assurance the Doctor accepted the invitation to leadership offered by the needs and possibilities of Rochester, and he was soon a force to be reckoned with in community life. His first efforts went toward providing the city with a library, and late in 1865 he joined with half a dozen other men to form the Rochester Library Association. He contributed fifty dollars to the book fund, helped to solicit subscriptions from others, and as a member of the executive committee took a leading part in selecting the first fifteen hundred books and establishing the collection in comfortable reading rooms above the bank.

The association also decided to sponsor an annual course of lectures, and Dr. Mayo was named with one other to plan them. The two men arranged series by current celebrities, state and national, including over a period of three years such figures as Wendell Phillips, Horace Greeley, Anna E. Dickinson, "the best and ablest representative of the rapidly increasing class of women known as the strong-minded," Fred Douglas, a negro orator of great repute, and Earle S. Youmans, a popularizer of science. The strong-minded woman drew the biggest crowd.

As a whole the lectures did not pay, however, and the association decided to try home talent. Would Dr. Mayo give a supplementary course to test the probable response? He would do the best he could.

But this was one of the occasions on which he treated a plan he did not like to subtle sabotage, or else he had an exaggerated opinion of the caliber of his public. He announced a course on, of all things for general consumption, anatomy and physiology! He must have planned to cover the areas of the body from tip to toe, for he began with "The Anatomy of the Brain." According to the newspaper report he had "a large and appreciative audience" and with the aid of brightly colored charts did a good job of making his technical subject clear. But he was not urged to continue the series.

In the meantime he had entered heartily into the activities of the local Republican party and had served a year as county chairman. In the spring of 1867 he was elected to the school board, and soon afterward the board decided to put up a new building. The Rochester school, still of the ungraded district variety, had been housed by turns in an abandoned log cabin, a remodeled carriage shop, and a vacant basement room, and was currently meeting in odds and ends of space in the courthouse. Intelligent citizens had long been protesting, thinking the town was large and prosperous enough to afford a respectable schoolhouse.

Prodded to action at last, the city fathers built with characteristic optimism and largeness of plan. Late in 1868 the superintendent of schools in Olmsted County reported to the state department of public instruction that Rochester had just completed one of the finest school buildings in the West—a brick building, five stories, sixteen rooms, single desks, furnace heat, cost $65,000.

Such a schoolhouse in Rochester? Not even St. Paul had anything like that. The state superintendent journeyed down to see it and went back to tell the legislature that Rochester had "the largest and most costly" school building in the state.

Dr. Mayo undoubtedly had a great deal to do with it, for he was given to just such big ideas for Rochester as the building represented, and education was one of the subjects on which he had strong convictions. Throughout his life he felt himself qualified and duty-bound to criticize the conduct of the school.

Once he was named chairman of the committee of citizens appointed annually to visit the classes and report conditions to the public. Most committees of the kind thought their duty done when they had penned a pretty tribute to the schoolmistress, but not the Mayo committee. The Doctor—for it was surely he who wrote the report—spoke his mind. He disapproved of the feeble voices and poor enunciation countenanced in one class and the hand-raising and finger-snapping allowed in another, because such disturbances surely hindered the thought processes of the more timid pupils. And finally,

there was an apparent restlessness, an apathetic indifference to the higher achievements of the school room, which showed us that some of the stronger wills before us had not yet been convinced that they were trifling with their own best interests.

It would seem from the action of some of these children as if they thought our City Fathers had . . . erected, at great expense, a gigantic playhouse for very large children with small ambitions; instead of a school house for instruction.

3

When the Republican party caucus nominated Dr. Mayo for election to the school board for the fourth time in the spring of 1870, a disgruntled faction led by John Edgar, a zealous church member and temperance leader, labeled him an infidel and a friend to Demon Rum and bolted to the Democrats, thereby accomplishing the defeat of the entire Republican ticket.

Since the successful Democratic candidate was no more a teetotaler or churchgoer than Dr. Mayo, the charge that Edgar and his friends acted from personal spite rather than moral principle seems justified. In any event, from that time forward frequent verbal jousts between Dr. Mayo and the pious Edgar added spice, sometimes too much, to Rochester politics.

Normal touchiness on the subject of religion had been intensified in Rochester by the activities of a group called the Society of the Friends of Progress. According to the ministers of the gospel, its members were infidels. They denied the divine origin and supernatural element of Christianity and through the study of science and philosophy were seeking to formulate a faith "consonant with the laws of nature" that would work for "the elevation of the human race."

# The Old Doctor

The age of science was crossing the threshold of the Western World, and among the gifts it brought was a clean, cold question mark for traditional values and beliefs. The warfare between science and theology was beginning, and with it the conflict between modernism and fundamentalism within the church.

Thomas Huxley and Herbert Spencer were leading the battle for Darwinism in England, as was Ernst Haeckel in Germany. And they were doing more than offer a new theory of man's origin, or even a new biology; they were pleading the cause of science as an intellectual discipline and urging the application of its critical spirit to the daily doing and thinking of mankind.

Of the three Huxley was the most easily understood and therefore the most widely known, for he was making it his mission to carry the gospel of science to common men. He wanted to get their minds off heaven and hell and onto the job of improving life on earth. "We live in a world that is full of misery and ignorance," he wrote, "and the plain duty of each and all of us is to try to make the little corner he can influence somewhat less miserable and somewhat less ignorant than it was before he came."

Souls who took their religion seriously and their Bible literally were shocked by such materialism and by the theory of evolution from which it came, but to Dr. Mayo, Darwin and Huxley brought the thrill of discovery. Their ideas delighted and stimulated his mind. He added their works and those of Haeckel and Spencer to his library as fast as they appeared, read Huxley's essays aloud to his friends, and discussed and defended Darwinism by the hour. No wonder he was labeled an infidel.

The theory of evolution gave no wrench to his spiritual moorings, for he had been bent toward science by the training of his youth and had never yielded more than a superficial allegiance to any church or creed. "He was an Episcopalian, but he didn't work very hard at it," was the way his elder son summarized his father's religion. Dr. Mayo himself defined his position by quoting Bismarck, "I never felt the need of any [religious faith], and therefore never had any," and adding an echo of Huxley's humanitarian creed, "My own religion has been to do all the good I could to my fellow men, and as little harm as possible."

# Rochester Then

Freethinker and confessed unbeliever though he was, Dr. Mayo was not a scornful cynic in religion. He felt sincere respect for simple, honest faith always, and he did not care what church or creed inspired it. He got on as well, if not better, with Catholics as with Protestants. Easily and comfortably he stood with the parish priests at the bedsides of his many Catholic patients, and he and the fathers became fast friends.

His attitude toward morals, or mores if one prefers, was equally unorthodox. He cast no stones at the prostitutes of New York or at the drunkards of Rochester. The former moved him to sentimental pity and the latter called him when they got into trouble in a street brawl, called him both as physician to patch up their wounds and as a friend to plead their cause with the magistrates.

Toward the weaknesses of such persons he was tolerant, reserving his censure for dishonesty and corruptibility in high places, for he thought education, opportunity, and wealth carried an obligation to be strong. In his standards for conduct in public office he was the sternest of puritans, not one whit the lenient liberal.

He would have denied the charge of puritanism vigorously though, for to him puritans were carping busybodies who tried to run the brewers and cigar-makers out of business in order to keep men from drinking and smoking, who wanted to raise license fees to absurd heights and so get rid of billiards and bowling, who talked the town into an uproar because the young folk dared to dance at a public sociable. Toward them and their attempts to force their prejudices and proscriptions upon the entire community he could feel no charity at all.

Amusements were as necessary as sermons, he stoutly maintained. He did not smoke himself but he saw no reason why others should not do so if they wished. He liked a nip of whisky on occasion, kept a quart or pint of it on hand at home, and thought a tankard of porter or ale often the best possible medicine for what ailed folk's spirits. Teach temperance, yes; legislate prohibition, no, a positive and uncompromising no.

That attitude, exaggerated by his opponents into an all-out defense of the saloon and the whisky ring, led to his defeat in 1870 and was made an issue against him in many a later campaign.

93

For several seasons bad weather had worked havoc with the local wheat crop, and striving frantically each time to stave off ruin until a good season next year should relieve the stringency, many farmers borrowed heavily at whatever rates of interest were asked of them. Some had mortgaged everything they possessed, down to the plow in the field and the next year's crop, and many a farmer and his wife went about their work with grim faces in the tense summer of 1869. If the wheat crop should fail this year— But nature smiled, and the yield was bountiful.

Too bountiful. The price of wheat, which had been trending gradually downward from the peak of two dollars and more a bushel in the palmy days just after the war, now dropped sharply, to sixty cents, fifty cents, forty cents a bushel. Forty cents, when it cost the farmer from sixty to eighty cents to raise and harvest it!

Creditors were seized with alarm and hurriedly took legal action to recover their investments. A local panic resulted. When the lien and mortgage foreclosures listed in the Rochester newspapers mounted to more than fifty a week, other towns cried shame, for although the slump was general throughout southeastern Minnesota, Rochester was harder hit than most places, since its business had been brisker, its borrowing and lending and buying on credit more extensive.

The national economic forces contributing to their plight were beyond the horizon of most of the losers, so they fastened upon grievances nearer home, of which the chief was the stranglehold of the railroad and the "wheat ring."

Freight rates were both exorbitant and discriminatory. Being the only carrier out of Rochester, the Winona and St. Peter Railroad raised its rates there to compensate for losses at points where it had to meet competition. By refusing to handle the shipments of independent warehousemen, it had secured a monopoly for its own elevator, which was charged with resorting to unfair grading practices to increase its profits. By granting rate rebates to a group of cooperating wheat dealers the railroad helped to eliminate the competition among buyers that had given the farmer his bargaining power. He could now store, sell, and ship his grain on monopoly terms, or he could let it rot in the field. He was at the mercy of the railroad and the wheat ring, and he found no mercy in them.

In the spring of 1870 the price of wheat again neared seventy-five cents, and the farmers who had been able to hold out for such an eventuality rushed to sell. Whereupon the railroad, with insufferable insolence, upped the freight rates from eight to fifteen cents a bushel. The farmers swore "oaths loud and deep," and gathered in angry, excited knots on the street corners and called public indignation meetings. Slowly came the realization that although individually they were helpless, collectively they could be strong. They had the power of the ballot and must unite to elect legislators and executives who would represent them instead of the "soulless corporations."

## 5

That was the beginning in and around Rochester of the social phenomenon historians call "the agrarian crusade." During more than two decades Dr. Mayo was an outstanding local leader in that crusade, for reasons that he explained in one of his last campaign letters:

I am often asked by my friends why I, as a professional man and doing a good business, should bother myself about these things. In reply, First, it is every man's duty to take an interest in the city affairs. Second, as a physician I am better capable of understanding the situation than most other people. I have in a professional way ridden over this county for more than twenty-five years. Having seen a generation grow up to manhood, I have personally known of the struggles and privations of many families in their efforts to attain a medium competence. I have seen many of them ruined by the snaky ways of the wily money loaner who has become rich upon other men's ruin. I have seen men robbed of their earnings by combinations of wheat and coal rings and a railroad which has given them the opportunity to plunder, and to carry away their plunder.

The despair and destitution the little doctor met at close hand on his daily rounds called into full play the quick, flooding sympathy that put him always on the side of the underdog. The man on top was *ipso facto* in the wrong. Seeing those he blamed as the authors of this wretchedness protected by the laws and abetted by corruptible politicians, Dr. Mayo was moved to action. He believed firmly that a government ought to be by and for the people—the many, not the few.

# The Old Doctor

His activity began in the fall of 1870. When the Republicans made their nomination for congressman in fulfillment of a political bargain agreed to two years before, Dr. Mayo, "unwilling to yield servile submission to a packed convention," promptly joined with a few Winona men of the same stripe in an effort to mobilize the disaffected Republicans and the Democrats behind a "people's candidate" on an anti-railroad, anti-monopoly, and free trade platform. They set out on a canvass of the district to enlist support, and when one Republican leader after another declared his approval of the project Dr. Mayo felt sure the bolt would be a success.

Apparently the Republican machine began to think so too, for the party organs changed swiftly from a tolerant amusement to an attack that by its fury betrayed alarm. They must have been sure that most of the bolters could be cajoled or bribed back into line and equally sure that Dr. Mayo could not be, for they were soon concentrating all their venom on the Doctor. And a nasty lot of it there was.

But the Doctor reacted with dignity to the raillery and invective, and was goaded only once into making a reply in print:

I am charged by the Rochester *Post* with acting from no other motive than ordinary personal enmity; and some of the smaller partizan sheets seem at a loss for epithets vile enough to characterize my conduct, and for what? Why, for daring to exercise a right that belongs to every man. . . . For my part I was willing to leave the matter with the voters of the district to determine at the polls, had I not been unmercifully dragged before the people of the entire State, and forced into a vindication of my course by giving the reasons for my disaffection.

Unhappily, however, the reasons he gave were not matters of principle but only the same sort of personal attack, though not so abusive or nearly so vulgarly offensive.

## 6

When it came time to make a public stand Dr. Mayo's supposed allies lost their political courage, dropped away one by one on some pretext or other, and left him entirely alone. Whereupon he joined the Democrats, took an active part in their convention, and devoted all his energies to electing their county ticket.

# Rochester Then

That brought him into alliance with Harry Young, his Hoosier friend who had edited the *Le Sueur Courier*. During the Civil War Young had acted as war correspondent in Virginia for the *New York Times* and the *New York World*. Then the trouble with his lungs that had sent him to Minnesota in the first place came back and, desperately ill, he headed once more for Dr. Mayo, in whose skill he had absolute confidence. The Doctor sent him west to Lake Traverse for a winter in the wilds, and now, restored to health, he was back in Rochester editing the Democratic *Federal Union*.

In later years Dr. Mayo was sometimes thoroughly exasperated with Harry Young, considering him insanely egotistical, impractical, too narrow a Democrat for the party's good, and Young undoubtedly had good cause to reciprocate the irritation at times, in spite of his boundless admiration for Dr. Mayo. But on this occasion the two men worked together in entire harmony and practically took over the management of the campaign.

Olmsted County never got a more thorough stumping than they and their candidates gave it that year. Since Dr. Mayo was willing and seemingly endowed with inexhaustible energy, he was scheduled to speak almost every night in some town hall or crossroads schoolhouse. Some of the speeches he made were published, and if his delivery matched his words it is easy to see why he was called "our most effective speaker." He sometimes began with carefully styled generalities, but when he turned to the problems of the people his phrases took on vigor and concreteness.

On the railroad issue he rebuked those who urged a boycott of the cars and a return to horse-and-wagon hauling. A retreat to oxen and the lumbering old stagecoach was as unthinkable as exchanging the mechanical mower for the scythe. "I am no enemy to railroads or to mechanical and scientific advancement in any and every direction."

No, the evil lay in the men who owned and managed the lines. "If I could treat this railroad company in my profession," he declared, "I would give them such a puke as would bring their corns from their toes through their stomachs." Instead he prescribed a stiff dose of government regulation, refusing to believe that by granting a charter the state surrendered its right to protect the people.

On the subject of the protective tariff foisted upon the nation by the eastern manufacturers and their agents in the seats of government he grew dramatic and sentimental, making much of the poor widow struggling to support her orphaned children. She must pay toll to heartless men of wealth for her shelter and clothing, even for fuel to keep up "her waning fires on such nights as we involuntarily cry, God help the poor." She "goes to the throne of grace and prays for justice, and the bloated monopolist to the throne at Washington, to get protection while he robs the poor."

Such speeches were rewarded with success. Although the Republicans carried the district, Olmsted County, one of the strongest Republican counties in a consistently Republican state, went to the Democrats. Jubilant at the victory, they staged a big celebration in Rochester, and Harry Young saw to it that Dr. Mayo was given full credit for his share in the achievement—while the disconsolate editor of the Republican *Post* made public lament that his party had thrown away enough brains to set the Democrats up in business.

7

Rochester suffered greatly from the slump in the wheat business. Some of its business firms went into bankruptcy, others moved away, and the main street was lined with vacant storerooms. Houses stood empty too, and prairie schooners were once again a familiar sight, but now they were going, not coming. Family after family left to make new homes in Dakota Territory. One large group of prospective emigrants even organized a colonization society and sent representatives ahead to select a townsite beyond the Red River and prepare it for their coming.

The decline was reflected on all sides. One constant reminder of it was the Cook House. Ambitious citizens, dissatisfied with the crude little boardinghouses that passed for hotels, had clamored for a new hostelry to impress visitors with the prosperity and importance of Rochester. Finally John R. Cook, the banker, began the erection of a new business block to house storerooms on the first floor and a hotel on the three above. With complacent pride the citizens watched the structure rise, knowing it would be the finest and largest hotel in southern Minnesota. No one dreamed it might be too big for the town. But there it stood now, empty except for a few stores and offices because Mr. Cook could find no one with temerity enough to undertake its management.

All in all, remembering happier times, Rochester was sunk in gloom. Dr. Mayo was willing to admit that "as a mere town of exchange and barter, as mere middle men for the trading commerce in wheat and farm machinery . . . we have already attained our acme and the day of retrogression is upon us," but he was stoutheartedly sure that if the citizens would only bestir themselves to develop some new lines of activity good times would come again and growth would resume.

So he became a sort of Io's ox-fly in municipal affairs. He would not let the city fathers rest, but was always urging them to make some improvement or expansion. The "Bear Creek improvement project" was his special pet. He wanted the city to build up the roadbed of College Street so as to dam Bear Creek, one of the streams flowing into the Zumbro River. Besides providing more water power for new industries and saving the cost of repairing College Street every time the Zumbro developed a freshet, the scheme would turn the flats along Bear Creek into a pretty lake whose shores could be made into a park. At present the flats, almost in the center of town, were an eyesore, good for nothing but a rubbish dump and a cow pasture.

Dr. Mayo's enthusiasm almost carried the day, but the opposition mustered strength enough to get the project shelved just in time. The Doctor did not give up hope though, and kept raising the question at every opportunity.

## 8

Twice during the seventies Dr. Mayo was the Democratic candidate for the post of school commissioner, but he did not expect to be elected, having put himself on the wrong side of the political fence in Republican Rochester. Consequently, when in 1882 he was elected mayor as the candidate of the Democrats and also of a "People's Anti-Monopoly convention," no one was more genuinely surprised by his victory than he. "My election as chief magistrate shows a sudden and extraordinary change in the views and temper of the people," he told the aldermen. The change seems to have been a fresh resentment against the practices of the wheat ring. The Doctor's opposition to that monopoly was well known, whereas his Republican opponent was actually one of the wheat dealers.

The new mayor had an exaggerated notion of the importance of his office and was proud of his election. He had no intention of being a passive figurehead who merely put the motions at council meetings and lent official dignity to public functions. He was going to get things done. The very first council meeting gave promise of stormy sessions ahead, though the inaugural address began pleasantly enough:

For a good many years I have been very intimate with your mayor. I know him very well. So far as this council is concerned, he has only one purpose, one object in view. I have not the slightest objection to telling you the secret by which he hopes to gain success. His purpose is to govern this council in accordance with the rules laid down for him, his object the best interests of the city. Of his ability to perform, you will be the best able to judge at the end of the year.

But then he advised the majority to mend their ways and encouraged the minority to do their best for the city in spite of opposition. He knew, he said, that already they and he and the people who had voted for them had been "denounced from the pulpit as atheists and communists, in the silly twaddle of a Court preacher, who truckles to his rich parishioners."

Finally he demanded that the council do something at once about providing the city with a decent seat of government. The musty loft in which they met was a disgrace, and to reach it one had to go through a dark and muddy alley, up a rickety stairway, and through the dark kitchen of a tenement cluttered with kettles and washtubs. When visitors came to see him as mayor, he would be expected to take them to view the council room, as he had been taken on visits to officials in other cities. Well, he certainly would never bring anyone *here*!

Some of the aldermen supposed they could rent a better room, and offered a resolution to that effect. That would be all right as a temporary expedient, snapped the mayor, but Rochester was going to get a new city hall at once. Things had come to a pretty pass when the city marshal had to beg desk space in one of the tobacco shops.

His statements aroused the resentment of some of the men who had served on the council before; the room had been good enough for former mayors and councils, why not for Dr. Mayo? They moved to lay the resolution on the table.

If they passed that motion, threatened the Doctor, he would not set foot in the place again. He would not do city business in such a hole. They did pass the motion, and he stalked out, refusing even to put the motion to adjourn.

To build or not to build a new city hall became the question of the day. Public meetings were held to discuss it, and the newspapers sent reporters to tabulate the opinions of representative citizens. The agitation continued for months, and though Dr. Mayo did not get his new council rooms during his own term of office, a city hall was built the following year.

So it went throughout his term, the mayor and the council majority always at loggerheads. Dr. Mayo was entirely lacking in the qualities of compromise, patience, and subtle suggestion necessary for the success of an executive who has not dictatorial powers. He was suited more to command than to persuade. So nothing of much moment was accomplished while he was mayor and he was not reelected.

In 1885, however, he was elected alderman from his ward and for four years carried on his agitation for civic improvements from within the council. He thought Rochester ought to have a waterworks to provide the citizens with a steady supply of good water, and he hired engineers to prepare a feasible plan, which he then proceeded to urge upon the council. For months he talked and argued the matter against strong opposition, and although his plan was not adopted, the council finally granted a franchise to a private company.

Dr. Mayo was content, but there were some folk who remained hostile to the idea of any water system at all, and they called it an act of God when an epidemic of sunstroke broke out among the workmen who were digging the new wells. What grounds they could find for the Almighty's objecting so vigorously to the provision of a city water supply is beyond understanding, but Dr. Mayo ordered that a cupful of oatmeal be added to each bucket of drinking water for the workmen, and, whether as a direct result or not, the sunstrokes stopped.

He waged similar battles for a system of sewers, a gas works, and an electric light plant. In time he saw them all established and heard people give him credit for sowing the seeds that produced them. But in each case his proposal encountered bitter opposition at first. Men said the city could not afford the improvements. To which the Doctor, reasoning in surprisingly modern vein, replied that Rochester could not afford *not* to afford them:

My opinion always has been that the government is responsible for the comfort and wealth of its people and the growth of the nation. The city council is responsible for the wealth and growth of the city.

In the winter and often in the summer time a great many men willing to labor and even asking for employment are to be met about the streets idle and needy. Now, if these men were employed in improving public buildings and streets, we will say that you merchants and townspeople would be taxed higher to pay them $6 or $9 a week.

But what is done with their wages? It is put out among your shoe men, grocers, and other merchants and so returned to you.

By utilizing these men thus, you not only provide for them and their families, giving them means of becoming respectable and independent and educating their children, many of whom are growing up in ignorance and misery, but you would push the city.

## 9

Affairs in Rochester did not in the least exhaust Dr. Mayo's energies; he continued to participate in county and district politics all the while, working usually with the Democrats, but always actively in support of any coalition with the ephemeral reform groups that flickered across the screen at election time.

Most of the reforms they proposed were toward increasing popular control of the government, and Dr. Mayo advocated them enthusiastically. Not all of them, however. He could not accept the idea of woman suffrage, for instance, feeling only scorn for women of the "bloomer species" and for reformers "of the male gender but female persuasion" who supported their cause. He thought it would be a crime to degrade such a gentle, charming creature as woman to equality with common man, and besides, such equality was contrary to all the laws of nature.

The pernicious influence of the railroad and the wheat ring had become a bogey that Dr. Mayo saw in everything and everyone that opposed him, but he did not imagine the whole of the evil he fought against. When it was so general throughout the nation, there is no reason to doubt that it existed in Olmsted County. Some of Dr.

Mayo's early allies had given up the struggle against it as a hopeless cause, and they were amused at his continued efforts.

They told him that when every phase of the nation's life was run by "rings" of some sort, political or economic, his tirades against the local samples were of as little use as the treatment of a corn when a man was suffering from typhoid fever, pneumonia, *and* smallpox. He might better accept the situation, they said, and instead of fighting political corruption make up a purse and put it where it would do the most good.

But Dr. Mayo was not cut to that pattern. And in time these men came to feel a grudging, then a wholehearted, admiration for his incorruptibility and persistence in the crusade for his principles.

In earlier years Dr. Mayo had often indulged in personalities in his political addresses and letters but seldom in the vituperation and name-calling that passed for political argument. His experience in the forum, however, taught him to use the weapons of his opponents, and he learned to match invective with the masters of it.

Moved on one occasion to answer two particularly abusive editorials that appeared in the *Post,* apparently written by his perennial enemy, John Edgar, he spiced his really admirable defense with uncomplimentary references to Edgar, calling him a fool, liar, polecat, a man "of brass and boldness, if not brains," and a money-loaner who lived off the poverty of the county.

The letter was not unusual for that day, but Dr. Mayo did not make sure of his target before he let the arrow fly. Edgar had not written the editorials in question, and he gleefully kept the threat of a suit for libel dangling over the Doctor's head for weeks. By the threat of a similar suit against the *Federal Union,* he forced the paper to repudiate Dr. Mayo's statements and then used the repudiation as ammunition in the next campaign.

## 10

No literate person in Olmsted County could have been unaware of Dr. Mayo's position on any public question. He was forever addressing some group on something—the holiday crowds at Fourth of July or Memorial Day exercises; the German citizens when they staged a parade and bonfire to celebrate the victory of their fatherland in the war with France; the Irishmen when they met to express collectively their indignation at the plight of Ireland; all sorts of workingmen's, farmers', and citizens' rallies, many of which he himself called together. In addition he made a speaking tour of the county in almost every fall campaign, and sometimes covered the district too.

Many of his speeches were published, and together with his frequent letters to the editor and communications and reports to the city council and the board of trade, they fill an astonishing number of columns of fine print on an equally astonishing array of subjects.

So it is not surprising that when Dr. Mayo was the candidate of the Democrats for state representative or state senator in the latter eighties, the *Federal Union* was at a loss for something to say about him. Everybody knew Dr. Mayo; everybody knew what he stood for. What could the editor add? People agreed with him and would vote for him, or they did not and would not.

More and more of them did so agree and so vote. In 1886 he lost the election by just two hundred votes, and in 1888 the victory should have been his. He missed it by one vote, but he probably lost more than that in one village, where his name was left off the ballot.

In the fall of 1889 the Farmers' Alliance entered the political field as a third party, and the following spring Dr. Mayo joined the local Alliance unit. He considered himself entirely eligible, for he was again a farmer. In 1875 he had bought a farm on the outskirts of Rochester and the next year moved his family out there to live, at least during the summer months. Although he hired a man to supervise the actual work, he managed the farm himself and became very much interested in improvements in farm machinery and in livestock breeding. Someone writing for the *Rochester Post* at the time described the place:

One day this week we accepted an invitation from Dr. Mayo to ride out to his pleasant farm home, situated on the south side of College street, about one mile east of Broadway. The Doctor's farm embraces thirty-five acres, consisting of plow-land and natural meadow, being well adapted to the raising of both grain and stock.

On a gentle eminence some twenty rods from the street are the buildings which are approached by a pleasant driveway lined on either side with young thrifty Lombardy poplars. From this site, a beautiful and magnificent view of the city, Zumbro valley, and the towering bluffs, together with portions of the far-stretching prairie, is had.

# Rochester Then

The Doctor is putting up a large and elegant two-story upright or addition to his residence, which, when completed, will be one of the most convenient and imposing residences in the city. Among the desirable features of the new building are two large bay windows and a tower some forty feet in height with an observatory at the top [for Mrs. Mayo's study of astronomy].

A large convenient barn, affording ample stabling and granary, is a prominent feature on this farm.

Dr. Mayo has an eye to good stock, [such] as blooded cows and some choice breeds of hogs, while his large flock of English pigeons, with their beautiful plumage and constant chattering and cooing, are very pretty to look upon and listen to.

With the projected improvements completed, the Doctor will have a home which for beauty, convenience and situation, will be exceedingly pleasant and desirable.

Dr. Mayo took his avocation seriously. Concerning his eligibility for membership in the Farmers' Alliance, he wrote to Ignatius Donnelly:

It can make no difference whether my profession keeps the farm or the farm keeps me. I am like other farmers; if it was not [for] physic I should go [to] the devil as soon as other farmers. My profession enables me to hold on to the world by the skin of my teeth until we can bring the r.r. to time.

Not long thereafter Donnelly, during a visit to Rochester, recorded his opinion of the Doctor in his diary: "the leading physician and anti-monopolist of the town; an intelligent, capable man." Donnelly was then the state lecturer for the Farmers' Alliance, and it was probably through his influence if not by his appointment that Dr. Mayo was named Alliance lecturer for the Rochester district.

In August 1890 the district Alliance, assembled as a political convention, nominated Dr. Mayo for a four-year term in the state senate, and two months later the Democrats agreed to what amounted to a coalition with the Alliance by endorsing the same candidates. Dr. Mayo was not present at the convention, perhaps by prearrangement, so a committee was sent to escort him to the hall. The loud cheers that greeted his appearance brought on the "ebullition of feeling" that often prevented his speaking, but he got control of himself and thanked the convention for the honor, admitting that his friends on the committee sent to fetch him had warned him not to "slop over."

Whenever he had done that, he assured them, he had been plain Dr. Mayo doing and saying what he pleased regardless of the consequences. Now he was their candidate and would conduct himself with all dignity and give them no cause to blush for him.

This time he won the election.

## 11

Ignatius Donnelly was also elected to the senate, and the two men exchanged "a thousand congratulations!" They felt that at long last "the sky is crimson with promise" and they laid plans for working together "to control the Senate if possible."

But they did not find it so easy to work together as they had expected. The Alliance had elected enough of its candidates to give them the balance of power in the legislature, and Donnelly was their acknowledged leader. Wishing to put Alliance men into all the offices of both houses, Donnelly asked the Doctor to see to it that the Democratic candidate for chief clerk of the lower house withdrew in favor of an Alliance man. Dr. Mayo refused. That would be unjust; Smalley was a sound man, whatever party name he wore, and besides, Dr. Mayo owed as much to the Democrats as to the Alliance.

The Doctor would be responsible for splitting the Alliance men and the Democrats if he did not give in, because Donnelly threatened to tell the Alliance men to vote with the Republicans. But if Donnelly thought he could bluff his colleague into acquiescence, he did not know his man. Dr. Mayo told him he could go plumb to hell and stay there, and the delighted bystanders gave an undisputed decision to the bristling little doctor.

He did not make any phenomenal record as senator. It was easier to say what ought to be done in legislative halls than to do it when he got there. He served on several important committees and secured the passage of some special bills for the benefit of his constituents, but he had bad luck with his major bills. He introduced three (two for the regulation of railroads and one for the regulation of medical practice) and worked especially hard for the passage of two others (one for a constitutional amendment permitting the levying of a state income tax and one for the establishment of grain elevators on railroad right-of-ways), but none of them became law.

It must have given him great satisfaction, however, to share in the enactment of a law that eventually eliminated the unfair grain-grading practices of which the farmers had complained so long.

Dr. Mayo ended his active career in politics when he retired from the senate, at the age of seventy-four. But for more than ten years longer he was an honored adviser in district Democratic councils. He kept well abreast of political developments and was never without positive convictions on any issue or any candidate.

# CHAPTER FIVE

# Horse-and-Buggy Doctor

Dr. Mayo did himself an injustice when, in declining to undertake the promotion of a cooperative insurance scheme among the members of the Farmers' Alliance, he excused himself to Ignatius Donnelly by saying, "You know I must give more or less attention to my profession." In only a few campaign moments did he neglect his professional duties for the sake of politics. With a manifestation of energy in his wiry little body that moved his friends to head-shaking wonder, he carried on the two main phases of his life side by side, each influencing his progress in the other.

When he began to practice in Rochester he got no such discouraging reception as Dr. Ayer had given him in Le Sueur; there were enough patients here to keep several doctors busy. Where men transact their business and find their amusements they are quite likely also to seek their doctors, so Rochester was already the medical capital of a good-sized country district.

It even boasted what might be called a clinic, if the meaning of that word be stretched a bit. The institution was called the Rochester Infirmary and was owned by two brothers, Drs. Edwin C. and Elisha W. Cross. The older brother, Edwin, with an excellent medical education and ten years' experience in practice, had wandered westward from Vermont in 1858, seeking a promising spot in which to settle. He found it in Rochester, and within two years was so busy that he sent for his younger brother, Elisha, also well trained and experienced, to help him. Three years more and Rochester was claiming for the Cross brothers the largest medical practice in all of southern Minnesota.

By that time they had bought an old grocery store, remodeled it into an infirmary, and equipped it with all the necessary apparatus for the thorough practice of homeopathic and hydropathic medicine. They provided facilities for "Shower Baths, Full Baths, Half Baths, Sitz Baths, Douches, Plunges, and all other Baths necessary for the treatment of diseases . . . fully supplied with an abundance of *Pure Soft Water,* at any required temperature. . . . Also Vapor Baths, pure or medicated, for the treatment of diseases of the skin."

They were also prepared to dispense, singly or in assortments for the family medicine shelf, the thirty-four kinds of white pellets that constituted the homeopath's weapons against disease. And to the unfortunates who might need surgical treatment they offered the solace of having the operation performed with instruments made to order by the best French instrument makers.

In their profuse advertising the Drs. Cross solicited especially the patronage of "patients from a distance," promising immediate personal attention at all times either at the infirmary or in the patient's home.

The sick came from all over Olmsted and adjoining counties. When a broken leg did not mend under a local doctor's treatment, the sufferer was taken to the Drs. Cross. When an injured man remained unconscious from what the village physician called "a mere scalp wound," the Drs. Cross were summoned to trephine the fractured skull.

Beyond doubt Edwin Cross was a man of acumen and knew well how to administer his own reputation, but he was skilled above the average too. He was a man of great bulk, with heavy dark brows above a forbidding face. As he rode his powerful black horse through the streets of Rochester, he carried his huge shoulders hunched close to his head, so the youngsters called him "Monkey Cross." He was rough and gruff, not given to wasting time in sympathy. Patients feared him, especially women in confinement, but they employed him.

Elisha, to the end of his days known as "young Dr. Cross," had equal physical proportions and equal ability as a doctor, but was less impressive, being more amiable and less obviously aggressive.

The systems of medical practice to which the Cross brothers adhered did not in the least prejudice their standing in the community, for only in the minds of doctors themselves was there any clear distinction among the various medical sects. Since the profession was unorganized and medical practice entirely unregulated in Minnesota, as it was everywhere else, good men and outright quacks mingled under all the labels.

# The Old Doctor

To the lay public a doctor was a doctor, and his abilities and personality rather than his school of medical thought determined his status. Indeed, reacting against the copious bloodletting and heroic dosage with emetics and purgatives that had become the rule in medical practice, patients were inclined to welcome the gentle medication of the homeopath and the pleasant water cure of the hydropathist.

In 1866, however, Dr. Elisha Cross refused to continue under the sign of homeopath and dissolved the partnership with his brother. The latter maintained the infirmary for a few years longer; then he too saw the writing on the wall and returned to the fold of the regular profession, quickly becoming a leader in the local and state medical societies. Thereafter the two brothers resumed their old partnership at intervals and, working jointly or alone, continued to be Rochester's busiest and wealthiest doctors throughout the first half of the 1870's.

With the kindly Elisha Dr. Mayo got on very well, but he and Edwin never more than tolerated each other, and often not that. From the first they took opposite sides of almost every civic and political question. To a man like Dr. Cross, Mayo seemed an impecunious, impractical idealist whom one could comfortably ignore except when he made a confounded nuisance of himself with his radical ideas, and Dr. Mayo thought E. C. Cross more concerned with money-making than any man, let alone a doctor, had a right to be.

Early in the 1860's Dr. Cross prescribed for a man in Marion, who subsequently was killed in the war. Seven or eight years passed. Then his widow got a job doing domestic "week work" and asked her employer to pay Dr. Cross's bill and take the amount from her wages in weekly installments. He agreed, paid Dr. Cross twenty-five dollars, and Dr. Cross receipted the dead man's bill.

The doctor told the story, and the paper published it, as a commendable example of personal integrity and determination to pay one's just debts. But Dr. Mayo saw in it only the man of wealth exacting his pound of flesh.

Eminently successful too was Dr. Hector Galloway, who had come to Rochester from nearby Oronoco in 1864 to become Dr. Mayo's assistant in the provost marshal's office. He was a man of great girth, ponderous in movement and slow in thought. Once when Mrs. Mayo was taken ill while Dr. Mayo was away, she called Dr. Galloway to prescribe for her. He sat by her bedside and pondered. She might have this. Or perhaps that. Maybe a little of this medicine would help her, or on second thought, another might be better. He wondered.

Mrs. Mayo lost patience. "Dr. Galloway, you're just like my old rag bag. There's a lot in it, but it takes a devil of a time to find it." Later she confided to a friend that Dr. Mayo would have had a sick person "in medicine" in the time it took Dr. Galloway to decide how to begin the examination. But he was sound and sure, and when Dr. Mayo wanted a consultative opinion on a local case he usually called in Dr. Galloway.

The big man had no push, and no gift whatever for pretense or palaver. He once told a Democratic convention which had drafted him to run for office that they had chosen the wrong man; they needn't expect *him* to travel around the countryside kissing the babies and admiring the pigs! But he was popular with patients and soon acquired a large and lucrative practice.

Dr. J. S. Allen was another of the busy Rochester medical men, but the little doctor had his doubts about him, because he seemed obsessed with something he called "dropsy of the heart." No fewer than five persons within a month came to Dr. Mayo with such a diagnosis by Allen.

One young woman had symptoms that quickly convinced Dr. Mayo she was pregnant. He told her so. "But Dr. Allen says I have dropsy of the heart," she protested. "He said the slightest exercise might make me drop dead. I've stayed in bed for two months, afraid even to walk across the floor."

A little further examination, and then, "Madam, you can arise, take up your bed, and walk. There's nothing wrong with your heart." She did so, and he saw her safely through her pregnancy—for less than the forty dollars Dr. Allen had charged to scare her.

## 2

The resident doctors did not have the care of the sick all to themselves. Rochester was a veritable honey-pot for the itinerant quacks who journeyed from town to town, staying at each for a few days or weeks and leaving behind a trail of useless nostrums, worthless advice, and disappointed hopes.

# The Old Doctor

In Christmas week of 1868 three of these men were simultaneously laying siege to the pocketbooks of Rochester and the surrounding countryside: Dr. Ballou, a spiritualist healer; Dr. Duvall, a "natural healer"; and Dr. Jones, an oculist and aurist from Chicago.

Dr. Ballou and Dr. Jones were unlucky to be competing with the sensational Dr. William P. Duvall "of the Western Healing Institute," who used no instruments or medicines to work his cures, just the natural healing power manifest in him since his tenth year. The patient had only to sit in his presence for a few minutes and all pains and ailments would pass away. It might take several weeks for the effects to appear, but cures were sure and permanent.

When such well-known sufferers as the village dressmaker and the proprietor of the Bradley House announced in worshipful accents the miracles Dr. Duvall had wrought within them, Rochester was convinced and opened its heart and its purse. Anyone could see what a saintly man he was, with those flowing locks, those soulful eyes, and that warm, soothing voice.

After several weeks of land-office business Dr. Duvall moved on to serve other communities, but Rochester citizens followed his doings as chronicled in the local paper with great interest. Soon there was word that he had taken to himself a lovely young wife. O happy girl, to be the bride of so good a man! Six weeks later came the sad news that Mrs. Duvall was dead. *What* a tragedy! The *poor* man!

Then came the facts in quick succession. Mrs. Duvall's death was mysterious, an autopsy revealed a lethal dose of strychnine, and the doctor was under suspicion. Nor was he Dr. Duvall, just plain William Pott, a botanic doctor of Newark, New Jersey, all of whose three previous wives had died under similarly suspicious circumstances. He was found guilty of murder and sentenced to life imprisonment.

What a rogue! To think of the way he had "fleeced . . . credulous people out of their hard-earned dollars" by his "senseless mummery."

For a time thereafter Rochester viewed traveling healers with a skeptical eye, and the editor reminded them of Dr. Duvall each time a new one appeared. But soon the memory of disillusionment faded, and the procession began again, as successfully as before.

Striking is the unanimity with which men like Duvall emphasized *chronic* diseases. Their power was always chiefly displayed in, or their attention especially given to, ailments of long standing in which the knowledge and skill of honest doctors were as yet ineffectual. The quacks were quick to see a potentially rich harvest in the vast accumulation of sick folk who wearily made the rounds of the doctors' offices without securing benefit. These were the folk to whom the Mayo brothers brought the effective techniques of a new surgery a few years later.

## 3

Though courteous, kindly, and often a sympathetic confidant, Dr. Mayo was not a man to offer or invite familiarity. Men might call him Mayo and a very few William, but no one called him Bill, not even his wife. An outward sign of this inner inhibition was a strict code of professional conduct, extending even to dress. Perhaps because of style maxims he learned when he was tailoring in Lafayette, he seldom appeared in public except in a long-tailed, double-breasted coat and tall top hat. That was the badge of a calling of which he was proud.

Dr. Mayo thus garbed and "going somewhere in a hurry" became one of the familiar sights of Rochester. In town he always made his calls on foot; for country trips he kept four or five horses of his own and sometimes had to rent others from a livery stable, for his daily rounds soon covered most of the roads radiating from Rochester. He would drive out one road, come back, change horses, drive out another, and so on, until the necessary calls had been made. And always he drove like mad.

One bitingly cold winter day Burt W. Eaton, a rising young Rochester lawyer, found it necessary to get to a neighboring town in a hurry. He hired a cutter with driver from one of the stables, muffled himself in furs, and started off. They were making good time when suddenly they heard hoof beats and a faint halloo behind. The next thing Eaton knew he was sitting in his cutter in a snowbank beside the road, while Dr. Mayo dashed by with a wave of thanks.

As he and his driver dug and pulled to get the cutter free, Mr. Eaton fumed. Wasn't he as good as the Doctor? And wasn't he in a hurry too? But the driver explained that Rochester liverymen always gave Dr. Mayo the right-of-way; *he* was making a sick call. They all knew the sound of his voice, and whenever they heard him shout they pulled over to let him pass.

Dr. Mayo's maxim was "Don't spare the horses when a human life is at stake." But he *never* spared his. He enjoyed driving and he loved good horses. Not for him the easy-paced nag that would stand without hitching. He wanted an animal with spirit and speed, so he always bought the runaways no one else could handle; he knew they had "guts" and could go, he said, and he could usually manage them. But not always.

One of his worst smashups occurred one morning as he was starting on a trip to High Forest. The team was skittish, he was careless, and soon they began to run. Seeing that they were getting out of control, he guided them toward a clump of trees, thinking the obstacle would stop them, but they simply straddled a tree and kept on going. The violent collision of carriage with tree threw Dr. Mayo against the dashboard, stunning him for a few minutes.

When he regained consciousness his nose was bleeding hard, but he seemed otherwise unhurt, and some men working near by helped him get the horses and the wrecked carriage back to the farm. Stopping only long enough to clean the blood from his face, he hitched the team to another buggy and started again for High Forest. When he returned some time after noon, he examined his nose, found the bone was broken, set it himself, and went on about his business.

He never lacked grit. When a sore appeared on his lower lip he watched it carefully for some three months, then decided it was cancerous and must come off. Assembling instruments and needles, he took a stiff shot of whisky, seated himself in front of a mirror, and directed an assistant in the swift excision of a triangular piece of the lip. Little Charlie was looking on and remembered that "of course he hollered," but he stanched the flow of blood and stitched the lip together himself.

He was just as decisive with patients. On a professional visit to the Granger farm one day he noticed little George hovering all ears among the grownups and addressed a pleasant question to him. When the child answered, Dr. Mayo snapped to serious attention.

"Why, that child is tongue-tied," he exclaimed. "Come here, George," reaching into his pocket as he spoke. Unsuspecting, the boy climbed onto the Doctor's knee and obediently opened his mouth. In an instant Dr. Mayo snipped the membrane under his tongue with the little pair of scissors he carried in his pocket case, and when the tongue healed George Granger could speak like other children. He grew up to be a lawyer, a judge, and legal adviser to the Mayos.

4

Perhaps during his early and more leisurely months as examiner on the draft board, Dr. Mayo had developed a simple but complete routine of physical examination that he now applied in private practice to every new patient, regardless of the specific complaint that brought him in. He had the man strip to vest and drawers, put him on the table, and began with his head. Was the hair dry? Did the eyes focus properly? How about the teeth? Were the glands of the neck enlarged? Now sit up and bend forward, and backward. We must not miss any stiffness in the spine.

And so on from head to foot. But the examination took only fifteen minutes, and by it he often found some ailment the patient did not know he had or traced his complaint to an unexpected source.

Let other doctors boast of their operating chairs of brocaded plush and crimson morocco; he designed his own examining table, of plain wood covered with a thin mattress, under which was kept a detachable board that could be fitted onto the foot of the table when a long flat surface was needed. So well was this adapted to its purpose that with but few modifications it is still the type of table used in the examining rooms of the Mayo Clinic.

The case histories Dr. Mayo elicited from patients were not of the kind that occupy the present-day intern. In later life he scoffed at what he considered a tendency to lose important diagnostic symptoms in a fog of minutiae. He wanted to know it if the patient passed blood from the bowels, for instance, but he did not think it necessary to ask what the man's great-grandmother had died of.

The idea of accumulating case records as a valuable source for the statistical study of disease had not yet penetrated to the rank and file of the profession. A notation of the patient's name, his disorder, and the fee charged made up the customary entry. But Dr. Mayo sometimes felt an urge to review a case at length in writing.

# The Old Doctor

He must have resolved on New Year's Day, 1866, to keep a record of his major cases from that time forward. Convenient to his hand lay the old ledger in which Mrs. Mayo had kept her millinery accounts. A short time before, the Doctor had punched holes through the used sheets, tied them carefully out of the way with a piece of pink tape, and started to use the ledger as a scrapbook, copying into it excerpts from things he read.

Among some from Hall's *Journal of Health* was one on the beauty of gray eyes, and another entitled "School Rooms Should Be Attractive," taken from the report of the school in Duxbury, Massachusetts. Immediately following a series of paragraphs on agriculture by Edward Everett, Dr. Mayo began his case stories.

That first resolution of 1866 lasted until January 14, but on January 1, 1867 he firmly began again and kept going until January 18. In 1868 he wrote nothing, because he was busy with a new venture as coproprietor of one of Rochester's biggest drug stores, and a year later he was busy dissolving the partnership. So his resolutions produced only about a dozen case records from his own pen. They bear little resemblance to the clipped, stripped models of the present day. He wrote them as little stories, in which he recounted everything the patient said and the doctor answered, even to the anecdotes they exchanged.

Little Octavia Gray fell from a horse in October. After three months of home treatment she was brought to Dr. Mayo to see what he could do about the paralysis on one side of her face. He ordered her parents to use the Galvanic battery and come back if that didn't work. In the ledger he admitted that he was puzzled. "Querie, where is the injury?" he wrote, and then reviewed and rejected all the likely possibilities.

A few days later he was called to Rock Dell to see Ole Nelson, a Norwegian youth of twenty. The Rochester papers had been making merry at Ole's expense, because he had drunk too much one night and woke up the next morning atop a slab in the graveyard. But the lad had frozen his fingers and toes so badly that Dr. Mayo had to amputate them. He found the family of eight or nine members living in a log cabin sixteen feet square and sent them all to the loft above, except for the father and one sister whose help he needed. After a bad moment when the first finger hemorrhaged the job was quickly done.

Next was a difficult confinement, in which the child was born dead after thirty-six hours of labor—instrument births were still frowned upon in the profession—and to stop the severe hemorrhage Dr. Mayo scooped up snow outside the cottage door and packed it into the vagina.

And then a series of entries tracing the day-by-day progress of a case of tubercular meningitis in a child of nine years. Again Dr. Mayo used snow in place of ice in packs for the child's head, but in spite of his best efforts the patient died. Whereupon he sat down at his desk and wrote a long review of the case and the treatment. What might he have done differently, and more successfully?

In November 1866 a farmer in Dodge County, another "Norway man," was butchering a steer when the knife slipped and entered the calf of his leg. Feeling no pain, he ignored the mishap and finished his job. Then he noticed that his boot was full of blood. Unable himself to stop the bleeding, he sent to the nearest village for the doctor, who wrapped a handkerchief around the leg, inserted a stick, and twisted it tight, then left, instructing the patient to twist the wrapping tighter if the bleeding did not stop. When the man's wife could not stanch the bleeding and the leg began to swell, she sent again for the doctor, but he merely ordered her to twist the handkerchief tighter still.

Ten weeks later the distraught wife sent a messenger for Dr. Mayo. The call reached him early one morning and he started out at once. The thermometer stood at twenty-two degrees below zero, with a brisk wind blowing and the snow drifting high across the road, but the little doctor got through and reached the bedside about noon.

He found the patient extremely emaciated and very weak, his leg a swollen mass, its calf punctured with sinuses discharging pus. The stench of decay filled the room. With the patient "partially under chloroform" Dr. Mayo began to clean away the clotted blood and decayed flesh. In the midst of the operation the man's pulse stopped. To all appearances he was dead. Snatching a bottle from his bag, the Doctor began dropping tincture of camphor between the man's lips, and in fifteen minutes he had recovered sufficiently to permit resumption of the operation.

When the wound had been cleaned as well as possible, Dr. Mayo began looking for the bleeding vessel. He finally located the flow, "no thicker than a bristle," coming from a tibial artery. The offending vessel was tied off, the wound dressed, and the patient left resting comfortably. The next day he was much better, the swelling had subsided, and the danger was past.

More puzzling was the case of Mr. Johnson of Rock Dell, who had been suffering from retention of urine for three days. Confidently the Doctor introduced a catheter. With no effect. Was the instrument clogged? No. Then what was the matter?

It took suction of considerable force to start the flow of thick, clotted pus that had been causing the stoppage. When more than four ounces of that had been removed and then a quart of thick, red urine, the patient was much relieved and Dr. Mayo returned home for the time being.

To the old ledger he confided his bewilderment. Where did the pus come from? Where was the abscess, and what was the cause of it? "The people were Norwegian, understood little of English, the patient no English. All I could gather about the history of the case was that the man had been sick about eight weeks."

He argued the possibilities at length but could come to no satisfactory conclusion. So he ended the record, "Left open for further thought and research."

## 5

"Left open for further thought and research." That showed a doorway ajar to the future.

Dr. Mayo was necessarily an empiric of the old school. He used the clinical thermometer and the crude wooden stethoscope, the only instruments of precision yet available, and he had made urinalysis an unfailing part of his examination routine. Over a lamp or a candle by the bedside he would boil a bit of urine in a teaspoon, testing it for sugar with a few drops of Fehling's solution and for albumen with acid, both of which reagents he always carried in his bag. More elaborate analyses he made later at the office.

Aside from that meager scientific aid, he and his fellows still had to depend on their own five senses to tell them what was wrong with the patient, and the height to which they had developed the art of clinical observation and physical diagnosis is the glory of their tribe. Practice trained their senses to recognize and their minds to interpret with astonishing accuracy the clues a deranged physiology left in the eyes, the tongue, or the skin of the sick man. Their snap diagnoses made on a symptom or two seemed intuitive at times only because they were so unconsciously conditioned by accumulated experience.

The difficulty was that many of them were such hard-shelled members of the old school that they could not see any need for improvement, any possibility of something better. To that number Dr. Mayo did not belong. He was a friend of progress in medical science as much as in transportation, communication, or farm machinery. Some of his Minnesota colleagues called him a student of disease, and so he was, not of the kind to advance the frontiers of medical science, however, but rather one to widen the horizons of his own knowledge and understanding to include those frontiers as they expanded.

He checked his diagnoses by postmortem examinations whenever he could get permission from authorities or relatives, and he examined pathologic specimens under the microscope. His use of that instrument made him unique among the doctors of his community. His model was an old, low-powered one, rapidly becoming obsolete, and techniques for its direct use in medical practice were not yet ready, but even his attempt to study diseased tissues removed at operation or postmortem was enough to set him apart among Minnesota practitioners.

Similarly, his unabated enthusiasm for chemical analysis—he always had a laboratory in one corner of his office or in an adjoining back room—was important not for its direct effects upon his practice but for its indication of an attitude of mind that, consciously or not, was in league with the future.

Dr. Mayo's medical library, which had been little more than a five-foot shelf of manuals and textbooks he had probably used in medical school, grew rapidly in the 1860's and faster in the 70's, with books that reflected his interests faithfully. Most of them were well-chosen works by outstanding authorities on the several fields of practical medicine, but there were some on chemistry, on the use of the microscope, on the new histology, and the newer embryology. To those he added what medical journals were available, of which the most popular with Minnesotans in the sixties was the *Chicago Medical Journal*.

# The Old Doctor

## 6

All those who feel an interest in the advancement of the Profession will meet at the office of Dr. Allen on the 15th of April, at 2 o'clock in the afternoon, to take into consideration the formation of a Medical Society for Olmsted County.

The notice, appearing in 1868, was signed, quite surprisingly, "Many Citizens."

Dr. Mayo, feeling a deep interest in the advancement of the profession, attended the meeting. After adopting a constitution and electing a president, the doctors turned to drawing up a common schedule of fees: for a visit in town $1; in the country, $.75 per mile and double at night; to deliver a baby, $10; to dress simple fractures, $5 to $25; compound and comminuted fractures, $25 to $75; capital operations, $25 to $100. Having thus advanced the profession, the new society adjourned until its next *annual* meeting.

When that convened Dr. Mayo shocked the society into life by reading a paper on "The Character of the Earth's Elements, Its Formation, Development, and Ultimate Destiny, and Its Inhabitants." For six months thereafter the medical society met every two weeks, usually at Dr. Mayo's home, to continue the discussion of Darwinism he had started.

Sometimes they turned aside to hear Dr. Galloway outline his "philosophy of disease"; Dr. Mayo explain the processes of digestion; John H. Whitney, a Rochester inventor whom they had elected to honorary membership along with Harry H. Young, describe an "entirely feasible appliance for aerial navigation"; or Dr. Allen discourse on "Electricity and Lightning Rods." But always they went back to evolution.

The summer's heat put an end to the meetings, and in the fall the society returned to its legitimate sphere of action, and presently to a state of suspended animation.

For a season its place was taken by the Rochester *Conversazione,* a group of doctors and others who met every two weeks for "conversations" on such divergent matters as how the human voice is produced and whether Bible-reading should be allowed in the public schools. Dr. Mayo was the mainspring of the group, and when he was not in town its meetings were adjourned or postponed for lack of attendance.

The time was ripe for something more than abortive attempts at medical organization in Minnesota. Early in 1869 a group of St. Paul men undertook to revive the state society organized during territorial days but dormant for more than a decade. They called the regular surgeons and physicians of the state to assemble in St. Paul—and to encourage response they persuaded the railroads to promise free passes home to all doctors who should attend.

Dr. Mayo was among those present, and he played a substantial part in the convention's deliberations. Declaring the old society defunct, the doctors organized a new Minnesota State Medical Society, which has remained a vital force in Minnesota medicine ever since. For more than ten years Dr. Mayo was among its active leaders and for another ten among its advisory elder statesmen.

Membership was not required of the state's doctors and it carried no special privileges or premiums in practice, so only the most alert members of the profession found time and energy for participation. Dr. Mayo made some interesting friends among them. One was Dr. John H. Murphy, *the* pioneer surgeon of St. Paul, whose crude manner and untutored ways have put him in the pillory as the horrible example of pre-antiseptic surgery, but who was quite the most popular surgical consultant and the most authoritative expert for court purposes in the state.

His position was being challenged and was soon to be taken over by Dr. Franklin R. Staples, beloved dean of Winona doctors. Staples was a bigger man than Murphy, with more professional consciousness. He was president of the state society in 1871, vice-president of the American Medical Association in 1877, president of the state board of health for fifteen years, and for five years a member of the examining faculty of medicine set up by the first effective medical practice act in Minnesota.

Jolly, roly-poly James B. McGaughey, Dr. Staples' most trusted friend and colleague in Winona, was too retiring to achieve the leadership of which he was capable. But he won the respect and affection of Dr. Mayo, and his sons after him, by his unaffected honesty and complete freedom from professional jealousy.

Probably the ablest man and the most profound thinker in the group, and certainly the most scientific-minded, was Dr. Charles N. Hewitt of Red Wing. Sober, earnest, wholeheartedly devoted to medicine, he sacrificed his career as a surgeon in order to put "state medicine" on its feet in Minnesota, and thoroughly deserved the title of Minnesota's "apostle of public health."

Foremost in direct influence on Dr. Mayo was the affable Dr. Alexander J. Stone of Stillwater, later of St. Paul. A congenital pioneer, he established the first medical journal in Minnesota and the first medical school in St. Paul, and later attained distinction as a medical editor and educator. His fellow doctors liked him personally, but in the early years of the medical society many of them shook their heads over his unseemly enthusiasm for new methods and theories in the treatment of diseases of women.

## 8

Participating in the "collision of intellect" among such men gave Dr. Mayo a periodic renewal of the perspective a man is likely to lose in the daily grind, the perspective that shows him he is building a church, not merely laying one brick on another. His professional consciousness deepened, his pride in medicine grew, and with it his concern for the good name of the medical profession.

Paramount among the problems discussed by the society in the 1870's was "the diagnosis and treatment of quackery." As a result of action taken by the society at its first meeting, the state legislature enacted a law regulating medical practice. Hastily drawn and full of defects, the law did more harm than good in several respects, and the public raised such an outcry about "class legislation" for the benefit of the regular doctors that the society's representatives worked as hard in the next session to get the act repealed as they had to get it passed. They succeeded, and though many members, including Dr. Mayo, kept urging the need for such a law, none was enacted until 1883.

In 1872, largely through the efforts of Dr. Stone, the legislature was persuaded to legalize dissection in Minnesota by granting to medical men and schools all unclaimed bodies. But for the time being the society could do nothing more than talk about the need for higher standards in medical education and the growing threat of malpractice suits.

# Horse-and-Buggy Doctor

In spite of the best care a doctor could give, fractures sometimes left deformities and limbs had to be amputated. In such cases the patient could always find a lawyer willing to sue the doctor for malpractice, and nine times in ten the jury, looking only at the deformity or the stump and not at the conditions that might have made it unavoidable, would award the damages.

And why not? pointed out the leaders of the society, when doctors themselves appeared on the witness stand to support the charges of negligence, implying that nothing of the sort ever happened in *their* cases. Half the time it was a doctor who started the difficulty by indiscreetly telling a patient what a fool or a rogue his former physician had been. Doctors had better stick together on this matter if they did not want to pay separately.

Dr. Mayo apparently took such discussions well to heart, for when next a malpractice case crossed his path, he reacted far differently than he had in the suit against Dr. Ayer in Le Sueur. Dr. E. C. Cross was the defendant. It was charged that in taking care of a broken arm for the plaintiff he had made the bandages and splints so tight they had obstructed circulation, causing mortification and necessitating eventual amputation of the injured limb.

Dr. Mayo suggested the theory on which the defense was chiefly based, that the artery had been injured and the blood supply shut off when the arm was broken and not when the splints were applied. He supported this theory on the witness stand and in company with several other prominent doctors, including Dr. Staples of Winona, made it so plausible that Dr. Cross won the verdict in both the district and the state supreme court.

That Dr. Mayo should show such wit and spirit in the defense of a man he was known to detest caused so much surprise and speculation in Rochester that one man finally ventured to ask him why he had done it.

"I did it for the profession, not for him, damn him."

# CHAPTER SIX

# Pioneer in Surgery

Dr. Mayo was a general practitioner, as all American doctors were and would continue to be for at least another decade. But surgery was what he wanted most to do. There was a positive quality about successful surgery, a sense of tangible accomplishment in an operation well done, that gave him satisfaction. Up to that time, however, he had not done any unusual amount of it.

Surgery was still, as it had been in his medical school days, mostly a matter of repair work on the surfaces and extremities of the body, and accidents provided the chief need for it. Industrial hazards, in mine and mill and foundry, were lacking in Rochester, but there were plenty of kicking or runaway horses that sent their riders or the carriage occupants to the doctor, and there were also ample hazards in farming.

Farmers and their wives seem to have been slow to learn that moving mechanisms will not yield to human flesh. The whirring knives of the new reapers did not stop when fingers and toes got in their way; the revolving knuckles of the tumbling rod in the threshing machine took lightning-quick, twisting hold of any loose garment that ballooned near them. In harvest time observers reported that those maimed and mangled in accidents with the new farm machinery were keeping the surgeons of Rochester busy day and night.

There lay one opportunity for specializing in surgery, if Dr. Mayo could achieve success above that of his fellow doctors. There was another in the special field of practice his friend Dr. Stone was so interested in.

The number of sufferers from the disorders to which the reproductive organs of women are liable was in that day greatly increased by the lacerations, displacements, and infections left by the crudities of ignorant and unskilled midwifery, and the treatment of the diseases of women made up a large share of every doctor's practice.

But there was really little the doctors could do about them. Not yet knowing the causes of infection, they were all at sea about inflammatory diseases of the pelvis. They could hardly escape associating inflammation of the uterus with placental remains left behind at the time of parturition, but they attributed other troubles to such causes as a chill or overexposure to cold during the menstrual period. As treatment they applied blisters and poultices externally, dosed with morphine or ergot internally, or tried to reduce a swollen cervix by drawing blood with leeches or by multiple punctures of the tissues. In severe cases of ulceration they resorted to the use of caustics, including the baneful silver-nitrate stick that caused more damage than it repaired.

Many "female complaints," often so severe as to make the woman a bedridden invalid, were caused by displacement of the uterus. It was advanced practice then to treat this by pushing the organ back into place and attempting to keep it there by packing the vaginal cavity with tampons of gauze or by inserting a mechanical support called a pessary.

Such methods of treatment were seldom effective, and in every community a growing number of ailing women wandered restlessly from doctor to doctor and quack to quack, hoping to find someone who could give them relief.

Cultivation of the field by qualified practitioners was beginning in the 1860's. Two decades before, James Marion Sims of Alabama had learned how to repair vesico-vaginal fistula, an accident of childbirth that made the women who suffered it truly pitiable. In a fine instance of frontier ingenuity, he fashioned from a pewter teaspoon the duckbill speculum that made the body parts accessible to surgery and from a half-dollar piece the silver-wire suture that made the surgical technique effective.

The doctors could not believe the reports of Sims's success, so he moved to New York and showed them, not only that he could do it but how to do it themselves. Moving on from that point, he became the "father of modern gynecology," and the Woman's Hospital he established in New York was its cradle. During the sixties and seventies he and his able assistants and successors devised and disseminated, through the printed page and their trained disciples, one new method after another for the successful treatment of the diseases peculiar to women.

Dr. Mayo was aware of these developments through his reading, and he was venturing to perform a few of the operations he read about. He was doing some fairly extensive plastic surgery on the perineum and the cervix, and on August 25, 1866 the *Rochester Post* reported "An Important Surgical Operation":

Dr. Mayo performed an operation a few days ago upon Mrs. Titus of Mantorville.

Mrs. Titus had been suffering for several months from the growth of a tumor in the abdomen; its size had become so great as to render her perfectly helpless and endanger her life. Before the operation she measured 54 inches over the tumor.

The operation was performed by making an opening in the abdomen about an inch long and deep enough to reach the sac of the tumor. There was discharged from the opening nearly five gallons of thick, gluey substance.

When the doctor left, the patient was feeling very comfortable and much relieved by the removal of the enormous burden. Dr. Mayo was assisted in the operation by Dr. Dearborn of Wasioja, who has charge of the patient.

We understand that Dr. Mayo gives special attention to this class of Female diseases.

Tapping an ovarian tumor when it required an abdominal incision, even so small a one, was more than other Rochester doctors were yet daring. But Dr. Stone, who had spent a year as an assistant in a Boston hospital, was full of tales about more remarkable things men in the East were doing, and though other members of the state medical society might smile at Stone's enthusiasm or frown when he carried it into action in his practice, Dr. Mayo grew restless in the knowledge that he might do more and better work if he knew how.

Consequently in the fall of 1869 he announced to his wife that he was going to New York for several months to study general surgery and gynecology.

## 2

He spent much of his time at Bellevue Hospital. It had undergone many reforms since his service there in the forties, but by 1870 its surgical wards were so full of infection and the mortality rate was so high that the public was once more ready to demand measures that would make the hospital "fit to receive and house the sick." Dr. Mayo had nothing to say about that state of affairs and probably was not aware of it, for despite the outcry, conditions at Bellevue were actually no worse than in most of the hospitals of Europe and America in those days before the adoption of Listerism.

In the long letters Dr. Mayo wrote back to the editor of the *Rochester Post* he described only the general aspects of the hospital that might be expected to interest lay readers: the huge building and its beautiful grounds, the many clean and roomy wards, the big drug department with its shining laboratories and its storeroom full of barrels of beer, whisky, porter, and ale (this with relish, for the benefit of Rochester prohibitionists), and the photograph gallery exhibiting stereoscope views of pathological specimens. "You don't like to look at them? Well, it is all a matter of taste. Everything has a beauty, after you get used to it."

The first ambulance corps in the world had just been established at Bellevue, and Dr. Mayo was much impressed by such a wonder.

When an accident occurs in any part of the city, there is a dispatch sent from the police headquarters of the ward in which the accident occurred, and the ambulance is on the ground in a few minutes after. The injured are picked up, and at once taken to the hospital. Truly this is quite as astonishing as any of the fairy tales, and a perfect realization of the Eastern story of Aladdin and his wonderful lamp.

Of course the insatiable little doctor did not limit his experience of New York to hospitals and study. He made the rounds of the churches to compare the eloquence of their preachers and the seraphic voices of their choirs. He went to the opera and the theater, on one occasion to see Edwin Booth play Hamlet. He attended inquests, and wandered for an hour or two from slab to slab in the city morgue musing on the characters and fortunes that had brought these men to their common end, "dead on admission." He walked slowly down Fifth Avenue, viewing the palatial residences and the fine horses and carriages.

Any person visiting New York should make it a point to stroll along this highway of wealth and fashion once, at least. . . . If he is fond of fine stock, the sight of the horses alone, in their rich trappings, moving with conscious pride of their own beautiful proportions, will more than pay for the trouble; but, in addition to this, he will be struck with the gorgeous richness of the ladies' dresses and, at time, forced to admire—aye, almost worship at the shrine of womanly beauty.

On his way home from New York Dr. Mayo stopped off at Philadelphia and went out to Lancaster to visit the Atlee brothers, the great apostles of ovariotomy. The operation for the removal of ovarian tumor had first been performed by Ephraim McDowell on the Kentucky frontier in 1809, under circumstances that make one of the most dramatic and most often told stories in American medical history. McDowell's success in that and succeeding attempts made the operation a nine days' wonder, but after its originator's death it fell into disuse; it was too seldom successful in other hands.

John and Washington Atlee revived the procedure about 1845 and set about demonstrating its practicability for saving lives. When Dr. Mayo arrived, Washington Lemuel, the younger and abler of the brothers, was nearing his three hundredth ovariotomy, with an average mortality of slightly over thirty per cent.

The little western doctor was moved to deep admiration, but watching the Atlees' work did not give him the courage immediately to attempt the operation himself. In spite of their success and that of the few others who were following in their footsteps, the main body of the medical profession condemned such a procedure as foolhardy. Any abdominal operation was a method of the executioner that no wise and humane surgeon would use. Ovariotomists were "belly rippers who ought not to be at large."

The attitude is vividly illustrated by the story of the general practitioner in Jericho, Vermont, who took one of his patients to the Woman's Hospital in New York, having heard that the doctors there could do something to cure ovarian tumors. After seeing his patient settled in bed for a day's rest before the operation, the old Yankee sauntered into the staff room to ask how the surgeons would go about getting "the darned thing out."

An intern explained, while the man from Jericho listened in horror.

"What," he shouted, "do you mean to tell me you've got to cut her wide open?" When the intern nodded, he hurried upstairs to tell his patient he had made a mistake; she must not let these men operate on her. But she had more courage than he.

He watched the operation next day, and at its end addressed the surgeon. "Do you expect the woman to come out of that alive?"

"Of course," said the surgeon.

"Well, I don't," snapped the old doctor. And the next word the hospital had from him was a telegram sent from some point on his way home, telling them what to do with his patient's remains. Fortunately the instructions were not needed.

That occurred about 1875, and in spite of the New York surgeons' nonchalance in the presence of the man from Jericho, they were not taking ovariotomy at all as a matter of course. Every such operation was an event that attracted doctors from all over the city to watch the performance and note the outcome.

A few months after his return to Rochester, Dr. Mayo was faced with a case of ovarian tumor that had got beyond treatment by tapping, but he called Dr. William H. Byford from Chicago to perform the operation, the same Byford who with Dr. Deming and Dr. Mayo had attempted to revive the old Indiana Medical College in LaPorte. He had long since exchanged Evansville, Indiana, for Chicago and had become that city's outstanding authority in the new gynecology. He performed ovariotomy on occasion, but in this case he decided the risk was unjustified.

3

While Byford was in Rochester, Dr. Mayo asked him to look at another puzzling case. Three years before, a woman had come to him complaining of headache, backache, and a host of other symptoms from which she had suffered for fourteen years. Doctors in New York, whence she had lately come, said she had "falling of the womb" and fitted one pessary after another without noticeable benefit.

Upon examination Dr. Mayo found the trouble was caused by a good-sized rectocele, a hernial protrusion of a part of the vagina, the retaining perineum apparently having been lost through laceration during labor. His first attempt to correct the difficulty was a failure, partly because of trouble with the anesthetic. But in a second attempt he used an ingenious method of his own devising and was greatly pleased with himself when it proved successful.

For two years he heard nothing more of the case and assumed that the woman was well. Then one day as he was passing her house she called out, "Oh, Doctor, come here a minute. I want to see you. I want to tell you that thing is coming out again."

He made an examination and sure enough, there was the rectocele as large and troublesome as ever. "Well, Mrs. H., I will try again. I will make another effort for you."

When the effort failed the Doctor was stumped, but Mrs. H. was cheerfully sure that he would succeed eventually and was quite willing to submit to anything he suggested. "As there was but little danger of her seeking other aid," said Dr. Mayo, "I took time to look up the literature on the subject more carefully."

In accordance with surgical practice at that time, all his efforts had been in the direction of returning the protruded parts to their proper place and fashioning a thick wall of tissue, an artificial perineum, to hold them there. Now as he read and studied, he asked himself why he could not make sure of a cure by radical removal of the rectocele. He worked out a plan of procedure that seemed feasible, but he hesitated to try it on his judgment alone.

By that time he was corresponding with Dr. Byford about the case of ovarian tumor, so he outlined the history of the returning rectocele and the radical removal he proposed. Byford was dubious. He had never heard of any such operation, and he would be afraid of fatal hemorrhage.

So the matter stood when Dr. Byford came to Rochester. He examined the rectocele and suggested a method of dealing with it. Dr. Mayo followed his suggestion, but it didn't work.

Then he screwed his courage to the sticking point and in May 1871 performed the radical operation he had planned. With the patient under ether and the hernial bag emptied of its contents, he fastened a clamp behind it to shut off the circulation, carefully put in the necessary sutures, and cut off the rectocele close to the clamp. Quickly he seared the cut surfaces with an iron he had heating in the flame of a spirit lamp near by. The bleeding was very slight.

The patient rallied nicely, the wound healed rapidly, and from the fourth day forward the woman was up and about, cured at last. The result of his audacity must have contributed greatly to Dr. Mayo's confidence in his own surgical judgment.

# Pioneer in Surgery

## 4

In reporting that case at the next session of the Minnesota State Medical Society, Dr. Mayo interrupted his characteristically circumstantial narrative long enough to say, "At this point I wish to make public acknowledgement to Miss Harriet Preston, M.D., a graduate of the Women's Medical College of Philadelphia, for her very able assistance to me while performing this and other operations on women, such as artificial perineums, and amputation of the cervix uteri."

That was an unmistakable rebuke to his listeners, for they had been voting regularly for three years past against admitting Dr. Preston of Rochester to membership in the society. She was one of the small vanguard of women who, unwilling to be forced into a life of teaching or making hats, were seeking to enter the practice of medicine, and the Minnesota profession was receiving her with something less than open arms.

While Miss Preston was in attendance at the Women's Medical College, the students of that school were granted admission to the clinical lectures at the Pennsylvania Hospital in Philadelphia. The result was a tempest. Some of the lecturers resigned in protest, the male students jeered and hissed the women who dared to avail themselves of the privilege, and the public poured censure upon the hospital trustees. The conflict was finally resolved by limiting the attendance of women to the Saturday clinics and reserving for Wednesdays those cases requiring "a degree of exposure improper in the presence of a mixed group."

Although Dr. Mayo held no brief for the emancipation of woman in the mass, he championed Dr. Preston's cause from the start. She was a competent and thoroughly qualified practitioner, and he believed her motive to be the same as theirs, her own and the profession's advancement.

He talked in vain. At first the doctors based their refusal to recognize Dr. Preston on various pretexts, but at one of the annual debates on the matter they came out with the truth. Dr. Mattocks of St. Paul did not want a woman around, because then the men couldn't say what they wanted to, and Dr. Blood of Owatonna thought it was immodest of Dr. Preston to insist when they had showed they didn't want her. "He had observed that women who stepped aside from the usual course of obtaining a living adopted by women were strong-minded women with whom it was desirable to have nothing to do."

Not until 1880, after Dr. Preston had moved to St. Paul and been granted membership in the Ramsey County Medical Society, did the state society reverse its decision.

Although Dr. Mayo did not get far with the men by his stand on the question, he did with Dr. Preston. That being a painfully modest age—medical students were taught to keep their eyes fixed on the ceiling while they fumbled through a manual examination of well-draped women patients—she built up a very large practice among the women of the Rochester community, and she referred her major cases and those requiring surgery to Dr. Mayo. That was no mean aid to the development of his practice in gynecology, and it grew rapidly.

5

In 1872 Dr. Mayo was elected the third president of the state society, convincing evidence of the standing he had won in the profession.

His presidential address the next year was something new in the way of such efforts. It bore the title of "The Relations of the Profession to the Public and Each Other," but there was a great deal more of "to the Public" than of "Each Other" in it. Stripped of its literary draping, it was a plea for the doctors to assume social and political leadership in their communities. That was their privilege and their duty. To practice medicine well they must understand the emotions of men and the ambient conditions of society as well as the anatomy and physiology of the body, and that understanding they ought not to waste but must apply in social action.

Minnesota was being peopled by many nationalities and from the fusion of these in time would come one true American character. The doctors could further that process. Admitted to the inner family circle, when the bars of reticence were let down by illness, they could, if they would, see the ordinary human hearts beneath unfamiliar outward manners. Let them try to understand, not condemn, strange customs that might to some seem vices. Then let them act as the interpreters of one group to another.

And they must be tolerant of different social classes. He had found that people tended to condemn the rough and ready men in the lower strata of society, to consider them coarse, unrefined, and therefore degraded and worthless. What a mistake! Such men were necessary, even vital, to the nation. Not just because they were needed to work its mines and mills and factories, but even more because without such an ingredient of brawn, of men strong in action, a nation would be "deficient in time of war and other great emergencies . . . and must degenerate into effeminacy and fall an easy prey to more brutal and ambitious neighbors."

Dr. Mayo did not entirely neglect more obviously medical matters. He spoke of the outstanding success that had been achieved since he took office. The state legislature, at the suggestion of the medical society, had established a state board of public health. That was cause for pride, but now it was up to the doctors to cooperate with the members of the board and supply them with the statistics for which they asked.

Yes, statistics. Medicine must have them too, now that science was taking the place of guessing in that field. Testing every theory in the light of many facts accumulated from many sources "prunes the mind of all luxuriance of imagination and ministers little to the poetry of life and less to its superstitions." But whether sweeping away cherished convictions was for better or for worse in social and religious spheres, it could only do good in medicine.

6

Now some of Dr. Mayo's medical friends began urging him to leave Rochester. That small town could not offer sufficient scope for the development of his abilities, they argued. Why don't you come up to St. Paul? Here are hospitals and a medical school and stimulating professional companionship. Here are more patients and a chance for specialization. You're foolish to waste yourself down there in the sticks.

Dr. Mayo's vanity was flattered, and his impulsive nature leaped to embrace the new idea. It seemed good, and the arguments reasonable. Surely St. Paul would offer greater opportunities than Rochester could, especially in view of the slough of depression into which Rochester had fallen. Moreover, at the moment Dr. Mayo's stock in local public affairs was low, for his crusade for reform had him at loggerheads with every faction in the town's politics except his own little coterie of faithful Democrats.

Dr. Charles Hill of Pine Island, not far from Rochester, was moving to St. Paul. He was a congenial person and a good doctor, and he was looking for a partner. So in April 1873 the Rochester newspapers announced that Dr. Mayo was going to St. Paul to establish himself in partnership with Dr. Hill. The public expressions of regret sound more than perfunctory. Even the opposition newspaper called the Doctor's going "a public loss," and declared that he would be missed by as many warm personal friends as any man in town. The Olmsted County Medical Society came briefly to life and called a special meeting to pass resolutions of regret at losing Dr. Mayo and to offer best wishes for his success "in his new and larger field." When the day of his departure came a host of friends "attended him to the cars."

Since Mrs. Mayo and the children remained in Rochester, the Doctor returned every month or two to see them and to visit some of his old patients. He was never more his headstrong, foolhardy self than on one of those trips. He stopped off at Kasson, eighteen miles from Rochester, to see a patient, and was overtaken by one of those raging blizzards the Northwest occasionally suffers. Whirling madly before the wind, the fury of snow piled itself high on everything, including the railroad tracks. There was nothing to do but wait until nature had calmed herself and the tracks could be cleared.

Dr. Mayo waited from Friday night till Monday morning. Then his fund of patience, never large, was exhausted, and he announced his intention of proceeding to Rochester on foot. His snowbound companions were utterly amazed. On foot? Through eighteen miles of thick, trackless drifts? Why, the man was mad!

But he would not be dissuaded. And he got through. He reached Rochester, attended to his business, and was ready to return to St. Paul by the time the trains were moving again.

In St. Paul the new partners rented a handsome downtown office, announced themselves available to patients, and received a cordial welcome from the city press. They immediately joined the Ramsey County Medical Society, and at its next election Dr. Mayo was made vice-president. Three months later he resigned the office and returned to Rochester to stay.

Why? To Rochester friends he had reported that his prospects in St. Paul were good, but perhaps they remained only prospects. Perhaps he discovered that if there were more patients in St. Paul there were also more doctors to claim them. That is a likely guess, since Dr. Hill also returned to his former place of practice. Or the two men may have found the amenities of city practice far too formal, too impersonal, for their liking.

Speculation on what might have been leads to the reasonable belief that if Dr. Mayo had stayed in St. Paul there would have been no occasion for writing this account of his life, so important in the Mayos' development was their location in Rochester.

7

Upon his return to Rochester Dr. Mayo rented an office above Geisinger and Newton's drug store and took up where he had left off the year before. His old patients were glad to have him back, and he was soon as busy as though he had never been away.

Perhaps in St. Paul Dr. Mayo had learned the advantages of keeping stated office hours. Previously, like his Rochester colleagues, he had always announced that he would be in his office from eight o'clock in the morning until nine in the evening. But of course he was not, and that was bad policy. When a visit to the doctor meant a trip of many miles on horseback or behind a team, patients were not inclined to dally or come back tomorrow; if their doctor was not in they went to somebody else.

So Dr. Mayo adopted the practice of limited hours and, barring emergency calls, he kept to them scrupulously. He would start an hour or two earlier in the morning, if necessary, to get the country visits out of the way and be in his office by eleven o'clock. His out-of-town patients came to know exactly when they could be sure of finding Dr. Mayo in, and they timed their trips accordingly.

But emergencies keep no hours, and in those days one could not *call* the doctor, one must *send* for him. If Dr. Mayo chanced to be at the farm instead of in his office at the time, and the patient was new or loosely attached, the messenger was quite likely to give the summons to another doctor.

It is not surprising then that the first telephone line in Rochester was one connecting the Mayo farmhouse with Geisinger and Newton's drug store. On December 12, 1879 the Rochester *Record and Union* announced the novelty.

The telephone line between Dr. Mayo's office and his residence is now up, the machines, or instruments, whichever they are, in position and everything working splendidly. Conversation can be carried on just as rapidly and accurately as though the persons talking were only separated by a few feet instead of a mile, and familiar voices can be recognized as easily. Parties wishing to summon the Doctor between 6 [o'clock in the morning] and 9 o'clock in the evening can do so by making their wants known at Messrs. Geisinger and Newton's drug store. After 9 p.m. and before 6 a.m. it will be necessary to find Mr. George Tilsbury the night watch, who will operate the instrument between the hours named when occasion demands. This will prove not only a convenience but a positive benefit to both the Doctor and his patients.

## 8

There were no more New Year's resolutions to produce case records in the Doctor's own writing, but from 1874 on, the newspapers published enough accounts of his cases to reveal some aspects of his practice.

Those newspaper accounts, which continued to appear well beyond 1900, have been cited as evidence that the Mayos indulged in unethical advertising. That view of them is unhistorical, for it applies the taboos of today to an age that did not share them. The publication of such items was sanctioned by general usage, and every doctor in the community enjoyed the "advertising" if his cases had news value.

However, the ethics of the practice was being debated. In 1870 the Hennepin County (Minneapolis) Medical Society resolved to expel any member who persisted in reporting his cases to secular journals, and from that time on, its members led the crusade. But many doctors whose reputation was beyond question did not agree. In his official address as president of the state society in 1881 Dr. A. J. Stone gave it as his opinion that "in cases of accident or grave surgical operation . . . as a matter of news called for by the public, the press had the right to all the particulars, including the name of the physicians in attendance, and that the particulars should, as a matter of justice, to prevent error, be furnished by the physician himself."

The editors and not the doctors took the initiative in the matter, for case histories were the sort of news their readers liked. In Rochester a reporter for the *Record and Union* made the rounds each week to ask what casualties the doctors could report, and the editor simply could not understand why the worthy gentlemen of the Hennepin County society should "deem it for the best interests of society in general and the profession in particular, to . . . forbid the publication of all proper and legitimate facts about a surgical operation." He hoped the Olmsted County society would not imitate them without good reason.

Moreover, the editor did not depend solely upon the doctors for such news items. He went directly to the family or friends of the patients, or picked up the information in the market place, and sometimes had to publish an apology for having assigned a case to the wrong doctor, saying "the parties who informed us misspoke the name." One might think that people would have objected to having the intimate details about their cancers and ruptures, their misshapen limbs, or their bloating and bleeding broadcast impartially to friend and foe, but apparently they did not. People have resorted to stranger ways of getting their names in the newspapers.

## 9

Naturally the newspaper accounts of cases do not provide a rounded picture of Dr. Mayo's practice, for the editor was not interested in the common ailments that made up the bulk of it. He reported epidemics and occasionally a case of Bright's disease in which the patient was so "filled up with water" that he could not breathe, or an abscess in the chest from which Dr. Mayo removed a cupful of pus, or a hemorrhage from the lungs that laid low a prominent citizen. But for the most part he gave space only to the accidental injuries and other ills that necessitated surgery.

A sampling of these press items will show how predominant still was the ripping, crushing, bruising action of the farm machines among the causes of more serious mishaps.

Mr. John Jondro went to see "Ireland as it is," as rendered last Friday evening, at Heaney's Hall, by Marble's theatrical troupe. He took a "reserved Seat" for which he paid rather dearly. Climbing to the top of a step ladder he insisted on remaining there, but by some mishap he fell, fairly bringing down the house. John says he will occupy a vacant seat next time. Dr. Mayo set the broken bone in his forearm.

A Mr. Hanson, of Rock Dell, met with a terrible accident while threshing, last Friday. His hand was caught in the gearing in some way, and torn all to pieces. Dr. Mayo amputated the injured member, and the man is doing well.

Mr. G. Sampson of Salem, got within kicking distance of a horse last Saturday evening, and when he got away, it was with two teeth and part of his jaw bone imbedded in his tongue. Dr. Mayo attended the injured man.

Mr. Thos. O'Gorman was badly hurt last Saturday by the horse-power of a threshing machine near Stewartville . . . his arm was twisted till it was broken in a number of places, and his breast badly bruised at the same time. . . . Mr. O'Gorman was brought to this city and his wounds were dressed by Dr. Mayo. He is now in a fair way to a speedy recovery, but will always have a stiff arm.

John Dolan, who lives on the High Forest road, made a brutal assault on his wife on Thursday morning of last week. John is a confirmed inebriate and while under the influence of liquor is no better than a brute. On the day mentioned he was drunk. . . . Becoming enraged he threw a tumbler at his wife which struck her on the forehead, making a severe gash and severing the temporal artery. Dr. Mayo was called, and he had great difficulty in stopping the flow of blood and preventing Mrs. Dolan from bleeding to death. Some one ought to enter a complaint against Dolan and have him dealt with as he deserves to be.

Saturday morning last, Dr. W. W. Mayo, assisted by Dr. E. W. Cross, performed a surgical operation on Miss Clara Higbee, at Hadley Valley, cutting off her right leg six inches above the knee. Some six years ago Miss Higbee was riding and a storm coming up, she caught cold in the limb. Inflammation set in, the limb swelled and the bone above the knee became affected and at last rotten, so that large sores formed and pieces of bone came out. She has been confined to her bed all these years and her suffering has been severe. She bore the operation with great fortitude, and is getting along very nicely.

James Stevenson, who lives on the Marion road, near the city, met with a severe accident last Friday. He was threshing at Mr. Rafferty's place, and part of the thresher becoming covered with straw he stepped upon the feed-board to remove it. He slipped and his foot got caught in the cylinder and was completely crushed. Dr. Mayo was called, who found it necessary to amputate the leg below the knee. The muscles were pulled out up to the calf of the leg.

Amputate, amputate, amputate. For everything from the bite of a cat to the misdirection of a woodsman's axe. Persons with missing extremities must have been commonplace in the community.

If a limb is diseased cut it off, was one of the oldest principles in surgery, and improvement had occurred only in the direction of greater neatness and dispatch. The technique was the thing, the surgeon most honored being the one who could dismember a limb in the fewest seconds. Whatever excuse for such shortsighted sacrifice of future usefulness may have existed in the days when operations were performed on patients awake to pain had passed with the coming of anesthesia. But the practice lingered on.

A saner idea had been slowly gaining ground, however, since the time of the great James Syme of Edinburgh. He had practiced and preached the obvious but revolutionary principle that it is better for a man to have a stiff leg or arm than to have none at all, better for the surgeon to excise a diseased joint or length of bone than to cut off the entire limb, even though it takes a little longer.

Dr. Mayo had acquired that principle and applied it to the limit of his knowledge and skill. There were plenty of severed members in his record, but there also appeared with growing frequency instances like these:

Dr. W. W. Mayo, assisted by Dr. E. W. Cross, performed the operation of exsection of the bone of a man's arm, named Ole Syvertson from Grand Meadow, who had had that member broken last September by the tumbling rod of a threshing machine. The arm had been set, but the bone did not grow together, and portions of it rotted and crumbled, making great running sores. The process was what is called Esmark's bloodless operation. About four inches of bone were taken out, the ends brought together and a union will take place. The operation was performed Wednesday and was very successful.

A son of J. C. Patton, of Rock Dell, has just passed through a very trying operation for a disease of the leg bone. The leg was cut open from knee to ankle, and two-thirds of the bone cut and chiseled out. The bone was dead, apparently, and of course was doing damage. Dr. Mayo performed the operation.

Dr. Mayo was ahead of his Rochester fellows in that and he sometimes disagreed sharply with them as to the need for amputation. He and Dr. E. C. Cross were once called together to see a young man with a badly injured hand. They looked it over, and Dr. Cross said it must come off. Dr. Mayo said no, and he won, assuming responsibility for the outcome. When the man died half a century later, he still had his hand.

Judged from the newspaper items, Dr. Mayo's surgical practice differed from those of the other Rochester doctors also in the greater number, and even more in the greater scope, of the operations he performed for the removal of external tumors and cancers. These are more noteworthy for their daring than for their probable success, although to the newspapers and in lesser degree to the surgeon himself the immediate recovery of the patient was then the criterion for success.

Dr. W. W. Mayo, assisted by Drs. Bowers, Nichols and Sanborn, removed a tumor of a cancerous nature from the cheek of Mrs. J. Hickox, Wednesday. It was situated at the bottom of the right ear, and an artery ran through the base of it. The operation was very delicate and dangerous to perform, but under Dr. Mayo's skilful hands it was safely done, and Mrs. Hickox is doing well.

Dr. Mayo removed a tumor from the top of D. E. Wilcox's head, Friday morning. The tumor was eating through the bone, and had eaten through one layer. The operation was successful.

Dr. Mayo removed a cancer from Mrs. Nat. R. Booth, last Sunday, at the residence of W. S. Booth. It was as large as a hen's egg, and the whole left breast was taken out. Drs. Mosse and Berkman assisted. The operation was entirely successful.

## 10

Modesty forbade the publication of details about Dr. Mayo's gynecological operations, but there were enough of them to rank him high among the half-dozen Minnesota men who were specializing sufficiently to be called gynecologists. Since 1871 the state society had maintained a standing committee on gynecology, and in 1874 Dr. Mayo was named its chairman.

Up to that time only five attempts at ovariotomy had been made in the entire state: three by Drs. Murphy and Wharton of St. Paul, one by Dr. Hewitt of Red Wing, and one by Dr. Stone of St. Paul. All five patients had died. In reporting his case to the society, Dr. Stone declared that he was not in the least ashamed to admit failure in a procedure that was still stigmatized in the best surgical circles of the world as an "American audacity."

Little wonder then that when in 1875 Dr. Warner of Mankato realized that a patient of his was threatened with death from an ovarian tumor, he decided to take no chances with a Minnesota surgeon and called Dr. Washington L. Atlee from Pennsylvania to perform the operation.

Dr. Atlee never forgot his trip to Good Thunder, Minnesota. It occurred in March, and Minnesota weather again produced a storm of blizzard proportions for the occasion. Dr. Atlee's train being stalled, he learned that he could keep his appointment on time only by driving twenty-five miles across the open prairie. Old settlers warned him that it would be madness to attempt the trip in such a storm, but he found a driver willing to take the risk and started out across the white waste. They lost their way, the sleigh hit a submerged fence post and overturned, and the driver wanted to give up. But Dr. Atlee insisted upon continuing the journey, finally reached the patient's home, and was rewarded by success in the operation.

The first successful ovariotomy by a Minnesota doctor was performed the next year by a young St. Paul surgeon. Then came three more failures, and that constituted the reported record in 1880.

Early in January of that year Dr. Mayo was called to see Mrs. Jacob Waggoner, a young matron who lived just across the alley from him in Rochester. She complained of a swelling in her side, which proved to be an ovarian tumor, but it was still too small to justify such a last resort as operation.

Mrs. Waggoner then became pregnant and in May suffered a miscarriage. A bad case of pelvic infection followed, and thereafter the tumor grew rapidly, until by October it was interfering with respiration. Dr. Mayo recommended removal, but Mrs. Waggoner refused it, so he tapped the growth, draining off its fluid contents. It quickly refilled and continued to grow.

The woman's general health failed, she grew thin and weak, and could not eat. She was facing death and the operation could mean no worse, so she gave her consent.

Carefully Dr. Mayo planned. Under his instructions the patient's husband, who was a blacksmith, forged the instruments, among them some clamps fitted with hooks made from the teeth of an old mowing machine.

On December 14 the operating force assembled at the Waggoner home. Dr. J. E. Bowers, superintendent of the Rochester State Hospital for the Insane, was on hand to give the anesthetic, and to render other assistance there were Mrs. Mayo, Dr. David Berkman, the young veterinarian whom Gertrude Mayo had married in 1877, and Dr. Gould, Dr. Mayo's partner at the moment. Young Will and Charlie were there too, "peeking through the door."

With the patient under chloroform, Dr. Mayo made the incision, as small as he thought practicable, plunged a trocar into the tumor, and drained its contents into a tub ready for the purpose. Then he applied the homemade clamps, which had been heating in a little charcoal furnace such as solderers used, and began to pull the tumor out bit by bit. It was a large one, weighing some twenty pounds.

All went well until a big pelvic abscess lying behind the growth broke and spilled its contents into the abdominal cavity. That was bad, but Dr. Mayo sponged out the pus as thoroughly as he could, inserted a drainage tube, and stitched up the incision.

The operation consumed nearly an hour and the patient showed signs of severe shock, but she rallied and regained consciousness. Three days later the newspaper concluded a notice of the event with the statement that "the lady is doing well." And in the next week's issue:

Upon inquiry at the house of Mr. Jacob Waggoner, we were much gratified to learn that Mrs. W. was doing well and out of danger. We are personally glad this is so, for it is not much to the credit of a state like Minnesota to have to send all patients who require difficult and dangerous surgical operations to Chicago for treatment. The citizens of Rochester must feel equally glad with us that there is one amongst us (Dr. Mayo) who has the nerve and courage to undertake to relieve suffering humanity from this dangerous disease.

Mrs. Waggoner's operation was the favorite topic of conversation for weeks, and the lady herself was one of the wonders of the town. Dr. Mayo had "cut her wide open," and she lived!

That operation was the first of a series. Its successful outcome led to enough others like it during the next decade to make Dr. Mayo the foremost ovariotomist in Minnesota by a good margin.

Obviously, Dr. Mayo did not operate in a well-ordered world of men in white. His was "kitchen surgery," attended with all the informality and makeshift that term implies. The theater was usually the patient's home, the operating table one from the kitchen, or the parlor sofa, or even a door taken from its hinges and laid across two saw-horses. For transients and the homeless Dr. Mayo requisitioned the use of a room in one of the smaller hotels, the American House, Merchants' Hotel, or the Norton Hotel.

The room was seldom large enough, and Dr. Mayo often refused to permit the presence of anyone but those who were helping him or other doctors who had come to watch. But the friends and neighbors who had gathered to support the patient's family through the ordeal mulled about the doorway or in the yard outside, excited and curious.

Modern men, accustomed to strict asepsis in operative routine and surroundings, can scarcely credit the stories of pre-antiseptic methods, stories of men who operated in whatever coat or shirt they happened to be wearing, covering it perhaps with a linen duster or an apron stiff with the stains of previous operations; who stropped their knives on the soles of their shoes before they began and while using one knife held another ready between their teeth, its blade nestling among their whiskers; who economized on the water that must be carried in from the well by squeezing the blood from the sponge instead of washing it out; who washed their hands after, not before, the operation.

Word of the work of Pasteur and Lister was getting around by 1880, but more as the story of an outlandish new fad than as the report of scientific truth. Microbes still belonged to the realm of fantasy, and the concept of antiseptic cleanliness was still beyond the comprehension of most men. As for the aesthetic cleanliness of instruments, sponges, and towels—well, wasn't that rather a silly whim when the operation itself was so messy?

Little is known specifically of Dr. Mayo's methods. Being fastidious in dress and person, he may have kept his few instruments fairly clean, free at least of dried blood between operations, but they were certainly not sterile. Some of them he carried in a little case or even loose in his vest pocket, where he could reach them easily to lance a boil or clip the ragged edges of a minor wound. Before removing moles or a wen from the scalp he did bathe the parts thoroughly with alcohol, so he may have paid rather more than customary attention to preparation of the operative site.

He may have removed his long black coat for the task, to allow himself greater freedom of movement or to save the garment from soiling. But perhaps he shared that peculiar sense of values which made it a matter of pride for the surgeon to perform an amputation or other major operation without spotting the whiteness of shirt cuff or front. It is said that Dr. Henry J. Bigelow of Boston, one of the nation's ablest surgeons at the time, always operated in a "well-valeted dark blue Prince Albert coat with a rose in the buttonhole," and that he always gave his appearance a critical once-over in the mirror before entering the surgical amphitheater of the Massachusetts General Hospital.

Like all his fellows Dr. Mayo expected infection to develop in the incision or stump, but he had got far enough to know that it was not the ideal, for he congratulated himself when the wound healed "almost entirely by primary intention," that is, almost entirely without complications from postoperative infections.

## 12

Such was the professional development that combined with Dr. Mayo's crusade for reform in government to make him known "nearly everywhere in the state." Men who listened to the little doctor discuss their problems at some campaign rally in October were likely to think of him when little Mary got diphtheria in December. As his reputation spread from family to family and neighborhood to neighborhood, his practice grew to an enormous size.

He became a prime favorite with the numerous Irish Catholics, and his case accounts are spattered with Pats and Mikes and Dolans and Dees. And with Campions. These were a prolific tribe, seemingly with a branch in every town and township of the county. One of the lively young ones, known as "Brick Jack," in later years recalled the good old days when he was a boy. "When one of the Campions took sick there were three things we always sent for . . . Old Doc Mayo, Father Riordan, and a jug of whisky."

So on the map of Olmsted and adjoining counties the cluster of dots representing Mayo patients steadily thickened and the circle of the Mayo ride widened. By 1883 it covered an area of forty square miles around Rochester.

To this was added an extensive consultation practice. As Dr. Mayo's ability grew and his reputation was enhanced by conspicuous successes, the village and country doctors roundabout who had been calling the Drs. Cross of Rochester or Dr. Hewitt of Red Wing or Dr. Staples of Winona—or even Dr. Atlee of Pennsylvania—now began to summon Dr. Mayo of Rochester.

Even his own neighbors gradually began to realize he was one of the best doctors in the state; the awakening of Dr. Elisha Cross is more or less typical. He was called upon to treat a young woman for purpura hemorrhagica, or land scurvy, a disease that manifests itself in great purple blotches on the skin caused by internal bleeding. Purpura as severe as hers was then almost invariably fatal even under the care of men like Dr. Murphy and the young firebrand, Perry H. Millard of Stillwater.

Dr. Cross summoned Dr. Staples to his aid, but the patient got rapidly worse, so finally her parents changed to Dr. Mayo. By regulating her diet and dosing her with turpentine he cured her, though it took him a year to do it.

After that whenever Dr. Cross got a case he did not feel able to handle alone, he called in Dr. Mayo, and for a year and a half he and Dr. Mayo shared an office as partners. In time Dr. Staples himself and Dr. Stone of St. Paul were also asking Dr. Mayo's opinion on cases of ovarian tumor.

For dozens of doctors in south central Minnesota it became habitual to send their surgical cases to Dr. Mayo and to consult him in medical cases that baffled them. They learned that they could trust his honesty as well as his ability, for his opinions were given quickly and directly to them and to the patient. He would have no part in what was called "closed consultation"; that allowed too much opportunity for unethical practices. He insisted that the doctors confer openly, in the presence of the patient or his family, so that all might know of any difference of opinion and take part in determining the procedure to be followed. Honest doctors respected Dr. Mayo for this stand, and he made some deeply admiring friends among them.

145

# The Old Doctor

By 1883 Dr. Mayo had one of the three largest practices in southern Minnesota. That much at least it is safe to say, and his practice may well have been the largest. The only possible competitors were Dr. Hewitt and Dr. Staples, but Dr. Hewitt was giving most of his time and effort to the cause of public health, and Dr. Staples shared the area about Winona with several able men. Nor did Dr. Mayo's practice stop at the state boundary lines. It had begun to reach into the communities of northern Iowa, and even across the border into Dakota Territory, among former residents of Rochester.

## 13

To note the sum of Dr. Mayo's activities in the early 1880's is to marvel at his capacity for effort despite his sixty-odd years. To his tremendous practice with all the hours of horse-and-buggy traveling it entailed, his continued activity in the state medical society, and his incessant participation in city and county affairs, he added intermittent service on the Rochester board of health.

In its earlier years the task of the board was merely to maintain a pest house for use during epidemics and to abate "nuisances prejudicial to health," which included such duties as arranging for the removal of animal carcasses left lying unburied on the river bank and piles of offal accumulated on the premises of the slaughterhouses and butcher shops; impounding the cattle, pigs, and sheep that ran loose fouling the city thoroughfares; and prodding the citizens to clean up their stables and privies. Those were elementary measures, but they aroused opposition. When the board announced a campaign against throwing garbage and manure into the alleys, the editor thought the doctors were going too far. What did they think the alleys were for?

After the state board of health was organized in 1872, the local board took on duties less ephemeral in effect, such as the collection of statistics on the prevalence of disease in the community, the administration of vaccination and quarantine measures advised by the state authorities, and also their program for educating the people to give up some of their cherished individual liberties in matters of health.

Dr. Mayo became much interested in these matters. He bought a manual of methods for public health officers and began trying some of the analyses of food and water it described. Because of his acquaintance with members of the state board, especially with Dr. Hewitt, its executive secretary, Dr. Mayo became a sort of agent of the board in and around Rochester. When an epidemic of influenza was reported from Pleasant Grove, for instance, Dr. Hewitt asked Dr. Mayo to drive over, learn what facts he could about the situation, and collect samples of the water from some of the wells for analysis.

Of course in all his activities Dr. Mayo had help from time to time from the medical students for whom he was acting as preceptor, but there is little more known of them than their names. The Doctor's way with young men is evident, however, in the stories of the boy working in the dentist's office next to Dr. Mayo's and the prescription clerk in the drug store downstairs. At Dr. Mayo's insistent advice the former quit being an office boy and went off to study, and later to practice, dental surgery in Paris.

The prescription clerk was Henry Wellcome. Dr. Mayo took an interest in him, and was soon giving him lessons in chemistry and physics and urging him not to be content with the life of a poorly trained, small-town druggist, but to go away to school and fit himself for a real professional career.

Henry was a lad with ears to hear and, given practical assistance by Dr. Mayo, he took a thorough course in pharmacy at colleges in Chicago and Philadelphia and then went abroad for further study. In London he secured a position with a manufacturing chemist by the name of Burroughs. Soon he was married to his employer's daughter and the firm was Burroughs and Wellcome—a name well known in the world of medicine and pharmacy today.

When Henry Wellcome left the United States the manufacture of medicines in tablet form had just begun, and it had not yet started in England. Burroughs and Wellcome introduced it there. Tablets of standardized size and content were much easier to prescribe than the old powders and homemade pills—and much more easily carried to those far places of the world that Englishmen were going to explore and colonize. The firm was phenomenally successful almost at once, and its proprietors became men of great wealth.

Wellcome devoted his money to many and widely varied philanthropies, most of them for encouraging research in science. The work of the Wellcome Bureau of Scientific Research is known to scientists throughout the world, and for it the founder was knighted by the king of England.

Henry Wellcome often returned to the United States and to Rochester, always finding occasion to speak with gratitude of the part Dr. Mayo had played in his career. Once in an address before the American College of Surgeons he described him as "one of my most valued preceptors, and the one who, in my youth, inspired and guided me in my studies, and insisted upon my qualifying myself for a career in the field of science."

## 14

For many years Dr. Mayo's best assistant was his wife. Applying her ability for self-education to her husband's books and journals, Mrs. Mayo acquired a knowledge of medicine that some friends of the family considered very nearly equal to the Doctor's own. He did not scruple to ask her opinion on a puzzling case, and she frequently went with him to see a patient. She helped too in his operations, and was so often present to assist in reducing fractures and applying splints that she acquired the knack of doing it herself.

Her ability was known and respected in Rochester, even by the other doctors. One of them was having trouble one day getting a dislocated shoulder back into place, and seeing Mrs. Mayo pass the door he called her to come in and help him. She did more than help; she promptly applied her husband's methods. Placing the injured man flat on the floor, she took off her shoe, put her foot firmly under his arm, and gave the arm a mighty tug. The deed was done.

Her younger son once described another phase of her helpfulness:

Patients used to call at the house for father; there were no telephones, and if mother knew he was out in the country she would keep the patients interested, discussing their troubles and problems, until he returned, even if she had to prepare a meal for them. Often the neighbors and the country people came to talk to her about their families, their troubles, the children, and the babies, with as much satisfaction from a social standpoint as they got from consulting my father when sickness descended on them. When father was taking special studies in the East, or in Europe, patients came to mother to talk about illness, and she told them of the simple remedies, which would tide them through the most common illness. Mother was a real good doctor herself.

# Pioneer in Surgery

Mrs. Mayo made a good confidante, for she was a wise woman. She had a strong sense of humor too, and a witty, pleasantly sharp tongue. According to one neighbor, she made "thousands of friends" in the city, and whatever her religious views were, she was as active in the Episcopal Church as her heavy duties at home permitted.

But domestic matters sometimes stalked her even at divine worship. Rochester folk long chuckled about the time she almost disrupted the Sunday morning service. In the midst of it she suddenly jumped to her feet, cried aloud, "Godalmighty, I left my bread in the oven!" and went streaking up the aisle toward the door.

Dr. and Mrs. Mayo sometimes attended a public entertainment, church festival, or social together, but they went less often than Mrs. Mayo would have liked. Frequently when she was looking forward to some evening of amusement, perhaps already dressing for the occasion, something more pressing would demand the Doctor's attention and he would announce that he could not go. If the reason was professional, Mrs. Mayo did not object.

Those two forceful personalities did not always pull smoothly in double harness. It was well known to their close friends that for long periods of time they spoke to each other no more than necessary to keep the affairs of the household going and the children free from strain. Dr. Mayo was an obstinate man, by no means easy to get along with, and his wife had a mind of her own that she proposed to use.

They agreed on most fundamentals. Sometime during the 1870's English relatives investigating the family history discovered that for some service to his king Captain Totten, Mrs. Mayo's grandfather, had been granted a piece of land in what is now New Brunswick, extending east and west as far as a man could ride on horseback in one day and north and south as far as he could ride in two days. Learning that the land in question was now valuable, the English descendants of Captain Totten instituted suit for title to it.

Lawyers came from England to persuade Mrs. Mayo to join in the litigation. The idea angered her as deeply as it did her husband. They would have nothing to do with the suit. It was unjust, for the land should belong to those whose labors had made it valuable. Apparently the court agreed with them, for the suit was decided adversely for the Totten heirs.

Mrs. Mayo joined willingly in her husband's impulsive generosity, though it sometimes disrupted the household routine and meant added burdens for her shoulders. One day he brought her four children to care for, ranging in age from six to twelve. Their mother, a patient of his, had just died and they had no place else to go. Other homes were later found for the two younger girls, but the two older ones lived with the Mayos until they married.

A few years later one of the colonizing schemes of the day brought to the Rochester area a party of some sixty young Englishmen, second and third sons of impoverished aristocrats who thought to better their fortunes in the New World. The idea of the promoter was to hire them out as farm hands until they learned the ways of American agriculture, but the boys, blithe and unaware, had come fully equipped with dress suits, guns, and fishing tackle. Some of them found farm life and the rigors of a Minnesota winter more than they could take.

Dr. Mayo was indignant about the whole affair and felt himself morally responsible for the boys. They kept coming to his office for help and advice, and before the winter was over he had taken no fewer than eight of them home for Mrs. Mayo to look after until they could find more suitable work or could arrange for passage back to England.

Such demands upon her good nature Mrs. Mayo met with equanimity and a generous measure of sympathy. It was Dr. Mayo's championship of the underdog in the mass that she could not approve. Her judgment was more balanced than his, her tolerant understanding deeper and inclusive enough to take in the banker as well as the widow and orphans. She knew that some of the economic distress that sent her husband into a tirade against the wheat rings and the railroads was quite as much the fault of individual shiftlessness and bad management as of general conditions or the cussedness of the wealthy.

Moreover, since she had to keep the family clothed and fed on the Doctor's income, she was understandably cross when he went off for two weeks at a time on political campaigns and neglected the business that provided that income.

She had a good business head and knew the Doctor's big practice could keep the family in comfort without strain. When Dr. Mayo set off for New York in the fall of 1869 he gave her his account books, saying she could collect enough of what his patients owed him to support the family while he was away. She undertook the job with alacrity, and never had the Mayos lived so well and so easily as they did that winter. Knowing that, Mrs. Mayo was exasperated when she had to struggle to make ends meet.

## 15

The stories of Dr. Mayo's houses in town and on the farm, of his trips, books, horses, carriages, his relatively generous contributions to civic projects, and his readiness to invest money in one venture or another do not give the impression of insufficient funds.

Never a year passed without the paper's reporting some improvement that Dr. Mayo was making on one of his properties, and sometimes the improvement was extensive and costly. He did not always go to the conventions of the American Medical Association as a delegate with expenses paid, and in the summer of 1876, just after buying the farm, he spent three months in Europe. Nor did his sons have to work their way through medical college, as some doctors did and do.

Yet Will and Charlie could not remember that their father ever had any ready money. The Mayos always had to practice the strictest economy in their daily living, and Dr. Mayo, himself told Ignatius Donnelly that his practice of physic enabled him only to hang onto the world by the skin of his teeth. His activities were often financed on credit, and although all accounts agree that he always paid his bills, the horse might be dead before he got it paid for.

The trouble was that no one had ever taught Dr. Mayo to make a budget and keep it balanced. Not that he would have bothered to do so if he had known how. He was as impulsive in spending money as in everything else, and he had a marked inclination to sacrifice the bread and butter of life for its jam. In a rush of enthusiasm he would hire an engineer to plan the Bear Creek dam, take a trip to Europe, or have a fancy new gig built to order at the carriage shop—and let the old suit or carpet or churn serve for another year. Unwise? Improvident? Perhaps, though there is a view of living that counts the grasshopper wiser than the ant, the feast worth the famine.

But that does not entirely explain why in spite of his large practice he was never listed with the Drs. Cross and Dr. Galloway among Rochester's rich men whose incomes were large enough to be taxable.

# The Old Doctor

For that his haphazard, easygoing business methods were chiefly to blame. Posting his books was a task he did not like, so he put it off as long as he could.

Mrs. Granger, living on a farm some miles from Rochester, was confined to her bed for something over a year and a half and required almost daily visits from Dr. Mayo for most of the period. Her husband did not want the bill to mount beyond his ability to pay it, so after the first few months he told the Doctor he wanted to pay what he owed.

"I haven't got my books up to date and I don't know how much it is," replied the Doctor. But Mr. Granger insisted. "Well, then, give me fifty dollars."

A few months later the man raised the same question, got the same answer, and paid another fifty dollars. Then shortly after his wife had recovered sufficiently to dispense with the Doctor's services, he stopped by to settle the bill in full. Dr. Mayo still did not know the amount of it. "But give me fifty dollars and we'll call it square." And that was the end of it.

At last his daughter Phoebe and later Gertrude's husband took over the bookkeeping and brought a measure of system into it. But they could not put system into the charges and collections. The Doctor hated to set a fee and detested asking for money. He would have preferred the old way of the honorarium: I'll do the best job I can and you give me what it's worth to you. Not until he was himself being pressed by some urgent need would he send out bills.

To that habit was added an incurable softheartedness; he could not put down a charge for poor folks. Whether his social and political views were right or wrong they were sincere, and he lived according to them. He would not take money from a struggling widow or a farmer bent low under a load of debt. Accept a mortgage in payment? Sue to collect an account? Not Dr. Mayo. He had seen too much of the ruin such methods wrought.

So the Mayos were grateful for patients like Mr. Granger who paid promptly and in cash. Others paid in vegetables, meats, milk, whatever they could spare, and some, a goodly number, did not pay at all. But in Dr. Mayo's treatment of them it made no difference which class they belonged to; if a man was sick his financial status did not count.

To some this attitude was, and is, incomprehensible. Dr. Mayo's farm hand could not understand it. He would mutter and sputter as he hitched up the horses, going all profane at times about the Doctor's readiness to answer a call from a patient they both knew to be a confirmed deadbeat. What kind of business was it to waste your time and energy on somebody who didn't pay?

But to Dr. Mayo his daily work was not a business. It was a profession, and one of service. To answer the call of any sick person at any time was a sacred obligation he had assumed with the title of doctor. *Sacred* is the right word, for that code was his religious creed.

And he got his reward this side of heaven—in something more than virtue's own sense of satisfaction too.

## 16

Tuesday, May 31, 1881, was Dr. Mayo's sixty-second birthday. His sentiment not being of the kind that makes much of birthdays, he went quietly about his ordinary routine.

In the pleasant early evening, however, he was glad to oblige a friend who had asked him to take her riding for a breath of air after supper. As the fast-stepping grays were speeding the carriage back toward town, his companion decided she would like to stop for a chat with Mrs. Mayo before going home. So Dr. Mayo turned in at his own gate.

The place was ablaze with the light of torches and a crowd of several hundred persons filled the yard and the porch. As the carriage drew abreast of them, there was a fanfare from a band and a rush toward the buggy. Dr. Mayo's Rochester friends and patients had gathered to surprise him.

He *was* surprised, utterly. After he took in the situation and shook hands all around, one of the men stepped forward, called for silence, then addressed the Doctor:

I have been requested to assure you that this seeming raid upon your premises is one of a peaceful character, and that no injury to your person or to your property is contemplated. That our mission to your beautiful home this evening is one of love and respect for you is fully demonstrated by the smiling, happy faces that greet you on every side. . . .

The great majority of those present have at some period of their lives been your patients, and we wish now to thank you for your kindness and devotion then extended to us and for your skill in restoring us to the robust health that all present seem now to possess. . . .

For nearly a quarter of a century you have been our friend and physician, ever true to the trust reposed in you, and ever equal to any occasion. By night as well as by day, through darkness and storms, you have visited the poor and destitute sick in their cabins, from whom you never expected to receive any pecuniary remuneration, as freely and as promptly as you have visited those who were able to pay for your services. Through all these years of your patient and untiring labors to relieve the sick and the suffering you have never hesitated in the performance of the responsible duties of your profession.

Appreciating these and many other noble qualities of your nature, we thought this, the anniversary of your birth, the most fitting occasion to make some acknowledgment of the great service you have rendered this entire community. I, therefore, in the name and in behalf of those present, present to you these books as a token of our high regard for you as a kind and obliging neighbor, a faithful friend, and a trusted physician.

These were five beautiful volumes, bound in morocco and gilt-edged, comprising a de luxe edition of Wilson and Bonaparte's *Natural History of the Birds of the United States*. (The newspaper revealed next day that they had cost one hundred and ten dollars.)

The little doctor was completely overcome. He tried to reply but could not speak for the emotion that choked him, and half the crowd were likewise moved to tears. Finally he managed a few sentences.

My Friends . . . I know not what to say to you; I would like to say much, but the ebullition of feeling prevents me from expressing more than my thanks for this evidence of your good feeling toward me. . . . I have been a citizen among you, knowing you all, meeting you daily, but I did not know that I had done or deserved more than any other citizen. . . . I have endeavored to do my duty as a physician in a manner satisfactory to myself and to the public, and never thought my efforts were so far appreciated by the community as to bring out a public expression of this character.

He concluded with a reference to the gift. Nothing could have been more acceptable to him, for books had always been his companions and friends; from them he had learned all he knew that was of use to others.

The ceremonies over, refreshments were served and the evening was passed in general conversation, mixed with selections by the Rochester Cornet Band.

Present to share in the Doctor's happiness were his entire family: Mrs. Mayo; Gertrude, now Mrs. Berkman, direct, positive, outspoken, very like her father in manner and temperament; Phoebe, gentle and winning, for the past five years an invalid as the result of an injury to the spleen suffered when she was thrown from a carriage as she made the sharp turn into the farm driveway; *and* the two boys. Will had just arrived from medical school on the six o'clock train, having come home for the summer a day early in order to be present for the occasion. Charlie, a lad of seventeen, was still in high school.

What thoughts stirred in their minds as they listened and watched that night? Pleasure, pride, excitement, of course, but were there also ambition and a determination to earn such a tribute for themselves someday? Or any thought of that future when these patients would be theirs?

# The Mayo Brothers

# CHAPTER SEVEN

# Will and Charlie

"From the very beginning Charlie and I always went together. We were known as the Mayo boys. Anyone that picked on one of us had the two to contend with."

From those words imagination can conjure a picture: There is Will, a slender boy, with fair hair and dreamy blue eyes, a little lonely, wanting companionship and love; he is the older brother, slight but strong, active, spirited, able. And with him almost constantly, in play and at their chores, is Charlie, short, stocky, with thick dark hair and big brown eyes that no parent or teacher could withstand when they turned innocent and appealing, an affectionate boy, needing oversight and protection, for he was the little brother and he was not strong.

Put just so, that is mere fancy. But in some such relationship must have been formed that infrangible brotherhood that was to be the wonder of all who saw it and on the strength of which both men were to reach the heights.

The boys spent long hours reading together, shooting marbles, fishing through an afternoon at Oronoco or Zumbro Falls, or hunting arrowheads and other more grisly relics in the old Indian burial grounds atop the bluffs surrounding Rochester. In spring "pigeon days" they sometimes hitched Will's pony to a buggy and drove over to the roost in a tract of timber about twelve miles from town to club a bagful of the young birds from the trees. That was then good sport and business too for youngsters and grownups alike, because the passenger pigeons ate up the farmers' grain and there were such thousands of them they darkened the sun in their flight.

The boys seldom missed a circus. Charlie especially loved the strange animals and varied shows and could hardly wait for it to arrive, once its coming had been announced. The summer he was nine or ten, he and a playmate sneaked out at four o'clock in the morning and walked down the road for two hours to meet the red wagons on their way to town. When the trainers allowed them to ride back on top of one of the animal wagons, the stay-at-homes were envious and the two adventurers twice happy.

One time Will watched the parade from on horseback. His mount, so the tale goes, was frightened by the elephants, and in its terrified cavorting jumped over a hitching rail and back again, causing a commotion in the crowd. "But Will never batted an eye." There, in the child, is a glimpse of that control in a crisis that became a distinguishing characteristic of the surgeon.

To his family Charlie seemed quieter, more serious and studious than Will. "He was always reading or writing or making things," his sister recalled. They were all proud of him, for he had a skill with things mechanical that astonished them all. Was there a stove, a pump, or a churn that didn't work? Charlie could fix it. Was a gadget wanted for some purpose in house or barn? Charlie would contrive it.

When the two brothers were in their early teens, Charlie persuaded their father to buy them a little steam engine that would turn wheels to do the family washing, cut wood, or work the well pump. When the engine came, and forever thereafter, its working was an unfathomable mystery to Will. He would push and pull and pry, turn this screw and that one. To no avail. "I could never make the cussed thing go." Then Charlie would come and with a simple twist or two set it chugging. When repairs were needed, he took the engine apart, found and fixed the trouble, and put all the pieces back in their proper place. "Absolutely magical" this seemed to Will.

There is a family tradition that Charlie at fourteen, with no instruction other than the pictures and descriptions he had seen, rigged up a telephone from his father's office to the family farm home. The instrument worked so well that the telephone company threatened suit for infringement of patent when they heard of it.

Whatever the truth of the tradition, it is a fact that in 1879, when Charlie was fourteen, the first telephone in Rochester was put in to connect Dr. Mayo's office with the farmhouse. But the newspaper report, though it treats this as a novelty, does not seem to refer to a contraption devised by an ingenious youngster. Perhaps Dr. Mayo to avert the threatened lawsuit authorized the telephone company to install one of its own instruments in place of Charlie's homemade device.

# Will and Charlie

At any rate, this child so much at ease with nuts and bolts, wires, screws, and coils, this child with so marked a flair for assembling disparate parts into a functioning whole, was natural father to the man whose quickness to originate the saving wrinkle or recipe in surgery left his professional brethren agape with wonder.

## 2

The Mayo boys displayed no precocious brilliance in childhood. They were gifted, to be sure, but not with abilities so phenomenal or so clearly predestined to medicine as to obviate the influence of circumstances.

They went to school at Rochester Central, that "model of magnificence and elegance" the school board had built across the street from their home. Although the occupation of the building had been followed by a thorough revision of methods to make the course of study conform to the current notions of good pedagogy, the pupils still spent more time learning to parse sentences, declaim properly, and reckon by long division, fractions, and decimals than in such innovations as American history and "brief lessons in natural science."

Will and Charlie did not show the "apathetic indifference to the higher achievements of the school room" condemned by their father, but neither were they teacher's pets, unnaturally well behaved and absorbed in study. Will was lively, so full of teasing tricks to torment the girls that they did not like to play with him. He got on easily enough with his lessons, except in arithmetic, which he could never master and, probably because of that, always heartily disliked. For Will Mayo could never have endured wearing the dunce cap; he was too proud and too sensitive to ridicule. He reacted violently and without humor to anything that turned the joke on him and made him feel a fool.

On one occasion he went to a show given by a playmate, Jimmy Ells, the son of a Rochester druggist and a little devil from all accounts. The admission was ten pins, and the theater a barn. As part of the entertainment Jimmy was to demonstrate his prowess in sleight-of-hand by finding two eggs under someone's hat. He chose Will's hat, and the eggs were rotten. When Will got the egg out of his eyes, he grabbed a hatchet and started for Jimmy. By his own admission, if someone had not tripped him on the way he would have done his first surgery then and there.

Another time, when he was riding on the tailboard of a grocer's wagon and did not heed a command to get off, the driver flicked him with the tip of the whip, then laughed to see him jump. Will's temper flared, more at the laugh than at the sting of the whip. He snatched up a handful of stones and hurled them in a fury at the driver, with a string of words that were neither gentle nor genteel.

If a hypersensitive ego is acquired and not inborn, the causes of Will Mayo's are lost with the details of his first years, for his barriers were up early. Withdrawal, protective pride, independence, all were there, creating an inability to be one of the gang, an incapacity for easy intimacy and informality. He may have felt surges of boyish affection and comradeship toward his companions, but he did not express them, or inspire others to express them, in playful hair-pulling or in throwing an arm across another's shoulders. Playmates would do that to Charlie, but not to Will. And he would not have liked it if they had.

His choice of pastimes was in keeping with his disposition. One of the familiar, remembered sights of Rochester for those whose school-days fell with his was that of "Will Mayo dashing spiritedly around the streets on his little bay pony." Dr. Mayo had got him the pony as soon as he was old enough to ride, and it was his pride and pleasure for several years, until he had to relinquish it for his sister Gertrude to ride to and from the school near town in which she was teaching. Then Will fell heir to a horse from his father's stable.

He learned to ride well and without fear, but not without accident. On one occasion when the wills of master and mount collided, he rode toward a tree to get a switch, but the pony acted first. Will's left arm struck a rock and was broken just below the elbow. Someone near by helped him to remount, and the child, just eight years old, rode home alone, a mile and a half. The story of that mishap to "Willie Mayo, son of Dr. Mayo" was the first of his many appearances in the newspapers.

The next year, in a trial of horsemanship for boys under eighteen at the county fair, Willie placed second in a field of four. In after years the local graybeards, recalling this early achievement of their most successful neighbor, ended with a chuckle, "That was the only time Will Mayo ever came out second best."

When Charlie started to school in the "baby room" at Central, he did not seem to like it, for he often played hooky. Each time he ran away his mother took him firmly back to school until the lesson was learned and the habit broken. At recess he would run across the street to mother for a piece of bread spread thick with butter and brown sugar. Sometimes he had to sprint to get back in time, and then the old janitor known and loved by generations of Rochester youngsters would call "Hurry!" and keep on ringing the bell until the boy could get up the stairs and into his seat. "Which proves that it's just as good to stand in with the janitor as with the superintendent," remarked Charlie some years later.

He always stood well toward the top of his class, but he also stood well up in mischief. He was so often the ringleader in the fun that Charlie Mayo and his chum, Albert Younglove, were the teacher's chief suspects when anything was amiss in the classroom.

At last the black marks against him were too many—or else he was guilty of some misdeed unusually vexatious—and he was summoned before the principal. That gentleman intended a birching and twirled a sturdy stick in his fingers as he read the culprit a homily on the advantages of being a good boy. Then he asked Charlie whether he had anything to say.

"Yes, please, if you could wait until this afternoon, I'd like to get my other pair of pants."

The schoolmaster struggled to stay severe, then surrendered to a laugh. "And that was the end of that."

## 3

A high school was the crowning distinction of Rochester Central, for that feature of the public school system was just emerging from the shell. The state provided common schools and a university but left the gap between to be filled only by private or sectarian academies and the preparatory department maintained as a necessary but unwelcome adjunct of the university.

Many Rochester citizens thought the addition of a high school too ambitious and grumbled about the cost, but for Dr. Mayo it was not good enough. The enrollment was small, the attendance haphazard. Two or three teachers, unimpressive in their mental equipment, turned out from five to ten graduates a year. And there was only one course of study, which included too much mathematics and too little science and languages to suit the Doctor. But there being no alternative he sent Will to the high school for two or three years.

Then in the summer of 1876 Mary Finch, a teacher of good repute in Rochester, announced the opening of a private school in which she would teach Latin, French, and German, and in the fall Will Mayo began an intensive study of languages in Miss Finch's select school.

Miss Finch soon had to meet competition, however. For eleven years Sanford B. Niles had been superintendent of schools in Olmsted County and in that time had become recognized as one of the outstanding educators in Minnesota, but through one of the irrational changes of heart the electorate sometimes suffers, he was defeated in 1876 by a lesser man. Immediately, with the aid of his wife Priscilla and a promising young teacher, Horace H. Witherstine, Niles opened the Rochester Training School. The course of study included the common and higher English branches, Latin, Greek, German, French, music, drawing, and painting. "Fitting for college" was to be a special function of the school, and for this work Niles employed the assistance of Joel N. Childs, a "thorough classical scholar" highly recommended by President Folwell of the state university.

Dr. Mayo felt that to study with Sanford Niles and teachers of the sort he was gathering around him was an opportunity Will ought not to miss. True, there were tuition fees, an item not to be dismissed lightly when income was chronically insufficient. But Mrs. Mayo advertised for boarders and the Doctor probably paid some attention to his collections, because Will was in attendance at the Rochester Training School when it opened on January 2, 1877.

It met in Heaney's Block, upstairs. Below was a public hall known as the "opera house." A narrow, wooden stairway climbed to the second floor, where a dusty hallway led between two rows of offices to the schoolrooms ranged across the back. (One of the offices was occupied by Burt W. Eaton and his law partner, Frank B. Kellogg, who as secretary of state under Calvin Coolidge was to give his name to the Kellogg-Briand Pact.) There were three schoolrooms, all light, pleasant, and well furnished according to the standards of the day, for they were fitted with single desks.

The Niles school was at once a success. For the first term it enrolled one hundred and thirteen students, many from nearby county areas, attracted by the reputation of the headmaster. Christopher Graham and his sister Dinah were there, both to be associates of the Mayo brothers later, and John J. Lawler, a future bishop of the Catholic church, J. Paul Goode, who was to make his mark as a university teacher of geography, and J. D. Farrell of Oronoco, later president of the Spokane, Portland, and Seattle Railroad.

Farrell may have been one of those who answered Mrs. Mayo's advertisement for boarders, but he seems to have received more from the family coffer than he contributed to it, for he is said to have earned his board and schooling by helping Will and Charlie take care of their father's horses.

Physical training was not in the course at Niles's academy, but it could be had near at hand. "Prof. Sam Manchester" conducted a "Rochester Gymnasium" in other rooms of Heancy's Block, and at two public exhibitions given by his pupils Willie Mayo was among the performers. "Leaping the horizontal bar, whirling, tumbling, parallel bars, ladder, dumb bells, club swinging, handsprings, and somersaults; all exercises requiring both activity and strength, were performed by the boys, to the entire satisfaction of the audience."

Charlie was not one of Manchester's pupils, perhaps because his strength was not up to the gymnastics, but otherwise he followed Will's course, transferring to the Rochester Training School after two or three years of high school and a spell of private study with a Mrs. McMahon.

On the whole then, in a day when schooling often stopped with three or four years of random attendance in an ungraded class, and at best seldom included more than eight years of rudimentary graded work, Will and Charlie Mayo were fortunate in the preparatory education their parents secured for them. Though who can say of what use it was to them? Charlie in particular was always an indifferent speller, impatient with insistence on anything more than a phonetic approximation. As he once told a secretary, any damn fool would know that *bellie* meant belly, and *phisicks* physics. There is nothing to indicate that all the brothers' study of Latin left them any residue of pleasure or profit, and as for French and German, Dr. Will once admitted, in telling how he had kept up with medical publications: "I had to depend on abstracts largely for the foreign literature. I spoke German very little and read it and French too slowly to be of real value. In striving to understand I lost the purpose of the understanding."

4

The brothers' young friends were always a little afraid of Dr. Mayo because he seemed so severe, and he could be strict enough when there was need. But the boys' mischief did not bother him. "They're no worse than I was," he told the brakeman of the freight train they sometimes rode to and from the farm. When Will came home sick after his first attempt at smoking, Dr. Mayo's only question was "Why did you do it, Will?"

"The other boys were, so I did too."

"Listen, Will," said his father, "don't ever do things because other people do. Do them because they're right."

"The Doctor had one weakness," said Mrs. Mayo of her husband. "It was for book agents. He knew and loved good books. Oh, many a time I planned to buy a dress for Trude or something for the boys or the house, only to have a book agent come to town and tip over my bucket of milk." His library was the living room, walled with well-filled shelves from floor to ceiling, and Will remembered that living room to the end of his days: "I can see Father now, standing on a wooden chair, reaching up to take books down, or, with one book under his arm, another held between his knees, looking into the pages of a third."

The books there were of a general character and covered many subjects. There were novels, which Will and Charlie were encouraged to read: some by Scott, full of dramatic history the boys remembered much longer than they did the lists of dates and names they had to learn at school; many by Dickens, whose word pictures of the wretched poor opened the social eyes of the sons while they fed the righteous indignation of the father; and the Leatherstocking Tales of James Fenimore Cooper, which moved Dr. and Mrs. Mayo to reminiscences of their own experiences with the Indians. For the boys the tales of the

# Will and Charlie

Sioux Outbreak were so thoroughly mixed with *The Deerslayer* and *The Last of the Mohicans* that the Minnesota Valley was always for them the real scene of Cooper's stories of romance and adventure.

Into the mixture of fact and fiction would come sooner or later the name of Cut Nose, the wild Sioux whose bones were lying in that big iron kettle in the Doctor's office. See, here they are. Then, picking up the skull, Look how small his head was. But he was very tall. Here's the femur, see how long it is. Thus began the first lessons in human anatomy, for the boys learned their osteology from that skeleton of the Indian warrior.

They were introduced to other sciences in the same casual way. Mrs. Mayo taught them botany while they worked together in the garden or rambled in the fields and woods along Bear Creek. Astronomy too they absorbed with enthusiasm under their mother's guidance, with books from the shelves to supplement and clarify what they saw through the four-foot telescope Mrs. Mayo had put together and mounted on a tripod in the observatory that topped the Mayo farmhouse.

Long hours of looking made the heavens ever after wear a friendly face for Will, even when affairs had crowded from his mind so much of what his mother taught him that he could recognize little more than the Milky Way and the Big Dipper. When he was himself rich enough to gratify any whim in building his house, he asked only that it have a tower like his mother's.

The boys picked up physics and chemistry from their father, who talked to them often about John Mayow, their illustrious ancestor, and the great John Dalton. "When my brother and I were small boys, he told us much about this tall, gaunt, awkward scholar, the keenness of his intelligence, his modesty, and how little it was realized in his day that the atomic theory was more than the vagary of a scientist." That from Will; this from Charlie: "Father was always talking about Dalton. He simply enthused him with chemistry."

From casual chats about men like these, perhaps over test tube and burner in the crude little laboratory in a back room off the Doctor's office, Will and Charlie learned something of the methods and manners of scientists. But they met the principles of science full face, in reasoned, defensive statement during their high school days, when their father set them to reading Darwin, Huxley, Haeckel, and Spencer. The freethinking Doctor did not think those writers at all unsuitable for teen-age boys, and they in turn found them fascinating. It is not likely that they would have met those men so intimately in even the best of high school science courses.

## 5

Though the library in the living room was large, the bulk of the Doctor's books, those having to do directly with his profession, were kept in his office. To acquaintance with these the boys came in good time as the natural consequence of their daily activities. From the time they were old enough to be of any help, Will and Charlie were expected to work as well as to study and play. "Father wanted us to be handy." He believed in useful children and did not allow his sons to acquire the art of loafing.

Even as little fellows they had chores to do. They drove the family cows in the morning to the pasture lot half a mile from home and fetched them back at night, and as Mrs. Mayo had no hired help, they were expected to assist in doing the washing and weeding the garden. They carried water in from the well and kept the woodbox filled, usually with Charlie handling the saw and with Will swinging the axe. Mrs. Mayo made her own butter at that time, so the boys must have served many a turn at the tiresome task of moving the handle of the old dash churn up and down till the butter came. And if it was too long in coming, the children knew a way to hurry it up— just sneak in a little hot water when mother wasn't looking. But be careful, for if the water was too hot or you added too much, the butter would be a mess, and then how you'd catch it!

After Dr. Mayo bought the farm—"to keep Will and Charlie away from other boys" he once said—there was plenty of work to keep them busy. They and their sisters had to help Jay Neville, a young Irishman who had recently attached himself to the Mayo household and was in charge of the farming. "I picked potato bugs, and raked hay with a jug of beer under the hay rake," said Charlie later. "They used to have big umbrellas over open buggies, so I put one on the rake. I thought I did most of the work on the farm."

Despite the tone of that last sentence, Charlie acquired a love of farming then that resulted in his making a hobby of it later. But Will would have none of it. Jay, or his father, set him to learn the trick of plowing with a sulky plow. He learned that, but little more. His experience can perhaps be inferred from an analogy he used dozens of years later: "Some of the jolts we got in learning our work were comparable to those a boy on the farm gets when learning to plow; he hangs on and stumbles across the furrows, occasionally has the handles of the plow jerked against his abdomen, but finally learns to plow." One noon he came in from the field and firmly announced that he was through. He was going into town to get a job in the drug store.

He found a place in Geisinger and Newton's drug store below his father's office, beginning with menial tasks like sweeping out, washing bottles, and scrubbing the mortars and pestles. He soon advanced, however, to the position of prescription clerk, filled a few years earlier by Henry Wellcome, Dr. Mayo's protégé. No special training in pharmacy was required then for compounding medicines; that was another of the skills acquired by apprenticeship. A year or two's experience in that line would be good for one who intended to write prescriptions himself.

The hours were long, from seven in the morning to six and sometimes nine o'clock in the evening, and the pay was only four dollars a week. With his first month's salary Will did a service for Charlie. Clothes were handed down in the Mayo family, so that whenever Dr. Mayo's double-breasted Prince Albert coat got shiny, Mrs. Mayo, with commendable thrift and the best of intentions, cut it down for one of the boys. "Charlie looked so funny in that coat, long-waisted, and with little tails. So I bought him a new suit, a store suit, and he was so happy." Neither of the brothers ever forgot the pleasure they shared in that suit.

When Charlie finished school, he went to work in the drug store too. "Will had and I wanted to." For a while he worked alone as prescription clerk, but the volume of business finally forced the owners to hire an assistant for him, a responsibility that made him very proud.

## 6

Against such a background of being useful, added to the accepted informality of the country doctor's practice, the cardinal fact of the

# The Mayo Brothers

Mayo boys' childhood and youth appears natural and inevitable: They helped their father in his work as they helped their mother in hers, and so they were learning the practice of medicine almost from their cradle days.

They began by taking care of the horses, cleaning the office, and driving their father on his rounds. Will could remember having the responsibility for the horses when he was so small he had to climb up in the manger to throw the bridle onto the neck of one high-headed horse called Frank. He enjoyed the duty and took pride in the horses his father raised, keeping a record of them in the family Bible: Hamiltonian Frank, foaled in 1859, Mustang Billy in 1860, Lexington Kate and Blacksy Girl in 1873, Chestnut Tom in 1877, and so on, with comments, like "fast trotter," or "as the wheat, solid and good."

The boys were expected to sweep out the office and dust it before they went to school. "As soon as school closed each day, father had me come to the office," said Charlie. "If he was delayed, I had to clean up some room in the office and then I drove the horse on the round of calls, taking up this work as my brother dropped it. Father said it saved him much time hitching and unhitching the horse; often he would have to go a block to find a hitching post. . . . It took until six o'clock or later to make his eight to fifteen calls."

When Dr. Mayo left the boy sitting outside the house some of the calls seemed interminably long, "especially in marble-playing time." Driving the Doctor's spirited horses was tiring too, but Charlie found a way of wrapping the reins around his neck and under one arm so that he could drive with the strength of his shoulders when his arms got tired.

In retrospect both boys were grateful for the education by association they got on these trips.

In the long drives of many miles into the country, father talked about many things, for he was interested in everything; nature, botany, geology, and especially the chemistry of life. He often took me into the house with him to see patients, even when I was a boy.

Once when I had seen a patient with him several times, I said, "He looked better today."

I had noticed that father peered intently at the patient's tongue, and put his finger on it, and at the side of it, not very cleanly perhaps but very effectually.

# Will and Charlie

Father asked, "You noticed his tongue was dry in the center, and also at the sides?"

"Yes," I said.

"Well, he will be dead within twenty-four hours."

Father said that a tongue which is dry on the upper surface is the sign of a serious condition; the patient may recover, but probably will be left with chronically poor health. When the tongue is dry on the upper surface, and at the sides as well, death is impending.

As the boys grew a little older their work at the office gave them the same training. Neither Dr. Mayo nor his patients saw anything untoward in Mrs. Mayo's being called in to set bones and dose babies, nor did they think it queer or undignified for the father to press his sons into service, and even his daughters if the emergency was great. Will and Charlie progressed from washing windows and sweeping floors to rolling bandages, applying them and the plasters and poultices used under them, helping to put on plaster casts, and similar jobs that would be done today by a hospital intern or an office nurse.

There is a story told about a young man who came to deliver produce of some kind to the house. While he was there, Dr. Mayo came into the kitchen, noticed a boil on the boy's neck, whipped out a knife, and lanced the boil, almost before the young man was aware of his intentions. Then he went on about other business, calling over his shoulder, "Will, come dress Bill's neck for him, will you?"

Transfer that episode to the office, where the Doctor, busy with a queue of patients, would need help of the same sort, and it becomes clear how and why the Mayo boys were able to acquire all the minor skills of a doctor.

Of more importance than those was what eyes and ears took in while the work was going on. Again and again the boys heard the significant questions to be asked in taking a case history, saw the points to be looked into in a thorough physical examination, listened to the diagnosis and prescription that followed from the findings. Doubtless when the patient had gone they asked their father the why of the things he did, and from frequent repetition they learned many of Dr. Mayo's tested principles of diagnosis and prognosis, which he often put in succinct, homely sayings they long remembered.

But probably their most important acquisition from office work and country drives was an introduction to the art of diagnosis on the basis of clinical observation. In association with their father William and Charles Mayo got an early training in finding the significant symptom and reading it aright. And to supplement his practical demonstrations, Dr. Mayo took from his shelves the old stand-bys, Gray's *Anatomy* and Holden's *Anatomical Landmarks,* insisting that the boys learn their contents to give "anatomical significance to physical examination."

## 7

Dr. Mayo was still at the business of "further thought and research" while his sons were working with him, indeed more actively at it than earlier, for he had more means for apparatus and for travel. And he returned from a trip to St. Paul, the East, or Europe with many new things to describe to the boys.

On one occasion that Will remembered, he came home with a dramatic story to illustrate the new principle that anesthesia had made possible for surgery. He had attended a clinic in New York at which James R. Wood and John McCormick both operated. Wood, noted for his speed in operating, a quality to be appreciated when the surgeon did his work on conscious patients, operated first, completing an amputation at the thigh in two minutes, and the crowded amphitheater echoed with applause. Then McCormick, an English surgeon, performed an equally difficult operation carefully and without haste, turning when he had finished to say quietly, "Not how quickly but how well."

From such a trip to New York or Europe came a new impetus to Dr. Mayo's interest in the use of the microscope. The instrument, like the medical uses for it, was still evolving, so that by the seventies the Doctor's model was out of date, and on this trip he had seen some of the new, higher powered ones.

He returned home on a train that reached Rochester about nine o'clock in the morning. Will and Charlie and their sister Gertrude drove down to meet him with the horse and old two-seated buggy with a canopy top. In preparation for his coming the boys had made the office spick-and-span and so were pleased when he said he would like to go to the office before driving home for breakfast. After commending them for the clean windows and floors, he picked up his little old microscope and took it along out to the house.

# Will and Charlie

At the breakfast table he distributed the presents he had brought, and then, placing the microscope on the table, he pulled from his pocket a circular describing the new model, the present he'd like to have for himself. It would do wonderful things, no gainsaying that, but it cost six hundred dollars, and there was no money left after his vacation trip. So to buy the instrument he'd have to put a mortgage on the house. Mrs. Mayo's Scotch prudence balked a little. Four children, and the times so hard. Would they ever get a mortgage paid off? But finally she said, "Well, William, if you could do better by the people with this new microscope and you really think you need it, we'll do it."

They did it, and legend says it took the Doctor ten years to pay off that mortgage. But Will was of the opinion that the circumstances under which the new microscope was bought helped to give him and Charlie an especially keen interest in its use. Nor was the financial stringency so great as to prevent the Doctor from adding to his library a new manual of histology, a book on section cutting, and one on the use of the microscope in clinical and pathological examinations.

He taught the boys to fix in alcohol the tissues he removed at operations and to cut and mount sections, technical procedures which at that time took several days. If they followed those steps with eager study of the results through the microscope, as they certainly must have, they were being introduced to microscopic pathology in the embryonic stages of that science.

They were already acquainted with the rudiments of gross pathology, for Dr. Mayo frequently took them along to his autopsies. He began taking Will when the boy was so small he could not see if he stood on the floor; so Dr. Mayo set him up on the head of the table, where he could lean forward and hang onto the hair of the corpse to steady himself while he watched. Always on such occasions the Doctor took care that the boys should see just what he did and what he found.

As in other phases of the work, watching grew into assisting. For Will the climax of this training came just a few months before he set out for medical school. One of his father's patients died, and since the disease had taken a perplexing course, the Doctor decided to do a postmortem. The night was gusty with storm winds; the way led across the river to the Bradley House, an abandoned hotel in which the patient had lived alone as a sort of caretaker; and the work had to be done by the light of a lantern.

Dr. Mayo received a call just as they set out, so when the examination of the body was finished, about ten o'clock, he left Will to close the abdomen and take the pathological specimens to the office. The boy would not let his father know he was afraid, but "I can feel yet," he wrote many years later, "the weird atmosphere of that squeaky old house, with its long shadowy corridors, and I remember the struggle I had to complete the job and force myself to walk slowly to the front door. The creaking of the old hotel signboard swinging above the entrance as I stepped out was the last straw, and I made good speed down the street." The dissecting room at medical school could hold no terrors after that.

Here again the practical experience was complemented by a good deal of reading. One book was Sir James Paget's *Lectures on Surgical Pathology*. Paget was a great London surgeon who had added to his technical skill an unusual knowledge of pathology by preparing a descriptive catalog of the specimens in the Hunterian Museum of the Royal College of Surgeons, and he had the wit to apply this knowledge to clinical problems. That was the basis for the course of six lectures he gave before the Royal College, which, in their printed form, Will Mayo read as a schoolboy. Paget's terse style and trenchant observations made such an impression on his mind that he could quote some of the generalizations in the book more than two score years after he read them.

It may well have been Paget's book that introduced Will to John Hunter, the great eighteenth-century student of gross pathology. In a day when the pathologist as such did not exist, when he had to be a practitioner pursuing mammon as well as science, Hunter refused to let the necessity for what he called "the eternal chase after the damned guinea" keep him from making systematic, scientific studies of disease. Rising at four o'clock every morning to work with his specimens before beginning the day's routine of practice at the office, he founded the science of experimental and surgical pathology. The thirteen thousand specimens that he assembled, prepared, and labeled neatly in black with his own hands constituted the museum collection of the Royal College that Paget cataloged.

# Will and Charlie

John Hunter became a hero to Will Mayo, providing inspiration and arousing admiration that apparently never lapsed. The place of honor in the office of the chief of staff of the Mayo Clinic, on the wall directly across from his desk where he could see it whenever he raised his eyes, was always reserved for the portrait of John Hunter by Joshua Reynolds, given to Dr. Will by his friend and fellow surgeon, Lord Moynihan of Leeds.

## 8

Used to helping their father in any way they could, the boys naturally moved with him into the field of gynecologic surgery. Will often acted as his first assistant, and there were a number of important odd jobs that Charlie could do. For tying off the blood vessels and closing the wound Dr. Mayo used silk and linen thread, and it was Charlie's task to cut hanks of this into the desired lengths, coat them with a mixture of beeswax and shoemaker's wax, and then twist the strands into two-ply or four-ply ligatures and sutures. With these he would thread an assortment of needles, stick them through the lapel of his coat, and stand where his father could reach for the ones he wanted. In between times Charlie might be called on to heat the instruments in the fire or to stand behind Will and handle the sponges.

It was one time when he was serving in these capacities that the accident occurred which resulted in his becoming his father's anesthetist. Since anesthesia was still new enough for the layman to fear it, it was the custom to have some physician of established reputation give the anesthetic, and on this occasion Dr. Mayo's anesthetist was a doctor well known in Rochester, a homeopath of wide practice and experience. He was a surgeon and had served as coroner for Olmsted County, but obviously he was not accustomed to major operations on a breathing, pulsing body.

Dr. Mayo made a small incision, inserted a trocar into the tumor, and as the fluid contents drained out caught them in a tub at hand for the purpose. Then by means of clamps worked by thumbscrews he began to pull the tissue of the growth out through the incision. The base of the tumor was pulled back and forth in the process, producing a peculiar sucking noise like that made "by a cow's foot in the mud." This was too much for the nerves of the anesthetist and he fainted.

After a quick survey of the possibilities, Dr. Mayo kicked over a cracker box at the end of the sofa and said, "Here, Charlie, you stand on this and give the anesthetic."

"He did it well, with perfect composure," said Will, but Charlie added a few details: "When she stopped wiggling Father would tell me to stop, and when she started again I would drop some more. I did fine, but like doctors called in to help another, I was looking at the operation and paying no attention to the patient."

That was a much loved and often told tale among the Mayos. Their memories placed it when Charlie was nine years old, or at most, twelve. Documentary evidence based on the identity of the anesthetist and the patient would seem to make him eighteen at the time. At any rate, Charlie took over the work of anesthetist at so early an age that some women patients were afraid he was too young for the responsibility.

## 9

The central fact that emerges from all these episodes and descriptive details is that the Mayo boys served a thorough apprenticeship in medicine and surgery which brought them into close contact with the realities of practice long before they entered medical school.

In the process of transferring the responsibility for training doctors from preceptor to college, the pendulum was to swing too far away from "the old apprentice system that brought the student . . . face to face with the patient at the very beginning of his studies." During the transitional period many medical students received their entire training in schools having such meager clinical facilities that they could add little bedside demonstration to their program of didactic lectures, and men like William Osler decried a system that sent a doctor out to deliver a baby without his ever having seen a case of labor.

William and Charles Mayo ran no risk of such lopsided training, because they had an appreciable experience with patients and diseases in the flesh before they began their formal schooling. They were born at the right time, neither too early to ride the wave of advance in medical science and surgery that followed upon the work of Pasteur and Lister, nor too late to reap the advantages of the old school at its soundest and best.

The quality of medical education under the preceptorship system depended largely upon the caliber of the preceptor, and Dr. Mayo was of the best. And instead of the usual two or three years of association, his sons had a youthtime of it at increasingly close range. The office and country rounds, the sickroom and autopsy table, the library of medical books and journals, osteology, pathology, chemistry—these were for them familiar sights and occupations. Medicine was not a thing apart, a series of laborious lessons to be learned, or a means only as good as any other for earning a living; it was the very stuff of living. "We were reared in medicine as a farmer boy is reared in farming." So Will put it.

That would not be possible now. Surgery has moved into hospitals, the postmortem into autopsy rooms, and that the practitioner's sons should be underfoot in either is unthinkable. The doctor's office has been spruced up, and his manners formalized along with it. Business-like methods, up-to-the-minute records, and a trimly efficient nurse as assistant and receptionist have replaced the top hat and Prince Albert coat as the badge of professional dignity. Amid such order curious children would be out of place. And what would patients say today if their doctor's sons came along to watch procedures at the bedside!

## 10

The roots of more than the Mayos' practical facility in medicine can be found in their boyhood. The Doctor was vitally interested in the problems and needs of his profession, and on those long country drives or in conversations at table or before the fire at home he introduced the boys to the principles and ethics of the physician. One may be sure they heard in positive terms what he thought of disreputable professional practices, and the lesson of the Cross malpractice case with Dr. Mayo's "I did it for the profession, not for him, damn him" was not lost on his sons.

He took Will and Charlie, even when they were little tykes, along to the meetings of the local and district medical societies. There they listened to the exchange of ideas among colleagues on such problems as the control of quackery and the patent medicine racket, the need for licensure and for higher professional standards. There too, as well as in their home, they met their father's friends, among them some fine examples of the pioneer physician at his best.

# The Mayo Brothers

At a meeting of the Minnesota Valley Medical Association in Man-kato, Will met Dr. Asa W. Daniels of St. Peter, Dr. Mayo's associate in the days of the Sioux Outbreak and one of the grand old men of the Valley. "So you're going to study medicine," said Dr. Daniels. "Well, it's the most satisfactory of all the professions; it is doing for others. I have always been physically well, and let me advise you that when you go into the practice of medicine and begin to go about the country seeing patients, be careful what you eat. I have found it wise to ask for a boiled egg, a baked potato, and hot toast, and to drink tea or coffee, something that has been boiled and is still hot." That was experiential wisdom, in the days before Pasteur.

Another of the men Will and Charlie came to know was Dr. N. S. Tefft of Plainview. Having come to the upper Mississippi before Min-nesota became a state, he had built up an enormous practice as a sur-geon and an enviable reputation as an enterprising and influential citizen. He was vigorous, outspoken, extreme in his likes and dislikes, a strong believer in evolution, a "freethinker [who] takes all occasions to express his disbelief in orthodoxy," the possessor of a tender social conscience that made him a leader in the incipient third parties that expressed the political unrest of the day—in short, he was an intellec-tual twin to Dr. Mayo.

But what the Mayo boys remembered chiefly was his pluck in carry-ing on his professional duties. He was a man "with dangling lower extremities, crippled by infantile paralysis, carrying his heavy body around on crutches, doing country practice, but nothing was allowed to interfere with his work. He would start off through the snow in winter, and if he did not return at a certain time, the livery man would take a team and go to find him. Perhaps he would be in a snow drift; hardly able to blanket his horse, and waiting down under the robes for rescue."

It was good for the two brothers to know such men in the early youth that is "a period of generous self-surrender to ideals." They grew up in a tradition that the life of a doctor must be one of service, that his profession demanded of him a response to every call, whether there was pecuniary reward in it or not. They were probably present on more than one occasion when a call from the country came in late at night or in the midst of a heavy snowstorm, and Jay Neville tried to persuade Dr. Mayo not to answer it. "They won't pay you anything. You know they won't."

"But, Jay, you don't understand. Those people are sick, and they need a doctor." And the Doctor would drive away, while Jay muttered after him, "But they never pay."

It must have been while the boys were helping in the office, perhaps when they went to mark up the ledger after the patients had gone, that they heard their father say, as Charlie remembered so well, "Now, those folks are poor. Don't put them down in the book."

## 11

It is a pregnant fact that the Mayo boys grew up during a period of depression and hard times. The dreams of a happy prosperous future, of a comfortable home and an education for the children, with which the pioneers had come to the new land had faded for many into the bitter reality of drouth and debt, bad crops, low prices, and lost homes.

Will and Charlie saw the situation and its causes through their father's eyes. They had not the experience then to see it otherwise, and they learned his principle of *noblesse oblige*. "Our father believed that a man with unusual physical strength or with unusual intellectual capacity or opportunities owed something to the people. He should do for others in proportion as he had the strength to do." Time and again the brothers offered that as sufficient explanation for things they did that won them the plaudits of the world.

Realists have called Dr. Mayo quixotic, with a smug smile to emphasize their own superior wisdom. But tilting at windmills is not a bad example to set before the young if service to society and not the pursuit of personal profit is what one wants of them later. If Diogenes struck the father when the son swore, it is permissible to credit this father with a goodly share in the ideals of these sons.

But by no means is it to be implied that Mrs. Mayo played no part in shaping the characters of her boys. Wise friends of the family, sure that Will and Charlie did not get all their ability and ideas from their father, have left a caution to biographers, "Don't forget the mother." But unfortunately there is no record of what Mrs. Mayo believed and taught. One can only draw conclusions from the tone of wonder in which her sons spoke of her tolerance, her understanding, and her charitable spirit. "She accepted what good there was in folks and did not criticize the bad. I never knew her to say a hateful word about anyone," said Dr. Will.

All in all, Dr. Charlie probably erred only in degree when he told a group of Rochester folk assembled to do him honor, "The biggest thing Will and I ever did was to pick the father and mother we had."

# CHAPTER EIGHT

# At Medical School

"It never occurred to us that we could be anything else but doctors."
So Will Mayo insisted again and again in later life, but there was a
moment of conscious decision nonetheless. The Old Doctor asked
Father O'Gorman's advice about training his sons for medicine, and,
according to Jay Neville, Will's own final resolve was taken the morning he decided to forsake the plow for the sink and bottle rack of the
drug store.

In spite of organized medicine's loud lament that the evil works of
diploma mills and quacks were causing the profession to lose caste with
the public, the individual physician was often a prominent and
honored figure in his community. He was not a laborer but a professional man, set above the rank and file by added education and special
knowledge and skill. He was one to be envied and imitated by youths
who sought to rise in the world. Knowing that, Will Mayo was not
one to be satisfied with any lesser position in life.

But when medicine had been definitely chosen, the Mayos had a
more difficult decision to make: To what medical school should Will
go?

The schools, all too plentiful, were on the whole a sorry lot, little
changed since William Worrall Mayo's days at Indiana Medical College. They still set no requirements for admission, were still ungraded,
and still granted their diplomas at the end of two sessions of five or six
months each. The preceptorship that had saved the situation in the
earlier day had become only nominal, many a student seeing nothing
of his preceptor from the time he registered as his apprentice until he
returned with his degree. So ten or twelve months was the total time
many a doctor gave to his training. As the advocates of reform pointed
out, it took longer than that to learn the trade of a machinist, a printer,
or a river-boat pilot.

Teaching in the schools was still of the "windy, wordy" kind under which students "heard much, saw little, and did nothing." They heard elaborate word pictures of disease, saw little of patients or illness at first hand, and did nothing themselves at the bedside or in the laboratory. And that at a time when scientific medicine was at the practitioner's door.

From the laboratories of Europe new facts in pathology, physiology, chemistry, and physics were popping out like corn in a pan, and in European hospitals great clinicians were adding these to their own critical observations and careful records to differentiate diseases and describe them for all to recognize. Chemists were laying the foundation of a rational drug therapy, and to accepted diagnostic aids like auscultation and percussion were being added laboratory methods like the blood count and the test meal and such instruments as the ophthalmoscope, laryngoscope, and others in the formidable series of -scopes that today extend the sight of the physician into all the cavities and hollow organs of the body.

Medicine was on the march, but American medical schools were not keeping step. The new medicine could not be adequately taught by the lecture method; it could be learned only by practice and experiment in the laboratory and at the bedside. And of such instruction there was virtually none in the schools. Even in the New York schools affiliated with metropolitan hospitals and dispensaries medical students of the seventies and eighties were not taken into the hospital wards or the dispensary examining rooms. They did not record the case histories, group and interpret symptoms, make diagnoses, and suggest treatment under supervision.

Instead they sat, a hundred or several hundred strong, upon remote seats in an amphitheater and looked down upon the feet of the patient and the back of the surgeon while he operated. Or they watched from the heights while the professor of clinical medicine placed his stethoscope upon the chest of a patient, listened gravely, and announced the presence of sounds indicating an unhealthy heart. Most of them received the degree in medicine without ever having felt a sick man's pulse, listened to the sounds of lung and heart, or stood at the side of a woman in labor.

Leaders of the medical profession were well aware of the shocking state of the schools. Since 1846, when the American Medical Association was organized for the express purpose of raising the level of medical education, protest and denunciation had been voiced in a crescendo, but the waves of words spent themselves without effect against the wall of the proprietary system. Most teachers of medicine were owners of the schools in which they taught, and their incomes were directly dependent upon the number of students. They could not afford to set up entrance requirements that would "force candidates to defer the study of anatomy and chemistry until they had mastered the simpler mysteries of reading and writing"; they could not afford to institute longer sessions that might conflict with the farm boy's working schedule, or more sessions that might turn him from the study of medicine entirely; they did not dare introduce new courses and equipment that would add to the expenses and reduce the profits of their enterprise.

So reform waited, while the proprietary schools multiplied beyond belief and engaged in furious competition for students, stooping at last to the expedient of personal solicitation and sending out drummers to intercept prospective students as they got off the train or registered at the hotel. Here and there appeared the notorious diploma mills, which did not bother to give any courses at all but sold the degree in medicine, with all the rights and privileges appertaining thereto, to all applicants at fifty or a hundred dollars per spurious sheepskin. In the words of William Osler, the American system of medical education was a byword among the nations.

2

Dr. Mayo knew all about this problem. As a member of the committee on medical education of the Minnesota State Medical Society he had helped to prepare a lengthy report setting it forth and commending the example of Harvard College, which had led the way in reform by adopting entrance requirements—elementary to be sure, but a beginning—a three-year graded course, and an annual session of nine months. So the Doctor knew what to look for in choosing a school for Will.

Minnesota offered no real possibility in 1880. It had only the St. Paul Medical College, more a hope than an actuality, a few students meeting with an instructor or two in some vacant basement or second-story room. Dr. A. J. Stone was its dean and its janitor as well as the teacher of every subject in its curriculum except chemistry. He was an able member of his profession, but one of whom it was said that the less he knew on a subject the more brilliantly he could talk about it. Dr. Mayo did not let his friendship with Stone blind him to the fact that the St. Paul school was not the place to send Will.

But in 1880 the medical school of the University of Michigan moved into the first class by following Harvard's example, and Michigan stressed instruction in the medical sciences. "The apparatus in the Department of Chemistry and Chemical Physics, is probably unsurpassed, if indeed it be equalled, by that of any medical college in the country," read the catalog, and without exaggeration apparently. By the fall of 1880 the chemistry laboratory at Michigan was housed in its own three-story building, with eleven workrooms providing table space and equipment for two hundred and sixty-nine students at one time. Even at Harvard and Yale, and indeed in most European centers, the laboratories were small by comparison and were intended more for the research of the professors than for the first fumbling experiments of undergraduate students.

The moving spirit for science at Michigan was young Victor C. Vaughan, who later became the dean of the medical school and had a remarkable career as practitioner, administrator, and educator in medicine. In 1876 Vaughan, having taken his doctor's degree in the liberal arts college, matriculated in the medical school and at the same time was made the instructor of a new course in physiological chemistry. As far as he could discover, the two microscopes he was using for his classes were the only ones available to students in the entire university. Some of the teachers had instruments, but they did not use them; they kept them carefully out of harm's way under dustproof glass covers. Only the professor of anatomy sometimes let his students see how bits of bone and muscle looked when magnified.

Vaughan persuaded President Angell to authorize him to purchase six new microscopes at the Centennial Exposition in Philadelphia, and he learned the technique of using them from a railroad engineer who was an amateur microscopist in his hobby hours and was glad to exchange his knowledge for the privilege of using the fine, high-powered models his professor friend had bought.

# At Medical School

Thus Vaughan moved along, wheedling appropriations from the authorities for more microscopes and other instruments, more rooms and tables, until now in 1880 the university could announce in its prospectus that in addition to an unequaled chemistry laboratory it had a physiological laboratory equipped with

microscopes, a stereopticon, sphygmograph, and numerous other instruments for extended practical work. . . . Students in the college, without additional charge, thus have the opportunities of practical instruction in Experimental Physiology and Histology, both physiological and pathological; and this supplemented by instruction in Pathological Anatomy and Medical Chemistry, is designed to afford facilities to students for research and specific and minute study exceedingly rare in this country, the want of which is deeply felt by all advanced medical practitioners.

If Dr. Mayo hesitated before choosing the University of Michigan for Will, it was because of a doubt about the clinical facilities at Ann Arbor. The town was so small that from the start the school's chief problem had been to find enough patients to demonstrate to its students, and solving the problem had been the big task of Moses Gunn, the first professor of surgery.

When the rumor spread that the young University of Michigan might establish a medical department, Gunn was studying medicine in Geneva, New York. He and his roommate, Corydon L. Ford, talked over the possibilities for such a school and decided they were good. So when he had won his diploma Gunn set out to speed the birth of the Michigan medical school—leaving in a particular hurry because he carried in his trunk a body that had arrived too late for use in the Geneva dissecting room that term.

Arriving in Ann Arbor on a snowy February day, Gunn hung out his shingle as a surgeon, laid out the corpse on a table, and let it be known that he would introduce prospective medical students to the mysteries of anatomy in his back room, after night had fallen. The scheme worked well; the anatomy class was soon flourishing and Gunn was in a position to aid in the organization of the university medical school and secure for himself the chair of surgery on its faculty.

It was customary then for the professors in a medical school to act as consultants in their special fields for the surrounding communities, and Gunn solved the problem of clinical material at Ann Arbor by merely extending this practice. He announced to the physicians and surgeons of the state that they could bring their difficult cases for free consultation with the experts of the university faculty if the patients were willing to appear before the school classes for demonstration purposes. In a short time the response to his offer was providing patients enough for two demonstration clinics a week.

For many years there was no hospital in the town. The doctors and patients from a distance stayed overnight at some hotel or boarding-house until, during the seventies, one of the houses on faculty row was turned into a receiving station for patients. It was called the University Hospital, but it had no wards, no dressing rooms, and no operating theater.

On clinic days the students carried the patients on stretchers across the campus to the college building, and there before the assembled classes each case was examined and the operation, if one was needed, was performed. Victor Vaughan, as the physiological chemist, examined the urine and blood, and on occasion proudly demonstrated to his colleagues and the students a find of diagnostic significance—such as urea in the perspiration of a man dying with kidney disease, or crystals of tyrosin and leucin in the urine in a case of cancer of the liver.

The results for the patients were good, and the professors were able to persuade the legislators that they were serving the state sufficiently to warrant the erection of a hospital. So in 1877 the first real university hospital in the United States was built in Ann Arbor. It was a wooden building of the pavilion type developed during the Civil War and large enough to accommodate one hundred and fifty patients as well as a surgical amphitheater. When it was built, the school assumed that in ten years or so it would be so badly infected it would have to be burned. That was reckoning without Pasteur and Lister.

Naturally the school's prospectus made much of this hospital and the opportunities for clinical teaching it afforded, enough to still any doubts Dr. Mayo had about the clinical courses at Michigan.

### 3

So on September 16, 1880 Will Mayo took the noon train from Rochester to the East to enter upon his medical studies at the University of Michigan. He was then nineteen years old, slender and not very tall, but straight and strong. This was his first trip from home alone. What he thought or felt he never said, but to his teachers he seemed just "a green Western boy."

Little is known of his daily life at Michigan, and even the official record of his courses and grades has been lost in the shuffle of the years. His only extracurricular activity seems to have been boxing, in which he gave a good account of himself, winning the university championship in the 133-pound class.

When Will Mayo reminisced of his medical school days it was of classmates and teachers at work that he talked. One of his friends was Franklin Paine Mall, a frail lad from Iowa who tried to harden himself physically by defying the winter cold without an overcoat, though he sometimes indulged in a scarf around his neck. "A choice spirit," Will found him, first and last a student even then. He became one of the distinguished anatomists of his time and a power for reform in medical education.

Another chap that Will Mayo knew well was Woods Hutchinson, nephew of Jonathan Hutchinson, the learned London practitioner remembered in Hutchinson's teeth, the notched incisors considered a sign of congenital syphilis. The nephew was a tall man with a long face, red hair, and a mind full of facts about all things medical, but he lacked the talents of a successful mixer, made few friends in college, and was only moderately successful later in practice.

Dr. Will never gave a name to a third classmate he described. The boy was the most promising member of the group, won all the honors at graduation, and had an impressive presence and the knack of getting on well with people. Everyone predicted a great career for him. And the first reports after graduation showed that he was fulfilling expectations, for he had quickly built up a flourishing practice.

Then with details from his own lips came suspicion. Where did he find so many movable kidneys to be fastened and so many diseased ovaries that ought to come out? For Dr. Will disillusionment was complete when he heard the man boasting one day that there had never been a postmortem on a patient he had lost. "We all make mistakes," he said, "but I take mighty good care that nobody knows about mine." Adopting one by one all the persuasive and deceptive methods of the quacks, he was finally beaten at the game by the men he aped and died a failure, in the eyes of his colleagues at least. So when Dr. Mayo spoke of him, with a regretful shake of the head over talents gone to waste for the lack of moral fiber to direct the use of them, he called him merely X.

Among the professors Dr. Will remembered was Alonzo B. Palmer, dean of the medical school and professor of the practice of medicine. He was a kindly old man nearing his three score years and ten, with a devotion to the Presbyterian church so intense that when a student failed Palmer's quiz on Saturday he tried to offset the failure by letting the dean see him entering church on Sunday.

Palmer was a clinician of the old school. He had taken to his heart the use of auscultation, percussion, and the early -scopes, but beyond that he was not receptive to the new ideas in medicine. He loved to teach and would forego a consultation any time for the chance of another hour before his class, but it was lecturing, not clinical teaching, he rejoiced in.

The two men whose forte was clinical demonstration were George E. Frothingham, professor of ophthalmology, and Donald Maclean, successor to Moses Gunn in the chair of surgery. Young, handsome, able, and dramatic, these two were the idols of the student body, though they were suspect to most of their colleagues because of their unorthodox religious beliefs.

Frothingham was perhaps the most brilliant man on the staff. He had carved his own niche by concentrating on diseases of the eye and ear when that field was almost entirely neglected by the regular profession. Soon he was attracting so many patients the general surgical clinic could not handle them and a special one was established for him. The school officials found that his results, spectacular then, in making the blind see and the deaf hear were good arguments to lay before the legislature when seeking an appropriation.

"Gentlemen," Frothingham would address the students in his first clinic of the term, "I will be able to show you in the clinic throughout the year most of the diseases to which the eye is subject and many of the accidents and injuries to which it is exposed. Yes, I will show you many of these many times. I will operate before you twice a week, but you must know that you will profit none by my operations unless you know the anatomy and physiology of the organ thoroughly. I can demonstrate the fundamental principles. The world will be your clinic."

### 4

An incident in Frothingham's clinic led to what Dr. Will later, with unwonted cynicism, described as "about the sort of thing one would expect of a group of immature young enthusiasts."

Medical students then were commonly a rough and ready lot, "lusty, bearded adults," who talked, clapped, stamped, and jeered at will, making no outward sign of any respect they felt for the professor, who suffered their lack of manners with Job-like patience. The playfulness often took the form of seizing some luckless boy in one of the front seats and passing him from row to row of the amphitheater until the last row received him and set him upright, half afraid to return to his seat lest he be made to take the unpleasant journey all over again. Such a prank disturbed Frothingham's clinic one day during Will's freshman year.

One of the seniors asked to be excused from the next clinic to go into Detroit to hear a lecture by the noted agnostic, Bob Ingersoll. Before giving his permission Frothingham began a little lecture on the bad taste of calling a distinguished man like Ingersoll by the nickname Bob. Why, he asked, should Thomas Paine, one of the great constructive forces in the United States after the Revolution, always be called Tom, while Jefferson is never anything but Thomas?

He got no further. A red-haired, red-whiskered medical missionary of forty years jumped to his feet, protesting with vigorous voice and gesture against such atheistic teaching. His seat was in the second row, an invitation to mischief, and in an instant, his harangue choked to an angry sputter, he was on his way up from hand to hand. The boys at the top failed to stop him and he went head foremost through a window and into a lilac bush, where he collected some bruises and an undeniably bad temper.

The sequel was a furor of publicity that rocked the university community. Following the usual course, it smeared Maclean as well as Frothingham, put into their mouths words they had never uttered, twisted others into unintended meanings, and pictured the medical school as a veritable hotbed of atheism, a menace to the morals of youth, a nest of vipers in the bosom of the state. Whereupon the orthodox members of the faculty turned against their two unbelieving brethren, stirring up a storm within the school that threatened to wreck it and did not subside for a year or more.

Some of the freshmen were greatly upset by the fuss and fury. They knew Frothingham had not said the things ascribed to him, nor Maclean either, and they did their best to establish the truth. A small group of them, including Will Mayo, continued their discussions throughout the next year, extending them to include a consideration of the weaknesses of their future profession. It needed higher scholarship, better teaching, and more loyalty among its members, and there ought to be some "supporting, protecting fellowship" among doctors, something to make them unite against common foes instead of fighting each other.

So they argued, and to the mind of one of them, Robert Stevens of Mount Clemens, Michigan, came the idea of organizing a medical fraternity dedicated to those ends. He chose five classmates to help him realize his plan: Will Mayo, Benjamin G. Strong of New York, Charles M. Frye of Massachusetts, Frederick C. Bailey of Michigan, and John L. Gish of Indiana. These were the founders of Nu Sigma Nu fraternity, which received its charter and adopted its constitution on March 2, 1882.

Robert Stevens "supplied most of the sense in the constitution and bylaws," said Dr. Will, "and I, it must be confessed, supplied most of the nonsense." Since Stevens was experienced in fraternity ways and procedures and probably supplied the practical details of rule and ritual, the "nonsense" was perhaps the statement of aims and ideals to which the boys subscribed.

By fall the group had ten members who rented a house, lived together, and shared expenses throughout their senior year. They elected to honorary membership their two idols, Frothingham and Maclean, who took a lively interest in the enterprise, and it is said that Nu Sigma Nu's espousal of the two black sheep did not facilitate the work of its members under other professors.

But the boys had wrought better than they knew. Within a few years alumni of the Michigan fraternity were asking permission to organize branch chapters in the communities to which they had gone, and the practice spread until today Nu Sigma Nu is recognized as one of the great honorary professional fraternities. It numbers some forty chapters and ten thousand members, including some of the most able men of medicine in the world.

5

The clinics at Michigan were of the prevailing sort, a parade of patients at a distance. Though much was made of the new hospital wards, there is no evidence that they were as yet used for bedside teaching. Their contribution to the educational facilities seems to have been merely the provision of more cases for the demonstration clinics.

There were still the two morning clinics weekly in medicine and surgery, but to them had been added daily diagnostic clinics, given at noon from twelve to one o'clock. Although only the seniors were required to attend these, as far as he could remember Will Mayo did not miss one during his three years. They were held in the low-ceiled amphitheater of the hospital, which was reached by outside stairs leading up from the campus. The front seats were officially reserved for the senior class, and the juniors enforced their unofficial right to those next highest, so the freshmen sat at the top, where the least of what happened below could be seen. But even at the freshman heights, Will was thrilled.

"I can visualize my freshman class sitting on the back seats," he wrote, "too far away to see the technic of the operation, but inspired by the fact that operations were going on; by seeing the assistants as they performed their duties; by seeing the members of the senior class called down to be quizzed on diagnosis and permitted to take some minor part in the operations."

He had heard his father describe such demonstrations of diagnosis and treatment, but these were the first he had seen for himself, and he found in them a stirring call to ambition. Those patients had come miles, hundreds of miles some of them, seeking relief from pain and disability. They had come to the men at work there, his teachers, because they, by their superior skill and knowledge, could heal and restore where lesser practitioners were helpless. What a satisfaction it would be so to command the confidence of patients, doctors, and students, to move among them able and assured, to be the man everyone admired and depended on.

When Will had reached the right to a senior seat, he did not need it, for he was among the chosen, an assistant to Dr. Maclean at the operating table.

Canadian born, Donald Maclean was a graduate of Queen's University, Kingston, Ontario, and of the medical department of the University of Edinburgh, Scotland. He had received his medical degree in 1862 after four years of training, in the course of which he had served as house surgeon and assistant for the great Scottish surgeon, James Syme, and he had been called to the chair of surgery at Michigan from a similar post at his alma mater in Ontario. He quickly won the devotion and confidence of Michigan physicians and surgeons, many of whom would have the advice of no other consultant when they struck a perplexing case.

The important question of course is where Maclean stood on Listerism when Will Mayo was his student, for surgery was then poised between two eras: before Lister and after Lister.

6

When anesthesia swept the barrier of pain from the path of surgery, that form of therapeusis under the leadership of men like Syme and Liston moved rapidly forward. Not to invade the cavities of the body —those were thought to be forever beyond the curative hand of the surgeon—but to improve the technique of amputation, the methods of wound repair, the handling of fractures, aneurysms, and the like.

Then came Joseph Lister. He too could originate and improve methods in this surgery of necessity, but as he walked through his wards at the Glasgow Infirmary he was often discouraged. There in long rows lay his surgical patients. He had brought them through the operations successfully, but there they lay, nearly all of them tossing restlessly in high fever, their stumps or wounds honeycombed with cavities that dripped foul, yellow pus. There they lay, fighting for their lives against a seemingly inevitable and commonly fatal septic infection.

No wonder the old woman in East-End London had answered, when she was asked to consent to a minor operation on her daughter,

"S'orlright. S'easy enough to give consent, but wot I wants to know is 'oo's going to pay for the poor girl's funeral?"

Under such circumstances every advance that invited the surgeon to attempt more operations, even anesthesia, was as much a curse as a boon to mankind. Sepsis must be eliminated. But how? By prolonged observation and induction Lister had come to the conclusion that inflammation and suppuration were the result of putrefaction, which in turn was produced by something in the air. But what that something was he had no idea.

Then one day a chemist in Glasgow suggested that he read the published findings of Louis Pasteur. That young French chemist had demonstrated conclusively that fermentation and, by analogies long known, putrefaction and infection were wrought by micro-organisms, bacteria. Lister seized upon this clue eagerly. Here was hope! If bacteria were the cause of infection and they could be excluded from wounds, healing would take place by first intention, without fever, inflammation, or suppuration. Since the organisms might lodge on any solid, on hands, instruments, dressings, even on dust particles in the air, everything must be kept clean—not just aesthetically clean, but antiseptically clean. Even the air must be made sterile if possible.

On that principle Lister developed a new surgical method, in which he used carbolic acid as an antiseptic—in solutions for cleansing hands and instruments, in plasters and putties for sterile dressings, and in a steam spray for purifying the air.

There were as yet no rules or tests to tell Lister whether his procedures achieved the sterile surroundings he desired, but empirically he knew they did, for his wards no longer stank of decaying flesh, were no longer hopeless hells of fever and inflammation. His patients made uneventful recoveries, their wounds healing without disturbance in the natural processes of repair. He had shown that sepsis could be prevented, and how it could be done. He had cleared the road to surgical horizons unseen.

In 1864 Lister read Pasteur, in 1865 he first applied lint soaked in carbolic acid to an open wound, in 1867 he announced his method and its amazing results. Awareness of his work dawned slowly on the medical world. Surgeons from Continental Europe came to his clinic, gasped at the operations he dared to perform, and marveled, not as of old at the speed of the operation, but at the speed with which his patients recovered. They went home to try antisepsis in their own clinics.

Volkmann of Halle, who was about to close his hospital because pyemia was taking an insupportably heavy toll in its wards, and Nussbaum of Munich, who was being driven to the same step by the ravages of erysipelas, applied Lister's methods as a last resort. The infections died out, the hospitals were saved, and the clinics of Volkmann and Nussbaum became important Continental schools of antiseptic surgery.

By 1875 appreciation was widespread enough in Germany to turn Lister's tour of the nation's medical centers into a triumphal march, and in 1879 an international medical congress in Paris literally went wild when he appeared before it.

## 7

Surely, one might think, with such international acclaim for Lister in 1879, American medical students would be learning Listerian methods and principles by 1883. Not at all, for Listerism took root slowly in the United States. "First Listerian operations" were still dotting the American surgical scene all through the eighties.

Revealing indeed are the descriptions by participants in those operations. All of them show the same general conditions and attitudes. Interns and assistants, since trained nurses were not yet on hand, spent days of preparation beforehand, boiling the necessary gallons of water, scrubbing the operating table, soaking the sponges and instruments in antiseptic solutions, carbolizing the dressings, sutures, and ligatures. Then came the operation itself, an ovariotomy perhaps, since that, being the major operation of the day, would provide a real test of the method.

All the important medical men of the community have gathered to watch the great experiment. Everyone is nervous and flurried lest some detail of commission or omission nullify the elaborate preparations, but though the surgeon and first assistant may be wearing aprons of rubber or oiled silk or, in extreme affectation, linen dusters or black dissecting-room gowns, all the others are in ordinary street clothes.

The steam atomizers are started, some from wall brackets and others in the hands of assistants who train them directly onto the field of operation. By the time the patient has been anesthetized and wheeled in the room is dimly gray in a fine odorous mist of antiseptic. The gallery moves in close to see through the haze, the incision is made, and the task of removing the tumor is begun.

When the operation is finished and the incision has been scrupulously swathed in the prescribed eight layers of carbolized gauze topped with a layer of mackintosh and another of gauze, the hands of the surgeon and his assistants are numb from the acid and everyone is wet to the skin with the spray.

And the patient? With fear and fervor she is watched, her progress noted. No rise in temperature after so large an abdominal wound? What about the dressings? Normally they would be changed once, and in severe cases twice, daily, but Lister says to let them alone as long as there is no fever and no hemorrhage. Still, perhaps one had better look. So the surgeon nervously lifts the edges of the dressings, just for a peek, with the carbolic spray playing over the wound and gauze all the while; the flesh is dry and cool; no pus and no inflammation!

As the days go on without disaster confidence mounts, and on the tenth day, according to Lister's instructions, the dressings are removed and the stitches drawn out, again in the dripping presence of the spray. The incision is still dry and without matter; it has healed by primary intention, perhaps the first instance of such healing either surgeons or assistants have ever seen.

Every such experience made converts for the new deal in surgery, but they were long a minority. The body of the profession remained unconvinced or actively unbelieving. Many rejected the theory of antisepsis for the same reason that obstetricians recoiled when Holmes and Semmelweis told them the puerperal fever they so dreaded was carried by their own hands; they could not believe, could not admit, that they who came to heal might bring death. Some scoffed at the belief in anything so fantastic as microbes, and others, ready to believe but not understanding the ways of bacteria, argued that while Lister-ism might be needed in crowded cities and in old, "tainted" hospitals, it was superfluous in the pure air of the country or the bracing ozone of a healthful climate.

The chief stumbling block was the general identification of the principle of antisepsis with a detail or two of its method. Missing the point that vigilance against contamination at every step was the end to be sought, an astonishing number of doctors thought that by an "indiscriminate squirting of carbolic acid" or by the mere application of carbolized dressings they were practicing Listerism.

This fatal misapprehension was encouraged by the work and words of the brilliant, truculent Lawson Tait, famous gynecologist of Birmingham, England. He rumbled and thundered his opposition to antiseptic surgery, pointing to his own truly admirable record as proof that simple cleanliness would achieve results equal to those of all the Listerian falderal. Neither he nor those who cited his example recognized his own methods as a form of asepsis.*

Added to such differences of opinion were the practical difficulties of the procedure. It was expensive and irksome, and it took time to develop the aseptic conscience in men unaccustomed to so strict a discipline. It was not easy for the older surgeons to break the habits of years, to remember that once they had washed their hands in antiseptic they could not move a chair, scratch their noses, or shake the unwashed hands of a visiting colleague without having to observe the cleansing rite all over again.

It took time too to educate men to realize the difference between aesthetic and antiseptic cleanliness. They were not quick to understand that though a marine sponge was rinsed clean enough to satisfy a New England housewife, it might still be filthy with microbes, and that even if a surgeon's hands were free of surface dirt, deadly bacteria might still lie deep in the pores of his skin or under his finger nails.

Because of such difficulties and deficiencies in understanding, many men of the eighties who tried what they thought was Listerism did not obtain the results claimed for it, and so quite sincerely they scorned

---

* The present precise differentiation of asepsis from antisepsis did not develop until after the coming of steam sterilization, rubber gloves, gowns, masks, and all the other appurtenances of modern aseptic surgery. In the eighties the two terms were commonly used as synonyms. The few who did make a distinction between them used *asepsis* for the methods of preventing infection and *antisepsis* for the methods of fighting the spread of infection once it had occurred. Both involved the use of chemical antiseptics. Indeed one Listerite of the day insisted that "Wounds treated strictly according to the Listerian method do not become septic, therefore the method is not antiseptic but aseptic."

the practice of antisepsis as a fashion or, worse still, a reprehensible form of self-advertisement.

The consequent battle waged with words was spirited, and medical journals and transactions bristled with the pros and cons. And in the meantime only a relatively few leaders, chiefly the younger ones, practiced the new surgery without reservation, a few more toyed with it half-heartedly, and the majority, especially those not connected with city hospitals, continued contentedly in the good old way.

## 8

With such confusion among practicing men of medicine, it was not to be expected that the medical graduates of 1883 would go forth confirmed advocates and masters of antiseptic surgery. But it would seem at first thought that the students at Michigan had an unusual advantage in this respect, for Donald Maclean had worked with Joseph Lister when the two were house surgeons for Syme in Edinburgh. Their association had ended before Lister read Pasteur, but having known Lister, Maclean might be expected to follow his career and give ear to his ideas with rather more sympathy than most.

And apparently Maclean was early in his attempts to give Listerism a trial, for Victor Vaughan recalled "the old days in the seventies, when, as Maclean's assistant, [he] had spent hours drenched in the poisonous sprays of carbolic acid." During Will Mayo's junior year in surgery, Maclean was still, or again, "trying out the merits of the carbolic acid spray." Unfortunately, however, he was one in whom absorption of the acid produced a toxic condition, so that he had to discontinue its use, and when Will became the surgeon's assistant he was spared Vaughan's unpleasant experience with the spray.

The spectacular steam spray and its saturating mist always remained in the memories of observers to the exclusion of more fundamental matters, and neither Vaughan nor Mayo ever recorded whether or not their professor tried out the merit of other parts of antiseptic surgery. Dr. Will did say that Maclean was "always cleanly in his work, and one could see that he had early Listerian principles in mind," but in those words is a note of the faint praise that damns. Most likely Maclean's Listerism was superficial.

On the whole, it is safe to say that Will Mayo finished his course at Ann Arbor with only an incidental introduction to the revolutionary theory that was to create his own great opportunity. He was aware of the controversy of course, probably knew something of antiseptic methods and something of the claims made for them, but he was not prepared to practice them. In view of the weight of authority against Listerism, he may even have been inclined to shrug it away as of little value.

## 9

Anatomy was taught by Corydon L. Ford, who had followed his roommate Gunn to Michigan, and Mayo always considered him the greatest teacher of anatomy he had ever heard. "I can see him yet as he stood before the class," he wrote. "He had a club foot and because of this disability carried an ivory headed cane on which he swung round as he demonstrated the anatomical details of the cadaver and the drawings on the blackboard. By his forceful personality and his intense love of his subject, he made the too often dull study of general anatomy as interesting as a novel."

Contrary to custom, Ford preferred to make his own dissections while he talked, and he did them beautifully and rapidly. When he had finished one he would swivel the table around toward the class with a flourish, pointing upward with his cane to emphasize his words, "Now, gentlemen, forget that if you can."

Ford did employ a demonstrator to substitute for him in the dissecting room, and for a large class the demonstrator had student assistants to supervise the work of their less able fellows. Both Will Mayo and his friend Frank Mall won the position of underdemonstrator for their junior and senior years. Together they spent long extra hours in the dissecting room, which like all such rooms then was a dirty, noisy, foul-smelling place. Modern methods of embalming and of refrigerated storage for bodies were not known, and unless the weather was very cold, painstaking dissection was a nauseating job. Nor did the habits of the students help matters; while they worked or watched, they smoked and chewed and spat, contributing much to the general unpleasantness.

Under those associations Will Mayo conceived a distaste for smoking that lasted throughout his life. Mall hated it too, and when he came to take charge of the dissecting rooms at the Johns Hopkins

Medical School, he forbade smoking on the premises. In fact, he instituted a general housecleaning in manners and methods, developing the means of preserving and storing bodies that are in general use in medical schools today.

Mall and Mayo had almost identical training in anatomy under Corydon L. Ford, but they reacted to it very differently. Ford's teaching, which made an extraordinary impression on most students, luring men from the arts college to crowd into the upper seats at his lectures and stimulating even the janitor of the school to become a proficient dissector, left Mall, the future anatomist, completely cold, but it fired Will Mayo with an enthusiasm for anatomy that he never entirely lost.

Mall's potential interests lay in research, in anatomy and physiology as sciences, sufficient ends in themselves, and those interests were not awakened at Michigan. Not until Mall was sharing in the laboratory life and problems of His and Ludwig in Europe did he feel an attraction that would not be denied. When he came to teach anatomy himself, his reforms in method were all in the direction of encouraging research on the part of the students, of stimulating them to find and solve problems for themselves. He had no time for the business of impressing upon passive minds the established relationships between anatomy and the practical arts of medicine.

But this last was precisely the field in which Corydon Ford excelled. He taught anatomy only as it applied to the active work of the physician and surgeon, and this seemed wholly good to Will Mayo, then and later, so that he once wrote in praise of Ford:

He presented anatomy not alone as a fundamental science which it was necessary to master for the purpose of laying a foundation for clinical medicine, but as a living thing to be considered in almost every professional act. He was closely in touch with the clinical issues of his time, and with anatomy he taught most valuable lessons in physiology and pathology, so that the student gained knowledge of his subject in its relation to his work. The university courses in surgical anatomy were excellent, yet Ford taught us more surgical anatomy than we learned in these special courses, and he also taught us medical anatomy, in order that we might see the patient from the anatomic standpoint, and recognize pathologic deviations from the normal in the early stages.

Would Will Mayo's talents have been put to a different use had he, like Mall, spent a year or two in some European laboratory after graduation? The chances are that had he gone to Europe he would not have spent his time in a laboratory but in the clinics of men like Billroth and Tait, for the life of the scientist held no appeal for him. His place was never in the seclusion of the laboratory, but out at the busy crossroads of practice. He came to appreciate the fundamental importance of science to medicine and developed a deep interest in the progress of medical science, but what he wanted from it was knowledge that could be applied in the better treatment of sick men and women.

Nevertheless, his association with Mall and with Woods Hutchinson made him, even in his medical school days, conscious and tolerant of a divergent spirit. He recognized in them a fruitful interest in the science of medicine but little manifest concern with its art, an interest in humanity in the mass but not in the individual. In them he found for the first time an attitude that always puzzled him and made him slightly resentful. He could never understand why research for the benefit of generations yet unborn should be considered noble while work for the relief of suffering in the present generation was thought to be necessarily tinged with sordid commercialism.

## 10

That predominant interest in the clinical phases of medicine helps to explain why Dr. Will never included in his recollections of the medical school at Michigan any account of his work in the fine new laboratories the prospectus had described so proudly. Only one incident survives. A new chair in physiology was established in 1880–81, and Victor Vaughan was given the task of selecting the man to occupy it. Wishing to introduce at Ann Arbor the "practical biology" that Huxley and Foster were teaching in England, Vaughan asked Henry Newell Martin, a disciple of Huxley's who was teaching at Johns Hopkins University, to suggest a man for the post. Martin recommended Dr. Henry Sewall, who was forthwith appointed—and wisely, for he became one of the country's great clinical physiologists.

He began his work at Michigan in the spring of 1881. It was not possible to start laboratory work at once, so he relied upon lectures and demonstrations for the remainder of the year. When examination time arrived, Sewall wondered how much physiology he might reasonably expect the students to have absorbed in the few months of lectures, and Vaughan suggested that he try an informal conference with a few of the best students to see how much they had learned.

William Mayo, Franklin Mall, and Walter Courtney were chosen. Sewall did not expect much of them, but he got even less. In disgust he told them, and Professor Vaughan too, that not one of those three would ever succeed in medicine, either in science or in practice. Naturally when all three had achieved national prominence in their respective fields, Sewall's pronouncement became a favorite story.

That incident suggests the inchoate state of the medical sciences at Michigan during Will's student days. He found the actuality less glowing than the catalog promise, for the readjustment of the curriculum to the added year was slow. With superb indifference to the principle of the reform the older teachers filled their share of the extra hours merely by requiring the customary repetition of their lectures. Certainly their wise words were well worth a second hearing by these students!

For the students who did not think so the administration provided elective courses in the natural sciences to be taken in the liberal arts college during the senior year. Will Mayo elected some and long remembered the contact he thus had with the beloved Alexander Winchell, one of Michigan's grand old men, a geologist who was known to thousands as a popular writer on scientific topics and as an able champion of Darwinism.

In retrospect the medical course at Michigan is not impressive: no practice in the examination or care of patients, the most meager demonstration of the new surgery, instruction in only the rudiments of the new medical sciences, the curriculum disorganized and padded. Perhaps, as Mall contended, the work was little beyond the high school level, the transition to college grade just beginning.

But the school can be depreciated on these grounds only from the viewpoint of today. Will Mayo might have fared better at Harvard, where the new system was of longer standing and so better organized; he might have got better clinical training in one of the New York schools affiliated with the metropolitan hospitals, though they made little enough use of their opportunities in that respect; and he certainly would have profited from a year or two in European clinics.

But failing those, he could have done no better than at Michigan and he could have done much, much worse.

In any event, on June 28, 1883, in the presence of his sister Phoebe, who came on from Rochester to represent the family at the ceremonies, "Will James Mayo" received his sheepskin and the right to call himself a doctor.

## 11

In the preceding June the American Medical Association had held its annual convention in St. Paul, and Will Mayo, home from Ann Arbor for the summer, went with his father to attend the sessions. He was excited by this, his first experience at a national society gathering, and by the presence of the great men of the profession, men whose writings he studied in school or read in the professional journals.

Among them was Dr. John Light Atlee, the elder of the two Atlee brothers of Pennsylvania. Washington, the younger and greater of the brothers, had died, and in the course of the session the president of the section on obstetrics and women's diseases paid high tribute to his memory. He told what a daring operator Washington Atlee had been, so bold and heroic that few had dared to imitate him, so advanced and original that even yet only a few could appreciate the excellence of his teachings. When the venerable, white-haired older brother rose to acknowledge the tribute, he described his long and cherished companionship with his brother, the struggles, failures, and successes they had borne together.

A little later the nominating committee, of which Dr. W. W. Mayo was a member, recommended Dr. Atlee for the association's president in the coming year. The election was unanimous, and the new president was escorted to the platform amid prolonged applause. In a few moving words he accepted the honor—but not only for himself: "I accept it also with gratitude as a tribute to the memory of a dear brother, who were he now living, would more deservedly occupy this position."

Those words will have a familiar ring to anyone who ever heard William J. Mayo accept any of the honors that later came to him. It cannot be stated as fact that the episode awakened or encouraged dreams in young Will's mind, dreams of what he and Charlie might be able to accomplish in their turn working together, but more than forty years later he described the incident vividly and accurately, bearing witness to the impression made upon him by the story of the Atlee brothers.

Certain it is that three years later, when Charlie was ready to enter medical school, the Mayos were already thinking of him and Will as partners in practice. In a family council they decided that Charlie should go to the Chicago Medical College, "because there he would get a different viewpoint."

Will had a hand in that decision no doubt, though he never publicly expressed any dissatisfaction with his course at Michigan. On some of his trips to and from Ann Arbor and on a recent journey to New York he had stopped off to visit the clinics in Chicago. He had seen Dr. Edmund Andrews, professor of surgery at the Chicago Medical College, at work in the amphitheater of Mercy Hospital, and he may well have visited the college itself, only a block away, to see its huge dispensary in action. He would have learned, too, that the student in Chicago was not limited to one hospital and one college staff, for visitors were welcome at the clinics of Charles T. Parkes, Christian Fenger, and Nicholas Senn, and in Will's view, colored by his supreme passion for clinical medicine, such opportunities for observation would outweigh many disadvantages.

By this time the Chicago Medical College, nominally affiliated with Northwestern University but entirely independent in location and administration, had made its three-year course compulsory, though the annual session was still but six months long, and it was offering a fourth year of instruction to those who desired it. There were excellent men on its faculty, and it too was beginning to boast of laboratories and science courses.

So in the fall of 1885 Charles Mayo set off for Chicago, accompanied by his father, who probably went along to make a round of the clinics and see for himself what the city had to offer.

## 12

Chicago Medical College maintained no dormitories, and the students roomed in pairs usually somewhere near the school, which was located on the corner of Twenty-sixth Street and Prairie Avenue. Charlie, having completed his registration, came out of the three-story red-brick building and waited on the steps for a few minutes, not quite certain what to do next. Soon another lad emerged from the building who was also alone. Charlie introduced himself amiably and learned that the other was Harry C. Whiting of Mount Pleasant, Iowa.

"We talked together for a few minutes," recalled Dr. Whiting, "then he asked me if I had secured a room. On my answer that I had just arrived and had made no effort to find one he asked me if I would not like to go in with him. We agreed not to discuss politics, since he was a Democrat and I was a Republican, nor religion, an agreement we kept for the two years we bunked together.

"Mr. Wakem, the registrar, gave us a list of nearby rooms. Our first place of call was on Indiana Avenue, three blocks from the college. The room was on the third floor, back, up a winding stair. It had a mantel bed, which was shut up in the day time and let down at night. On the mantel we arranged our medical books. We had a study table with a student light, three chairs, and a large closet in which we kept our trunks, clothes, and junk. Like a number of the Chicago Medical College and Hahnemann College students, we took our meals at Mrs. Henry's Boarding House, on the corner of Twenty-fourth and Cottage Grove avenues."

The first year the two roommates chummed with Charles W. More, a boy from Janesville, Iowa, who was living in the same house; later he established a hospital in Eveleth, Minnesota, and became an associate of the Mayos in the state medical society. The second year Whiting and Mayo moved to another room, not greatly different, just east of Cottage Grove Avenue, and there they made the acquaintance of another pair, Edward C. Morton of Wyoming Territory and James Morgan of Chicago. The four remained inseparable friends throughout the remainder of their college years. They even dressed alike, in heavy mouse-colored corduroy trousers because they were inexpensive. Charlie wore his dark hair pompadour, but it was generally hidden under an old shapeless cap. Most of his friends thought him careless and indifferent about clothes.

They found him a good companion, friendly and pleasant always, though inclined to be somewhat retiring and quiet, with little to say about himself. "He was companionable, but not aggressively so." There was no social life within the college and little for the students to do when they left school but go home to their desks and books. Occasionally they gathered to talk, smoke, and drink a glass of beer, and though Charlie did not smoke he sometimes joined them in having beer. But by and large, the boys were "an earnest lot," and they had come to Chicago just to study medicine.

## 13

As a student Charlie was only average. "He was not conspicuous in any way, neither brilliant nor dumb—just one of us," according to one of his classmates. And the record bears him out by listing neither failures nor honors for Charles Mayo.

In later years, when he had achieved worldwide fame as a surgeon, there were some who asserted in attempted derogation that C. H. Mayo had failed his college course in anatomy. But the official record of his courses and grades is still extant in the files of the Northwestern University Medical School, and on the numerical rating from one to ten then in use, he was graded 8.5 in descriptive and practical anatomy, 8.0 in surgical anatomy. He received the full 10.0 in dermatology and in—"punctuality"! His lowest grade was 7.0, which he got, strangely enough, in the principles and practice of surgery.

One thing that Charlie's schoolday friends recalled almost as with one mind was his uncanny ability to locate the operations he wanted to see and his absorbed interest in them. Night after night during his first two years he would greet his roommate with the same story, "I saw Dr. Senn [or Dr. Andrews, or Dr. Fenger] do a fine operation today," and then he would proceed to describe every move the surgeon had made. Surely he carried over something extra from those occasions to his work in surgery, but perhaps it was too much of the "practice" and too little of the "principles" to impress the professors.

Charlie was known for his habit of choosing a seat with great care, down in the center front, three or four rows back, where he could see clearly the blackboard charts and the clinician's every move. He himself used to tell how this predilection for front seats, added to his small stature, made him often the victim in the prank of passing a boy up through the rows of the amphitheater.

It is difficult to evaluate the training he was given at the Chicago Medical College, for the specific details are few and Dr. Charlie made no helpful comments. There are familiar and respected names on the list of his teachers and some titles among his courses that suggest a moderately progressive spirit. Dr. Frank Billings had just begun to teach physical diagnosis, which he learned in Europe and was one of the first to introduce into the medical curriculum in this country. Dr. William E. Casselberry was teaching materia medica and therapeutics when Charles Mayo was his student, but he took to specializing in nose and throat disorders a few years later and made signal contributions in that field. Dr. Walter Hay, the professor of nervous and mental diseases, was one of the early American specialists in neurology and a founder of the American Neurological Association.

In view of Dr. Charles Mayo's later interest in the advancement of the public health program, it is worth noting that he studied "State Medicine and Public Hygiene" in college. Dr. Oscar DeWolf, who taught the course, was the first public health commissioner in Chicago and did such an excellent job of cleaning up the filth-ridden city and formulating effective rules for municipal sanitation that the British Association for the Advancement of Science elected him to membership in 1882. The long, hard fight it took to win acceptance for his measures made him a good man to teach students the part education must play in forwarding the cause of public health.

In the practice of medicine Charles had as teachers the "untiring, irrepressible, uncompromising, and incorruptible" Nathan S. Davis, noted dean of the school, and the cultured, scholarly John H. Hollister; in surgery the popular, able Edmund Andrews and the less distinguished Ralph N. Isham. All four were veterans and had been co-founders of the college. Gynecology was taught by E. C. Dudley, still young but a capable practitioner whose services as a consultant were already in demand throughout an area extending west to the Twin Cities.

To indicate what form the teaching of practical medicine and surgery took, there remains only the catalog description of what it was intended to be. No clinical classes were provided for the freshmen; they were even advised not to attend clinics but to concentrate on the lectures, three a day, in preparatory subjects. During the second and third years the lectures were supplemented by two hours of clinical instruction daily.

# At Medical School

This was given at the several hospitals to which various members of the staff had appointments, but mainly at Mercy Hospital, located within a block of the college and under the exclusive control of its faculty. Cases of the sort that constitute the usual office practice were provided by the South Side Dispensary, maintained by the college in its own building chiefly to supply teaching material. Through its eight specialty departments passed some ten thousand patients a year.

In small groups of six or seven, the second- and third-year students alternated between hospital and dispensary for their clinical classwork, spending a week at a time in each. The schedule was planned to give every student two weeks of work in each department of the dispensary. These were not full-time weeks of course, but weeks of the two hours a day allotted to clinical courses.

The hospital instruction consisted largely of the customary demonstration of ambulatory patients or of surgical operations in the amphitheater, but sometimes clinics were held in the wards at the bedside. Then the students were "allowed" to examine the patients for themselves, and in their third year, in groups of two or three, they were permitted to observe the progress of obstetrical cases under the care of the house physician. However inadequate, this was an advance.

Most of the surgeons whose methods Charles Mayo studied seem to have been converts to Listerism and to have insisted on antiseptic precautions, though of varying sorts and degrees of completeness; and in Chicago hospitals was appearing a new and nobly useful aid, the trained nurse, to facilitate the practice of the system in all its routine details. So it is likely that the younger Mayo graduated with a fair understanding of the new method and its advantages.

He concluded his formal training with the third year. One of the requirements for the degree was a certificate of age and character, which his father supplied with admirable succinctness: "To whom it may concern, This is to certify that Chas. H. Mayo is over 21 years of age and is of good moral character. W. W. Mayo." When Dr. Mayo penned that brief note he did not suspect that it would someday be framed and cherished as part of the historical records of the Northwestern University Medical School.

The degree in medicine was conferred on Charles Mayo on March 27, 1888, and this time the proud father was present at the exercises.

# CHAPTER NINE

# From Father to Sons

"Dr. Mayo has moved to his new rooms in the Cook block, opposite the post office," announced the Rochester newspaper one day early in May 1883. "He has large reception and consulting rooms, and an operating room. All the rooms are light, airy and cheerful, and nicely furnished. There is no pleasanter office in the city. His son will return from Ann Arbor, Mich., about the first of June and assist the Doctor in his extensive practice."

Those new offices were a gesture of celebration, not only by a pleased father welcoming his son to an equal place in joint labors, but by a triumphant craftsman seeing the promise that his handiwork will survive him. Dr. Mayo was building up an office practice that filled every minute of the hours he allotted to it, a country circuit that extended some forty miles in every direction from Rochester, and a consulting practice that reached up to the Twin Cities and dipped into Iowa and Dakota. Of all this he was the mainspring, but he was nearing three score years and ten.

A doctor's practice is a mortal thing, mortal as the human being at its core. Fashioned by the slowly cumulative skill of a man and faith in a man, it may dissolve with an expelled breath. The product of a lifetime's labor in medical practice will perish with its creator unless there is a successor to whom he may transfer, while he is still active and his practice intact, the mantle of custom and confidence he has woven. For Dr. Mayo his two sons were such successors, and they were ready in time.

For them the opportunity was golden, the advantages patent; they were heirs to one of the largest practices in the Northwest, and allowing for the brief period necessary for the mantle to settle securely on their shoulders, they could begin at a point it had taken a lifetime to attain. Continuity from father to sons was a fundamental factor in the rapid growth of the Mayo practice.

## From Father to Sons

Shortly after Will graduated and returned to Rochester there was a social gathering at the Mayo farm, and among the guests was Charles N. Start, district judge in Rochester and an old friend of the family. In the course of the evening he found himself next to his host's elder son. Oh yes, the boy was just out of medical school. And what do you plan to do now? After a year or two in your father's office, what then? Will you be off to Minneapolis, St. Paul, or Chicago?

The questions were casual, the usual sort in such circumstances, but the reply was not. It fairly took the judge's breath, it was so direct, so serious, so sure. "I expect to remain in Rochester and to become the greatest surgeon in the world." That was William James Mayo at twenty-two.

A romantic young fool, the judge may have thought. Become a great surgeon in Rochester? It would take a superman to beat the handicap of such a location. But young Will saw nothing incompatible between his ambition and his intention to remain in Rochester; he saw no insuperable obstacle in the western, small-town site. It is just possible that he even saw what an inestimable advantage that particular location would be.

2

In their efforts to convince patients that the young Dr. Will was as able as the Old Doctor, the Mayos got a measure of help from the official seal of the state. The persistent efforts of the regular medical profession to weed out quackery by legal recognition of qualified practitioners were at long last bearing satisfactory fruit. After 1875 one state after another adopted acts to regulate medical practice, and Minnesota fell in line in 1883.

Early in that year the regents established a faculty of medicine in the University of Minnesota, not for the purpose of teaching but to examine and recommend qualified candidates for the degree. This was intended to be a substitute of sorts for the legal recognition the state was withholding. But almost immediately the state legislature moved to exclude the unfit from practice in Minnesota by making the university faculty of medicine a state examining board with the power to certify acceptable applicants. Those who could present a diploma from a medical college in good standing were to receive certificates from the board without further question, but others must pass an "elementary and practical" examination.

Although the law exempted from its provisions all who had been practicing within the state for five years or more, Dr. W. W. Mayo refused to take advantage of the exemption. Father and son together presented their diplomas, paid their one-dollar fees, and received their certificates on November 12, 1883.

The equality of father and son before the law was all very well, but it was a tussle to make the sick folks believe they were equal in healing skill. "Toe-in-the-door-days" the Mayo brothers called these early years in practice, for like unwelcome salesmen they had sometimes actually to use their toes to ensure themselves a crack through which to state their case when they answered a call in their father's place.

Dr. Will was very young and looked younger. He was boyishly slender still, his face smooth and round. His eyes were wide and blue, and though their glance could be keenly direct it was as often dreamily full of the long, long thoughts of youth. His brisk professional manner and the instrument bag of the physician could not at once convince patients that this boy was a doctor they could trust.

A call would come in from the country and the Old Doctor would send his son, but the farmer would send him back, saying that by "Dr. Mayo" he meant W. W. Mayo. If the father thought he could do so without alienating his patient altogether, he would send the boy back to try again. In one instance he sent Dr. Will four times before the patient finally gave in, saying with a grin that if in Dr. Mayo's opinion this stripling was a doctor it was all right with him because Dr. Mayo's opinion was what he wanted.

There are a number of such anecdotes from those early days, all telling the same story: The Rochester folk did not want the services of the young Dr. Mayo, while the Mayos were determined they should have them. One woman of a prominent family to which the Old Doctor had long ministered was again pregnant. As before, she engaged Dr. Mayo to deliver the baby and when labor began sent for him, secure in her confidence in his skill.

But when "Dr. Mayo" arrived it was Dr. Will, and the woman was furious. She told him to get out, she wouldn't have him, she wanted his father and wanted him right away. Dr. Will was very soothing. Father would be along in a minute or two; he had just come on ahead to make sure that nothing was amiss. Dr. W. W. Mayo did arrive finally but Dr. Will saw the case through, successfully delivering a daughter, without entirely mollifying the mother, however.

When the young doctor was given the chance he proved himself able and earnest, worthy of confidence by his own merit, thus facilitating the transfer of practice his father was trying to effect. The lawyer, Burt W. Eaton, was one of the Mayo clientele, and called the Drs. Mayo to attend his mother when she was taken ill late in May 1884. Dr. Will arrived alone, explaining that his father had gone to Washington to attend a meeting of the American Medical Association. He pronounced Mrs. Eaton very ill indeed, outlined his proposed plan of treatment, and set to work on it, all without question or ado.

But Mr. Eaton was uneasy. Finally he said, "Look here, Will, you're a young man and a new hand at this game. My mother means everything to me, and I'd like to call in old Dr. Cross." Will swallowed hard but he agreed, and Dr. Cross was summoned. He assured Mr. Eaton that the young doctor was entirely right in his diagnosis and was doing all that anyone could do. Then he left and the case was Dr. Will's, without doubt the first serious one he had faced alone.

Throughout the day and evening he stayed with the patient, never leaving her bedside. About three o'clock the next morning he came out of the bedroom, white and weary but smiling. "She'll be all right now," he said. And she was. The Eatons did not ever again insist upon having the Old Doctor.

The story of one less successful treatment is best told in Dr. Will's own words: "An old Irishman, a friend of father's, had lumbago. In that day salicylic acid was supposed to be good for rheumatism and I gave him some. He came in ten days later and in a loud voice told father about it . . . said that he had been in desperate agony, that Will had given him this medicine, and now he was all right. He congratulated father on his wonderful son. I was feeling pretty good. About an hour afterward I went downstairs to the street, and there directly in front of the building was a traveling medicine wagon, for Wizard Oil, with a ballyhoo man and a negro to pass out samples of the oil and to take up money. On the wagon, in the seat given to patients, was my old Irishman, telling loudly that he had been to all the doctors for his rheumatism, that none could help him, but that he had used Wizard Oil and now was cured."

Some who knew Dr. Will Mayo in later years have found it hard to imagine him driving a horse on country rounds, but that is the way he began, facing as a matter of course the floods and washouts, heat and dust, snow and freezing cold of the turning seasons. In the wintertime the Mayos always carried a shovel in their cutter in case they encountered snowdrifts that were too deep for their horse to flounder through.

The frontier wildness had not entirely gone from the region they covered. One blustery day in the very cold January of 1885 Dr. Will made a long drive to answer a call in Mower County. It was getting dark when he approached his destination, and the snow had drifted across the road so high that he decided to leave his team and cut through the woods about a mile afoot. He had no sooner entered the timber than he became aware of two wolves watching him from very near by. With chills chasing up and down his back he took to his heels, flourishing his medicine bag at the beasts to scare them off, but they followed him to the very door of his patient's cottage.

3

One might expect to find these years a period of pause in the growth of the Mayo practice, a plateau season in which the Old Doctor marked time while Dr. Will was making ready to carry the work onward and upward again, but that was not the case. There was continuous, accelerating expansion, to which the father contributed equally with the son, and that not merely by the force of momentum but by active effort.

The practice grew particularly in the proportion of surgical cases. Like nearly all their brethren, the Mayos were still "physicians and surgeons," for though exclusive specialization in general surgery may have stepped over the threshold in the metropolitan centers of the East it had not yet arrived in the West. Doctors could not support themselves by surgery alone because there was not yet enough of it. So the Mayos handled their share of the community's childbirths, indigestion, kidney trouble, and typhoid fever, measles, whooping cough, and the dread diphtheria. But it was surgery they wanted, surgery they courted, and surgery they got in increasing proportion.

From a collection of more than one hundred and fifty newspaper items for the years from 1883 to 1889 a few samples may serve to illustrate their surgical cases at this period:

Drs. Mayo and Son were called up to Kasson at midnight, Wednesday, to operate upon Mr. Cooper for strangulated hernia. Mr. Cooper is 73 years old and had been suffering great pain for several days. Being so prostrated with pain and vomiting, it is very questionable if he recovers by reason of delay in the operation.

The boiler to a steam thresher burst last Thursday on the Farm of Mr. Wedeskes near Pottsdam, breaking Gustave Geltner's leg, injuring his knee, and crushing one hand. Drs. Mayo were called to attend the injured man.

August Helmer's son, about eight years old, received a bruise on his right leg, about a year ago. It did not heal up and this week the Drs. Mayo excised about five inches of the bone.

Drs. Mayo removed the entire lower lip of Peter Hoganson, of Rock Dell, Wednesday, for cancer. A new lip was formed by bringing up the tissues from the chin below, and the patient is doing well.

[A Mr. Clements stopped a fight between four men.] The one that had his head cut was a fearful sight, his cap being one mass of blood. This frightened Mr. Clements so that he hastened to the city after a doctor, fearing the man was seriously injured. Dr. W. J. Mayo went out and dressed the wounds, and found his head terribly mangled but there is no danger but that he will recover, as there is too much of the evil one in him to get fatally injured in a row.

Mrs. Barney Clark was fearfully gored in the stomach by a bull on Wednesday morning while she was passing through the pasture to milk a cow. Drs. Mayo were called and it is thought Mrs. Clark will recover.

Drs. Mayo operated upon John Dever of Millville for a bad case of club foot, it being turned over so far that he walked on his ankle, but they straightened it in fine shape.

About two years ago Mr. Dexter Payne of this city, discovered something on the back of his hand that resembled a wart, and supposed it was one so paid no attention to it. In a short time it began to grow, and he consulted with a physician about it. The doctor did not consider it anything serious, but it continued to increase in size, and he finally went east to have it treated. He returned without receiving any relief. Last week he consulted Drs. Mayo, and they at once pronounced it a cancer, and that it would be necessary to have his arm amputated to save his life, as the cancer had gained such a hold, that the hand could not be saved. Last Friday the operation was successfully performed, and Mr. Payne is doing as well as could be expected. If it had been taken in season, a pair of shears and nippers would have done the business and he would have saved his hand.

That sort of thing made up the bulk of the Mayos' surgery and virtually all of their colleagues'. There were about ten other doctors in Rochester, but the Mayos' strongest competitors, now that the Drs. Cross were retiring from the pursuit of practice because of age and failing health, were Dr. F. R. Mosse and Dr. W. A. Allen, both crusading homeopaths and personable gentlemen with large followings.

4

The measure of what the Mayos could show in more radical surgery may be taken from the Old Doctor's progress in gynecology, especially in ovariotomy. As the word of his first successes in removing ovarian tumors spread through the countryside, neighboring doctors, unable to perform this operation themselves, referred their ovarian cases to him. Particularly cooperative was Dr. Ida Clarke, the able successor to Dr. Harriet Preston, who had moved to St. Paul. Dr. Mayo was a friend to Dr. Clarke as he had been to Dr. Preston, and she was listed as an assistant in many of his operations on women, probably in cases she had referred to him.

With such assistance Dr. Mayo piled up a record of thirty-six ovariotomies during the decade, with twenty-seven recoveries and nine deaths. A mortality of twenty-five per cent would be disastrously high today, but it was not so when a tabulation of ovariotomies throughout the United States showed a mortality of 20.93 in 86 cases in hospital practice and 30.4 in 311 cases in private practice. In Minnesota Dr. Mayo's record was unique, unequaled as far as the reports show either in total number or in number of successes.

The general attitude toward surgery contributed to the high mortality. When the knife was considered a last resort, the surgeon was not thought justified in removing an ovarian tumor until it got so large that family, neighbors, and friends could see that unless it was taken out the patient would die. Should the doctor by chance diagnose ovarian tumor when it was the size of an orange, he had to stand by, not always reluctantly, until it had grown to the dimensions at least of a full-term pregnancy before he could recommend surgical intervention. Then, of course, delay had made the risk of the operation greater.

Twenty-seven successful ovariotomies. To reveal the full import of that fact and its influence on the growth of the Mayo practice, imagination must bring the figures to life by reading into them the individual human experiences they so coldly conceal. Twenty-seven times something like the following must have happened.

A circle of friends and relatives fearfully watched a woman get weaker and weaker while her belly swelled steadily toward the point they knew meant death. Despairingly they turned to their doctor. Could he do nothing to help? He plunged a trocar into the mass and drew off a quart or two of fluid, bringing some relief, but only temporarily. Soon the tumor refilled and went on growing relentlessly. Perhaps the doctor tapped it a second, even a third, time before he admitted that he had done all he could. But maybe, he said, Dr. Mayo over in Rochester could do something more. In some cases like this he had cut the abdomen open and removed the tumor at its roots. Of course it was a drastic measure and might mean the end at once.

The agonizing choice was made, and one day the family and friends watched the woman lie down upon her kitchen table to submit to chloroform and Dr. Mayo's knife. An hour or two later they watched her awake again and as the days passed saw her recover health and strength, her size restored to normal, her life so seemingly near its end prolonged for many years.

They had a story to tell, those who watched from close at hand or from next door, a dramatic tale that made a choice morsel for tongues set free over a piece of needlework or a cup of coffee. From mouth to mouth, home to home, neighborhood to neighborhood it passed, till hundreds had heard it, some of them far from the point of origin. And with it spread the name of Dr. Mayo of Rochester, the worker of the miracle. There are women still living who remember having first heard his name when as girls they heard just such a story told in their homes.

Only by similar reconstruction against the contemporary background can the effect of news stories like the following be adequately gauged:

[In November 1884:] Thos. Mahony of Rochester, had his arm terribly mutilated in the gearing to a threshing machine. . . . His coat sleeve was caught and drew his arm into the gear, and took the skin from it from the wrist to the shoulder. It was a frightful looking spectacle, large patches of the skin being torn completely away, leaving the naked flesh and muscles exposed to sight. Irwin Tolbert brought him into the city and the Doctors Mayo dressed the wound. It is doubtful if he ever recovers the full use of the arm.

[In December:] Young Mahony has so far recovered from his injury as to be able to come into the city last Saturday to have his arm dressed. He says his arm pains him but little now, and he is hopeful of having a good arm yet. He can move it and it has commenced healing. The Doctor has commenced to skin-graft it, as there was so much of the skin destroyed that it would hardly heal over without the assistance of skin-grafting.

[The following April:] Young Mahony of Rochester was in the city last Saturday. His arm that was so terribly lacerated in the gearing of a threshing machine last fall, has entirely healed, and he has the use of it as well as ever.

Tuesday afternoon, Mr. Sumner Snow of Farmington, was kicked by a vicious stallion, thrown down and stamped upon by the brute, injuring him very seriously. The hoof struck him in the hip causing a compound fracture of the hip bone and cutting a hole in his abdomen. The Drs. Mayo were summoned, Wednesday morning, and reduced the fracture. The hip bone had to be wired together with silver wire as the muscles drew the sections apart. He was also badly cut and bruised by the stamping. He will recover.

## 5

The movement of stories was widening the area of the Mayo practice and so was the movement of people. Immigration to the new land of promise in Dakota Territory, which had begun with the hard times of the late sixties and early seventies, was at high tide in the eighties and brought two new states into the Union in 1889. Wet seasons and good crops had wiped out the momentary doubts aroused by drouth and grasshopper devastation, and once again little boys in the sod-house homes of northwestern Minnesota could while away the hours watching the lumbering prairie schooners, forty or fifty each day, roll slowly along the old Pembina trail into the newer West.

The railroads were also pushing rapidly westward across Dakota, and to bring population to the hinterlands behind the tracks they joined with territorial officials in singing a siren song of waiting acres. The song was heard and heeded not alone by immigrants from Europe but by the young men of the settled states who as always were eager for adventure and more economic elbow room than the established communities could offer.

Into the stream flowing toward the new Fargo, Flandreau, Wahpeton, Aberdeen, Brookings, Bismarck, Pierre, DeSmet, Minot, Sioux Falls, and Devil's Lake, the southeastern counties of Minnesota continued to spill their share of restless men. A merchant of Rochester returned from a tour of the Dakota settlements in 1885 to tell his associates on the board of trade it was no wonder the population had declined; not a Dakota town could you enter without finding men from Olmsted County.

The new communities were not isolated from the old, for the railroads were strong bridges. Over the tracks of the Chicago and Northwestern men could move easily between Rochester and Dakota, and the local news columns show that they did so. In season eight, ten, a dozen items an issue announced the visits of Dakota sons and daughters to relatives in Rochester. Men worked through the summer on their Dakota farms and returned to spend the winter in Rochester, Dakota storekeepers came back for new stocks of goods, young lawyers and teachers came home for wives—and sick men and women came for treatment by Rochester doctors.

The Dakota doctors, few, scattered, and untried, might do for minor complaints, had to do for acute illness, but when a chronic malady allowed time, former residents of Rochester journeyed back to Dr. Mayo or to Dr. Allen, who had always taken care of them and their parents. And it may be supposed they recommended these men they knew and trusted to their new neighbors who had need of special medical care.

A Mrs. Vail of Dakota, nearly blind from wild hairs in her eyes, traveled to Rochester for a series of operations by the Drs. Mayo which gradually restored her sight. David Dyson of Dakota, son of Robert Dyson of Rochester, was ill with a disease of the spinal column which so crippled him that he could not stand erect and finally could not work or even walk. He was taken to the Drs. Mayo, who found and drained an abscess that was causing the trouble and then applied a

217

plaster cast and a supporting iron rod to his back. He was soon straight again, three inches taller, able to walk and to return to his work. Such dramatic successes brought many patients from Dakota to the Mayos.

And that in spite of instances less successful. Miss Hattie Libby of Fargo was referred by her Dakota physician to Dr. Mayo for the removal of an ovarian tumor in May 1884. For two years she had been refusing an operation, trying instead the baths and electric currents by which various quacks promised to cure her. Finally she got diffuse peritonitis and nearly died.

When she arrived in Rochester completely worn out, Dr. Mayo was about to start for Washington to attend a medical convention. He left her to recruit her strength under the care of Dr. Will and Dr. Ida Clarke, but when he returned she was so ill he doubted the propriety of operating at all. Nonetheless he tried it as "a forlorn hope." Complications made the removal of the thirty-pound tumor unusually difficult, but Miss Libby rallied from the operation and began to gain, and the newspaper reported another success for Dr. Mayo. Then on the tenth day she suddenly collapsed and died.

6

There was no hospital in Rochester as yet. Plans for one were being made, but meanwhile the Mayos continued to perform most of their operations in the patients' own homes. For out-of-town residents they usually took rooms in the old Norton Hotel on the banks of the Zumbro River, but it was a problem to provide suitable aftercare there, especially for a patient unaccompanied by friends or relatives.

There were a few women in town who would act as practical nurses, one of the best being a Mrs. Carpenter who lived in a large square house in north Rochester, near the present site of the Samaritan Hospital. Her family being small, she had room enough to accommodate eight or nine patients and was willing to make her house into a nursing home. So the Mayos began taking more and more of their surgical cases there. They had no separate operating room but used a little portable table and operating outfit that they moved from room to room. Mrs. Carpenter was a good nurse on whom they could rely for intelligent care, and Dr. Will credited her competence with a share in keeping their mortality low.

# From Father to Sons

Often a number of their fellow doctors gathered to watch a major operation. They were welcome, and to make it easier for them to attend, the Mayos soon began to schedule their more important operations for Sunday mornings at Mrs. Carpenter's. When a case of unusual interest was on the docket they tried to let the men in the nearby towns know so they could drive over if they wished. At such times Dr. Mayo talked informally as he worked, answered questions from the onlookers, and explained what he was doing and why. Here were the beginnings of the Mayos' surgical clinics.

## 7

In all this activity, insofar as the patients would permit, young Dr. Will was sharing equally within a year after his graduation from medical school—in all, that is, except ovariotomy. The senior Dr. Mayo had great confidence in his son's surgical ability. On the way home from the first operation he saw Dr. Will perform he bubbled with admiration. He talked of nothing else to the young priest who had been present at the bedside and who was riding back to Rochester in the Old Doctor's buggy. "Yes sir," he told Father Lawler, "that boy will make a great surgeon; he's going to make his mark in the world." But his confidence did not extend quite far enough for him to allow the boy to open abdomens and remove ovarian tumors; that was too hazardous an operation for anyone but a man of experience and proven skill.

Dr. Will did not at once challenge his father's opinion. Instead he set out to develop a field of his own. The Old Doctor was doing very little ophthalmic surgery though there was need in the community for a great deal of it. Diseases of the eye were a field exploited in and around Rochester only by the itinerant "eye specialists," most of them quacks of varying degree. There, Will decided, was his opportunity; he would concentrate on the surgery of the eye and add another string to the Mayos' bow. But he must know more about the pathology and anatomy of the eye before he ventured to operate.

Dr. Charlie once said of Will that he was "filled with the genius of finding opportunities." On the outskirts of Rochester was a slaughterhouse berated by the city officials as a menace to the health of the community. To that unlikely place Dr. Will went for the knowledge he needed, and he spent many hours practicing his dissections and operations on the eyes of slaughtered pigs and sheep.

Then, sure of his knowledge, he sought a chance to demonstrate his new skill, and again he "found" an opportunity. At the county poorhouse were three inmates blind with senile cataracts. Dr. Will volunteered to remove them and did. In two cases he got perfect results and failed in the third only because beneath the cataract was an atrophied optic nerve, revealed by his shiny new ophthalmoscope.

One of the cured patients was an elderly woman who, in Dr. Will's words, "had sufficient strength to stump the county for me, exhibiting the cure," and soon the newspapers were telling of private, paying patients from whose eyes Dr. W. J. Mayo had removed cataracts. With continued study and practice at the slaughterhouse, he extended his efforts to other phases of ophthalmic surgery, and beyond a doubt he was the partner responsible for the following accomplishment:

The Drs. Mayo performed a very difficult operation upon Mrs. P. M. McDowell of Claremont, this week. A tumor had grown just under her left eye so as to push it nearly out of the socket. They took the eye out, letting it lay on her cheek, and removed the cancerous growth and then replaced it, sewing up the fine muscles that had been cut. The operation was entirely successful, she now being able to see better than before and to move the eye freely.

## 8

The end of medical school was truly a commencement for Will Mayo and for his brother too. Neither of them ever suffered for a moment the delusion that he had finished his education and had no more to learn. One of the most valuable contributions William Worrall Mayo made to his sons' career was his insistence that no matter how busy they might be or how heavy the calls of duty, they must give at least one hour a day to reading and study. Quick to recognize the good sense of this, Dr. Will formed a habit then that he never broke. To the end of his life he kept scrupulous account of his reading time, with unavoidable debits carefully set down to be paid up in full, though credits in advance were not recorded.

Most of his reading hours he gave to medicine. He bought books by the masters of his craft and searched their contents eagerly. Hilton Fagge's *Practice of Medicine*, Osler's *Practice of Medicine*, Grieg

Smith's *Abdominal Surgery*, and Jacobson's *Operations of Surgery* he found especially helpful. To Jacobson's manual he expressed particular debt, calling it "the greatest work on operative surgery I ever studied. Sound and sane, it covered the salient features of anatomy and physiology, and with wise caution indicated the peculiar procedures which would be best suited to meet individual conditions. I owe Jacobson much." For several years he depended so much on that book that he practically slept with it under his pillow.

He outgrew dependence on such systems and manuals quickly though, and came to find more stimulation in the articles in the *Journal of the American Medical Association,* the *Annals of Surgery,* the *Medical Record,* the *London Lancet,* and the *Northwestern Lancet,* to all of which he and his father subscribed.

"With few exceptions," he came to believe, "the progress of the surgeon lies in the medical journal. Medical journals are not only a source of information but also a source of news, and surgical news, like other news, is open to correction day by day. . . . Sometimes one is unduly influenced by a book because it seems so real, with its fine binding and heavy paper, that one sees, not the meager merit of the man who wrote it, but rather the building with the brownstone front and plate glass windows where it was published."

### 9

There is no understanding the young William James Mayo without giving full account to the driving urge to excel that possessed him. Again and again in story or sentence its strength is manifest.

In April 1885 he went to Washington to attend, as a spectator, a meeting of the recently organized American Surgical Association. This was an exclusive body of the surgical elite of the nation, and election to its fellowship was recognition of one's abilities by one's colleagues, the men best qualified to judge them. As he sat in a rear seat listening to the papers and discussion Dr. Will felt, in his own words, "like a hungry, penniless boy in front of a bake-shop window."

In momentary despair he wondered, "Is it possible for a small-town man to get into the company of these giants, and sit with the mighty?" Then his eye fell upon Dr. Jacob Rowland Weist sitting on the platform. Dr. Weist was a fellow of the association and its secretary, and he came, not from New York or Philadelphia or Boston, but from Richmond, Indiana. There was Will's answer.

It was his determination to get to the top of the ladder that dictated the program of continuing education on which he embarked, with the support and encouragement of his wise father. In getting started he was aided by the circumstance that the first two postgraduate schools in the country had just been organized in New York.

Graduate work in medicine did not yet exist. One might earn an advanced degree in physiology, chemistry, or anatomy, but nowhere could one find systematic, organized training in clinical medicine or surgery leading to a degree beyond the M.D. That phase of medical education was to come many years later and was to originate with William and Charles Mayo and the University of Minnesota.

Postgraduate work, however, was not new. American medical schools being what they were, intelligent and ambitious graduates had long sought to repair the deficiencies in their training by study abroad. Berlin, Munich, Vienna, Paris, Edinburgh, Glasgow, London, and Liverpool provided the postgraduate schools for American doctors. To make the rounds of those centers, watching, listening, and when possible working in the research laboratories already a part of European clinics was the accepted way to round off one's medical education—if one could afford it.

For those who could not the United States offered little. There was good work to be seen and much to be learned in New York, but its facilities and its able men were not organized for postgraduate instruction. Their clinics and courses were intended for undergraduates, and if a practitioner wished to share in them he had to enroll in one of the undergraduate schools and mix with the cubs in a routine ill-suited to his special needs.

Plans for a less wasteful use of New York's abundant opportunities were in formation from about 1875 on, but it seems to have been Dr. John A. Wyeth who brought them finally to realization in 1882. He had graduated from the old and honored medical department of the University of Louisville, had graduated *cum laude,* but in all his schooling not once had he entered a hospital ward or stood with a teacher at the bedside of a patient. Six weeks after he tacked up his sign in a small Alabama town he took it down again with a shiver of conscience, locked his office doors, and set out to learn how to *practice* medicine.

But when he got to New York he found no way of getting the instruction he wanted except by enrolling in another school of the sort he had come from, and it was that disappointing experience which fathered his determination to establish postgraduate instruction in New York. From the nucleus of an unorganized but active teaching corps at the DeMilt Dispensary his influence fashioned the New York Polyclinic, the first American postgraduate school, patterned and named after the famous *Poliklinik* of Vienna. Almost simultaneously a "supplementary faculty" seceding from the medical school of the University of the City of New York organized the New York Postgraduate School. Both institutions opened their doors for the first time in the fall of 1882. Both were for practitioners only.

They were distinguished by their exclusive concern with practical instruction in clinical and laboratory subjects. Not one didactic lecture did they offer. They were frankly "undergraduate repair shops" aiming to teach the young doctor in the quickest manner possible the practical technique his alma mater had failed to impart. For this reason their courses were short and their arrangements very flexible.

They offered for three or four hundred dollars a general ticket that would admit the bearer to any clinical or laboratory course offered by the school during the year, but a man with limited funds and time could enroll for short courses of a month or two in the two or three special fields he was most interested in. That entitled him to "private instruction" (in small groups no doubt) and would admit him to the school clinics and hospital services in those fields. His card, with a little aggression on his part, also secured him admission to almost any clinic or hospital in the city.

## 10

For his first course Dr. Will chose the Postgraduate School, which he attended from late September to early November 1884. Little is known of what he did there, but from one incident of which he spoke an interesting and significant sequence of events can be traced.

He spent much of his time in learning his way about among the New York hospitals and their surgical clinics, and settled upon those of Dr. Henry B. Sands at the Roosevelt Hospital as his favorites. He had chosen with unerring judgment, for Sands was the outstanding surgeon in New York, if not in the nation, and his surgical service at Roosevelt Hospital was the largest and best managed in the United States. Sands seemed a more brilliantly original surgeon than he was, for he had to a consummate degree the ability to take up quickly a new technique of promise and develop such a dexterity and perfection in it as to make the originator himself envious. He was a general surgeon, and until very recently had also practiced general medicine, but at that time he was especially interested in the malady known as perityphlitis or perityphlitic abscess.

This was not at all a new disease. It had been known to the ancients, who called it colic or iliac passion, but it had been known only in its clinical manifestations—sudden severe pain in the right lower quadrant of the torso, accompanied by fever, nausea, and constipation, and followed, if death did not immediately occur, by the formation of an abscess that caused fatal general peritonitis if it ruptured into the peritoneal cavity.

A long series of anatomic, pathologic, and physiologic studies had shown the trouble to result from inflammation, but exactly where in the body that inflammation originated was still a matter for dispute. There were some who thought it began with a foreign body or catarrhal discharge in the appendix and from there spread to the surrounding tissues, but these were a little heeded minority. Most physicians, that is, most of the few who were acquainted with the disease, thought the point of origin was the cecum and general region at the head of the colon. Whence the name perityphlitis, meaning inflammation of the peri-cecal tissue.

While pathologists were arguing about the etiology of the ailment, a few daring surgeons had made some progress in treating it. First and foremost in America was Willard Parker, who in 1867 announced that he had opened the abdomen and drained the perityphlitic abscess with success in three out of four cases. He advised that this form of surgical intervention be employed between the fifth and twelfth days of the malady's course, after the abscess had formed but before it reached the point of possible rupture.

While Parker was developing this idea, Henry Sands was his partner and learned from him how to diagnose perityphlitis and when and how to open the abscess. Since then Sands and his assistants had performed this operation nearly a hundred times and had reported their favorable results in the journals. Other surgeons in New York and elsewhere in the country were also beginning to use the procedure, but none of them so often as Sands.

That was how matters stood when Dr. Will Mayo was attending Sands's clinics. They were held in the afternoon beginning at two o'clock, and day after day Dr. Will was on hand at one o'clock to secure a front center seat in the amphitheater, from which he watched the operations with absorbed interest until the very end, sometimes until six-thirty or seven in the evening, long after the other spectators had gone.

Late one stormy night, as Dr. Sands was finishing the day's operations, an orderly brought him word that an emergency case had just arrived in the surgical ward. As he turned back toward the table Sands looked up into the amphitheater and saw its one remaining occupant. "I see you sitting here through every clinic. You can go away, but I must stay until my work is over. They tell me that there is an interesting case out in the surgical ward. Perhaps you would like to go with me."

Dr. Will welcomed the chance. In the ward they found the man very ill, vomiting and feverish. After listening to the history of the symptoms Dr. Sands motioned his young companion to feel the swelling in the right iliac region and then said, "I believe we have here a perityphlitic abscess described by my old teacher, Willard Parker. These abscesses sometimes rupture and cause fatal general peritonitis. I do not know why this region should be so susceptible to these foul abscesses. We will give the patient a little chloroform and open the abscess here in the ward."

As he worked, making the Parker incision over the area of swelling, opening the abscess, and putting in a drainage tube, he explained the operation to his keen-eyed companion. Finally he asked Dr. Will whether he had ever seen such an abscess before. Yes, he thought perhaps he had, said Dr. Will. He had just been thinking of a case he had seen when he was his father's office boy. The patient was a tall, thin man, a barber. He had inflammation of the bowels and was thought to be dying. Father introduced an exploring needle into the iliac region, found pus, and leaving the needle in as a guide, incised an abscess and drew off about a quart of foul fluid.

Dr. Sands chuckled his approval, agreed that that had probably been a case of perityphlitic abscess, and said that Dr. Mayo senior was a wise surgeon to leave the needle in as a guide to the collection of pus. It had taken him a long time to learn that trick, he said, and he had been humiliated more than once by not being able to find the abscess again when he was ready to open it.

## 11

That experience gave Dr. Will food for thought. He and his father and their colleagues had many cases of abdominal pain with fever and vomiting that they called inflammation of the bowels, or some-times cholera morbus. But they really knew very little about them, and the cases often ended fatally. How many were actually this peri-typhlitis in which evacuation of an abscess might bring recovery?

Within a week or two of his return to Rochester, as his memory placed it, a young Swede was brought in from the country with what looked to the alert young doctor very much like the perityphlitic abscess he had examined at Roosevelt Hospital with Dr. Sands. His father being away, the responsibility was Dr. Will's. With the grooved needle he probed for pus, found it, cut down into the abscess, and drained its contents. The young Swede recovered.

Dr. Will had other cases that he considered perityphlitis—although the editor would have none of the strange name so hard to pronounce and continued to report the trouble as inflammation of the bowels. In some of them medical treatment brought recovery so that he did not have to operate, and in one he had been called too late for surgery to help.

In the late summer of 1885 a young schoolteacher who lived near Rochester was taken suddenly and violently ill. There is reason to believe that the two Drs. Mayo did not agree on the diagnosis, the father thinking the trouble to be the usual inflammation of the bowels and the son insisting it was perityphlitic abscess, which a Parker inci-sion and drainage would relieve. In any case, the girl's parents refused to permit an operation and she died. Then Dr. Will secured permission to do a postmortem and by it clearly demonstrated the accuracy of his own diagnosis.

One would like to know exactly what he found in that autopsy. In telling of it later he said he had found the trouble to be appendicitis, but was his use of that term merely the retroactive application of later knowledge, or did he at the time actually locate the seat of the disease in the appendix? The question is of interest because the episode occurred in August 1885, and not until the following June did Reginald Fitz read his famous paper on "Perforating Inflammation of the Vermiform Appendix" before the Association of American Physicians. That paper, published in the *Transactions* of the association and between separate covers as a book, made it convincingly clear to everyone that virtually all cases of perityphlitis actually originated in the appendix and ought therefore to be called appendicitis.

Fitz did a classic job of marshaling and presenting his evidence. He gave a clear picture of the clinical course and diagnostic signs of the disease and stated his positive conviction that if the symptoms did not subside within twenty-four hours after their appearance the surgeon should remove the appendix. But Fitz was a pathologist, so exclusively associated with the autopsy table in the minds of his clinician friends that once when he was called to the bedside of one of them, the man thought he must be dead and Fitz had come to do the postmortem!

So the surgeons did not immediately follow Fitz's advice. Not until 1889, when Dr. Charles McBurney, successively assistant, associate, and successor to Sands at Roosevelt Hospital, described the famous McBurney's point in the abdomen, at which pressure would reveal a diseased appendix, and came out firmly in favor of early and radical operative interference, did appendectomy begin its march to general use.

Dr. Will was no quicker than others to adopt the radical measures Fitz recommended. He read Fitz's paper soon after it appeared, but it merely made him more sure in diagnosis and less hesitant about opening the abscess when it had formed. Which was quite enough to excite the interest of the community.

Drs. Mayo operated on a nephew of E. H. Derby's . . . for an internal abscess caused by inflammation of the bowels. The young man was in a very critical condition, but we are glad to say will recover.

[Three weeks later:] E. H. Derby of Viola, was in the city last Saturday, and reported his nephew, Chauncy McCormick, who was operated on a short time since for inflammation of the bowels, as rapidly on the way to recovery, and able to be taken home by the last of the week. Mr. McCormick is the second case operated on by Dr. Mayo, and both have been successful and the parties' lives saved, as there was no hope for them except by an operation.

A son of Ole Nelson of Rock Dell, who has been studying medicine at the State University, was taken ill recently with inflammation of the bowels, and was very low, when an operation was performed by the Drs. Mayo, assisted by Dr. Witherstine. A gangrenous portion of the bowel was removed, and the patient is well on the road to recovery. This is the eighth successful operation of this character made by the Drs. Mayo.

The more radical nature of that last operation is obvious. If the "gangrenous portion of the bowel" removed from Mr. Nelson was his appendix, the Mayos were well abreast of their eastern fellows in the use of appendectomy.

## 12

By the spring of 1888 Dr. Will felt that his experience with this sort of abdominal disorder was worth reporting, and he prepared a paper on "Inflammations Involving the Caecum, its Appendix, or Both," which he read before the surgical section at the annual session of the Minnesota State Medical Society.

"We all know," he began tactfully, "that the 'inflammation of the bowels' of the older writers was, in the majority of instances, typhlitis or perityphlitis, and as we become more familiar with the clinical symptoms . . . we are impressed with the many errors which have been made in diagnosis." Concisely and clearly he outlined the anatomy, pathology, and physiology concerned and the various clinical courses the disease might take. "While the term perityphlitis does not express the exact origin of the disease it is the one we have retained because in common use. Appendicitis would be the proper term."

Then he turned to the question of treatment and went on record unequivocally as opposed to an immediate resort to surgery. "It must be apparent to all that if the dictum of our most ambitious surgeons be followed, to operate in three or four days, many patients will suffer from a formidable operation unnecessarily." He thought few who could be saved by operation would die before the end of the first week.

For that period he advised rest, light food, and opium to relieve pain. Knowing the tendency of laymen to use, and of many doctors to prescribe, a cathartic at the first sign of anything wrong in the stomach or bowels, he warned that in this malady peristaltic action would spread the inflammation, prevent the desired localization, and perhaps even rupture the abscess and bring death.

He did not believe incision and drainage to be in order until the adhesions around the collection of pus were fairly firm. Any earlier invasion of the abdomen was in his opinion unsound practice because, he said, "anyone who has seen the stinking pus and feces from a perityphlitic abscess would be willing to wait for adhesions to render the operation extraperitoneal, rather than risk the slightest contamination of the peritoneal cavity." For him, obviously, that cavity was still sacrosanct.

Conservative though its conclusions were, Dr. Will's paper made his listeners sit up in surprise at its thorough survey of the subject and the amount of personal experience it revealed. Ordinarily one or two cases of an uncommon malady were enough to occasion a report to this state body, and on perityphlitis only two such reports of three cases had been made previously. But now came this lad from Rochester to speak authoritatively and knowledgeably out of his own experience. He had illustrated each of his points with case histories, nine in all, and some of these he said were typical of several others of the same sort. Why, he must have treated a score or more altogether!

Of course the *Transactions* of the assembly do not record the reactions of the group to Dr. Will's paper, but the impression it made on them may be guessed from the fact that they, the assembled surgeons of the state, promptly elected this young man, twenty-seven years old and only five years out of medical school, as the chairman of their surgical section for the following year.

## 13

There, in one sequence which it has been possible to reconstruct in fairly complete detail, is an almost perfect miniature of the pattern of action and circumstance that made the Mayo brothers world-famous surgeons.

At the dawn of modern surgery they went forth to learn the latest developments from others. With sound judgment they adopted what was good, and with consummate skill they applied and refined it. Around them, in southern Minnesota and adjacent states, a virgin growth of sickness waited to be brought under control. Because they were there first with the new surgery they stood forth in a wide area as men who could heal where others failed. More and more sick folk sought them, and they gained more and more experience and skill. Then with unprecedented numbers to add to unusual results they made reports to their professional brethren that startled them into incredulous, then admiring, attention.

In part, that pattern appeared in the Old Doctor's achievements in ovariotomy. Complete, it appeared again and again, on a larger and larger scale, at a faster and faster tempo—in stomach surgery, gallbladder surgery, thyroid surgery. And in the end it carried the name of Mayo to the farthest corner of the surgical world and made it known to more persons of the lay world than would recognize the name of any other medical man alive or dead.

## 14

The chairman of the state's surgeons could not admit that any operation performed by others was beyond him. In November 1888 Dr. Will was called to Kasson to examine a woman for what proved to be an ovarian tumor. Normally slight, she was now huge, and she had a nasty burn across her abdomen that she had got in reaching for something that was burning on the cookstove; her great belly had hit the stove before her hand could reach the pan. To examine her Dr. Will had her lie down on a horsehair sofa in the parlor, and as she attempted to turn onto her side at his request, the weight of the tumor upset her balance and she fell off onto the floor. Dr. Will had to call for help to get her up again.

When he heard his son's report, the Old Doctor set the operation for the following Sunday morning and sent word of it to the doctors roundabout. Then he received a note from Dr. A. J. Stone in St. Paul, asking him to come up for consultation on a case there, and he left, planning to be back by Saturday night. But he did not come. Nor did he arrive on the first train Sunday morning.

By the hour set for the operation, some fifteen doctors had gathered at Mrs. Carpenter's, the patient was waiting, and with her several relatives who had left small children alone at home. They could not be asked to come back later, so taking his courage in his hands, Dr. Will told the woman *he* would do the operation if she was willing. She was, and with the assistance of Dr. Charlie, Dr. Clarke, and Dr. A. W. Stinchfield of Eyota, Will removed the tumor. It was enormous, completely filling the washtub they put it in, and the watching doctors were greatly impressed.

Although everything had gone off very well, Dr. Will spent the day wondering what his father would say. A little fearfully he went down to meet the evening train, which brought Dr. Mayo and with him Dr. Stone. Dr. Mayo had stayed over in St. Paul to assist at Dr. Stone's operation and had brought that gentleman back to watch his own, which he was planning to do the next morning. He was in high spirits, gloating a little, Will thought, over the fine case he had to show his St. Paul friend.

Hesitantly Will told them he had done the operation that morning. His father was speechless. And Dr. Stone sat down on the station steps, beat his hat against the platform's edge, and laughed till the tears came at the thought of the boy's stealing his father's big case. Then the three men went down to Mrs. Carpenter's together, saw that the patient was doing well, and took a look at the tumor in the washtub. Dr. Will always felt that on that occasion his father fully realized for the first time that his son had become a thoroughly competent surgeon in his own right.

## 15

Reading his paper on appendicitis in 1888 was by no means Dr. Will's first appearance before the state medical society. He had got his toe in that door too through association with his father. The Old Doctor was so well known and respected among the state's physicians that when papers began appearing under the joint authorship of W. W. Mayo and W. J. Mayo the first name was sufficient endorsement of the second.

Dr. Will took up that phase of professional life with energy and enthusiasm. With his eye ambitiously on the national bodies of the profession's elite, he welcomed the experience and preparation to be gained from participation in local societies. Perhaps at his jogging and certainly under his father's initiative, the Olmsted County Medical Society, dead since the middle seventies, was reorganized in 1885, with Dr. W. W. Mayo as its president for two years. From that time forward its meetings, often held in the Mayo offices, were regular and well attended, and the Mayos always took a prominent part in the programs.

Dr. Will's membership in the state medical society began at the annual meeting in Stillwater in 1884. Dr. James B. McGaughey of Winona, elected president at that session, had long been a friend of the elder Mayo's and was a man who loved to help beginners along the way. So it is not surprising that he named W. J. Mayo to the committee on surgery, along with such men as Perry H. Millard, Charles A. Wheaton, and Frederick A. Dunsmoor.

Although only five or ten years older than Dr. Will, Wheaton and Dunsmoor had by their energy and ability already made themselves acknowledged leaders in Twin City medical circles. Dr. Wheaton, one of the Northwest's contributions to the "masters of American surgery," was even then giving unmistakable evidence of the remarkable ability to distinguish sound innovations from fads and frills that made him a sort of plumb line for Minnesota surgeons. Dr. Will once called him "the surgical hero of my youthful admiration." Dr. Millard was a member of the state university faculty of medicine and the secretary of the state board of medical examiners, and was shortly to become the dean of the University of Minnesota Medical School.

Such men were exhilarating company for the young Dr. Will, who must have found it a little breathtaking to be so quickly admitted to close association with them, but if so, the odds are they did not know it.

It was the custom for the committees on surgery, medicine, diseases of women, and the other nascent specialties to ask society members to send in accounts of their most interesting cases during the year, and their replies made up the committee reports at the following meeting, as well as the bulk of the published *Transactions*. Curiously, Dr. W. W. Mayo was never among those responding. He reported cases to the society, but in independent communications and not through the medium of any of the committees, not even when he was a member of one of them.

But now from the committee on which Dr. Will was serving came a "Report of Drs. W. W. and W. J. Mayo," and each year thereafter the Mayos furnished at least one paper for the program.

## 16

There was stimulation for Dr. Will in his association with this group of medical men, among whom the conflict between the old and the new in medicine was very marked. The pioneers of the Minnesota profession, men of the Old Doctor's generation, were, like him, still active in society councils, serving on committees and presenting occasional papers, but leadership was clearly passing into the hands of younger men who had seen enough of the new medicine to know that it was good and so were impatient with their elders' slowness in accepting it.

Some of these younger men, like Dr. Millard and Dr. James H. Dunn of Minneapolis, soon to be named professor of surgery at the University of Minnesota, had made a tour of European clinics and returned to view with cleared eyes the practices still prevailing in Minnesota.

Dr. Dunn was a particularly good friend to Will Mayo, who thought him the most learned surgeon of his time in the Northwest. "He used to come down to see us at Rochester, and he was always cold. We would build a fire in the grate, and he would drop into a chair in front of the fire, resting apparently on the back of his neck, stretch out his long, thin legs to the blaze and become reminiscent." Yes, he had seen many new and interesting things in Europe and in New York. "The funny thing about it," he would say, "is that when I get off and see these things, I make up my mind that I am going to do them, and when I come home I find myself sliding back into the old ways I have always used and have confidence in."

Such inert content with the old ways must have developed later in his life, for at this period he was a ready whip on the flanks of plodding colleagues. Extremely honest and outspoken, he spared no man his scorn whose amiable backwardness or lack of professional integrity aroused it.

But stronger in influence than natives like Dunn were several doctors of European birth and training whom the stream of immigration was bringing into the community. Most of them came from Germany and Scandinavia, where they had received a thorough grounding in the disciplines of scientific medicine and antiseptic surgery, the like of which had nowhere been available to their new Minnesota associates. As far as possible they practiced European methods, and to the degree their abilities allowed they brought a quickening contact with European medicine to the doors of Minnesota doctors.

## 17

When Dr. Will came home from medical school confused and uncertain about the merits of Listerism, he found his father's opinion and practice against it. The Old Doctor was careful to sponge out the abdomen after removing a tumor and to keep the contents of the cyst from spilling over into the peritoneal cavity, but he was not using antiseptics. At the end of two of his ovariotomy records stand brief notes that by their very presence suggest defiant rejection: "No antiseptics other than cleanliness" and "No antiseptics." Although the notes were undoubtedly made when the operations were done, in 1880 and 1883, they were not omitted when the records were published in 1885. The Old Doctor had not yet changed his mind.

If Dr. Mayo was not using Listerism it is safe to say that no practitioner in the immediate vicinity of Rochester was, and if young Will turned to the profession in the state at large, what he heard was not likely to settle his mind. In its report for 1880 the committee on surgery declared that it had been "unable to learn of a single case in which the Lister method has been followed in this State." The chairman went on to say complacently that "in this pure and bracing air and comparatively thinly settled country, there does not seem to be the need for that strict and methodical attention to the Listerian details that may have been found necessary in some crowded hospitals . . . whose very walls reek with the effluvia of generations of patients."

In that same year the letter of the committee on gynecology also requested expressions of opinion on Listerism. Only four replies were received, of which just one favored the new method—and that one came from a man who said he had as yet had no cases in which to test it.

Then in 1883 two voices sounded in the wilderness. Dr. Millard, as president of the society, declared positively for Listerism and said he believed the tendency to decry it was due to misinterpretation of its principles. At the same session a newcomer to the state, Dr. C. H. Hunter, just returned from a period of study under Lister himself, demonstrated the method before the assembled surgeons and gave a highly intelligent explanation of the ends to be sought. He made the point clearly that "the essentials of the method are an aseptic condition of the part to be operated on, of the operator and his instruments, and of all things that come in contact with the wound from beginning to end. . . . Neither the gauze nor the spray makes the method. A dirty finger or knife is much more dangerous than the absence of both." He concluded with an arrow straight to his target: "That other objection, that though all very well in old and crowded hospitals, there is no need of such care in the pure atmosphere of the Northwest, will be much more cogent when surgeons here cease to report deaths from long-continued suppurations, erysipelas, pyaemia, and allied diseases."

Except among the younger progressives practicing in the Twin City hospitals, the method made slow headway, and zealous champions more than once locked horns with stubborn opponents. In 1887 Dr. Dunn let loose his impatience. Graphically he contrasted what he had seen in European hospitals with the "torrents of pus" still flowing in the cases of Minnesota diehards. Scornfully he pointed out the stupidity of those who claimed that perfect cleanliness was all they needed. Could they not understand that *perfect* cleanliness was the very end sought by Listerism and was possible only through antiseptic sterilization? It took intelligence to become a true antiseptic surgeon, and perhaps most doctors could never be anything more than "men of gauze and germicides."

Association with Dunn and his fellows was undoubtedly one of the forces that brought Dr. Will off the fence, and the reports and books his brother brought home from Chicago were probably another. One of the books the brothers found helpful was Robert Morris' *How We Treat Wounds Today*, a practical manual of antisepsis, published in 1886, a sort of recipe book telling how to prepare the various solutions, dressings, and the like.

To those influences can be added Dr. Will's experience in New

# The Mayo Brothers

York. In the fall of 1885 he returned to New York for another post-graduate course, this time at the Polyclinic, where the courses in surgery were taught by Drs. John A. Wyeth and Arpad Gerster, and to Gerster more than anyone else Dr. Will said he owed his understanding and, one may suppose, his acceptance of antisepsis. He certainly would have seen it at its best in Gerster's clinics.

Gerster was of European birth and training, a Hungarian who had learned the new surgery in Volkmann's clinic at Halle when he stopped off there on the way to America in 1874. So thoroughly had its discipline become a part of him that he was one of the few who could have been the unnamed surgeon said to have winced at the clapping and stamping his surgical performance elicited and to have turned to say to the amphitheater, "Gentlemen, your applause is gratifying, but you have killed the patient." Gerster considered the crowded audiences and trooping assistants of the Polyclinic so unsuited to good surgery that he preferred not to operate there but to take his small private classes with him to Mt. Sinai Hospital, where he could keep conditions under better control.

He found that most of the students were interested only in therapy, in precisely what to do for this or that and when to do it. They cared little about the basic whys. "There was, however," he recalled, "among them an 'elite' of distinguished intellects, who by evident and gratifying signs showed a preference for fundamental pathological facts, a knowledge of which is the only basis for a sound therapy. One of these was William J. Mayo."

Gerster's teaching made a deep impression on Dr. Will. "It was a happy day for me when I came under his influence, and I shall always have for him reverence and respect." His influence on young Mayo's mastery of the antiseptic method was exercised as much through his book, *The Rules of Aseptic and Antiseptic Surgery,* published in 1887, as through personal contact. Dr. Will said he practically learned that book by heart. It ran quickly through three large editions, was the most talked-of book of its time in medical circles, and may well have been the strongest single factor in promoting the spread of the practice of antisepsis.

For Gerster stated simply, clearly, and convincingly the case for a discipline that might seem irksome until it had been mastered, and

236

more important still he described all the steps in the "handicraft of asepticism." He told the country doctor exactly what equipment he would need and how he should use it to turn a farmhouse kitchen or bedroom into an aseptic operating room—how many and what size tin dishpans or enamel basins he would need and how he could nest them for convenience in transportation, how to suspend the syringe full of antiseptic solution from the bedpost or the chandelier above the table, how to fold and arrange towels as a trough to carry the fluid from the wound into buckets placed on the floor below, and so on. The special procedures to be used in each one of the common operations were carefully described, and most of them were illustrated by photographs of Gerster demonstrating them.

The writing of this eminently practical little book was begun and some of the photographs taken during the month of October 1885, when Dr. Will was attending Gerster's clinics, and it always pleased him greatly that he was to be seen among the bystanders in one of the pictures.

## 18

Surgical skill was not W. J. Mayo's only ability to show itself in these beginning years. When he came home from medical school his parents were in debt, in part for the microscope bought years before and for a horse already dead, and perhaps in part for the costs of Will's own schooling. The young man soon put an end to the financial stringency. He was as willing as his father to give his services without charge when it was necessary, but he was methodical in charges and collections and felt no qualms about insisting on payment if the patient could afford it. Moreover, money did not slip so easily and unproductively through his fingers as it had through his father's, and of course as the double practice grew there was more and more money coming in.

Improvements in the offices followed each other in rapid succession. Rooms more easily accessible to patients were taken on the first floor of the Cook Block, and repainting, refurnishing, and recarpeting kept the community agog. Gas lighting and running water were put in, and heat was piped in from the new boilers of the Cook House next door.

Life at home was easier and more pleasant too. The Mayos entertained more often, and the Old Doctor began the frequent and extensive travels that filled much of his later years. From 1884 on he seems not to have missed a single convention of the American Medical Association, no matter where it was held. His wife began to get away too, to spend a winter in Florida, or to visit relatives in Michigan.

Dr. W. J. Mayo allowed himself little time for recreation. There were occasional parties, sometimes a camping trip to Lake Elysian, a wintertime jaunt to the gay ice carnival in St. Paul, or a day spent with young friends "ruralizing" around the lake at Oronoco. Perhaps he joined his brother and a young man friend or two on some of the occasions when they chipped together and rented a gig and a boat to give their best girls an outing.

Dr. Will's best girl was the chubby, red-cheeked, dark-haired daughter of Eleazer Damon, pioneer resident of Rochester, the town's jeweler, and at intervals one of its aldermen. Quiet, even shy, good-natured, and content with home and its duties, Hattie Damon agreed happily to Will Mayo's proposal of marriage, and the wedding took place on the young doctor's return from New York in 1884. According to the custom of the day, a friend conveyed his felicitations through a newspaper item:

A pleasant interruption to the daily routine of events was the occasion of the marriage of Miss Hattie May Damon to Dr. W. J. Mayo . . . at the residence of the bride's parents on Glencoe street, Thursday evening, Nov. 20. The skill of fair fingers had made the parlors beautiful with rare flowers and plants and tasteful decorations. In one corner was arranged a canopy of filmy lace of rare pattern, from the center of which depended a dove. On the wall [was] the monogram "D.M.," and in the opposite corner of the second parlor were displayed the bridal presents, elegant and costly, and withal useful, showing that none had forgotten. . . . The ceremony was performed by Rev. Mr. Bradshaw in his happiest style, and after many hearty congratulations came the call to the dining room. Here was displayed a table laden with all that could constitute a feast, and 'mid the fragrance of fruits and flowers the bride for the first time sits as a guest at her father's board. Happy pair! Happy evening. The memory of it will long linger in the hearts of all present, and as the recurring seasons follow on bringing as they will to all the care and pleasure, joy and pain, may they be so blended in your lives that the highest and best in life and character may result. M.

The young couple bought themselves an "elegant cherry bedroom set" and moved into the old Mayo house on Franklin Street. Mingled joy and grief did follow. In May 1885 Dr. Will's beloved sister Phoebe died from the splenic disorder that had made her an invalid for seven years, and it became a source of keen regret to him that he did not know then what he later learned about the spleen, for he could have saved her life by an operation. In March 1887 the young couple proudly announced the birth of a daughter, Carrie, but their joy in the coming of a son in August 1889 was cut short by the baby's death three months later.

The small cottage home did not satisfy the rising young doctor for very long. He bought the property at the corner of College and Dakota streets, on the site of the present College Apartments, tore down the old brick house, and ordered the construction of a model house and barn. When the building was finished the townsfolk were impressed with the size and arrangement of the barn, the elegance and spaciousness of the house, the three large fireplaces topped by handsome mantels, the covered driveway, the speaking tube from house to barn, the not yet common conveniences of gas light and city water. Dr. W. J. Mayo believed, as have enterprising business and professional men since the days of the Renaissance, that investment in the appearances of success pays good returns.

## 19

By so much accomplishment in professional and personal life was the elder of the Mayo brothers ahead of the younger when Charlie graduated from the Chicago Medical College and in his turn settled into practice at Rochester. By this time the state standards had been raised and the law tightened, so that Charlie's first task was to pass the examination required of every candidate for a license to practice in Minnesota, regardless of what diploma he held.

On the first Tuesday of April, following his graduation in March 1888, he appeared before the examiners at the capitol in St. Paul. The examination was long and hard, covering nearly a dozen branches of medicine, and of the twelve applicants only a few passed, but Charlie was among them and returned home with license in hand.

He fitted easily and naturally into the partnership, for he had been working in the office during summer vacations at such tasks as blowing the sulphurated gas that doctors were then using to treat tuberculosis. It may have taken a little time for the father and older brother to realize that Charlie need no longer play the assistant, but his surgical ability, quickly recognized by Dr. Will, soon put things right.

With the patients it was his turn to face the toe-in-the-door days that were all but over for Dr. Will, and in his case too the normal skepticism was aggravated by his youthful appearance. So for a while, as he confessed, he wore whiskers "like an old buffalo robe" to make himself look older. Speaking of those early days, he told how the patients "would talk through a crack in the door, and I would put my foot in it so they couldn't close it, and would explain that father was busy or called away. Could I do anything for them? I would, when given the chance, give a thorough examination with all my instruments, and it would take me quite a while, whereas father could detect the trouble offhand, and consequently by the time I had finished they would remark that I had given them the best examination they had ever had."

Almost immediately Dr. Charlie took over the surgery of the eyes. He was so much better at it, according to Dr. Will, that for the good of all concerned it was turned over to him. And soon he too had a patient to stump the countryside for him. A fighting Irishman living about three miles out from Rochester engaged the Drs. Mayo to remove the cataract from one of his eyes, but he wanted it saved so he could show it to his friends. Accordingly, Dr. Charlie wrapped it up in a little piece of oiled silk for Mike's convenience in carrying it. But since Mike had not yet got his glasses, he lost the bit of tissue without knowing it and thought the oiled silk was it. He had several fights trying to make his friends believe that piece of silk was what Dr. Charlie had taken out of his eye, and was convinced of his error only in the police court.

Unfortunately Charlie had barely started his professional activities when they were halted by illness. Probably more exhausted than he knew by the strain of intensive study, he fell a victim to whooping cough and could not get over it. When the racking cough hung on for nearly six months, his parents decided that he needed a change of scene.

Judge Start was about to leave for Europe on a business trip, and it was arranged for Dr. Charlie to make the crossing with him. They set out in January 1889. When he got to England, Charlie went first to his father's birthplace, Eccles, to visit his aged uncle and aunt. Characteristically, what he remembered best from that trip was the turntable of shipping he saw under construction in the canal between Eccles and Manchester. After two days with his relatives he went on to Ireland, where he picked up souvenirs, canes made from the celebrated shillelagh bog oak, for two Irish friends in Rochester.

Then he cut back across England to the Continent for a tour of the hospitals there. Lister was at work in London at the time, but for some reason Dr. Charlie missed seeing him. He did, however, attend a lecture by Pasteur in Paris. "Of course he spoke in French and I did not understand it, but I saw this great man. He had had a mild stroke, and he came in with a little drag to his left leg. He was gray, and wore a tightly fitting skull cap. His face was covered with a short beard. The hall would seat 150, and there were about sixty students present. He sat at a desk while he lectured, and spoke from notes, and most of the time his head was bent forward and down, which greatly muffled his voice and seemed to make it difficult for those present to hear him, for they all listened intently. I felt that to see this man was a great privilege."

In the Continental hospitals, especially those of Germany, Dr. Charlie made special note of the forms of antisepsis in use. The walls of the rooms were lined with large jars full of many different kinds of antiseptic solutions, each a different color; the bigger and better the hospital the more such jars it seemed to display. The operating tables, designed for use in the extremely wet operations then in vogue, were covered with rubber and flanked all around with drain pans to catch the pailsful of plain boiled water, sometimes warm, sometimes cold, that was sloshed generously over everything in sight. The surgical staff all wore rubber boots. Much emphasis was being placed on the careful scrubbing of the surgeon's hands and the cleaning of his nails, and a few men were already using gloves, white cotton ones that were boiled after each wearing. Asepsis in its present-day form was appearing.

Refreshed in mind and well again in body, Dr. Charlie returned home, to make good use of what he had seen abroad in the small hospital under construction in Rochester, as a delayed but direct result of the best known incident in the whole Mayo story, the tornado.

# CHAPTER TEN

# By Act of God and the Sisters of St. Francis

Tuesday, August 21, 1883, was a very hot day in Rochester. Weary and restless in the stifling heat, the residents hopefully watched black storm clouds pile up in the west late in the afternoon.

About six o'clock Will and Charlie Mayo, their day's work done, hitched a fast little mare to the light buggy and started for the slaughterhouse to get a sheep's head upon which to practice eye operations that night. As they drove along the narrow road through the woods north of town they watched the rolling clouds and remarked on their peculiar formation; they seemed to ray upward in three directions from a very black center.

When the young men reached their destination they found the slaughterhouse closed and the butchers starting for home. They were leaving early because of the impending storm, they said, and they advised Will and Charlie to make for their own home quickly in order to escape it.

Turning around to start back, the brothers saw the huge whirling cloud, funnel-shaped now, moving toward them, saw buildings sucked into its maw like wheat into a thresher and the pieces blown out in all directions like chaff. In alarm they whipped the mare to a gallop across the path of the storm, just in time too, for they got barely a block past the Zumbro River bridge when it was torn from its moorings by the wind and smashed to bits. As they crossed the railroad tracks on Broadway a grain elevator toppled and cars careened crazily down the rails. The din was terrible as planks, shingles, bricks, tree limbs, everything, went flying helter-skelter in the gale.

As they passed the intersection of Broadway and Zumbro Street the heavy cornice was ripped off the Cook House opposite and hurtled down upon the dashboard at their feet, bouncing off and breaking the wheels and shafts of the buggy. The terrified horse, loosed from the carriage, bolted down Zumbro Street and into an alley, and when the brothers jumped out to follow they were literally blown along the way. They took shelter in a blacksmith's shop just as its tin roof whirled away over their heads. They hugged the wall with the horse and watched until the wind subsided. Then they started for home, but turned back to run with other people when they heard there were dead and injured in north Rochester.

As in a detective story, the time of the tornado can be fixed by a stopped clock; the whirl of wind had picked up a little desk clock in some home west of town and set it down a block away, unbroken but with its hands stopped at twenty-four minutes to seven.

Considerable damage had been done in many parts of town, but north Rochester, called Lower Town, was a shambles. Scarcely a house was left standing, and the slaughterhouse was in ruins. The work of rescue began at once. With lanterns men searched out the dead and wounded and carried them into hotels or offices and some forty of them into the convent of the Sisters of St. Francis, where they were laid on the parlor floors until cots could be set up.

The doctors were quickly on the job, in the private homes to which they had been called, in their own offices, or in the hotels used as first-aid depots. Dr. W. W. Mayo, assisted by George Weber the druggist, took charge at the Buck Hotel, near the Chicago and Northwestern station on the edge of Lower Town, while Dr. Will and Charlie worked with those brought into the Mayo office. All night long the work went on, women helping too by preparing beds, bandages, medicine, and food.

Early the next morning at a mass meeting held in one of the town halls the mayor put the management of the relief work into the hands of a citizens' committee headed by Judge Start. The most pressing need was a suitable place for the care of the wounded, so Rommel's dance hall on Broadway near Center Street and the nearby lodge rooms of the German Library Association were turned into hospital quarters. Perhaps to avoid offending the physicians by singling out one of them, Dr. David Berkman, the veterinary son-in-law of Dr. Mayo, was named steward of the hospital to take charge of supplies and nurses.

Under his supervision wires were strung and curtains hung to divide the floor space into rooms, beds and bedding were moved in and made up by the women who had volunteered as nurses, and then the wounded were brought in from the scattered quarters they had occu-' pied during the night. By eleven o'clock thirty-four patients were established in the improvised hospital, and the doctors went to work on their gashes and fractures.

But before long there was friction. The doctors could not agree on what should be done for the patients. One of them who had heard somewhere that an emetic should be given the first thing in case of accident ordered that treatment for all the injured. Dr. Mayo was outraged by the idea—and also no doubt by the man's crass assumption of authority. When the fellow stubbornly persisted, the Old Doctor issued an ultimatum, "Either he gets out or I do." Clearly someone must be put in command, and the city council named Dr. Mayo to take charge of the hospital, with Dr. Berkman continuing as steward.

At once Dr. Mayo saw the need for a better organization of the nursing staff. The volunteers were willing enough, but they could not be depended on because they had homes and families to look after. It was urgently necessary to find nurses who could give their entire time to the job. He thought of the one hundred or so teaching Sisters of St. Francis who were at home in the motherhouse for the summer vacation; some of them ought to be available.

Next morning Dr. Mayo appeared early at the convent and said to the mother superior in his offhand way, "There ought to be a sister down there to look after those fellows," meaning the injured or perhaps the nurses, it is not clear which. Agreeing at once, Mother Alfred appointed two sisters to the task, and from then on until the hospital was closed, sisters supervised the nursing.

Meanwhile the dead and the destitute were receiving attention elsewhere. Mass obsequies had been held for a score of dead buried in a single day; three or four more died later from their injuries. To take care of those whose homes had been destroyed a storeroom near Lower Town was made into a public mess hall, where generous housewives, grocers, and bakers provided food, and public halls downtown were turned into temporary sleeping quarters.

The response was generous to the call sent out for relief funds. Minneapolis and St. Paul each subscribed $5,000, Chicago $10,000, Winona and St. Cloud each $3,000. Communities in Dakota to which

Rochester had sent help when grasshoppers stripped their fields a few years before now gave socials and entertainments to raise funds to return the kindness.

All told, the relief committee collected $60,441.51. With this they furnished clothing for 253 families, rebuilt 119 houses, and gave to each family about seventy-eight dollars toward new furniture. Thus gradually through the fall and winter Rochester life returned to normal.

2

But the act of God had left an idea in the mind of the mother superior of the Sisters of St. Francis.

It was by a long road westward that this order of nuns had reached Rochester. In 1829 a daughter was born to a locksmith in the Grand Duchy of Luxemburg, and she was named Mary Catherine Moes. Since her sister was also called Catherine, she later chose the name of Josephine. At a boarding school in Metz she learned the accomplishments proper to young ladies: French and German, singing, painting, tapestry and wax work, and embroidery. But Josephine Moes had too much iron in her character to rest content practicing such dainty arts. She decided to go to America to labor for the conversion of the Indians.

In the United States she joined the Sisters of the Holy Cross at Notre Dame, Indiana, taking the habit as Sister Alfred in 1854. But things were not all to her liking there, and a few years later she transferred her allegiance to the Third Order of the Sisters of St. Francis, joining a group teaching school at Turkey Creek, Indiana. From there she moved on to become the mother superior of a new Franciscan congregation at Joliet, Illinois, and when she had brought that to maturity and a position of influence she set out to open a convent school in Minnesota.

After a survey of the possibilities, she chose a location in Owatonna and signed the contracts for the building. But when Father O'Gorman's two Rochester parishes raised nearly three thousand dollars to buy a site, Mother Alfred decided that the Joliet sisters could afford to build two new schools. The academy in Owatonna was opened in September 1877 and that in Rochester the following December. A few weeks later the bishop of Chicago separated the Minnesota workers from the Illinois motherhouse, and Mother Alfred with twenty-four sisters formed the new Congregation of Our Lady of Lourdes.

Though the life of postulants in pioneer sisterhoods was hard, with wood and water to carry, snow to shovel, soap to make, and a vast amount of other work to do, the new congregation did not lack recruits. Among the first of these, in a group invested with the habit on August 6, 1878, was Mary Dempsey of St. John's parish, Rochester, who took the name of Sister Joseph.

By 1883 the Sisters of St. Francis of the Congregation of Our Lady of Lourdes numbered nearly one hundred members and were conducting an academy and a day school in Rochester, an academy in Owatonna, and a score of other missions scattered through Minnesota, Ohio, Missouri, and Kentucky. They were ready for new enterprises.

Shortly before the tornado the Right Reverend John Ireland, Bishop of St. Paul, in whose diocese Rochester then lay, suggested to Mother Alfred that the sisters might build a hospital in Rochester. The idea did not then appeal to her overmuch, because her sisters were trained for teaching, not nursing, but she thought better of it during the dreadful August days of 1883, made so much more difficult by the lack of adequate hospital facilities. Rochester needed a hospital, it would be a worthy enterprise for the sisterhood, and if it was a costly and difficult departure, so much the better perhaps. It would test their mettle.

Sometime after the temporary hospital was closed Mother Alfred paid a visit to Dr. W. W. Mayo. Did he not think it would be well to build a hospital in Rochester? His reply was quick and positive: The city was too small to support a hospital, it would cost a great deal, and there was not much likelihood of its success.

But Mother Alfred had made up her mind. Quietly she overruled the Old Doctor's objections and said that if he would promise to take charge of a hospital the sisters would finance it. When he insisted that it might cost as much as forty thousand dollars, she replied that they would spend that and more if necessary. Then, asking him to begin drawing up plans for the building, she went away.

So, according to the best evidence available, was St. Mary's Hospital conceived. The misconception that the Mayos were originally responsible for the venture got started early, and efforts to correct it have been unavailing. In an address at the hospital in 1894 Dr. W. W. Mayo made a special point of telling the story of Mother Alfred's visit and their conversation, and in 1904 he addressed a letter to the general public through the newspaper, hoping to establish the truth once and for all, that "the Sisters of St. Francis are to be credited with the inception [of the hospital] and the funds for its building" and that he acted merely as an agent to carry out their wishes.

## 3

It is not surprising that Dr. Mayo did not at once enthusiastically agree to the idea of a hospital in Rochester; he may well have thought Mother Alfred a visionary to propose such a thing. Hospitals ranked low in public favor then. Maintained for the indigent by a government agency, by some charitable foundation, or by a medical college for the purpose of providing material for clinical teaching, they were usually grim and gloomy places in which care was intermittent and sometimes entirely lacking. When trained nurses were few, the hospital could in nowise match the personal attention and interest of good home nursing. Then too, the records of even the best hospitals in the days before antisepsis fostered the general impression that one did not go to a hospital to get well but simply to die. Not long since, surgeons themselves in reporting their mortality rates had asked allowances for "the disadvantages of a hospital atmosphere."

So hospitals were not sought as sanctuaries by the suffering members of the upper and middle classes but were essentially charity asylums for the sick poor who had no place else to go and no one to look after them. They were classed with poorhouses, jails, and insane asylums.

Antisepsis, increased use of surgery, and the coming of the trained nurse were working a transformation, but it would take time to change the public mind, to make hospitals attractive even to the most affluent and transfer the care of the sick from the home and family to the hospital and trained nurse.

What hospitals there were in Minnesota in 1883 were concentrated in the Twin Cities and were not of a sort to attract paying patients. There were three in St. Paul, "one an achievement, one a hope, and one a promise." The achievement was St. Joseph's Hospital, the oldest and without doubt the largest and best equipped in the state; the hope was the City and County Hospital maintained jointly by St. Paul and Ramsey County; and the promise was the Episcopalian St. Luke's, recently divorced from the orphan asylum that had been a part of it since its founding. It was housed in an old-fashioned residence, and except for a man who acted as druggist and general factotum, one woman constituted its entire staff—superintendent, nurses, and dietitian all in one.

In Minneapolis there were the Cottage Hospital, begun as a dispensary "for supplying the deserving poor with medicine and advice, gratis," a maternity hospital for unmarried mothers, and the Northwestern Hospital for women and children, staffed entirely by women doctors and serving most of its patients free of charge, though some "paid a trifle each."

Outside the Twin Cities Duluth had one hospital, recently opened by the Episcopal Church, and in Winona "an old house down in the lower part of the city, dismal, lonely, and equipped with an old corded bedstead was all that the city could show in the way of appliances to lighten the sufferings of the unfortunate."

That was the lot in Minnesota when Mother Alfred announced her plan. There was not a hospital worthy of the name, even by that day's standards, in the whole expanse of southern or western Minnesota— nor beyond in Dakota, although two or three Sisters of St. Benedict were offering care to the sick in a few hotel rooms in Bismarck.

As it turned out, that very fact provided a large tributary area from which a Rochester hospital could draw its patients, but this possibility seems not to have occurred to Dr. Mayo. Considering only the immediate vicinity, he thought building a hospital in so small a town was a very risky venture. As of course it was. To see it through took courage, a strong will to serve, and the sort of optimistic faith in the future of the community that marks the pioneer at his best.

### 4

For nearly four years the hospital remained just an idea, but it was not forgotten. It could not be. The tornado had scarred the mind of Rochester, and for years afterward every approaching storm raised the awful fear of another catastrophe. Frightened women made their husbands dig cyclone cellars and hurried their families into them every time the wind rose, and such recurring alarms kept alive the thought that it would be well to have a hospital before nature struck again.

Meanwhile by hard work and frugal living the Sisters of St. Francis were accumulating funds. Every cent the missions could save was sent to the motherhouse, and to send more they encouraged donations of food and clothing and took in extra work for pay, the sisters spending their scant leisure in giving music lessons or crocheting and embroidering linens to be sold. Every durable gift they received that had any monetary value, even old clothes for which they had no use, they brought to the motherhouse when they came for the annual summer retreat.

Carefully Mother Alfred counted the nickels and dimes. Not one more than necessary did she spend for anything except permanent improvements and expansion. The sisters wore rough, two-dollar shoes and habits of coarse cloth, and sat down always to plain, sometimes meager, fare. It is said that five pounds of roundsteak and a fifteen-cent soupbone were a day's supply of meat for a household of some thirty boarders and from twelve to twenty sisters and postulants. Thus, by constant labor and stint, was the building fund for St. Mary's Hospital raised.

At last there was money enough to proceed, and Dr. Mayo chose the site, nine acres just west of the city limits on Zumbro Street. Mother Alfred approved the choice, for the location was far enough out from town to escape the noise and dust of the city streets, yet close enough to be reasonably convenient, and the plot itself had been made pleasant with trees and shrubs, while around it on three sides rose beautiful wooded hills quite unspoiled by human habitation.

At a meeting in the motherhouse on July 26, 1887 the Congregation of Our Lady of Lourdes voted to build the hospital, and four months later the purchase of the property was concluded, the sisterhood paying twenty-two hundred dollars in cash for it.

Now it was time for Dr. Mayo to present his plans for the building, nor did he take take the responsibility lightly; the hospital must be the best and most modern that the means allowed. He and his sons pooled their knowledge of hospitals elsewhere and found that it was not enough, for they had observed more of surgical technique than of hospital construction or management. So the Old Doctor and Dr. Will

249

made a special tour of eastern hospitals to study such matters as floor plans, lighting arrangements, and administrative organization.

They visited among others the new Methodist Episcopal Hospital in Brooklyn, where Dr. Lewis Stephen Pilcher was chief of staff and Dr. Henry P. de Forest the intern who showed them through the building. Long afterward Dr. de Forest recalled this visit by "a gentleman from the West, a physician by the name of Mayo, dressed in a . . . Prince Albert coat of black broadcloth," accompanied by his youthful son.

Out of this experience the Drs. Mayo made up their instructions for the architect, and when the plans came from him they sent them back "once and twice and thrice" until they got exactly what they wanted.

5

Interest rose with the building. Mother Alfred and the Mayos were excited of course. Endlessly they discussed plans and policies and speculated on the prospects of success. When Dr. Charlie expressed the optimistic opinion that the hospital would draw patients from "all these little towns around here," Mother Alfred proudly reported his words to the sisters, who were in need of reassurance, so little did they guess what the future was to bring.

The townsfolk were interested too, and it became quite the thing to do of an evening that summer of 1889 to walk or drive out and see how the hospital was coming along. For those too far away to keep track of the progress for themselves the Rochester papers made periodic reports, lengthening as the structure approached completion into detailed descriptions of the "imposing edifice," three stories high, built of brick with window ledges of roughhewn stone and four balconies on the west and north sides.

They described the entrance: "A flight of stone stairs leads up to the large double doors, over which is a cut plate glass window with the inscription, 'St. Mary's Hospital, conducted by the Sisters of St. Francis.' The doors are placed in a large brick arch, the lower part of which consists of carved stone ornaments."

Then floor by floor: In the basement, dispensary rooms for outpatients, laundry and vegetable rooms, an immense cistern to hold five hundred gallons of water, and especially the "foul air room" of the remarkable ventilating system that makes it "an utter impossibility for foul air to remain in any part of the building." (This last was emphasized as a promise that the building would be free from the usual unpleasant hospital odor.)

On the first floor, offices, reception parlors, dining room, pantry, and the kitchen, equipped with a large cooking range having an eighty-gallon boiler attachment from which hot water will be piped throughout the building.

On the second floor, wards and private bedrooms and the operating room, "a credit to its deviser. Part of the room is built out in the same manner as a bay window, and as it is on the north side the light will fall upon the operating table from the north and the skylights above. Surgeons unite in the opinion that a north light is the proper light for operating purposes, hence this room must be perfect. The floor of the room is inclined a trifle and is so constructed that it can be flooded with water, which instead of running into the adjacent hall, will run into a waste pipe."

And on the third floor, more wards and private rooms (making a capacity of forty-five beds in all), a chapel and sacristy for the sisters' devotions, and a large recreation room "where patients will be able to walk around for exercise, or will be provided with suitable reading matter."

The papers listed too the various bathrooms, closets, clothes chutes, the gaslight fixtures throughout, and the water faucets in the halls for use in case of fire. They were enthusiastic about the artistic staining of all the wainscoting and the beautiful floors of curly maple planed and rubbed to the smoothness of glass and "deadened with two thicknesses of deadening felt, which are laid between the floor and the lining." On the whole, they said, the building is neat, clean, and generally attractive, "as handsome as any residence can be," with every feature designed to make it pleasant and homelike for the sick—an expression of the prevailing impression that hospitals were not so.

That these descriptions are to be taken with salt appears from a note, a little tart in tone, that Sister Joseph inserted in the manuscript Annals of St. Mary's Hospital. She said the editor of one news story, wishing "to give as favorable an account as possible of the new building . . . described as already existing some features that at the time were only hoped for." But in any case the building was as perfect as the experience of the Mayos and the funds of the sisters could make it.

## 6

During the last days of September the sisters began making the building ready for occupants. Sister Sienna, Sister Constantine, and Sister Hyacinth went over every morning, carrying their lunch, and spent the day clearing out rubbish, sweeping, dusting, and scrubbing. Mother Alfred asked the public to help them furnish the rooms and shrewdly promised to acknowledge in the newspapers all gifts received, but the only acknowledgment that appeared was of a gift of books by Mr. Blakeley, the editor of the *Record and Union*.

The hospital opened without formal ceremony, the blessing of the building taking place some weeks afterward. The sisters planned to begin receiving patients on October 1, but the Mayos had an operation to perform the day before and the operating room was ready, so with a fine disregard for pomp and palaver they simply began. The operation was for the removal of a cancer of the eye; Dr. Charles Mayo performed it, Dr. W. J. Mayo assisted, and Dr. W. W. Mayo gave the anesthetic.

Within a week eight patients were admitted, Sisters Sienna, Constantine, Fidelia, and Hyacinth were assigned to duty in the hospital, and Edith Graham, a Rochester girl graduated from the school of nursing at the Women's Hospital in Chicago and the first trained nurse in town, was put in temporary charge of the nursing staff.

According to a policy repeatedly announced, the hospital was open to all sick persons regardless of their color, sex, financial status, or professed religion. It was neither solely a charity asylum nor exclusively a nursing home for the wealthy. It was sometimes referred to, even by the sisters, as a "noble charity," or a "free hospital," but in practice persons of all classes were to be received and given the same care. The accommodation of paying and charity cases in the same institution was an innovation in hospital management. John Shaw Billings had suggested it in his plans for the Johns Hopkins Hospital, but for many years the Baltimore doctors, even those on the hospital staff, took care of their paying patients at home or in little private hospitals.

# Sisters of St. Francis

Nor was St. Mary's intended to be a hospital for Catholics only. When that question was raised, Mother Alfred made the sisters' position quite clear: "The cause of suffering humanity knows no religion and no sex; the charity of the Sisters of St. Francis is as broad as their religion."

And finally, there was no intention of reserving the facilities of the hospital for the patients of the Mayos. True, it had been understood from the beginning that Dr. W. W. Mayo was to be in charge and he and his sons had planned the building and supervised its construction, but that was no cause for surprise. Though the Mayos were not Catholics, they had long worked closely with the priests and the sisters. When the latter established themselves in Rochester they made the Old Doctor their physician, probably on the advice of the parish fathers, and he quickly won their esteem and confidence, so that Mother Alfred turned naturally to him for guidance in all medical matters. Moreover, it must have been clear to her that he stood head and shoulders above any other Rochester doctor in the experience and interests that would bring success in hospital practice.

Dr. Mayo was to be merely the "physician in charge," however. Neither he nor Mother Alfred had any thought of excluding other doctors from St. Mary's Hospital. In all public announcements it was made clear that a patient could choose any doctor he wished, and that the hospital doors were "open to all physicians who wish to put their patients in the institution." But when Dr. Mayo tried to organize a staff he met with evasions and refusals. Although the men he approached were personally friendly to him and collectively welcomed the hospital, individually they refused to join in a venture that seemed already doomed.

Doomed because religious fanaticism was breeding antagonism to it. Increasing immigration was causing a resurgence of nativism in the United States, especially in the Middle West. The American Protective Association, successor to the Know-Nothings, forerunner of the Ku Klux Klan, and the most rabid anti-Catholic movement in the history of the nation, had been organized at Clinton, Iowa, in 1887 and had spread into the states immediately to the north and east. Seeing the bogey man of papal imperialism behind the door of every Catholic home and institution, the A.P.A., as it was popularly known, fanned Protestant and nationalist bigotry to a flame by forged documentary evidence of Catholic plans and falsified reports of Catholic strength in American politics.

The A.P.A. was strong in Minnesota, particularly in Minneapolis and Duluth. Its existence in Rochester is nowhere evident in the local newspapers, but its being a secret society may account for that. The Mayos remembered that it was present and ascribed much of the early opposition to St. Mary's Hospital to its influence. Ardent Protestants would have none of an institution that was managed by black-robed nuns and in which there was a chapel set aside for the exercises of popery, and they viewed with suspicion the alliance of the Drs. Mayo with the Sisters of St. Francis.

Alarmed by this sentiment and its threat to the success of the hospital, which had become very dear to his heart, the Old Doctor asked his friend, John Willis Baer, a prominent member of the Presbyterian church but a man above fanaticism, to become the nominal superintendent of the hospital in order to overcome the prejudice of the Protestants. Mr. Baer (who later became the president of Occidental College in California) goodnaturedly acceded to Dr. Mayo's request and for some weeks made frequent and ostentatious visits of inspection to the hospital—ostentatious until he got inside, where he became very unobtrusive indeed.

How much effect Mr. Baer's activity had in allaying Protestant prejudice is unrecorded, but it was not enough to persuade the Rochester doctors to accept staff positions. And it must certainly have aggravated the antagonism of some of the Catholics, who thought they too had a grievance in the sisters' choice of a non-Catholic doctor to manage their enterprise.

There was one Catholic practicing medicine in Rochester, a graduate of McGill University and a member of one of the town's most prominent Catholic families. But he was young, about the age of Dr. Will, and he made only occasional attempts at surgery. He seemed hardly qualified to head a hospital, and he himself seems to have felt no pique at being passed over. He maintained friendly relations with the Mayos, continued to consult them in his practice, and called them to attend him when he was ill. But his family and friends thought he should at least have been consulted in the making of plans and policies for St. Mary's Hospital. And looking back, the Mayos admitted that the matter had not been tactfully handled. In their zeal and enthusiasm they had not thought to ensure support by seeking the advice of others.

## 7

That milk was spilled, however, and the Mayos now had on their hands the whole responsibility for the success of the hospital, and that without the support of a united community. To make matters still worse, they did not have the full support of the Sisters of St. Francis either.

Mother Alfred was a woman of unusual intelligence, courage, and vision, and perhaps for that very reason, she may sometimes have been highhanded in her plans for the sisterhood. For the most part the sisters backed her decisions loyally, but the hard work and meager living exacted by the hospital venture frayed some tempers. A few of the sisters considered this departure from their teaching mission, especially now that its success was in doubt, a sign of advancing age and lessening wisdom in their mother superior. They complained bitterly to Archbishop Ireland, as he now was, and finally, although he had encouraged the undertaking, he arbitrarily retired Mother Alfred as mother superior in the late summer of 1889 and appointed Sister Matilda in her place.

After staying on at the motherhouse long enough to help her successor get a firm hold on the reins, Mother Alfred went to take personal charge of St. Mary's Hospital on November 5, 1889. She knew though that she could not hope to guide the destinies of this creature of hers for long, and before she resigned control of the congregation she arranged for the transfer to the hospital of a young sister whose remarkable abilities were already manifest to her discerning eye. Sister Joseph, the Mary Dempsey of Rochester who had taken the habit in 1878, was recalled from her teaching at the mission in Ashland, Kentucky, to take up nursing duties at St. Mary's Hospital on November 19, 1889.

Mother Alfred remained in charge until August 1890, when she was replaced by Sister Hyacinth, who in turn gave way to Sister Joseph on September 9, 1892. And a lucky day that was for St. Mary's Hospital.

# The Mayo Brothers

8

Dr. W. W. Mayo was now seventy years old. He was still alert, enthusiastic, and full of energy, and it was he in large measure who still commanded the confidence of patients. But at seventy the slope ahead, however gentle and long, is necessarily downward; the responsibility for success in the new enterprise must rest upon the shoulders of the two younger Mayos. The father became consulting physician and surgeon, and they the attending staff.

Dr. Will had proved himself extraordinarily capable in private practice, and Dr. Charlie, though little more than a year out of medical school, was already showing surgical ability equal to his brother's. But both were entirely without experience in hospital management and practice; neither of them had served an internship. "We were a green crew and we knew it," declared Dr. Will, in reminiscing of those days.

The little band of sisters—four at first, then joined by Sister Joseph within a few weeks, by Sister Sylvester in 1890, and by Sister Fabian temporarily in 1890 and permanently in 1892—were as untried as the doctors, and they were not at all prepared in either disposition or training for hospital service. They were used to nothing more unnerving than the pranks of children in the classroom, and for some of them the first operation they witnessed was a shock that remained a vivid memory for life.

An insight into what these sheltered, sensitive women had to overcome is afforded by the story of Sister Joseph's first major contact with the necessities of nursing. She was asked to assist at the examination of a male patient whose ailment required that his entire body be uncovered for observation. While one of the doctors and Miss Graham worked with him, the young sister stood off in the corner, her back turned, quivering with outrage and shame. As she left the room when the task was done she protested vehemently to Miss Graham that she could never do such work, that she would ask Mother Matilda to send her back to teaching at once. But she stayed on, and quickly learned the lesson that the needs of human suffering transcend the dictates of modesty. In her subsequent management of St. Mary's she was always on guard against prudery among the sisters, where it might lead to neglect in nursing.

To inexperience was added the further handicap of inadequate equipment. Either because the building had exhausted the accumulated funds or because the opposition within the sisterhood prevented further expenditure on the hospital, it opened with the most meager furnishings.

The Mayos equipped the operating room, crudely at first, but well enough to serve their immediate needs. Calling upon his mechanical skill, Dr. Charlie himself fashioned some extra instruments and built an operating table like those he had seen in European hospitals in the spring. He padded the top and covered it with oilcloth, then slanted three boards downward on the sides to carry the fluids into tin drain pans held in position by stirrups at the corners. With large "percolators" to hold the antiseptic solutions, plenty of tin basins in which to rinse instruments and sponges, and an array of syringes for squirting boiled water all around, the room was ready for the wet operations then in vogue.

The responsibility for furnishing the wards and private rooms was the sisters', and they were hard put to it to find the bare necessities. They attempted to open only three small wards and one private room at first. About a dozen iron cots had been provided, three or four dozen unbleached muslin sheets and pillow cases, and a few rough gowns. Outer bedclothing was scarce, so that not the least pressing task in preparing for a patient's coming was to find covering for his bed. The sisters had been given a few heavy quilts of garish pattern and a few others that were lighter and of better quality, but for blankets they had to wait until they earned the money to buy them.

The mattresses did not fit the cots and slipped around so freely on the crude springs that the nurses had to be alert to prevent them from sliding to the floor, carrying the patient and bedclothing with them.

The eight persons admitted in the first week exhausted the number of beds set aside for patients, and the sisters had to give up their own to make room for more. After that at bedtime they dragged out some extra mattresses and made up their sleeping accommodations on the floor.

There was virtually no furniture except beds, not a commode or a dresser in the hospital except one heavy black walnut piece sent over from the convent. The rough wooden stands that held the enamelware washbowls were fitted with oilcloth covers whose edges had been pinked by Mother Alfred herself. Odds and ends of dishes and linens were made to do for the trays at mealtime, and the knives and forks and spoons were heavy iron pieces that had to be scoured after each meal to keep them even passably presentable.

Since there was as yet no gas to fuel the pretty fixtures, the sisters carried lanterns to light their way through the hospital at night and hung one on a tree outside to guide the doctors or any others coming to the hospital after dark.

An elevator shaft had been constructed through the center of the building, but there was no elevator in it and no guards around it, so until a wooden railing could be built to enclose the opening on each floor, sisters came from the convent at night to sit on guard at the gaping holes. There was a dumb-waiter from the kitchen to the upper floors, but half the time it would not work and the sisters had to carry the trays of food up and down on foot.

Water was piped from the city main into a large reservoir in the basement, from which it was pumped by hand when needed. All the water used for cooking, cleaning, baths, and toilets had to be carried upstairs from this basement supply.

The sisters did not always have to carry out the sewage. A surface sewer in the yard behind the hospital took care of that, except when it backed up into the basement, as it did all too frequently. Then the odor summoned the sisters by day or night to come and clean up the mess, and for the next few days, until the cesspool could be put in order again, the long-suffering nuns carried out all the slops. Not until 1898 was the hospital connected with the city sewer system, and then at the sisters' expense.

The location of the hospital was more inconvenient than Mother Alfred had supposed it would be. Zumbro Street at that distance from Broadway was only a country road, ungraded, unpaved, and without bordering sidewalks. Visitors and patients with no conveyance of their own often had to trudge the mile from town on the footpath alongside the road, for Rochester's only hack service was a large yellow wagon that shuttled between the railroad station and the Cook House. Sometimes patients were driven out by the Drs. Mayo or in their absence by Jay Neville, now the general handy man around the doctors' offices.

The sisters walked into town each day to do their marketing, usually after supper, and they carried their own parcels home, for Rochester had no free delivery service yet. It had no telephone system either, and if it was suddenly necessary to call the doctors, as on one well-remembered occasion when a patient got hysterical beyond the nurses' ability to control him, one of the sisters had to leave her work and carry the message on foot to the Mayo office or home.

Those devout souls minded the distance from town most sorely when it kept them from religious services on Sunday. They tried to plan their work so that half of them could get away to walk in for the early mass and the other half for the later service, but their duties did not always permit such depletion of the staff. Sometimes a kindly parishioner would drive out to fetch them in his carriage after he had taken his family to church.

## 10

Against such odds of hardship, physical and mental, the faithful sisters worked with unflagging energy. Entirely without outside help, except for the sporadic assistance of some itinerant janitor whose incompetence was endured only because he worked for a pittance, these women carried an incredible load of hard labor. Their day ordinarily began at three or four o'clock in the morning and continued until eleven or twelve at night, and every third or fourth morning they rose at two o'clock to get the laundry work out of the way before the regular routine of the day began. The operating-room linen had to be taken care of every day of course, so it was washed and ironed in the evening between supper and bedtime.

After the first few weeks the sisters took over all the nursing as well as the housekeeping tasks. Since the Mayos had employed Edith Graham to assist them in their office practice and had merely loaned her services to the hospital to get the work started, she taught the sisters the rudiments of their new work in informal little classes, and then gradually shifted the care of the patients into their hands.

Her own work as far as the hospital was concerned came to be the giving of anesthetics. The Drs. Mayo saw no reason why an intelligent nurse could not be an able anesthetist, and since Miss Graham had not learned the art in nursing school, Dr. W. W. Mayo undertook to teach her how to administer chloroform. She learned the trick all right, but she was still so young that nervous patients did not trust her, so to calm their fears the Old Doctor continued to stand by her side while she gave the anesthetic.

On the mornings when surgery was scheduled Miss Graham would go to St. Mary's early, see that everything was properly ready in the operating room, and then act as anesthetist and remain with the new patients throughout the day. From then on the sisters were responsible for them. At first they were nervous and a little fearful and would ask Miss Graham please to look in the next morning just to make sure that everything was all right before the Drs. Mayo made their call. But they soon got over that.

When a critical case needed special care at night the sisters took turns at staying up to give it, remaining on duty throughout the next day too, since there were not enough of them for one to be spared in the daytime. A period of two days and the intervening night was not an unusual shift on duty. For the first three years there was no male orderly on St. Mary's staff, and the Mayo brothers added to their heavy practice the responsibility of nursing the male patients who needed special attention. They took turns on night duty, depending on the alarm clock to arouse them from the sleep they dared not entirely forego.

Under such conditions the local editor might well think it worthy of awe that in a succession of four hundred admissions to St. Mary's Hospital there were but two deaths. The dauntless sisters deserve a goodly share of the credit; they helped to make a success of what might for all the surgeons' skill have been a failure—by unceasing toil, by determination to make good, by willingness to offer whatever sacrifice the task demanded.

And also by the inspiration of their faith, no doubt, for to their labors they added prayer. Often while they worked lighted candles in their chapel kept vigil for them. When a critical operation had to be done they sent word to the convent for prayers, and many a rosary was said to bless the surgeon's work while he was operating. The Drs. Mayo did not share the sisters' faith, but they did not scorn it. One time when

Dr. Will was leaving a seemingly hopeless case, he said to Sister Joseph, "I know she can't live, but you burn the candles and I'll pay for them." And—so the story reads—the patient lived.

## 11

The low mortality rate must have helped greatly to overcome the general distrust of hospitals that the Mayos encountered among their patients. They could have kept St. Mary's filled twice over from their practice had not most of their patients shied away from hospitalization, preferring to be ill and convalesce at home.

However, by cajolery, insistence, and repeated explanation of the advantages, they persuaded first a few, then more and more, to enter the hospital. With what apprehension appears from the recollection of the former Miss Graham that "We almost had to lock some of the first patients in their rooms; they were so sure they were going to die if they came to a hospital." By the close of 1889 sixty-two persons had been served by St. Mary's, in 1890 there were three hundred more, and by the close of 1893 the grand total had passed a thousand.

To the great satisfaction of the Drs. Mayo the institution was paying its own way. When they saw the entire responsibility was to be theirs, they determined that the hospital must be self-supporting. There was good reason to believe that the sisterhood would not be willing to make up a deficit should there be one, and the Mayos did not wish to rely on public contributions. They even asked the sisters not to set out the usual little mite boxes for gifts to the poor. They wanted the hospital to earn the money for its own charity, as they did, and to this end they adopted the policy of telling their patients to pay the sisters' bill first and theirs for professional services second.

The hospital rates were eminently reasonable, at least by present-day standards: one dollar a day or six dollars a week for ward beds and from eight to ten dollars a week for private rooms. The receipts for the first eleven months were about eleven hundred dollars, and by thrifty corner-cutting on expenses that sum was made to yield a surplus, which grew larger year by year and financed all improvements.

One of the first uses to which extra money was put was to make the rooms pleasant. Good beds and bedclothing were bought, then rocking chairs, dressers, pictures, and mirrors. Daintier dishes and silverware were purchased for the dinner trays. On September 21, 1891 the first half-dozen silver knives and forks were bought, and the event was carefully recorded in the hospital annals, along with the fact that they were wrapped up between meals for better care.

The Mayos helped too. In 1891 they imported from Berlin a complete set of glazed enamelware operating-room equipment, which they donated to the hospital. That same year the sisters secured permission from the city fathers to set up telephone poles along Zumbro Street from the Mayo offices to the hospital, and Dr. Charlie installed the telephone with the aid of a mechanically minded neighbor boy. He and the same boy also installed the doctors' Christmas gift to the hospital, an electric annunciator by which the patients could summon the nurses when they were needed. The amateur electricians got some of the wires crossed, and at times "the bells would start ringing and would not stop; so the sisters got to carrying shears around with them. If a bell kept on ringing, swsshsh!! would go the wires, and next morning Dr. Charlie would have to resurrect the whole system again."

In that year too the shaft was finally fitted with an elevator. The kindhearted sisters fed a good many tramps in their kitchen, and among these one day was a traveled hobo who described to them a hydraulic elevator he had seen in Paris. Dr. Charlie decided to copy it for the hospital. With the aid of a plumber friend he excavated the necessary depth at the bottom of the shaft and screwed into the hole length after length of pipe, so as to form a sort of syringe. When the water was turned into this contrivance it pushed the elevator upward. But the thrifty Dr. Charlie could not bear to see the water wasted after each trip, so he ran a pipe up along one corner of the shaft into a tank on the roof. Then as the elevator descended it pumped the water up into the tank, from which it was piped into the toilets.

Just one thing was wrong with this elevator; it could be operated only from within the car, and it was sure to be standing at some other level when it was wanted. Once when Dr. Will was injured in an accident and was lame for a few weeks, it was necessary for him to use the elevator to get around in the hospital, and one of the sisters kept watch for his coming every morning so she could "go after the elevator for him."

As the number of patients mounted more help was a necessity, and the number of nursing sisters was increased to eleven, but that was still too few for the work to be done. When requests for more assistance were not granted by the mother superior, Sister Hyacinth in desperation tried the distrusted practice of hiring lay help. She drove into Rochester and searched out two likely girls to work as maids at a wage of six dollars a month.

### 12

The success of the hospital and its ability to support itself seemingly quieted the opposition within the sisterhood. At no time, even in the first months, did a decline in the number of patients provide an occasion for suggesting that the institution be closed, so its continued existence came to be taken for granted.

Antagonism in the community also died away. Late in 1889 Rochester and the Sisters of St. Francis came under the jurisdiction of the newly formed diocese of Winona, of which the Right Reverend Joseph B. Cotter was named the first bishop. A man of wisdom and great tact, he did much to still the ruffled waters, and under his influence the support of the Catholic community was assured.

The noisy Protestant minority subsided too, and for the moment all was serene. Friends of the hospital sponsored a public ball for its benefit and cleared some seventy dollars for its coffers, the Olmsted County commissioners adopted the practice of making a small annual appropriation to the hospital to pay for the care of the county's wards, and the three Masonic lodges in Rochester chipped together to pay one hundred and fifty dollars a year to maintain a free bed at St. Mary's for the use of their members—all pleasant signs that Rochester citizens were forgetting their distrust and suspicion.

Others less pleasant appeared. Some of the townspeople began to show a tendency to use St. Mary's as a pesthouse upon which to dump the heavy and dangerous care of infectious diseases. And gradually some of the Rochester doctors, now that it seemed quite safe, began to use the hospital facilities for their patients. Unfortunately they still seemed to regard the hospital as a last resort and so failed to recommend, or at least to persuade their patients to accept, hospitalization until the patient was at death's door. They probably did not purpose to transfer the death from their own records to that of the hospital, but in effect that was what they were doing.

The mortality rate of St. Mary's Hospital began to rise, just slightly, but enough to alarm the Sisters of St. Francis and no doubt the Mayos too, for they could appreciate how a continuance of this would menace the reputation of the hospital. At last the sisters took a bold step. They ruled that no patient should be admitted to St. Mary's Hospital until he had been examined by one of the Drs. Mayo.

Though the purpose of that ruling was merely to make sure that the privileges of the hospital were not abused, the effect of it was to close the hospital to all but the Mayos and those doctors who were willing to call them in consultation or refer cases to them.

## 13

One who was not so willing was Dr. W. A. Allen, their homeopathic rival. He was intelligent enough to see what an advantage the facilities of St. Mary's Hospital were giving these competitors of his and he was human enough to be jealous. Was there any reason why he could not have a hospital too? There were no other Sisters of St. Francis to provide it, so he would provide it himself.

In the spring of 1892 Dr. Charles T. Granger graduated from the Hahnemann Medical College, passed the state examinations with distinction, and came back to Rochester to begin practice in partnership with the busy Dr. Allen, and the following fall the partners announced that they were about to open a second hospital in Rochester. They rented a large house on the east side of town, remodeled it thoroughly to suit hospital needs, and engaged a matron and a trained nurse from St. Paul to manage it. In November the Riverside Hospital began to receive patients. The newspapers welcomed the new institution heartily because they saw in it more evidence of Rochester's preeminent position as a medical center.

The opening of the Riverside Hospital had no noticeable effect on the patronage of St. Mary's, which had by now entirely outgrown its original capacity and was showing symptoms of dangerous overcrowding. After much discussion and with the encouragement of Bishop Cotter, the Sisters of St. Francis ventured to begin building an addition.

And then the American Protective Association came to life again. A new wave of nativist sentiment swept through the country, reflecting faithfully the peak that immigration had reached in 1892. Feeling spread wide enough and rose high enough to put a number of A.P.A. candidates into office in the election of 1894 on a platform that had few planks not directly or indirectly aimed against Catholic institutions or policies. In this phase the tension was greatly increased by bitter controversy within the Catholic church itself, part of which revolved around the famous Faribault plan for merging public and parochial schools. That plan, of which Archbishop Ireland was the foremost sponsor, had been initiated in Faribault, Minnesota, and copied in a few other communities of the state, including Rochester. It drew the fire of Protestants and Catholics alike and provided ammunition for the A.P.A. guns.

As a result of all the turmoil, local Protestants renewed their vociferous opposition to St. Mary's Hospital and pointed to the rival Riverside as an institution that Protestants and patriots could enter without doing outrage to their convictions by furthering an agency of the hated and alien Catholic church. Drs. Allen and Granger saw their chance; they made a bid for more business by announcing that "contrary to what many suppose, the [Riverside] hospital is not a homeopathic institution, for any regular physician can have the benefit of any of the advantages afforded there, and can take their patients there for operations or care."

At this juncture two important members of the Presbyterian church fell ill, they were taken to the Riverside Hospital, and the Drs. Mayo were called to attend them.

It was a weighty decision the Mayos had to make when that call came in. To refuse it would more or less formally cement their alliance with the Catholic St. Mary's; to accept it would doubtless lead to the division of their practice between the two hospitals, for if they showed a willingness to serve patients at either institution, many would probably choose the non-Catholic hospital. But after all, why should the Drs. Mayo not so divide their practice? It was customary for physicians in eastern cities to hold appointments and attend patients at several hospitals.

But the Mayos were wise enough to see the advantages of centralizing their practice in one hospital under one staff—particularly a hospital and staff they controlled. The Riverside, small in capacity and in staff and so recently improvised from a dwelling, could not possibly offer the facilities or the quality of nursing care they had developed to their own taste at St. Mary's.

Moreover, the Mayos felt a strong moral obligation to the Sisters of St. Francis, who had just lately decided to put all their eggs in the Mayo basket and were even now adding to their investment. To divert a share, perhaps in time the larger share, of their practice to another hospital seemed wrong, a poor return for loyalty and confidence. And finally, the Mayos were not men inclined to knuckle under to public clamor or the pressure of opposition. They refused to attend patients or to operate in the Riverside Hospital. And the centralization of their surgical practice that followed from that decision was a primary factor in their phenomenal success.

## 14

At the time the decision brought them censure and criticism aplenty. One enraged pastor abused them publicly from his pulpit, calling them servants of the Catholics and accusing them of forgetting their sworn duty to the sick. Ostentatiously a section of the community took up the cause of the Riverside. Some thirty women, at the instigation of one of the Protestant ministers, organized a Riverside Hospital Aid Society and met to sew and quilt, gave benefit socials, and made plans to endow a bed for the poor. Given generous publicity in the press, these activities made a great stir.

Through it all, the Mayos were conscious of eyes askance and ears cocked in their direction to catch any sign of their reaction. Wisely, they went quietly on their way, ignoring alike the attacks made on them and the noisy support given to their rivals.

For more than two years the Riverside Hospital prospered, and then suddenly an astonishing announcement appeared in the Rochester paper:

Doctor Allen has been a resident and practicing physician in this city for many years, and has built up a lucrative practice. He has been eminently successful in his profession, and stands among the best physicians in the west. His practice of late has become too great for him, and he cannot give it all the attention that he feels he should, and for that reason he has concluded to drop it entirely and remove to St. Paul, where he will do office work only, acting as a consulting physician. . . .

# Sisters of St. Francis

The doctor's family will remain here until next spring, when they will join him in St. Paul. In the meantime he will visit the city once a week, probably on Saturdays, and will retain the mayoralty of the city. . . . Dr. C. T. Granger will take Dr. Allen's practice here.

A fortnight later, on September 27, 1895, the paper announced that owing to Dr. Allen's removal to St. Paul, the Riverside Hospital had been closed.

Whatever the true cause for Dr. Allen's hasty departure, the closing of the Riverside marked the end of opposition and local competition for St. Mary's Hospital. For it the road ahead now lay smooth and straight, mounting with scarcely a level stretch or a detour to the heights of worldwide service and fame.

Struggling together to succeed despite inexperience, hardship, and hostility, the young doctors and the Sisters of St. Francis had learned to depend upon each other. Forced to it by circumstances, the Mayos had shown that alone they could furnish all the patients the hospital could care for, and the Sisters of St. Francis in turn had demonstrated their ability to give all the doctors could ask in the way of nursing care. The hospital had no need of other doctors; the doctors had no need of another hospital. Each made the decision to rely solely upon the other.

The result, pregnant with consequences, was to give the Mayo brothers a monopoly of the *only* hospital facilities in existence throughout a wide area and the *best* in a still wider one.

# CHAPTER ELEVEN

# Young Doctors from the West

Few would have blamed the Mayo brothers had they settled contentedly into their comfortable berth at St. Mary's Hospital, barring all entrances against the freshening winds without. But then few would have heard of them had they acted so normally. Instead, by persistent efforts they kept the windows open wide and often made their way outside the better to feel the direction and velocity of the winds and to study the fast-changing aspects of the medical heavens.

The star of surgery was rising rapidly. With the advent of antisepsis the volume of operations increased and their scope widened. New procedures were devised, and old routines, abandoned as too risky, were revived, improved, and put into general use. Before Lister a hospital of two or three hundred beds might record four hundred operations a year, with twenty-five per cent of them amputations. After Lister a hospital of equal size might reasonably expect four or five thousand operations a year, with less than one per cent amputations.

The most striking general advance lay in lifting the taboo from the internal cavities of the body. For centuries the abdomen, the chest, and the skull had been forbidden territories to the wise and humane surgeon, but with the risk of infection wiped away he learned that an incision into the interior of the body need be no more dangerous than the amputation of a little finger.

The new attitude appeared first in the expansion of emergency surgery. The doctor faced with an abdomen ripped open by accident no longer hastily pushed the contents back into the cavity and sewed the wound shut, then waited with bated breath to see what nature would do with the mess. Now he could search for the bullet with impunity and remove it if possible, stitch up ruptured intestines, tie bleeding vessels, and in general start the repair of the damage. He dared even invade the abdomen deliberately in order to deal with such threats to life as obstruction of the bowels or a perforating ulcer.

# Young Doctors from the West

With success in emergency cases came the prospect of a surgery of expediency, of operating that would not be just a last desperate throw of the dice with death but a means of restoring health deliberately chosen in the early, curable stages of disease. The use of the knife and needle was about to become an accepted therapeutic measure in many disorders of the stomach, the gallbladder, the lungs, even the central nervous system.

But there was much to be learned first. With the forbidden cavities of the body opened before him the surgeon looked upon an unfamiliar mass of tissues, vessels, and nerves—unfamiliar because they were pulsing with life. To deal with them he must know more about descriptive anatomy and postmortem pathology, but beyond that he needed to learn also the physiology and pathology of the living body.

Just what could he do, where and how much dared he interfere, without jeopardizing bodily functions? Where lay the outer limits of the reserves nature provides to safeguard life? How many feet of the intestines could be removed and still leave enough to carry on the necessary processes? How much of the stomach could the body get along without? Could the pancreas or the gallbladder be spared?

Even when the answers to such fundamental questions were known, there still remained a host of others about the most efficacious techniques. In what position should the patient be placed on the table, where should the incision be made, how should the sutures be put in? If an artificial opening was made to detour the contents of the alimentary canal around an obstruction in the pylorus, where was the best place to make it to be sure it would function successfully?

Many such problems had to be solved by trial and error, and that in large measure on living patients, for animal experimentation was still young and its development was threatened by the noisy horror of antivivisectionists, whose sympathy for dogs overwhelmed their compassion for human beings. By what someone called "autopsies *in vivo*" the surgeons had to perfect and determine the exact uses for all the -otomies, -ostomies, and -ectomies that today confuse the lay reader of surgical literature.

Outstanding German surgeons and Lawson Tait of England boldly led the way. In some operations their results were amazingly good, in some frighteningly bad, but in almost all they were sufficient to demonstrate the possibility of success. So others took up the work of improvement, and there was a rush of progress in abdominal surgery, then in cranial, neurologic, and thoracic surgery.

Men could give their whole time to operating now; specialization in general surgery developed, and the surgeon was differentiated from the physician. In America as well as in Europe outstanding leaders developed great surgical clinics, from which poured a flood of new uses for surgery and to which patients flocked for healing and other surgeons for instruction. Because its results were dramatic and immediate, surgery took the limelight. General medicine, overwhelmed by the precocious brilliance of its latest child, lagged gaspingly behind.

This boom in surgery, at its height from about 1890 to 1910, offered medical men an unprecedented opportunity for fame and fortune. There were broad stretches of new land to be explored by surgical pioneers, trails to be blazed by men of originality and daring. Those who could grasp the skirts of chance would win acclaim among their colleagues for their contributions to knowledge and technique and find many patients among laymen because of their ability to deal successfully with hitherto incurable ailments. The possibility of such outstanding recognition no longer exists in anything like the same degree, for surgical procedures are now more standardized and surgical skill is more widespread.

It was to that situation chiefly that Dr. W. J. Mayo referred in a suggestion for his biographer: "Stress the unusual opportunity that existed in the time, the place, the general setup, not to be duplicated now."

## 2

With all the more determination because of their remoteness from the centers of activity, the Mayo brothers kept eagerly abreast of developments. Blessed with energy and endurance, full of ambition, and keenly aware of their own inadequacies, the two young doctors made time for continued study and travel and seized upon every opportunity to learn from others. They were never averse to confessing ignorance if by so doing they could learn.

The pages of the medical journals bristled with theories and suggestions, and the Mayos read them all diligently and intelligently, with sound judgment sifting the wheat from the inevitable pile of chaff. They attended medical conventions regularly—not to make merry at bar or club, but to listen earnestly to the papers and discussions.

At the session of the section on surgery of the Minnesota State Medical Society in 1891 the audience was apathetic and the discussion of papers desultory. Time and again when no one else was moved to comment, one of the brothers rose to say the paper called for discussion, and then started it off by offering some criticism or a supplementary case history. Sometimes one or two others followed him briefly, but more often no one stirred.

The program droned on to a paper about "Acute Intestinal Obstruction." The speaker considered carefully the possible ways of determining just what kind of obstruction had felled the patient, and then outlined the methods of treatment he thought best: opiates to relieve the pain, hot poultices, leeches or blisters applied to the abdomen, external massage, and enemas of warm water or olive oil. If after a fair trial these measures did not relieve the obstruction, then of course one must resort to surgery.

Surely that would touch off the fireworks!

But the audience just sat. No one rose to comment, and the chairman was about to call for the next paper. Then Dr. Will Mayo took the floor, fire in his eye.

I would like to know what we are here for. We from the country come up here to the city. We accept the hospitality of the gentlemen who live here. We find out that they are royal good fellows, but we come up here to learn something from them. We don't invite them down to our town because we cannot give them the amount of learning and experience, and all that sort of thing, that we can get here; so when we leave our business and come up here we feel as though they ought to talk to us. We think the papers should elicit something more than the experience of one man. We want the experience of the leaders who live up here in the cities.

I think these gentlemen are not doing all of their duty. I see Dr. Ohage, and Dr. Dunn . . . Dr. Moore and Dr. Dunsmoor. I see a great many gentlemen who could enlighten us, and we would like to hear from them. The paper of Dr. Ranson is one we ought to have discussed.

Then he proceeded to take decided issue with it. He did not approve of deadening pain, the instructive danger signal, with opiates. He did not think the physician should waste time trying to decide clinically what kind of obstruction existed. Call it obstruction and let the surgeon find out what kind it was and relieve it. He emphatically did not believe that surgery should be the last resort in acute intestinal obstruction. "As long as we make it the last resort, just so long will it be something that is fearful."

He sat down. The silence must have been electric. Then the section chairman, Dr. E. C. Spencer of St. Paul, spoke:

I think most of the instruction which the society has received, outside of the papers, has been from the members from the country, and especially the two from Rochester; so I hope you gentlemen from Minneapolis and St. Paul who think you can tell anything that the Doctors Mayo, of Rochester, do not know will get up and tell them.

One after the other the four men Dr. Will had named took the floor, and together they tore the paper to shreds. They argued some points among themselves, but when they got through they had made it impossible for anyone to return to his practice unaware of the possible danger of treating intestinal obstruction medically.

That was what Dr. Will wanted: "I would like to thank the gentlemen from St. Paul and Minneapolis in the name of the profession outside the Twin Cities for the noble way they have responded to my request."

3

Reading and hearing were good but seeing was better. Whenever the brothers learned of any new operation that sounded promising, one of them set out at the earliest opportunity to see it on the spot, study it in the hands of its originator, discover the hard-luck side of it that the man in his enthusiasm might have forgotten to report, and if it proved good master it for use in Rochester.

They early established the habit of an annual "brain-dusting," and kept down the cobwebs of routine by going each year, Dr. Will usually in the fall and Dr. Charlie in the spring, to spend a month or more in intensive observation of the work of other surgeons. Their purpose being to acquire methods they could themselves use, they preferred not to occupy their time with undiscriminating tours of many clinics, which gave them only a confused impression of undigested details, but rather to concentrate on one or two at a time, making a thorough study of the best clinics and masters of surgery in turn.

# Young Doctors from the West

As a merchant goes to market to buy the kind of goods he knows he can sell to the folks at home, so they went to learn the operations they had need of in their own practice. With care they selected the best man in the field they wanted to develop and made it their urgent business to learn his methods thoroughly. They were determined to do their work as well as it could be done at the time.

They were fortunate in being two, and at first three. One of them could always get away for the necessary length of time without seriously disrupting their practice. They were seldom away from Rochester at the same time, though in the early years all three of them occasionally went off to some medical meeting, leaving their practice in the hands of a Dr. Van Cleve of nearby Mantorville. They soon gave up that indulgence, however, and even after other surgeons had become their partners, Dr. Will and Dr. Charlie traveled together only when both were scheduled to give papers before some national group. For the most part they stuck to their rule: When patients came to Rochester they must always find a Mayo on hand to take care of them.

The two brothers had entire confidence in each other's ability and judgment. Neither hesitated to leave the other in charge at home and each passed on to the other the things he had learned while away. They took turns at traveling, sometimes so closely on each other's heels that the trains they rode would pass in the night and at the midway station to Chicago their thoughts would cross: There comes Will. There goes Charlie.

Whether they could afford these trips was never a question; they *had* to afford them, because they were necessary for professional betterment. At first the hardy and thrifty young men were content with coach seats on the poky, smoky trains that plied between Rochester and Chicago, but as affluence came and the consciousness of appearances deepened, in the older brother at least, they indulged in the comfort of a Pullman.

Not the least part of this comfort for Dr. Charlie, so people said, lay in the fact that when he had forgotten to clean the country mud from his shoes he had only to leave them out for the porter. Part of the education the Mayos got from their travels was in social conventions; they learned how much men judge from the choice of a fork, the press of a suit, or the shine of a boot. But to the end of his life Dr. Charlie could not be persuaded to bother overmuch about the fine points of spruceness.

4

Unfortunately Dr. Charlie left no accounts of his experiences on those early travels, but Dr. Will talked about his often, and in his papers are many stories of the men and clinics he visited. They help to sketch a backdrop for the action at Rochester.

New York drew the brothers first. Dr. Will returned to the Polyclinic in the fall of 1888 and again in 1889, and Dr. Charlie in his turn spent a month at the Polyclinic in 1889 and another at the Postgraduate School in 1890, receiving *ad eundem* certificates from both. After that the Mayos dispensed with formal enrollment in medical courses, but they continued to visit New York hospitals and the men in whose work they found merit.

Henry B. Sands was gone now, but Arpad Gerster was still an outstanding leader, and the Mayos attended his clinic often. More and more, though, they turned to a group of younger men: Charles McBurney, Frank Hartley, Robert Abbe, William T. Bull, and Robert F. Weir. These men had learned the radical operations introduced by the Germans and were using them, often against the vigorous protests of their older colleagues.

From them the Mayos picked up many a new operative procedure: for instance, from McBurney his own method of removing a gallstone impacted in one of the bile ducts, from Robert Abbe his ingenious "string-saw" operation for dilating strictures of the esophagus, from Robert Weir the symptoms and surgical treatment for perforating ulcer of the stomach and duodenum.

Frank Hartley, who made his colleagues gasp by his rash courage in operating on desperate cases and by the brilliant success he sometimes had with them, seemed to Dr. Will the most gifted of the group, but in the end he proved the most disappointing. He did, however, help to simplify and make less uniformly fatal the operation for the removal of the gasserian ganglion in cases of tic douloureux, a particularly troublesome form of facial neuralgia. Perhaps it was from him firsthand that Dr. Charlie learned to do the operation.

Dr. Will spent many hours on successive visits in the clinics of William T. Bull, trying to penetrate the secret of his extraordinary surgical

Early Rochester

The Cook Block, Mayo offices
from 1883 to 1901

Zumbro Street

*The end of medical school was truly a commencement*

Will's graduation class in front of the old medical school
of the University of Michigan, 1883

The graduation class of 1888, Chicago Medical College
Charlie is seated third from the left in the third row.

Charlie's crowd

*Toe-in-the-door days*
Charlie at 23, *above,* and
Will at 22, *right*

Hattie Damon, daughter of
Rochester's jeweler, married
Dr. Will in 1884.

Edith Graham, the first trained
nurse at St. Mary's, married
Dr. Charlie in 1893.

Amos W. Abbott

Archibald MacLaren

Charles A. Wheaton

Frederick A. Dunsmoor

James H. Dunn

James E. Moore

*Some of the outstanding Minnesota physicians and surgeons who influenced
the early careers of the young Drs. Mayo*

*Young Doctors from the West*
Dr. Will, *left*; Dr. Charlie, *below*

They were born at the right time, neither too early to ride the wave of advance in medical surgery that followed upon the work of Pasteur and Lister, nor too late to reap the advantages of the old school at its soundest and best.

The tornado of August 21, 1883

Mother Alfred, founder of St. Mary's,
with Sister Joseph

St. Mary's Hospital in 1894

Dedication of the first addition to St. Mary's Hospital, 1894

Against such odds of hardship the sisters worked with unflagging energy.

The sisters tried to make the private rooms at St. Mary's as homelike as possible.

"We were a green crew
and we knew it."

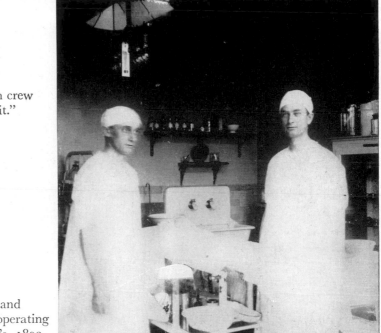

Sisters Fabian and
Constantine in the operating
room at St. Mary's, 1893

Dr. and Mrs. William J. Mayo

Dr. and Mrs. Charles H. Mayo

"She accepted what good there was in folks and did not criticize the bad."

"No man is big enough to be independent of others" was the most pregnant precept the Old Doctor gave his sons.

Christopher Graham

Melvin C. Millet

Augustus W. Stinchfield

Dr. Stinchfield joined the two Mayo brothers as a partner in 1892, replacing Dr. W. W. Mayo; Dr. Graham entered the partnership in 1895.

Edward Starr Judd

Gertrude Booker Granger

Henry S. Plummer

Assistants to the Mayo firm were soon
added: Dr. Booker Granger in 1897;
Dr. Millet in 1898; Dr. Plummer in
1901; and Dr. Judd in 1903.

Christian Fenger performing an autopsy at the Cook County morgue

*"That's the way to learn the fundamentals of medicine."*

Albert J. Ochsner

John B. Murphy

judgment, that essential but apparently unteachable sense that tells a surgeon "when to go in and when to get out." Bull was in charge of the emergency service at the Chambers Street Hospital in a crowded neighborhood of lower New York, a haunt of the underworld. He had to deal with so many stabbing and shooting cases that he was finally able to perform the first successful repair of a gunshot wound in the intestines—which another celebrated surgeon of the day said was a misfortune, because it would lead others to attempt the same operation, with disastrous results.

5

One of the famous, or notorious, feuds of this vital period was between the conservative New Yorkers and Joseph Price of Philadelphia. Price was introducing into the United States the radical ideas and procedures of the English titan, Lawson Tait, and was reporting such amazing success in abdominal operations, one hundred in a series without a single death, that the diehards simply refused to believe him.

When Dr. Will began to venture beyond ovariotomy in abdominal surgery, he was dissatisfied with his results. His death rate was too high, about seventeen per cent as he later remembered it, so he decided to see Joseph Price on his next trip.

The Mayo brothers were already aware of one of the principal weaknesses of their profession, and more than once they acted on the advice that Dr. Will later gave to his young associates: "When you hear that a certain celebrated surgeon is a liar, and that you are not to believe what he says, go to see him. Find out whether the trouble is his goodness or his badness. Sometimes a good man is cussed more vigorously than he would be if he were bad."

"I had heard that Price was a liar," said Dr. Will. "I had heard of his being fired from a certain medical organization, and then getting his friends together and getting back in. So I went to see him."

That was in September 1890, and it was Dr. Will's first visit to Philadelphia. With some difficulty he found his way to Price's hospital, called "the Tenement House School of Surgery" because it was located in a double tenement that abutted so closely on the Reading Railroad tracks there was scarcely room to walk between the rails and the house.

Price was out of town when Dr. Will arrived. A second and a third time he returned, but Price was still away. Then on the fourth morning as Dr. Will sat waiting in the bare little reception room, the door opened with a rush and a small man with graying hair and beard bounced in. Seeing the visitor, he snapped, "Who are you? What do you want?"

"I am Dr. Mayo from Rochester, Minnesota. I want to see Dr. Price."

"I'm Dr. Price. What do you want?"

"I want to see you operate."

"Sorry. There are more people around here now than I can bother with." And Price turned abruptly away, not looking in the least sorry.

With him had come Dr. Lewis McMurtry of Louisville, Kentucky, another prominent surgeon of the day. Winking at Dr. Will, he touched Price on the shoulder and spoke a few words to him. Price turned back. "How long have you been here?"

"Four days," said Will.

"Whom have you seen?"

"No one," he answered, then shrewdly sizing up his man, "I have been waiting to see you, but I shall go on to New York this morning."

"Don't do that. You won't learn anything there. Come on in."

The room to which he led Dr. Will was meagerly furnished. For an operating table there was only a wide board laid across two sawhorses, with a zinc washtub underneath and a small copper sterilizer near by. A splint-bottomed chair for the surgeon's use in vaginal operations completed the equipment.

Price's methods were just as simple. With a small handful of instruments—one knife, one pair of straight scissors, a few straight needles, and half a dozen hemostats to control bleeding vessels—he performed beautifully the most difficult and complicated operations. Every movement of his hands was quick and precise. Following Tait, he did not spray or irrigate with antiseptics, but he kept himself and his instruments scrupulously clean and preceded each operation with a thorough scrubbing of his hands, face, and beard. And he was outspoken in his scorn of any surgeon visiting his clinic who did not keep his hands and linen clean. His simple methods, considering the results he got with them, were a good counterweight to the growing tendency toward an arsenal of cutlery and an elaborate antiseptic ritual that often missed the essential points entirely.

# Young Doctors from the West

For three weeks Dr. Will watched Price at work, taking particular note of the Philadelphian's special field, the surgery of the uterus, ovaries, and fallopian tubes. Then he went home and in a few months reduced his own mortality rate in such operations to five per cent. For several years thereafter he spent a week or two each year with Price, and soon Dr. Charlie was doing likewise. The three men became fast friends.

Joseph Price's hospital, makeshift though it was, was his own, and he would not have it otherwise. He had begun his practice with a service at the Philadelphia Dispensary, where he became familiar with the lives and ills of a wretched people, the offscourings of a smug, corrupt, and badly governed city. To these poor souls he was tender and kind, often scraping his thin purse to its bottom in order to send some negro mammy to the country to recuperate from an operation he had performed without charge.

He had to do such operations in the patient's home, usually in surroundings of unspeakable squalor, where he could succeed only by cleaning up a small circle and staying within it. To improve upon such conditions he had rigged up his tenement hospital, where he continued to do an immense amount of charity work, entirely at his own expense. With characteristic independence and pugnacity he summarily refused the municipal aid proffered by Philadelphia politicians, saying he would have none of the strings he knew would be attached to their grants. *He* wanted to be able to hire and fire his own assistants and coal heavers.

Apparently he reserved his tenderness for his patients, for he certainly wasted none of it on his rivals. He was a master of sarcasm and sharp repartee, and it is no wonder that those he opposed hated him intensely.

At a medical meeting in Toronto that Dr. Will attended, a New York surgeon, one of Price's pet enemies, read a long and involved paper in which he attempted to describe how a surgeon could tell from the appearance of a loop of intestine just where in the length of gut he had got hold of it. The man concluded with a caution to his hearers that this work was still in the experimental stage, that he could not really tell much about it, and that he doubted whether it had any real value.

# The Mayo Brothers

When he sat down Joseph Price sprang to his feet and moved that the assembly give a rising vote of thanks to the gentleman for presenting the finest piece of original scientific work to come out of New York in the last twenty years. Impressed by this description of what they had just heard, the gathering rose to a man. Then someone saw the joke and began to laugh, and in a moment the whole crowd was roaring.

An incident Dr. Charlie witnessed shows how devastatingly cruel Price could be in his militant defense of surgery. He and his surgical associates in Philadelphia found themselves in competition with a practitioner who advocated electrotherapy as simpler and safer than operation for the treatment of pelvic disorders. Many honest, sincere men considered this method of real value, but not so Joseph Price. He began to follow up this competitor's work and kept on his trail for months.

Finally the electrotherapist announced his intention of making a report before the College of Physicians of Philadelphia, and Price advised Dr. Charlie, who was visiting him at the time, to attend the meeting. Before the scheduled hour Price arrived at the hall with a dray, from which he unloaded a collection of labeled jars that he arranged carefully on a long table at the front of the room. He listened attentively to the speaker's report, and each time a case history was given with the name or initials of the patient he leaned forward to pencil a note on one of the labels.

When the invitation to discussion was given, Price arose and exhibited one by one in the jars before him the pathologic specimens he had removed surgically from the patients the electrotherapist had just reported as cured. Here was a uterine tumor cut open to show the streaks of cauterization that were the electrical treatments' only effect on the growth; there was a uterus in which the electric needles had entered the wall far from the site of the tumor; and here were the tubes from a "cured" pelvic inflammation, still full of pus.

The effect was so overwhelming that the hearers were moved to sympathy for the crushed speaker of the evening, but Price had dealt a death blow to electrotherapy in Philadelphia.

Unfortunately Joseph Price had the fault common to so many great surgeons, an overmastering jealousy of any neighbor who showed signs of becoming too good. Dr. Howard A. Kelly, who was working with Price when the Mayos first made his acquaintance, was one of those who earned Price's bitter enmity by his exceptional ability.

Dr. Will and Dr. Charlie came to know several men who had that fault to an extreme degree, and a few who did not have it at all. That they were among the latter group was fundamental in the creation of the Mayo Clinic. "No man is big enough to be independent of others" was the most pregnant precept the Old Doctor gave his sons.

## 6

Among the Chicago men who contributed to the Mayos' surgical education the first place belongs without question to Christian Fenger, who by common consent is called the father of modern surgery in the West. Strangely so at first glance, for he was not a good operator. Dr. Will once said that much as he revered Fenger he always felt toward a patient entering his operating room as one would toward a friendly little dog coming into an experimental laboratory: "You poor devil."

Week after week for several years Dr. Will or Dr. Charlie, turnabout, made the journey to Chicago on Wednesday night in order to attend Fenger's clinic on Thursday, and afterward, if time allowed, to join the smaller circle in his autopsy room. Sometimes they stayed over to meet with the little band of students Fenger entertained in his home every Thursday night, discussing medical literature and reminiscing over a stein of beer about his experiences in the clinics of Vienna, Heidelberg, and Berlin. Such a day with Fenger, they found, stored their minds with pabulum for a week or two's chewing. "He gave me more mental indigestion than any man I ever knew," said Dr. Will.

Fenger was blunt, even boorish, in manner, unconventional and careless in dress. There was no diplomacy in him, only honesty without veneer. He moved with the lumbering gait of a bear, and his words came haltingly in a thick mumble, which when transcribed from shorthand formed beautiful English phrases. He was addicted to swearing, in all the eleven languages he spoke. Experience taught Dr. Will that when Fenger swore in English one might smile at him, but when he swore in German he was irritated, and when he took to Danish oaths beware, for he was viciously angry.

Fenger was a native of Copenhagen and a finished product of the Danish and German schools of medicine. Refused appointment to the chair of pathology at the University of Copenhagen because of the impediment in his speech, he had wandered off to Egypt, settling finally in Cairo. There he soon drew to himself so much of the surgical practice that his competitor, who had preceded him in the city, ruefully announced his intention of surrendering the field. Scrupulously fair, Fenger said no, they would decide by lot which of them should leave. He drew the short straw, and by that chance exchanged Egypt for America, Cairo for Chicago.

For so modest and unassertive a man, he stirred Chicago medicine to its depths in a remarkably short time. Borrowing the necessary thousand dollars, he bought the position of pathologist at the Cook County Hospital, which paid no return except the chance to see and study disease. The first teaching jobs he secured were relatively inconspicuous and he did most of his surgery in small hospitals on back streets.

Yet he quickly attracted an immense following among the younger practitioners of the Northwest and aroused fierce opposition in the old guard—because he possessed a knowledge and spirit the best American-trained men did not have in any comparable degree. The Scandinavian and German schools of medicine were leading the world in the application of science, especially the new pathology, to medicine. They were demonstrating how anatomic and physiologic facts could be learned by microscopic analysis, at postmortem, and more important still, at operation. And they were using the facts so gained to improve and extend the scope of surgery.

These northern European schools of medicine had the early defects of their qualities, however. In their intense interest in the study of *disease* they had lost sight of the *patient*. Understanding the processes and the course of illness was their objective, and they were frankly skeptical of the power of medicine to relieve suffering. Their meticulous work would mean the discovery of remedial agents for the future, but that was small consolation for the patient of the present.

Fenger was tainted with this therapeutic nihilism. He did not intentionally disregard the individual patient in his pursuit of accurate knowledge about disease, and he did not teach that to recognize and classify diseases was more important than to heal them. But his interest, beyond his power to control it, lay in diagnosis more than in treatment and in devising therapeutic measures more than in applying them successfully to the individual patient.

From Dr. A. J. Ochsner, a disciple of Fenger's, Dr. Will Mayo heard a story that illustrates this attitude. The wife of a friend of Ochsner's was seriously ill and the young physician was worried about her, so he sent for Fenger. The Danish surgeon made a careful examination and then said, "We must operate at once."

"Will she get well?" asked Ochsner.

"No, she will die."

"But will she get well if we don't operate?"

"God only knows," was Fenger's reply. Whereupon Ochsner promptly vetoed the operation. "Well, where is your diagnosis then?" shrugged Fenger.

On another occasion, when Dr. Will was present, Fenger made a brilliant diagnosis of a fibroid tumor of the brain and operated to remove it. While he was closing the wound the patient died.

"Dr. Fenger, the patient is dead," said the anesthetist quietly. There was no answer.

Again, more clearly, "Dr. Fenger, the patient is dead." Still not a word. Carefully the surgeon sewed up the incision and as carefully wound the bandages around it. Then he said softly, "You damned fool, to die just as you were cured."

For Fenger every operation was in essence a dissection, so that he stayed in the wound longer than most surgeons, longer sometimes than was safe, in order to learn pathologic facts from the living body. For the benefit of the watching clinic he would sketch on the blackboard the surgical anatomy and pathology of the parts he was to work on, and then with knife in hand he would explain and discuss them, forgetting the patient waiting under anesthesia.

When he had removed the specimen he was like a hound on the scent, walking about with the piece of tissue in his hand, examining and pointing out its pathologic features, until someone reminded him that the incision was yet to be closed.

Fenger's emphasis on exact diagnosis was salutary for young American practitioners so long as they did not carry it too far. When a doctor could do nothing about a lump in the abdomen whatever it was, it mattered little whether he was right or wrong in thinking it a tumor, but now it mattered' tremendously, for if it was a tumor the surgeon could operate to remove it.

So doctors crowded around Fenger's postmortem table in the morgue of the Cook County Hospital and his operating table in the Passavant Memorial Hospital. Men who in their own theaters wielded the knife more dexterously than he came to learn from him the meaning of things they saw in the body but did not understand, or looked at but did not see. He was the acknowledged master of physicians like Frank Billings, pathologists like Ludwig Hektoen, and surgeons like Nicholas Senn, Albert J. Ochsner, John B. Murphy, and the Mayo brothers.

Many years later, when the Mayos and their associates were planning a program of medical education, Dr. Will brought forth a picture of Fenger at work in the morgue surrounded by a group of absorbed spectators. "That's the way to learn the fundamentals of medicine," he said.

## 7

In the group around Fenger the Mayos made the acquaintance of Senn, Ochsner, and Murphy. They learned much from Nicholas Senn; there were few surgeons of his day, east or west, who did not, through his writings if not by direct observation in his clinic. The West was proud of him; he was its gift to the nation.

"I attended Senn's lectures whenever possible and always with profit," said Dr. Will, but so briefly as to give himself away. Like many others who knew Senn personally, Dr. Mayo admired and respected him as a surgeon but did not like him as a man.

Born in Switzerland and raised in Wisconsin, Senn had finished off his medical education with a lengthy period of study in the German clinics and then under Dr. Fenger. He built up a large private practice in Milwaukee, which he gave up only when his teaching duties in Chicago became too heavy to be handled by commuting.

His endurance and capacity for work were amazing. No matter how busy he was he always found time, late at night usually, for experimental research on the animals he kept in his stable loft, or later in the laboratory built under the sidewalk in front of his Chicago home. He was one of the first men in America to make use of systematic animal experimentation. He worked upon most of the major surgical problems of the day and raised many new ones, but he solved few His contributions were inspired and fermentative rather than conclusive; he set the tasks for others.

He was an excellent teacher. Despite a voice that Dr. W. J. Mayo remembered as unpleasantly harsh and strident, he could hold an audience engrossed and put his ideas across with clarity and force. That ability, added to his towering reputation, made his clinics popular with visitors. They were always crowded, and through them and his voluminous writings Senn did more than any other one man, unless it was John B. Murphy, to popularize the new surgery with the general profession. To adopt Dr. Will's figure of speech, Senn came into a land without music and soon had the populace singing.

But unfortunately his ability was equaled by his egotism, unrelieved by any saving trace of humor. He was dogmatic, dictatorial, intolerant of opinions not in agreement with his own, and in his office and clinic the orders to assistants and patients alike came fast and sharp. There was no room for argument, no time for human warmth. And he could not endure the presence of a possible rival near his throne. To share the limelight for even a moment made him ill-tempered.

Albert Ochsner was chief of staff under Charles T. Parkes at Rush Medical College and continued in that position when Senn succeeded Parkes. It was soon apparent, to Dr. Will Mayo at least, that the new professor of surgery was worried by Ochsner's ability.

One day Senn was giving a clinical lecture on a patient who had a hard mass in her abdomen. Exact diagnosis was difficult and the operation was to be exploratory. After reviewing the various possible diagnoses, Senn turned to Ochsner, who was standing quietly by, and said condescendingly, "Perhaps our chief of staff can tell us what is the matter with this patient."

Ochsner promptly said he thought the tumor was a lithopedion (a calcified fetus). Senn snorted his derision and quickly listed half a dozen reasons why it could not possibly be a lithopedion. Then he opened the abdomen and found—a lithopedion. The large audience cheered Ochsner to the echo.

Will Mayo was present on this occasion, and following Ochsner to the anteroom after the operation said to him, "This will end you in this clinic." Ochsner, who had not yet taken Senn's measure, asked what Mayo meant. "You will find out." And he did.

8

But Ochsner was not long without a position. Within the year he was appointed chief surgeon of the new Augustana Hospital. It was a small hospital, only twenty beds, but under his guidance and through his ability it grew to two hundred and fifty beds and became one of the surgical centers sought by visitors from abroad.

William Mayo was attracted to Ochsner at his first meeting with him in Senn's clinic and deliberately sought his acquaintance. The friendship ripened into what was probably the closest personal relationship Will Mayo ever had outside his family circle. "My elder brother, guide, philosopher, and friend," he called Ochsner, and many of his later journeys to medical centers were made in Ochsner's company. Neither man being jealous of his knowledge, the two shared their opinions and discoveries, each criticizing the other and helping to test and prove his theories before they were published to the profession at large.

Ochsner was the older by three years. He had taken a bachelor of arts degree at the University of Wisconsin before graduating in medicine from Rush Medical College in 1886 and had later spent nearly two years studying surgery and pathology with the masters in Germany. Always a surgeon rather than a scientist, he nonetheless was at home in the laboratory to a degree unusual among practicing surgeons.

There was nothing of the exhibitionist in him. He shunned the spectacular and refused to be daring in surgery merely for the sake of a good performance. He is seldom named among the outstandingly original surgeons of his generation, perhaps, as Dr. Mayo always contended, because he was so far ahead of his time and wasted so little energy in establishing his claims to priority that his name is not associated with many of his greatest contributions.

Ochsner was a sincerely simple and kindly man. With his quiet voice, low collar, and white bow tie he could have passed for a Lutheran pastor. His modesty amazed men who had less of it, and they marveled at the reputation and influence he gained in professional circles solely by virtue of an ability too great to be hidden and an unmistakable strength of character. He was quiet and unaggressive until questions of professional integrity and ethics arose. Then he was uncompromising and would not be silenced. After reading the warmly admiring tributes that others have paid to A. J. Ochsner, it is easy to understand why William Mayo was able to say, "Spiritually, morally, and professionally, I profited greatly from my association with him."

## 9

If Ochsner filled his canvas with pastel shades, John B. Murphy splashed his with vivid color. A mercurial, red-bearded Irishman, Murphy was truly the "stormy petrel of surgery." His achievements were always spectacular; they invited reporting and he frequently made page one of the newspapers. And how his brethren of lesser stature hated him for that! They called him a liar, said he stole his ideas and his patients, and accused him of deliberately courting publicity by histrionics.

No one could claim that John B. Murphy ever tried to screen his light; no one could deny that he was ambitious, that he dramatized everything he did, and that he played best to the grandstand. But the records do not substantiate the charges hurled at him; they were born of jealousy and nourished by envy. Murphy's crime was the possession of an incredibly quick and brilliant mind.

When the Mayos first met him, he was waging a dramatic fight to make the nation, doctors and laymen alike, conscious of appendicitis and its dangers. The Chicago profession had got his dander up when they brushed aside his plea for early surgery in that disease and suspiciously asked where he got all the appendicitis cases he was reporting. So he was out to show "the old fossils" he was right, and they were not taking kindly to his demonstration.

Then came the battle over the Murphy button.

In the early nineties abdominal surgery was somewhat hung up on the nail of intestinal anastomosis, that is, on the problem of how to unite successfully two open ends of the intestinal tract—how to join the gallbladder with the duodenum, or the stomach with the jejunum, or two severed ends within the intestines themselves. The problem was to find a method that would join the ends firmly without forming a scar to close the passage. Sewing the parts together was dangerous, because the stitches did not always hold, sometimes the bowel became gangrenous at the line of suture, or it took so long to perform the operation that the patient died of shock.

Many men were interested in this fundamental problem, and a number of experiments had been made with mechanical devices that might do the job. Nicholas Senn, for example, devised discs of decalcified bone to be placed one in each end of the bowel and laced together to hold the parts in apposition until healing took place. But for various reasons these did not work too well, and Senn soon abandoned them and went back to the use of plain sewing.

Then Murphy tackled the problem. He read everything he could find about the matter, and in the abandoned experiments of a French surgeon he saw an idea that had fallen just short of success. At top speed and with feverish concentration, as always, he set to work to overcome the defects in the Frenchman's device, and one day not long afterward he ran from the workroom shouting his eureka to his wife.

What he showed her was a gadget looking something like a sleigh-bell. Constructed on the principle of the common snap fasteners used by dressmakers, it consisted of two small metal bowls fitted with invaginating cylinders. Put a bowl in each end of the severed gut and snap the two together. What could be simpler? As the cut ends within the bowls sloughed off in the healing process the button would be released into the bowel to pass from the body, leaving an unscarred opening the exact size of the button used.

With the aid of his wife and assistants, Murphy tested the button on dogs and then on human patients, and in December 1892 he announced his invention to the profession. Here was a method of end-to-end union that was simple and safe, even in inexpert hands, he said, and it was quick. Anastomoses that had always taken hours to perform could be done with the Murphy button in half an hour or less.

In April of the following year Dr. Charlie and his father visited Murphy's clinic and for the first time saw an operation performed with the button. Impressed, Dr. Charlie took one of the gadgets home, showed it to Dr. Will, and explained how it worked. Only a few days later the use of that button saved the life of a patient the brothers must otherwise have lost, and that was the beginning of a long and highly important service the Murphy button rendered in the Mayos' progress in surgery.

There can be little doubt that Murphy's device cleared the way for advance in intestinal, gallbladder, and stomach surgery. Even the bitter opposition to it helped, for those who criticized it were moved to find something better to take its place. Eventually successful methods of suturing were developed and the button was superseded. But meanwhile it served an immensely useful purpose.

After that triumph in abdominal surgery, Murphy, on the advice of the greathearted Christian Fenger, branched out into research in one field after another—gynecology, nerve surgery, lung surgery. And in each of them he contributed something sensationally original. "His every shot hit the center of the target," as Dr. Will Mayo said.

Each time Murphy would think happily that he had at last won the acceptance by his colleagues that he craved, but then "Murphy Cures Consumption" or some such headline would break in the papers and the doctors would be hostile again, "outwardly because their profession was being dragged through a puddle of prosaic printer's ink, inwardly because Murphy was again in the news."

The Mayos' admiration for John B. Murphy was unbounded and unconcealed. They gave him a boost whenever they could and defended him stoutly against his critics. They considered him the greatest surgeon of the Northwest and one of the greatest of his generation anywhere. "As far as one could go he could walk with Murphy" was the elder brother's eloquent tribute.

But for all his ability and originality Murphy left no school of followers to carry on when he was through, because he gave no thought to fostering the development of others. His assistants worked *for* Murphy, not *with* him, and they were not encouraged to have any higher personal ambition than to serve their chief.

## 10

Medical news in the early nineties was full of the new Johns Hopkins Hospital. The munificent bequest of the Baltimore merchant that made it possible, the slow and thoughtful laying of plans for it, the revolutionary features of those plans, and the appointments to its staff were all of a sort and scale to attract widespread interest.

Then when the Johns Hopkins Medical School, planned in conjunction with the hospital from the start, came into being, the ambitious daring of its program added fuel to the fire of talk. It was to be of real university stature, with a course four years long and centered on research in laboratory and hospital ward. But beyond that the school set up unheard-of qualifications for admission; only those could enter who had a bachelor of arts degree with two years of training in premedical subjects and a knowledge of French and German. The profession raised its eyebrows. Even the Hopkins men themselves were a little frightened by the completeness with which their dreams had been translated into actuality. Did prospective medical students of such caliber exist? Jokingly Dr. Osler remarked to his colleague, "Welch, it is lucky that we get in as professors; we could never enter as students." Eighteen applicants met the requirements, however, and the first class at Johns Hopkins began in 1893.

The next year Dr. W. J. Mayo elected Baltimore for his annual period of study. He had been reading Osler's *Principles and Practice of Medicine* and like everyone else had found it surpassingly good. He had probably seen some of the issues of the *Johns Hopkins Hospital Bulletin,* stimulating from the first in its reports of original research. And he had heard enough about the new hospital to whet his curiosity.

Reaching the hospital early one morning, he found it as quiet as the streets outside, and for a time he wandered alone through the reception rooms. Then a light, quick step behind him made him turn to face a man with dark eyes, dark complexion, and drooping mustaches, who asked briskly but kindly, "Well, what would you like to see?"

"I'm a young doctor from the West and I have heard so much about this hospital that I should like to visit it, if I am not in the way."

"Not at all. Come with me. I am Dr. Osler."

After showing the young man where to hang his hat and coat, Osler led the way to the wards and introduced the visitor to his assistants. Then they went to work, blithely but intently, Dr. Will with the rest.

The thorough study given to each patient that morning made a strong impression on the young man from Rochester, especially the use Osler made of scientific procedures in diagnosis. The microscope was in constant use at the bedside, and Dr. Will saw two blood pictures of disease that he could recall vividly some forty years later.

# Young Doctors from the West

The clinical laboratory was a small one without any attendant in charge and so in an indescribable state of disorder, and the work done in it was rudimentary by modern standards—just a few chemical and microscopic analyses of blood and excreta. But the mere existence of a laboratory for purely clinical purposes was a sign that scientific tests were reaching the useful stage.

In the weeks that followed Dr. Will got a good introduction to a group of men and a spirit of camaraderie in work that have become almost a legend in American medicine. The Johns Hopkins Hospital had no large staff of consulting, visiting, and attending doctors, rotating in service to disrupt the organization every few months. Each of its units was under the supervision of a permanent chief who held the corresponding chair in the medical school. The medical clinic was in charge of William Osler, the beloved physician of Canada, the United States, and England in turn; surgery was the province of William S. Halsted, a shy, unapproachable perfectionist; gynecology was that of the young surgical artist, Howard A. Kelly, whom the Mayos had met with Price in Philadelphia; and the department of pathology was directed by the genial William Welch, known affectionately to hundreds as "Popsy."

Those were the famous Big Four of the well-known Sargent painting. With their assistants they formed a congenial, gay, cooperative group, for whom accomplishment of a high order was the normal business of life.

The place of the assistants in that group was unique in the United States. Following the model of the German clinics, the Hopkins chiefs had substituted long-term, paid residencies for the usual one-year, unpaid internships. They sought men of ability and promise who would be willing to stay on for several years in return for the opportunities of experience and study afforded them, and their purpose was to prepare these men for important positions in other hospitals and universities. So they made teaching a part of each man's work and encouraged him to exercise initiative, assume responsibility, make journeys of observation periodically, and get his teeth into some research problem of his own. Thus they had built up a staff, not of underlings in for a year or two and then out again, but of responsible younger associates, some of whom approached the stature of their chiefs.

And at Johns Hopkins research in medical science and practice was not a mere sideline for the individual to follow in odd hours; it was considered an integral part of his job, as legitimate and necessary a function of the hospital staff as teaching or taking care of the sick. There were at that time no research laboratories in the hospital itself, but near by was the two-story pathology building and not much farther away the medical school laboratories of anatomy, physiology, and chemistry. These, with the assistance of their able staffs, were available to the clinicians, and they made good use of them.

What Dr. Will thought of all this he did not say, but it is worth noting that the next journey of the Old Doctor and Charlie was to Baltimore, and thereafter the two brothers were frequent visitors at the Johns Hopkins clinics. The repeated appearance of the two young westerners, first one and then the other, caught the interest of Dr. Osler, and he showed it in characteristic fashion. From here and there on his own travels he sent a memento to the Mayos, usually a trinket or an interesting item about brothers, often brother physicians.

## 11

The Mayos spent most of their time in the clinics of Halsted the surgeon. Although they could not feel at ease with that reserved, silent man, they appreciated the quality of his work. Two original operations at least he showed them, one for the radical removal of cancer of the breast and another for the repair of inguinal hernia. But they owed him most for his demonstrations of general surgical principles.

For most visitors it was a shock to find, in this big new hospital that was a model in so many ways, cramped surgical quarters with makeshift equipment. The explanation offered is that John Shaw Billings, the man of vision who planned the hospital building, realized that surgery was in a state of rapid change and wisely decided to let the surgeons plan and furnish their own buildings in due time, when it was quite clear just what they needed.

The visitor's surprise in most cases soon gave way to something akin to awe, for in that little room with its old wooden operating table Dr. Halsted maintained standards and secured results of such uniform excellence as to put most surgeons to shame. He paid meticulous attention to the details of antisepsis, and though his routine may have been needlessly comprehensive at times it seems to have freed him from the anxiety about wound infection that bothered less careful practitioners.

At the time the Mayos began to visit his clinic Halsted was changing from antisepsis to the newer asepsis—from drenching the scene with chemical solutions to sterilizing everything that came in contact with the wound either by boiling or by dry heat in an autoclave. This was a great improvement, but it did not solve the problem of human fingers. The Hopkins men had tried wearing white cotton gloves but found them unsatisfactory.

A few years before, the head nurse of the Hopkins operating room had complained that the harsh antiseptics were making her hands painfully sore and that she could not carry on with them much longer. Because she was an excellent nurse and also a charming young woman —she later became his wife—Halsted tried to do something about the matter. Taking an idea from the heavy coachman's gloves Dr. Welch used for performing autopsies, the surgeon asked a New York manufacturer to make a special pair of thin rubber gloves for the nurse. They served her so well that the assistants took to wearing them too, and finally Halsted got some for himself. Now he was urging them upon other surgeons, having become a firm believer in their importance in the aseptic routine.

After a trial some men agreed with Halsted, but others did not think the merit of the gloves was sufficient to offset their impairment of the surgeon's sense of touch, and it was ten years or more before their use became general. The Mayos adopted them early, though gradually.

From another aspect of Halsted's surgery Dr. Will derived great comfort as well as valuable pointers. Because postoperative shock was proving a dangerous complication in abdominal surgery, there had been a marked resurgence of the emphasis on speed in operating, and rapid operators were claiming that the shorter the time of operation the quicker and less eventful the patient's recovery. This disturbed Dr. Will, for he felt himself to be a slow worker, and the dispatch with which men like Senn, Murphy, and Kelly did their work did not add to his peace of mind.

But in Halsted he saw a surgeon obtain results equal to theirs despite methods that were painfully deliberate. In fact, Halsted considered meticulous work a cardinal principle of good surgery. He maintained that if a surgeon covered the exposed viscera with warm moist pads to keep them from getting cold, was careful to handle the tissues gently so as not to bruise or strangle them, and took pains to tie off all, even the tiniest, bleeding vessels so as to leave the cavity dry and clean, he would have fewer cases of shock than if he operated at high speed.

He did not consider surgery an end in itself or merely a means to more knowledge; if an operation did not contribute to the increased well-being of the sick person, it was not good. When he saw the attitude of men like Senn and Fenger at its source and in its undiluted form in the German clinics he was moved to protest. He urged American surgeons not to go too far in following the German leaders, but to take instead a stand "for conscientious surgery with some interest in the result to the patient."

John M. T. Finney, one of Halsted's associates, likewise failed to share in the usual wholehearted approval of the foreign masters. He was so shocked by the needless cruelty he saw in some German clinics that he refused to visit them again and returned to the United States convinced that German surgery had advanced to its place of leadership by virtue of disregard for human life and suffering.

To such opinions the Mayo brothers listened all the more readily because of their own inclination to moderation in audacity.

## 12

Since Colonial days Boston had ranked with New York and Philadelphia as a center of medicine and surgery, but for ten years the Mayos steered clear of it. They had heard that its people were cold and inhospitable to visitors, and they shrank from the attempt to scale its ramparts. But Dr. Will wanted badly to see the work Dr. Maurice Richardson was doing in stomach surgery, and in the fall of 1898, having got fresh haircuts and provided themselves with dress suits, so they wouldn't look "too woolly and hayseedish," Dr. Will and his friend Ochsner ventured to Boston.

Arriving at the Massachusetts General Hospital early in the morning, they asked a janitor who was sweeping the walk in front whether there were to be any operations there that morning. He started to direct them to the office, then broke off to nod down the street, "Here comes Dr. Mixter; maybe he can tell you."

# Young Doctors from the West

Ochsner put their question about operations diffidently, but Dr. Samuel Mixter was affability itself. Yes, he said, he was doing some surgery that morning and he thought Dr. Arthur Cabot and Dr. Richardson were too. Come right along. They did, and had a full and pleasant morning, staying at the hospital for lunch and on into the afternoon.

Perhaps in expressing their thanks they told Dr. Mixter how they had felt about coming to Boston. At any rate, he invited them to have dinner with him, and when they hesitated, urged them, "Come on. I want you or I wouldn't have asked you." So they donned their dress suits and went to dine with half a dozen of Boston's great medical men: David Cheever, chief surgeon of the Boston City Hospital, John Honans, nationally known gynecologist, Cabot and Richardson, whom they had met that morning, and John Collins Warren, professor of surgery at Harvard Medical College.

Only four years later the Boston men asked William J. Mayo to come all the way from Rochester to tell them how to do what he was doing in stomach surgery, but that evening he tingled with the wonder of being accepted on equal terms in such a company. Perhaps something of this attitude was apparent in his manner and moved his host and fellow guests to an added measure of graciousness, for Dr. Will himself believed it was his very lack of sophistication, his youthful eagerness, that made the older men always so kind and willing to help him.

The two westerners returned to their hotel thoroughly happy and quite ready to admit that all they had heard about Boston men was a slander. Not until several years later did the cat escape from the bag. Then at some medical convention Dr. J. C. Warren approached Dr. Will to congratulate him on a mark of honor he had just received. "I remember the first time I heard your name," he said. "It was about ten years ago. Sam Mixter called me up late one afternoon and asked me to come to dinner to meet Drs. Ochsner and Mayo.

" 'Who are they?' I asked.

" 'Damned if I know,' he said. 'Just a couple of young fellows from the West. But come on anyway. They say that Boston is cold.' "

For three weeks the two young men stayed in Boston, attending the clinics at the Massachusetts General and the Boston City hospitals.

When he returned home Dr. Will wrote an account of his trip for the *St. Paul Medical Journal*, including a word about the cordial reception given him by the Boston medical men. His general verdict on their surgery reveals his own conservatism.

To my mind Boston is the home of what might be called American surgery, in this respect differing from the West, where surgeons not infrequently abandon old and tried methods which have given good results for the new method of some continental surgeon. Boston surgeons have confidence in their own judgment and in their own way of doing things. If a certain procedure gives good results, it is continued until something else is proved better.

The one fault Dr. Will had to find with the work in Boston also tells as much about him as about it: The surgery did not begin early enough in the morning or the clinics promptly enough to please him.

## 13

Dr. Will did not go abroad until 1900. Then, again in Ochsner's company, he went to attend the International Medical Congress in Paris, but he went early enough for a visit to Germany before the congress convened.

Apparently others had had the same idea, for the clinics of Berlin were so crowded with visitors that it was impossible to see either the surgeon or the patient at close range. So Ochsner and Mayo took to the provinces. Many good hospitals had been established as state institutions in the smaller cities in the days before unification, when Germany was a loose aggregation of free cities and petty kingdoms, and these were now staffed largely with surgeons who had trained as assistants to Billroth or Volkmann and had built up clinics that compared favorably with those of the capitals.

The best known of the surgeons the two Americans saw at work was Max Schede, then in charge of the University Hospital at Bonn. He ranked with Trendelenburg next to Billroth as a source for new surgical ideas and procedures. Dr. Mayo found him a quiet man, quick and sound in judgment. If he saw in Schede or the others he visited any of the ruthlessness noted by Halsted and Finney, he did not say so.

His main concern was with major operative methods, but he also took note of German practice in details that were then matters of controversy in America. He noted that none of the Germans wore rubber gloves for operating and that most of them preferred sutures to the Murphy button. He was impressed by the organization of the hospitals and the amount of space and staff devoted to the accessory sciences. Among the clinical units one wing or one entire building was always devoted to what is today called physical therapy, that is, to baths of all sorts, massage, the use of heat and electricity—forms of treatment then left largely to exploitation by the quacks in the United States.

Moving back to Paris after a month or more in Germany, Ochsner and Mayo gave their afternoons to the sessions of the medical congress. There were more than six thousand in attendance, some four hundred and fifty of them from the United States. The speakers were men with whose work Dr. Will was familiar through their contributions to medical journals, and he found it "very interesting to see the great surgeons of the world and hear them speak."

The forenoons were spent at the leading Paris clinics. Dr. Will was particularly impressed with the work of Tuffier, whom he called "the Murphy of France," saying, "I liked him for the things he did not do, as well as for the many things he did do." In Tuffier's clinic he saw his first demonstration of spinal anesthesia, but he did not like the looks of it. He feared it would do irreparable damage to the central nervous system.

### 14

Taking time off from the scheduled program one afternoon, a hot one in early summer, Dr. Mayo, Dr. Ochsner, and Dr. Harvey Cushing, the great neurosurgeon who was then working with Halsted at Johns Hopkins, sat down to rest a while in the shade on the steps of the Ecole de Médicine. They talked of the value of watching other men at work in their own clinics and sighed for the chance to do more such observing in the United States. It would be an excellent idea, they thought, for a few good American surgeons to form a club that would hold its meetings at the hospital of each member in turn, a new professional society that would occupy its sessions with observation and informal discussion over the operating table rather than with a long program of formal papers.

When they returned to the United States they mentioned their idea to other surgeons, who agreed that it was good. Finally, after three years of talk, Dr. James Mumford of Boston and Dr. George Crile of Cleveland decided to act. They called a meeting in New York on July 11, 1903 and organized the Society of Clinical Surgery. Its membership was to be elective and exclusive, limited to forty practicing surgeons, who twice each year would meet with one of their number for a clinical demonstration of his work. William J. and Charles H. Mayo were two of the original members, and the fifth meeting of the society was held in Rochester.

Obviously the Mayo brothers were no longer hungry, penniless boys looking with longing into the bakeshop window. They were now inside, visited as well as visiting for instruction. For the story of how that came to be it is necessary to turn back to events in Rochester during these years from 1890 to 1905.

# CHAPTER TWELVE

# Applying the New Surgery

The opening of St. Mary's Hospital did not transform the Mayos overnight from general practitioners into surgeons. Throughout the early nineties their surgery was only the graft of a special interest upon a general practice. At St. Mary's the surgical cases outnumbered the medical two to one, but even so, one or two mornings a week sufficed for the operations. The remainder of their long hours the Mayos spent in examining and prescribing at the office or at patients' homes. In one day in January 1890, during an epidemic of virulent influenza, they prescribed for seventy victims of "la grippe."

At a stated hour each day father and sons started out, each in a different direction, to cover the countryside. Among them now they had an array of smart carriages and ten or fifteen spirited horses. Like the motoring youth of today, Will and Charlie always had to pass everything they met on the road, so they had their share of smashups, fortunately none of them serious.

This general practice was itself a factor in making them turn a sympathetic ear to the claims of the new surgery, for looking critically and honestly at their work they had to admit that their medical treatment often fell far short of success. What really ailed these persons whom medicine did not help, and what could be done for them? In many cases surgery provided the answer.

One striking fact impressed itself upon the brothers early in their travels: The men whose work they found it worthwhile to study had almost without exception developed their abilities in charity service rather than in private practice. Some busy municipal hospital, university clinic, or free dispensary provided them with the multitude of patients and the variety of diseases they needed to give them experience and skill.

The Mayos' little home town did not offer any comparable opportunities, but it did have a state hospital for the insane with a thousand

297

or more inmates, and ninety miles to the west in St. Peter was another still larger. These institutions were undergoing transformation from asylums to hospitals; lay attendants were being replaced with trained nurses and excellent medical staffs were being built up. But neither of them possessed adequate surgical service, so the two superintendents jumped at the chance when the Mayo brothers volunteered to provide it.

Unofficially, they insisted, for they wanted none of the political complications they feared would attend an official appointment. Nor would they accept any fees for the work; the remuneration they sought was access to the postmortem material of the hospitals and the chance to perform any needed operations on the inmates. Each Saturday night one of them made the journey to St. Peter to do on Sunday whatever operations were necessary and whatever autopsies the superintendent had saved for his visit.

Although the amount of surgery these hospitals provided was relatively small, it was enough to give Will and Charlie some experience in almost every new operation they learned. Long after their need for experience had passed, however, they continued the service without fees, and whenever the hospital boards insisted on voting them a token of appreciation, they turned the sum back for the purchase of improved equipment for the operating rooms.

2

When the brothers turned to applying the new surgery in their own practice, their peculiar position at St. Mary's Hospital proved an inestimable advantage. Medical biography is full of the frustration and delay suffered by young enthusiasts where the hand of tradition was too heavy and the authority of inflexible seniors too strong. But Dr. Will and Dr. Charlie faced no opposition from an established order. There were no nurses to purse their lips in a prim remark that Dr. Blank had always done it *this* way, no staff of elders to raise a prohibitory voice against methods in advance of theirs, and no board of well-meaning but ignorant lay trustees to forbid what they did not understand.

The Sisters of St. Francis followed trustingly where the Mayos led, and though the Old Doctor might have interfered, there is no evidence that he ever did. Sometimes, fondling his own little pocket case of needles and knives, he scoffed at the number of instruments the boys thought they needed, and sometimes he asserted his authority by "changing the medicine" when he thought a patient was not coming on as fast as he should, but apparently he never prevented his sons from introducing a new procedure at St. Mary's.

Although the Old Doctor called himself a "bacterian" and was fascinated by the idea of microbes, he was always impatient with the fuss of the antiseptic ritual; yet he let the boys use it at St. Mary's from the beginning—and that was early for any hospital to practice Listerism consistently and exclusively. Dr. Will and Dr. Charlie followed the unpleasant rites of wet antisepsis for a few years, but they adopted the methods of asepsis as fast as they came in. It was a problem at first to adapt sterilization to the makeshift conditions of kitchen surgery—of which they did a considerable amount throughout the nineties—and Dr. Will performed many an operation with instruments he had sterilized over the spout of a bubbling teakettle on a wood-burning kitchen range. When Dr. Edouard Boeckmann of St. Paul devised a practical portable sterilizer the Mayos were among the first to use it.

They wore Halsted's rubber gloves at first only for operations on septic cases, to protect their hands from contamination with pus; then they wore them for work on parts of the body especially susceptible to infection, such as the veins; and finally, as they grew used to them, they came to wear them always.

That left the skin of the patient as a final source of infection. In an effort to root out and away the bacteria lodged deep in the glands of the skin it had become the custom to work long and elaborately over the site of the operation. Will and Charlie shared in this excess of zeal for a time. They had the sisters apply poultices of green soap and antiseptic packs and scrub with stiff brushes until the patient came to the operating table with the skin of his abdomen red and angry and spotted with pustules in which the germs were already at work. About 1897 they saw the folly of this and substituted gentle cleansing and the necessary shaving. Almost at once wound suppuration ceased entirely to plague them.

For the first decade the two young men did their operating as a team, each serving in his turn as the other's first assistant. It stirs the pulse to think of the potential abilities focused on those early patients as the brothers bent together over the table, every faculty intent, one seeing what the other missed, pooling their knowledge and ingenuity to meet a crisis when it came. And afterward, if things went wrong, fighting together with the nursing sisters for the life of their patient. Or in easier moments discussing the why of failure or success and the ways and means of improvement, over their books or a microscope slide or pathologic specimen.

Given the circumstances of childhood and adolescence, it was in these years, when problems were faced and fought through, when responsibilities were shouldered and successes won, *together,* that the bond of mutual love and admiration between William and Charles Mayo was cemented, a bond so strong that nothing could ever break it.

Both brothers must do all sorts of surgery if either was to be able to get away for study, and each seems to have tried his hand at every kind of operation on the calendar. Yet naturally a division of labor gradually developed between them. As the number of operations increased Dr. Will found more and more of his time occupied with pelvic and abdominal surgery, while Dr. Charlie took over the work on the eye, ear, nose, and throat, the bones and joints, the brain, nerves, and neck.

Dr. Will always maintained that their specialization was the result of Dr. Charlie's superiority as an operator. "I was driven to cover by a better surgeon," he said on one occasion. And on another, "Charlie drove me down and down until I reached the belly." But Dr. Will had got started on the belly before Dr. Charlie joined him, so it is more likely that the younger brother's quick skill in all kinds of operating left Dr. Will free to devote himself to the new abdominal surgery as the amount of it increased.

For convenience this specialization may be assumed throughout the story that follows, though it was by no means so clear-cut as it may appear. The brothers crossed the line into each other's domain easily and frequently.

### 3

When Dr. Will stole that ovariotomy case from his father in 1888 he entered the field that was to provide the bulk of the Mayos' surgery for a decade to come. Naturally, for in gynecology the new surgery first developed and in gynecology the Old Doctor had made the start. Expansion occurred not only in the number of operations but in their radical nature. During the first three and a quarter years that St. Mary's Hospital was open such minor surgery as the plastic repair of lacerations of the cervix and perineum accounted for 164 of the 195 gynecologic operations the Mayos performed. But in 1905 the total for the single year was 637, and nearly two thirds of them were radical operations.

When Pasteur made it possible to understand the processes of infection, Lawson Tait read in a pus-filled fallopian tube the true story of pelvic inflammation: The unclean fingers of the midwife or placental remains give rise to an infection in the uterus, from which it spreads through the tubes into the ovaries and surrounding tissues. Boldly Tait advised the removal of infected tubes and ovaries as the treatment for inflammatory diseases of the pelvis.

He was vigorously opposed, as were Joseph Price, Howard Kelly, and the others who carried his teachings to the United States. These chaps were making a great to-do over rarities, said the men of the old school, who did not consider the fallopian tubes important in the diseases of women. But the crusaders answered with plateful of specimens and sheaves of case histories.

The argument put gynecologic surgery in the limelight, and its scope was rapidly extended. First only the infected tube and ovary were removed; then those on the other side too were cut out to prevent the spread of the infection; and finally, when this failed to relieve the symptoms in all cases, the uterus, which after all was the source of the infection, was taken too.

That extension was possible because the operation for removing the uterus (hysterectomy) had been brought to a high state of technical perfection. It had been available for treating fibroid tumors and malignant disease since 1813, but the likelihood of hemorrhage made it so dangerous that it had not been widely used. Gradually, however, the technical difficulties were overcome, the mortality rate dropped, and from the late eighties on, the operation was within the practical reach of general surgeons. They went a little wild and were inclined to find in hysterectomy a panacea for all the ills of women.

Ovariotomy passed through somewhat the same phases. It was

only a step from removing the ovaries for tumor to removing them for pain in menstruation, and then for various nervous symptoms that baffled physicians. From this grew the theory that mental derangement was produced by the generative organs, and ovariotomy was advocated as a treatment for insanity.

That was the "hysterical adolescence" of gynecology. Dr. Will learned the new operations first from some of the Twin City surgeons who were using them and then polished up on the finer points during his visits to Joseph Price and Howard Kelly. But with the techniques he learned the debate about them, and he proceeded cautiously in applying them.

Conservative measures would suffice, he finally decided, when the inflammation had not spread beyond the uterus, but once the ovaries and tubes were thoroughly involved, only removing them would bring relief. This procedure, like hysterectomy, he felt, was a useful operation when properly applied, and it ought not to be blamed for the mistakes in judgment of those who could perform it more skillfully than they could diagnose the need for it.

No doubt Dr. Will, in spite of his caution, was sometimes fooled by neurotic women and sometimes persuaded by the enthusiasm of fellow surgeons into unnecessary operations, and he later admitted, "It would seem to me that the genital organs of woman had suffered from an excess of operative zeal, to her detriment and our discredit." But certainly by the use of the new operations he restored health and energy to scores of ailing women whom the medical treatment of that day had not and could not have helped.

### 4

We have heard of an operation very unusual in its cause and results which was performed by the Drs. Mayo, at St. Mary's Hospital, last evening. A lady from near Byron who had been in the hospital for three weeks, awaiting the birth of a child, was relieved by the Caesarean section, which consists of cutting into the cavity of the abdomen and extracting the child, and is so named because tradition says the great Caesar was born in that way.

The result of the operation in this case was not only the birth of the child, which weighed nine pounds, but also the removal of a tumor weighing twenty pounds. The mother and child are both doing nicely. The case is the first of the kind ever known in this part of the world.

# Applying the New Surgery

That item, which appeared in the *Rochester Post* on September 13, 1895, illustrates the kind of gynecologic case that was important for its dramatic quality rather than for the numbers to which it applied. Its unusual feature was not the use of caesarean section but the complication of the pregnancy by a fibroid tumor of the uterus.

Dr. Will had no difficulty in making the diagnosis when he was first called to see the woman in April, because she had been big with the growing tumor before she became pregnant. And although he and none of his immediate neighbors had ever faced such a case before, it was not unknown to medical men. A search of the literature gave him the histories of a few similar cases and the surgical procedure for handling them, but the question was whether he should interrupt the pregnancy at once or let it come to term and save the child.

After careful consideration he advised the woman to wait until near the time for confinement and then enter the hospital for delivery. But he must have been tormented with doubts, for she became thin and emaciated as her abdomen grew alarmingly large. She had to remain in bed most of the time and often needed morphine to relieve her pain. In August she entered the hospital, and when labor began three weeks later she was at once taken to the operating room.

Dr. Mayo's plan was to remove the part of the tumor that filled the vagina and extract the child through that channel, but when he had cut out a piece of tumor the size of a coconut only to have more of the mass take its place, he inserted a gauze pack to check the bleeding and turned to the abdominal route for removal. In an operation full of difficulty he delivered the baby, then removed the uterus and with it the soft, swollen mass of the tumor. The woman rallied quickly from the long operation and mother and child did well.

That was triumph enough, and the young surgeon might have been excused for congratulating himself. Perhaps he did, but he did not stop there. He reviewed the case carefully and talked it over at length with Dr. Charlie, seeking to answer these questions for himself: Had he been justified in letting the pregnancy come to term at the cost of so much suffering and danger to the mother? Had his initial attack on the tumor through the vagina helped or hindered the abdominal operation? In short, what should he do differently another time on the basis of his experience this time?

By persistently and systematically reviewing their cases in that critical fashion the Mayo brothers extracted the last jot of value from their own work, finding lessons in success as well as in mistakes. That is routine practice for any physician worth his salt today, but it was exceptional then.

## 5

The spotlight swung from gynecology to surgery for appendicitis. On the threshold of the nineties the more progressive surgeons were coming around to Reginald Fitz's conviction that removal of the appendix was the treatment to be preferred. But because of the growing differentiation between physicians and surgeons, the latter were doing less and less general medical practice and so saw few cases of appendicitis other than those referred to them as specialists. It was the physicians then who must be trained to recognize this malady early and accept the need of surgical treatment for it.

That was easier with the practitioners who thought they rarely saw a case of appendicitis than with those who said they saw lots of them but always cured them without trouble. Those men clung firmly to their belief in medical treatment. The measures they recommended varied considerably, from narcosis with opium to ice packs, enemas, calomel, sweet oil, or quantities of salicylate of soda. But whatever the specifics they swore by, they insisted that most of their patients pulled through.

Look at the mortality of operation, they said to the surgeons; it's twenty-five to thirty per cent. As many or more die under surgical treatment as under medical, so why hurry every patient off to the operating room?

They die in operation because you don't get them to us in time, retorted the surgeons. If you doctors would learn to recognize appendicitis and would call the surgeon in at once, the mortality rate would drop. And as for those patients you say you cure, follow them up and see what state of health they're in. Maybe you pulled them through one attack, but they're having others. You've just turned an acute case into a chronic one. That patient who suffers from periodic stomach and bowel upsets, so-called bilious attacks, is what you have called a medical "cure" of appendicitis. You ought to get that man to a surgeon *now*.

# Applying the New Surgery

The physicians shrugged in disgust; the surgeons were seeing appendicitis in every case of plain bellyache. They were going mad on operation again, as they had with woman's pelvic organs. What they really wanted was the hundred and fifty dollars the poor patient gave up along with his appendix.

The argument was really bitter, one of the classic battles of medical history. It raged throughout the nineties, all over the country but especially in the Middle West, where feeling ran higher and language plainer. No matter how slow or dull a medical meeting, the chairman had only to toss in a paper on appendicitis to wake it up and set men scrapping for the floor to give vent to their feelings. Many of the discussions in the Minnesota State Medical Society were enlivened by the presence of John B. Murphy, who was making it his mission to spread the gospel of immediate appendectomy. He often attended meetings of the various state societies in the vicinity of Chicago, always dramatizing and exaggerating his position in order to drive his points home.

Dr. Will and Dr. Charlie took little part publicly in the controversy, except to bring up the question occasionally. St. Mary's Hospital reported only twelve operations for appendicitis in 1895, and there is no way of knowing how many of those were excisions and how many merely the draining of an abscess. The smallness of the number, even allowing for the additional operations that may have been done in patients' homes, attests the caution with which the brothers were moving.

They were willing to grant the logic of operating immediately upon diagnosis, but when they faced the cases in practice they could not stick to any such rule of thumb. Operation simply was not safe in some of the cases they saw. Although their mortality rate was not the thirty per cent admitted by some city hospitals, it was still twelve to fifteen per cent, too high to justify operation if the patient had a chance without it.

Then Dr. Ochsner took Will Mayo into his confidence. He had worked out a method of treatment that seemed to reduce the operative mortality considerably, but he hesitated to publish it, partly because he wanted it more thoroughly tested first and partly because he was afraid the opponents of appendectomy would seize upon it as ammunition for their guns, which it was not. The patients he showed Dr. Will were the kind that had bothered him too; they had been ill for several days and had a high temperature, fast pulse, all the alarming symptoms of peritonitis. Ochsner simply put them on a fast and waited to operate until they had passed through this dangerous stage.

The essence of his idea was this: If a patient is seen before the appendix ruptures, the organ should be removed at once, but if the infection has already spread to the peritoneum it is not safe to operate. Instead, peristalsis should be stopped in order to aid nature in localizing the infection. Put the patient at rest and give him absolutely nothing to eat or drink, above all no cathartics. In a few days the acutely dangerous phase will pass and appendectomy will be safe.

That became famous as the Ochsner starvation treatment. It was first described to the profession at the international congress in Paris that Ochsner and Mayo attended together in 1900, and thereafter it was widely publicized and adopted, though Ochsner's fears proved well grounded. Hundreds of physicians, seeking to justify their own stubborn opposition to appendectomy, pounced upon the Ochsner treatment with glee. See, they said to their local critics, the great Chicago surgeon saves most of his appendicitis cases by not operating on them!

In 1908 the surgeons of the nation assembled in Chicago were told by various speakers that although the Ochsner treatment as understood by the average physician of the country was a damnable stumbling block to progress, nonetheless it was actually the greatest single advance in the treatment of appendicitis. And the Ochsner treatment had been available to the Mayo brothers several years before it was published. They put it into practice, and almost at once, according to Dr. Will, their death rate dropped to less than four per cent; then with experience and refinements in technique it went to one per cent and under.

At the same time the conception of chronic appendicitis expanded. Since the first of the decade it had been recognized that without operation acute appendicitis might recur in chronic form, and for such cases the interim or interval operation was recommended. Gradually it became clear also that much intestinal and stomach trouble of obscure origin was actually the result of a chronically inflamed appendix that had never given symptoms acute enough to be identified. That meant a tremendous expansion in the use of appendectomy.

The storm of argument finally achieved the aim of Murphy and his fellows. The plain people and their family doctors, whatever their opinion of operative treatment, were aware of appendicitis and more often than not scared to death of it. The bad appendix joined the much-publicized germs as public fright number two, and children walked in terror of the grape seed and cherry pit which if swallowed, their parents warned them solemnly, would bring a pain in the side and the dreaded operation.

Probably nowhere in the nation did the number of operations for appendicitis mount so quickly or so high as in Rochester. In 1900 the number was one hundred and eighty-six. In 1905, if the appendixes removed in the course of operations for other troubles are included, it passed the thousand mark. Approximately half that number were for chronic appendicitis—which reflects not only improvement in diagnosis but also the fact that a chronic sufferer can take the time to travel to his surgeon; in other words, it reflects the growing attraction of the Mayos for patients from a distance.

## 6

One result of antisepsis in surgery was to make feasible the exploratory incision. If the source of the abdominal trouble is obscure, said the progressive surgeons, open up the cavity and find out whether the cause is a condition you can do anything about.

Subject a patient to all the dangers of peritonitis just to find out what is wrong with him? Reckless, utterly irresponsible, said the conservatives. And besides it's a confession of failure in diagnosis.

Exactly, replied the surgeons. We do fail in diagnosis on clinical signs, so why not admit it in the only way that promises the patient relief from his troubles?

With this position the Mayos agreed. The Old Doctor once told a carping colleague in a medical meeting: "It is the custom with me and those associated with me, where there is a seriously diseased condition of either a man or woman's abdomen, and the diagnosis cannot be made without, to open the abdomen very frequently."

This custom led to their first operation for gallstones. In December

1890 a machinist from Sleepy Eye, Minnesota, many miles to the west of Rochester, presented himself at the Mayos' offices. For years he had suffered from spells of pain in his right side and a year before one attack had been followed by a prolonged illness and the formation of an abscess, which his physician had opened several times. Since then he had been forced to use opiates almost constantly.

Not sure what was causing his trouble, the Mayos suggested an exploratory operation, and he consented. When Dr. Will found a mass of adhesions surrounding a contracted gallbladder containing one large stone, he removed the stone and inserted a drain. In three weeks the patient was discharged, had soon gained forty pounds, and went back to work at his trade.

Diseases of the gallbladder, long known as a plague of adult mankind, were still the province of the physician. Postmortem examinations had shown how surprisingly often the gallbladder contained stones—so much more often than their presence had been suspected that it was generally believed most gallstones were "slumbering" or "innocent," that is, lying quietly in the gallbladder without causing any trouble.

The one recognized diagnostic sign of active stones was the excruciating colic that any practitioner could identify at a glance. This agonizing pain, which might last for a few hours or for a week or more, was thought to be a kind of labor that occurred when the stone passed from the gallbladder through the cystic and common ducts into the bowel. The end of the colic was taken to mean that the stone had passed. Unless it had got stuck in one of the ducts on the way. Then several serious results might follow: distention and rupture of the gallbladder, inflammation, suppuration, jaundice, death.

For this malady the therapeutics of the day prescribed morphine to deaden the pain, copious draughts of saline waters to prevent the formation of the stones, doses of some mixture like ether and turpentine that was supposed to dissolve the stones, and the old favorite, spoonsful of olive oil. Proudly the doctor would exhibit to the patient the stones he had passed with the aid of the olive oil, but actually the "stones" were soap balls formed by the action of the intestinal alkalies on the oil.

The futility of these measures was demonstrated by the fact that scattered through every community were men and women who had sweat through spells of colic for four, ten, even twenty-two years. Sometimes their gallstones slumbered for a month or two, but then something, no one knew what, woke them to new activity and the almost intolerable pain began again.

In 1890 surgeons were just beginning to advise operation for gallstones, though it had been known to be possible for some time. Dr. John Bobbs of Indianapolis in 1867 first had the audacity to cut into the gallbladder and scoop out the trouble-making stones, and the German surgeon Langenbeck had successfully removed the entire organ. But the mortality of operation was too high and the danger of death in gallstone disease too remote for the average doctor to recommend these procedures.

Removal of the gallbladder (cholecystectomy) was thought advisable only in such desperate straits as cancer, because the exact function of the organ was not yet understood, and because the operation was much more hazardous than removing the stones (cholecystotomy). In the latter the gallbladder was opened, the stones scraped out, and the organ stitched into the abdominal incision so as to form a fistula, or channel, for drainage and the escape of any stones that had been missed.

But the relatively simple cholecystotomy would not suffice for all gallbladder ills. In April 1893 Dr. Albert Plummer of Racine, Minnesota, sent one of his patients to see the Drs. Mayo. The man was seventy-one years old and very ill. He had been having attacks of gallstone colic for two years and for the past four months had been in almost constant pain, with vomiting, emaciation, and jaundice of the most pronounced degree.

This time the Mayos did not hesitate in their diagnosis; a stone was obstructing the common duct. A few years earlier there would have been nothing they or anyone else could do about it, but McBurney and Abbe of New York had recently outlined a method by which the biliary ducts could be opened and impacted stones removed. And Dr. W. J. Mayo had learned how to do that operation.

But he struck a snag. When he got the abdomen open he found the site of obstruction in the duct so inaccessible that removal of the stone was out of the question.

There was one alternative—to cut a backdoor for the escape of the bile by fastening the gallbladder directly to the bowel and cutting a permanent opening between them. But the patient was in such bad condition that he could not possibly last through the long procedure of a suture anastomosis, even if the Mayos were expert at performing it, which they knew they were not.

At this juncture Dr. Charlie remembered the gadget he and his father had brought back from Chicago a day or two before. Murphy's button was supposed to work in just such cases as this. Neither Charlie nor Will had had a chance to try it out to make sure they knew exactly how to apply it, but this was no time to hesitate on that account. Quickly Dr. Will made an opening in the gallbladder and another in the duodenum, fastened one half of the button in each, and snapped the two together. Then he closed the incision and got the patient back to bed.

How closely the young surgeons watched the progress of their elderly patient may be imagined. His recovery was quick and complete. The jaundice disappeared, his strength returned, and he was able to go home. For six years he remained well and active, dying in the end from an ailment far removed from the gallbladder and its ducts.

From that occasion on, for more than ten years, the Mayos leaned heavily on the Murphy button in their abdominal surgery, and rarely did it let them down.

## 7

The number of stones in a gallbladder is not of great importance; one good-sized concretion can be as troublesome as many small ones. But the Mayo cases that caught the attention of the public were those in which the stones numbered hundreds—or more. Witness this:

An operation was performed at St. Mary's Hospital within the past few days that savors of the marvelous. Nearly three thousand gall stones were removed from a woman. The number is known to be about three thousand for bacteriologist T. Spillane spent all one day counting them. The woman still lives and is sure to recover. The stones ranged in size from a pin head up to a pea.

That experience would command an audience for the woman who

had it today. How much more so in a day when major operations were novelties and in a community where the drab drudgery of farm life was enlivened only by talking and where there was little to talk about except the weather and the crops and the neighbors.

So word of what the Mayos were doing got around, arousing hope in the victim of gallstone colic or in any doctor who had a patient suffering from it. And the ten gallbladder operations of 1895 became seventy-five in 1900 and three hundred and twenty-four in 1905.

By that time the -ectomy operation had been so improved that it was almost as safe as the -otomy, and with the knowledge of the part infection played in the formation of stones had come the theory that any gallbladder containing these formations was obsolete and should be removed. The Mayos did not hold with this idea, though they greatly increased their use of cholecystectomy. It seemed better to them to strive for earlier diagnosis, so they could operate before complications developed. What they wanted was to get after those gallstones that were supposed to be slumbering.

For they were convinced that half of the so-called innocent stones were no such thing; they were merely thought to be so because the signs of their mischief were not recognized. Doctors had so long thought of colic as the one indication of gallstones that they were blind to the less obvious gastric manifestations of them. The Mayos themselves had been surprised into awareness of those by finding gallstones in cases of vaguely defined "stomach trouble," which vanished with the stones. Apparently the stomach served as an alarm box for a smoldering fire in the gallbladder as well as in the appendix, and perhaps in other organs too. Here was more work for the diagnostician, and then for the surgeon.

## 8

To the unhappy victims of hernia—fifteen per cent of mankind they were said to be—the medical men of the 1880's could offer only the makeshift of a truss to hold the viscera in place. Such abdominal supports were usually expensive, uncomfortable, and but partially effective, providing poor defense against the ever-present danger of strangulation, which occurs when the hernia cannot be reduced and the circulation is shut off in the protruded parts so that they become gangrenous. That patients did not willingly accept trusses as the remedy for their affliction was shown by the business they gave to any charlatan who advertised a rupture cure.

The hernia patient, used to looking after himself, usually tried to do so when strangulation occurred, and the doctor was seldom called until the choked tissues had begun to mortify and the patient was in an alarming condition. What the physician could do then may be illustrated by the practice of the Old Doctor. He would freeze the protruded mass by applying salt and ice wrapped in a handkerchief, and then split the skin to allow the pus and feces to escape. If the patient recovered after this, which he sometimes did, Dr. Mayo twisted off the spur of dead tissue with clamps and threaded buttons into the fistula to close it.

In such extreme cases as this Dr. Will began his work with hernia. Aided by asepsis and the new surgical techniques, he could open the abdominal cavity, relieve the stricture, remove the gangrenous portion of the bowel, and unite the severed ends. Soon he was also able to try one or another of the various operations proposed for the so-called radical, that is, surgical, cure of hernia.

These operations were young, the first practical one dating from 1889, and they were little used by surgeons because the results were notoriously impermanent. The best of the few men who were using them admitted to forty or fifty per cent of relapses, and others said gloomily that seventy-five or eighty per cent would be nearer the mark. Those were poor odds to offer anyone except a man in the extremities of strangulation.

Surgeons had a strong incentive for improving those results, because rupture through the line of incision was such a likely sequel to an abdominal operation that physicians were often reluctant on that account to recommend expedient surgery. Dr. Will found it discouraging indeed to have one and then another of the patients on whom he had operated for appendicitis or gallstones turn up a little later with a troublesome hernia. What did it profit a man to lose a diseased appendix or gallbladder only to gain in exchange a ventral hernia?

Gradually men like McBurney, Bull, and Halsted came to realize that by no procedure could they make the skin and peritoneum into an adequate bulwark against rerupture, that the underlying muscles and their accompanying fibrous tendons must be used as the retaining wall. When they put this principle into practice the percentage of relapse in hernia operations fell to five per cent, and surgical repair began slowly to replace the wearing of a truss. Up to 1893 the Mayos attempted only thirty-nine radical cures; by 1905 they were averaging about three hundred a year.

Umbilical hernias did not immediately share in the improvement, however. At the navel the muscles of the abdomen lie too far apart to be brought easily and successfully together, and the method used was to cut them loose from their moorings, pull them into apposition, and sew them together to form a wall at the site of the rupture. But that created a dangerous tension that often undid the work of repair. Besides, umbilical hernia occurred most frequently in obese persons whose abdominal muscles were so flabby and undeveloped that they were of little use as a retaining wall. Surgeons despaired of ever being able to cure rupture at the umbilicus.

In attempting to perform the customary operation one time Dr. Will had to make a transverse incision to get at the muscles, and then found them so far apart and so thin that it was impossible to use them. But that wide transverse gap had to be closed. Boldly he lapped the upper edge over the lower throughout all the internal layers of the abdominal wall and stitched them together. The patient's hernia was gone, and it did not return. But Dr. Will did not at the moment realize what he had done.

As he saw more of such cases he noted again and again that the patients' abdominal tissues were stretched and pendulous. When the patient lay relaxed on the table he could gather the sagging flesh in his fingers and overlap it a number of inches.

Overlap it. . . . There was an idea! Why not lap the fibrous tendons edge over edge for a couple of inches to form a wall of double strength at the critical spot? The resistance ought to be perfect. That was essentially what he had done in the earlier case, and it had worked.

Carefully he thought the method through, talked it over with Dr. Charlie, and perhaps tried it a time or two on the cadaver. Then convinced of its soundness, he performed it on a patient and watched the results. They were good; the union was lasting and the wall held. He used the method in a second case, a third, a fourth. He explained it to a few professional friends, Dr. Ochsner among them, and their experience confirmed his own. By 1903 he and Dr. Charlie had done thirty-five such operations without a death and with but one slight relapse. They had something useful to report to the profession.

## 9

Children *will* swallow things not meant to be swallowed. The old way of handling them in such an emergency, if the foreign body seemed to be stuck above the entrance to the stomach, was to turn the child upside down and shake him vigorously. In the consequent coughing and crying the offending object might be dislodged and fall out, but unfortunately, it might just as easily become more firmly and dangerously stuck. If the foreign body had entered the stomach, the patient was fed quantities of mashed potato to form a mass around it and carry it safely through the intestinal tract, but that did not always work and obstruction was an even chance.

The newer method was to make an incision into the trachea, esophagus, or stomach and remove the object by direct sight or touch. The Mayo brothers dealt with a number of cases in that way and had a goodly collection of prune pits, corn kernels, coins, and safety pins to show for them.

Some mistakes in swallowing were not so easily handled, however. Concentrated lye was then in common use in the rural households of the Northwest for making soap and for a number of general cleaning purposes. There were no laws to regulate packaging or labeling, no educational campaigns by press or radio to warn unwary mothers, and the poisonous, burning stuff, looking like sugar, often sat around the kitchen in open containers within easy reach of unsuspecting children.

The number of casualties from that source seems to have been large. A child might survive the immediate effects of swallowing lye, but as the severe burns in the gullet healed, contraction occurred and scar tissue formed to obstruct the esophagus. The unfortunate child could seldom swallow anything but liquids, and less and less of those as the stricture tightened. Slow starvation was the likeliest prospect.

If the doctor got hold of the case before the channel was too nearly closed, he could dilate the stricture by the use of bougies, slender cylindrical probes of various styles and graduated sizes. He could force one of these through what opening remained and by daily sounding with progressively thicker bougies he could enlarge the opening to near-normal size.

But sometimes the obstruction was so far advanced that the most patient efforts could not find an opening for the bougie. Such patients, almost all of them children, came to the doctor in pitiable condition, thin and pale, weak, pathetically hungry but unable to swallow the milk they craved.

For them surgical treatment was now possible. Christian Fenger had originated a method for passing a probe from below through an incision in the esophagus or the stomach, and for cases where even this was impossible Dr. Abbe of New York, working on the suggestions of the Germans, Schede and Trendelenburg, had devised an ingenious operation in which several strands of string were threaded from a stomach incision through the stricture and out the mouth. By using the string as a saw, an opening was cut in the obstructing scar tissue sufficiently large to admit the smallest size bougie, from which point dilatation could be carried on as before.

The Mayos had learned this "string-saw" method from Abbe and applied it in several cases with admirable ingenuity and patience. The successes they won were unusually satisfying to all concerned; an illustrative case history may show why.

On October 5, 1892 a little girl three years old was brought to St. Mary's. She had been unable to eat solid food since swallowing lye a year before and was now regurgitating most of the liquid nourishment given her. Unable to find an opening for even the smallest bougie, Dr. Will advised operation, but the parents refused it and took the girl home again.

Nine months later they brought her back, scarcely alive. The channel had closed completely and for four weeks they had been feeding her through the rectum. Dr. Will immediately made an opening into the stomach by Fenger's method, and for a month the child was fed through that opening. Then Dr. Charlie started the string-saw operation, and he worked for five weeks to enlarge the esophageal opening enough to admit a bougie. Two months later the child was discharged "in good general condition, able to drink milk readily and to take chopped meat and bread with little effort." A few years afterward the parents happily reported the child to be entirely well and eating quite normally.

## 10

The gastrotomies made in such cases to permit the manipulation of bougies and string-saws were the first incisions into the stomach cavity made by the Mayo brothers. Stomach ailments probably brought more patients to the doctors than any other complaint, but the Mayos had been surprised to see how often "gastralgia" disappeared with the removal of an inflamed appendix, "dyspepsia" with the drainage of a diseased gallbladder, and "stomach cramps" with the repair of a ventral hernia. Stomach trouble under its various names had long been a sort of diagnostic catchall for the vague miseries of the upper abdomen.

Naturally, and often correctly, the source of stomach disorders was thought to be bad diet habits, chiefly the overeating of greasy, fried foods, hot breads, and heavy pastries. The time-honored treatment consisted of emetics, cathartics, and chemical aids to digestion like bismuth, pepsin, and hydrochloric acid. For chronic "gastric catarrh" a glass or two of hot water taken each morning was a favorite remedy with many. As knowledge of the physiology and pathology of the digestive apparatus increased, however, it became clear that some disorders of the stomach were not chemical but mechanical in nature, and for those medicine could do little; they were logically the province of surgery.

But stomach surgery was in disrepute because of the frightful mortality attending the first attempts. Billroth, who was the first to practice operation in desperate gastric disorders, had been wry about his own results. "All the patients left the operating room in shock, from which some of them recovered," he said. More than half of them had died. Long after his methods and statistics had been superseded, surgeons had to fight the impression of fatality they had left.

By the nineties some progress had been made by German and English students of Billroth's, and a few American surgeons were entering the field. But stomach surgery had progressed little beyond the stage of use in emergencies to avert imminent death; much was still to be done to make it safe enough to be applied for the relief of disability.

Among the stomach sufferers they saw, the Mayos soon learned to spot one type with unmistakable symptoms. These persons told a story of chronic gastric distress lasting over a number of years, sometimes as many as fifteen or twenty. In the last year or two their trouble had taken a peculiar turn. Their food would not digest properly; it just lay heavy and sour in the stomach, causing them great discomfort, until they brought it up again by vomiting or by washing it out with the stomach tube, and they had to go through this unpleasant emptying process once or twice every day. Some of them were reduced to a liquid diet; all had lost much weight and were growing steadily weaker.

Theirs was chronic starvation caused by obstruction of the pylorus, the narrow outlet from the stomach into the duodenum. They had had a chronic ulcer of the pylorus, and in its repeated healing, reopening, and healing again, a mass of scar tissue had formed, closing the channel. This was the sort of mechanical difficulty medicine could not touch.

When Dr. Will turned his attention to the possibilities of surgical relief for these persons in 1894, he found two procedures available. Wölfler of Germany had originated a method of making an opening from the stomach directly into the small bowel to serve as a substitute for the blocked pyloric passageway. This operation (gastroenterostomy) was an admirable solution of the problem, but with suture anastomosis its death rate had been fifty per cent or over. Use of the Murphy button would cut that down, but not enough to make the operation really safe. Simpler, and so to be preferred where it would work, was the newer plastic operation (pyloroplasty) by which the pylorus was incised lengthwise and sutured crosswise to enlarge the pyloric opening.

Armed with these alternative methods, Dr. Will tackled pyloric obstruction, beginning with the worst cases of course, those in which relief was most imperative. Here is his record of his first case:

M. M., male, aged forty-six, American, admitted to St. Mary's Hospital January 10, 1895, with a history of gastric symptoms extending over a period of seven years. For the past two years he has vomited large quantities of partially digested or decomposing food once or twice in every twenty-four hours. He has grown weaker, and lost about 100 pounds in weight. Early in his illness he vomited blood a few times and suffered severe pains after taking food. . . .

Operation January 13, 1895. . . . Pyloroplasty was done, and the patient discharged February 15th, cured. When seen six months later, he had gained 70 pounds in weight and was doing his work on a farm.

Success of that sort was the rule in the cases that followed, but there were disappointing exceptions. The failure of the simpler plastic operation to turn the required trick necessitated a second operation often enough that Dr. Will inclined more and more toward the use of gastroenterostomy, and as the results of the latter operation improved and its risk lessened it became the operation of choice in his treatment of pyloric obstruction.

## 11

Unfortunately the obstruction was not always benign in nature. Cancer was thought to be much the commoner cause of it, but early in his experience with the condition Dr. Will Mayo began to doubt that assumption. He had had occasion to perform a postmortem in a case where the certified cause of death was "cancer of the pylorus" but in which he found the stricture to be benign, and that gave him something of a jolt. The man had died of starvation due to a condition that surgery could have cured. How often was this mistake made?

Obviously there was need for some means of differential diagnosis between these two kinds of obstruction, and the Mayos combed their case histories looking for significant signs of one or the other, but they could find none that proved reliable. Forced to admit that they could not tell the difference clinically, that a cancerous mass could be distinguished from a benign one only by direct observation at the operating table (and not always even there), they took the position that an exploratory incision was imperative in all cases of pyloric stricture. If it revealed a benign condition, curative surgery could be performed.

And if it revealed cancer? Just make the patient's last days as comfortable as possible, would have been the general answer, for cancer of the stomach was considered incurable by any method.

# Applying the New Surgery

Surgeons had tried cutting out the cancerous portion and even removing the entire organ, but the immediate mortality had proved prohibitive. Moreover, if the patient survived the operation the period of relief was so short, the recurrence of the disease so certain and quick, as to make one doubt whether the brief respite was worth the ordeal of the operation.

Dr. Will rejected so gloomy a view. He took a look at the patients on whom resections for gastric cancer were done and saw that all of them were in the last stages of the disease, some of them near death from hemorrhage and exhaustion, before they came to operation. It was a wonder any of them survived. If surgery could be applied earlier the results would be better.

Here again the stumbling block was the difficulty of diagnosis. It was so hard to be sure the patient's symptoms came from cancer and not from ulcer or something else, and while the doctor waited, trying to make sure, the disease got beyond the possibility of control.

Again the Mayos accepted the need for exploration upon suspicion. If the cause of the trouble may be cancer and is not quickly found to be something else, operate. But would the patient agree? The Old Doctor had always insisted that in such circumstances the patient must be told the full truth and allowed to decide for himself. The sons were as honest. They never hid the nature of the operation they proposed. And seldom did the patient hesitate. It was more often his attending physician who counseled delay—because he did not believe that stomach cancer was curable by early removal.

Often for all their efforts the brothers were too late and there was nothing to do but close the incision. Sometimes in such cases the succeeding days in bed so sapped the patient's remaining strength that he never recovered sufficiently to return home, and that got under the young surgeons' skin. It seemed to turn their good intentions into cruelty.

Finally they thought of silver-wire sutures, which had once seemed the answer to the surgeon's prayer for some means of permanent internal support. They were strong, sterile, and not subject to absorption, but they had failed in their promise because the tissues surrounding them tended to atrophy, and for a few years surgeons were busy taking out the silver-wire sutures they had so confidently put in.

Where life would be short, as in these cases of inoperable cancer, the objection to the sutures did not hold. They would furnish immediate and firm support, and there would not be time for them to do any harm. So thereafter, whenever exploration revealed incurable malignancy, the Mayos closed the incision with silver wire, and the patient was able to return to his family and friends within a week. That was a bit of human kindness.

But not all the cases were hopeless. By 1906 the Mayo brothers were able to report one hundred stomach resections for cancer, with a mortality and a record of permanent cure that compared favorably with results in cancer of other parts of the body where the value of surgery was generally accepted. In view of the fact that medical men had absolutely no hope to offer in this disease, the surgeons had proved their right to try operation.

## 12

Inevitably, experience with benign obstruction led the Mayos and their fellows at last to ask: What about the ulcer that produces this condition? Must we let it go its way to this result? Can't we interrupt these years of suffering at some earlier point?

Ulcer of the stomach was a medical disease. Only when it hemorrhaged or perforated was the surgeon called, in his accustomed role of the last resort, to stop the bleeding and patch up the hole. The pathology of ulcer had been studied only at postmortem or in such emergency operations, so that ulcer was viewed and treated in the light of its death-dealing complications, and no distinction was recognized between acute and chronic ulcer.

It was the same old story, told before in appendicitis and then in gallbladder disease. The exacerbations of chronic ulcer were being treated as acute ulcer, and the subsidence of the attack was being mistaken for a cure. But a condition of ten or fifteen years' standing is not acute, nor has it been cured.

What could surgery do about it? It seemed logical that if the ulcer area was put at rest with no gastric juices or food passing over it to irritate it, it would heal and remain healed. On that supposition the artificial passage from the stomach into the bowel that relieved pyloric obstruction ought also to work for open ulcers. In 1900 Dr.

# Applying the New Surgery

Will first performed gastroenterostomy in two cases of chronic ulcer, and in both the results were all he could ask for. So he continued to consider it the operation of choice and to perform it in an increasing number of cases.

But there were other surgeons, notably Dr. William L. Rodman of Philadelphia, who maintained that excision of the ulcer, or better still of the entire affected portion of the stomach, was more likely to produce lasting results. Dr. Will did not see why, and until he did he would not adopt the procedure, which was then much more dangerous than gastroenterostomy.

Then a curious fact began to appear. A surprising number of persons who came to operation for cancer had suffered from chronic stomach trouble sometime in the past, often many years before. Could it be that these persons had had an ulcer and that the ulcer had degenerated into a cancer? More careful attention to the histories in cancer cases showed that more than sixty per cent of them had at one time or other experienced the typical symptoms of ulcer.

That was a finding too suggestive to be ignored. Carefully Dr. Will and Dr. Charlie began to examine the cancers they removed for any evidence of previous ulcer. And they found it. Not often, but in at least two specimens it seemed to them undeniable that the malignant degeneration was occurring at the site of an old ulcer.

Other men, both pathologists and surgeons, were observing the same development, among them Drs. Ochsner and Murphy and Dr. Dunn of Minneapolis, but still others, of equal authority, challenged that interpretation of the evidence. The matter was highly debatable, but the Mayos were convinced. And if ulcer could turn into cancer, then it was unwise to leave an ulcer in the body, even at rest and healed. Better snip it out or, if there was more than one, remove the affected section of the stomach.*

As they progressed with this work on chronic ulcers the Mayos noticed that a rather surprising number of the lesions occurred in the duodenum. They noticed it, but not consciously enough to make them question the accuracy of the general opinion that duodenal ulcer was rare and relatively unimportant. Then at a meeting of the

---

*Medical men are now generally agreed that duodenal ulcer rarely, if ever, becomes cancer. About gastric ulcer the question is still debatable, but the majority opinion seems to be that stomach ulcer seldom degenerates into cancer.

American Surgical Association Dr. Will caught sight of the truth as he listened to Robert F. Weir of New York.

His [Weir's] presidential address in 1900 was on acute perforations of the duodenum, and his striking presentation of cases, and clear descriptions in relation to the pre-perforate symptoms which we now know to be those of chronic duodenal ulcer, impressed me greatly. They were graphic, they caught my imagination. When I came home I had several patients with acute perforation of the duodenum who gave pre-perforative histories almost identical with those in Weir's cases. I was encouraged to operate on some of the more serious chronic duodenal lesions, and was soon able to recognize and separate the chronic duodenal ulcer from the chronic gastric ulcer.

Once his eyes were opened to duodenal ulcers, Dr. Will found many more of them than he had suspected. Pyloric obstructions that he had thought due to gastric ulcer he now saw to be extensions of the lesion upward from the duodenum. And he also discovered that some of the cases that had baffled him when he tried to find the trouble in the gallbladder were actually chronic ulcer of the duodenum.

Early in his experience with surgery for ulcers Dr. Will was pulled up short by performing operations on some persons with typical ulcer symptoms in whom he could find no lesion, search as he would. Suspiciously he reviewed their histories and found them to be what the Old Doctor would have called "nervous dyspeptics." That was his introduction to the kind of neurosis which simulates the symptoms of chronic ulcer so exactly that the physician can rule out the possibility of an organic lesion only on the basis of the patient's disposition and a previous history of nervous disorders.

The Mayos steered cautiously clear of these poor souls whom they could not help and who could cast great discredit on this newborn field in surgery. And they got plenty of opportunity to learn how to spot them. When word spread of Dr. Will's work on ulcers, seldom a week went by without several neurotic women appearing to ask for a stomach operation. A little wearily Dr. Will warned his fellow surgeons against this "vast army of neurasthenics. . . . Many have already had their movable organs fixed (kidneys and uterus) and the removable ones removed (ovaries and appendix) and now are anxious to secure relief by a further resort to the knife."

If contemporary estimates were correct, medicine was failing to cure in more than seventy-five per cent of chronic ulcer cases, and since that had been so for years there was a goodly accumulation of sufferers to welcome the surgeon. Whatever their physicians thought, those persons themselves, as soon as they heard of the possibility of surgical relief, voluntarily sought it. The trend was just getting under way in 1905, and in that year Dr. W. J. Mayo, by then the foremost American authority on stomach surgery, performed two hundred and seventeen operations on the stomach and duodenum.

## 13

That in brief is the story of the Mayos' advance into differential diagnosis and surgical treatment of diseases of the pelvis and upper abdomen. A similar story might be told for other abdominal organs—the kidneys, the pancreas, the intestines. But the record given must suffice to explain the steady rise in the number of abdominal operations at St. Mary's Hospital, from 54 in the first three and a quarter years to 612 in 1900 and 2,157 in 1905.

The expanded usefulness of surgery was the fruit of a steady improvement in operative techniques that reduced the death rate and made permanent results more certain, but that long story can only be suggested by some highlights in the evolution of gastroenterostomy, which came into general use in the United States largely through the work of the Mayos.

Dr. Will quickly appreciated the usefulness of that operation for short-circuiting the current of digestion, but he trod warily in the use of it because of the tricks it was said to play. Some bad results in his own experience sharpened his interest in the causes for complications and failure, and whenever death occurred after the operation he made an extra effort to get permission for an autopsy to see whether the operation had been at fault and if so just where and why.

One of the moot questions about method was whether to use sutures or the Murphy button to make the union between the stomach and the bowel. Dr. Will, accustomed to use the button in other operations, began with it in this one. The objection to it was the fact that when the button had done its job and was released, it was likely to drop backward into the stomach instead of forward into the bowel, and no one liked the thought of what it might do in the stomach.

The brothers got the ingenious idea—it sounds like one of Dr. Charlie's—of tying to the intestinal side of the button a string about eight inches long with a double bowknot at the end, thinking that intestinal action upon the string would make it a tractor to pull the button in the way it should go. This device seemed to work moderately well, but they did not bother with it long, because no ill effects turned up in the cases where the button had dropped into the stomach.

Or so they thought for a long time. Then one day a woman was admitted to St. Mary's Hospital with what her doctor thought was an attack of appendicitis. Dr. Will had done a gastroenterostomy for her three years before for a bad case of pyloric obstruction, and she had recovered completely, gaining some forty pounds. Now, however, she had lost weight again and was on a liquid diet as before.

Dr. Will suspected a return of the old trouble and upon opening the stomach found an ulcer just above the artificial opening he had made three years before. The old Murphy button was lying in the bottom of the stomach, and Dr. Will feared, though he could not be sure, that it had caused the new ulceration. Perhaps the button was not so safe as he had thought.

Not long afterward he was convinced that it was not, when he lost one patient and nearly lost another because, in very difficult secondary operations, the newly joined organs pulled apart after the buttons had dropped away too soon.

These experiences inclined Dr. Will to listen more sympathetically to those who advocated sutures for anastomosis. The method of applying them had been greatly improved by Senn, Halsted, and others, so that they now gave results equal to those with the button. Gradually Dr. Will changed over to suturing, but a little reluctantly because he felt that part of his unusual success with gastroenterostomy was due to his use of the button.

## 14

Another point of controversy was whether the bowel should be fastened to the front or the back wall of the stomach. Dr. Mayo preferred the anterior position because there the surgeon could see the site of operation and so could do a better and quicker job than when he operated blind. However, so many others favored the posterior position that, in spite of the fact that his results were better than theirs, he decided to try it out. The results were no worse, but no better either.

There was, theoretically, an advantage in the posterior operation. The practice was to join the stomach to the jejunum (the section of the small bowel that follows the duodenum), and in order to do this the jejunum had to be pulled around the membranous mesocolon that separates it from the stomach. A loop of jejunum was left hanging unused after the operation, and this loop could be several inches shorter, so that less of the jejunum was thrown away, in the posterior operation than in the anterior.

That loop caused most of the trouble in gastroenterostomy. The contents draining from the stomach might pass into it and its peristalsis be insufficient to get them started back in the right direction, several feet of the small bowel might get caught in the loop and cause intestinal obstruction, or the loop might kink at the site of union so that the bile and pancreatic juices flowed into the stomach.

When such kinking occurred immediately after the operation the constant vomiting of bile so exhausted the already weakened patient that death was probable. Known to doctors as the "vicious circle," this complication was so often the sequel to gastroenterostomy that surgeons hesitated to use the operation at all.

Vicious circle plagued Dr. Will in his first fourteen operations, but then he made a slight change in his method. Like everyone else, he had been fastening the bowel and cutting the new opening at a point well up on the stomach wall, where there were fewer blood vessels to be dealt with, but now he began using a spot as low as possible, so that the weight of the dependent bowel would pull the baglike stomach into the shape of a funnel. In his next three hundred and sixteen gastroenterostomies there was only one case of vicious circle.

But elimination of the vicious circle did not eliminate bile regurgitation. Sometimes the angulation of the jejunum that caused it occurred three or four months after the patient had been discharged from the hospital, and then a second operation was necessary to join the two limbs of the loop of bowel so as to make a channel for the bile at a level below the opening into the stomach. This usually turned the trick, but a second operation was a mark of failure. There should be some way of doing the original operation so as to prevent the angulation of the bowel.

About 1903 Peterson of the Heidelberg clinic began reporting a no-loop operation that sounded good, and in the same year the German surgeon Mikulicz, probably the leading stomach surgeon in Continental Europe, came to Rochester and showed the brothers how to do it. It seemed to be much better than their method, so they promptly began to use it. The results were good but not phenomenal—four deaths and four cases of secondary operation in a total of forty-three cases—and the Mayos were a little afraid of the procedure because it required a crosswise incision of the bowel, which permitted so small an outlet from the stomach as almost to court difficulty. If this no-loop operation could be done with the usual lengthwise incision it would be ideal.

In October 1903 Dr. Charlie had occasion to do two gastroenterostomies while Dr. Will was away, and he boldly attempted the lengthwise incision. He accomplished it successfully, but it was difficult because there was no way of preventing leakage of the bowel contents while the operation was in progress.

In the meantime Dr. Will had turned to a trial of the method demonstrated to him by Berkeley Moynihan of Leeds during a visit to Rochester in the summer of 1903. His was a loop operation, but it involved the use of clamps he had devised to simplify the technique. In fifty-three gastroenterostomies by this method Dr. Will found the primary results good, only three deaths, but within the year seven patients had to have a second operation for regurgitant bile.

Finally on January 1, 1905 Dr. Will, seeing that with Moynihan's clamps the lengthwise incision would be easily possible, returned to the no-loop operation as done by Dr. Charlie in 1903. In the succeeding six months he performed fifty-six gastroenterostomies with only one death, but there were still two cases of secondary operation.

Determined to get rid of even that much failure, Dr. Will settled down to a close study of the anatomy and physiology of the parts involved. As a result he made a slight shift in the angle at which the jejunum was joined to the stomach, and during the second six months of 1905 he performed sixty-five gastroenterostomies, with no deaths and no secondary operations.

# Applying the New Surgery

## 15

Meanwhile Dr. Charlie's versatile fingers were standing the team in good stead. With apparent ease and gratifying success he could turn from the fine work on the eye to the broader motions of an excision of the knee joint, or from the tricky manipulation of a cranial nerve to the removal of a bunion. The stories of only a few of the fields in which he worked must serve to illustrate how the usefulness of surgery expanded in all of them.

To improved and extended eye surgery Dr. Charlie soon added the newer specialty of ear, nose, and throat, visiting in turn the clinics of all the best eastern specialists in that field. He did considerable work on the mastoid and the sinuses, but the development of chief importance, in number of cases at least, came in surgery of the tonsils and adenoids. Operations on the tonsils were by no means new. They had been described and recommended by surgeons of ancient Greece and had been practiced through most of the centuries since, but only for bad cases of tonsillar abscess and quinsy. Mere enlargement and mild tonsillitis, however often an attack laid the patient low, were not thought to call for surgery.

The removal of adenoids did not come into use until the last quarter of the nineteenth century. Indeed, not until the last decade of that period were the adenoids generally recognized as the cause of the common respiratory troubles in children. When swabbing and spraying the throat and snuffing powders into the nose failed to correct difficulties in breathing, the doctors comforted themselves and the parents with the knowledge that such difficulties vanished as adolescence passed.

Then throat specialists began to trace those and other troubles to the adenoids, and they began to urge the removal of the growths in many cases of deafness, annoying noises in the head, and easy susceptibility to colds. Another conflict between the general practitioner and the specialist was on.

The removal operations were as yet imperfect, did not always bring relief, and sometimes proved dangerous, largely because of hemorrhage. Pointing to those facts the physicians asked why they should recommend surgery for a condition the child would outgrow anyway. The specialist answered that the child might outgrow the abnormal enlargements but not the defects they had caused. He urged the doctor not to let the tonsils and adenoids stay in little Johnny who took cold so easily, or Mary who developed earache whenever she got her feet wet, or Jimmy who was "all stuffed up with catarrh."

The Mayo brothers took no recorded part in this argument, but the side they chose may be seen in the climbing rate at which Dr. Charlie cut out tonsils and adenoids. He devised his own instruments for the procedure; crude they are said to have been, and not conducive to painless operating, but they were as serviceable as any on the market and certainly to be preferred to the fingernails, which the progressive Osler still recommended in 1892 as the instrument of choice for scraping out the adenoids.

Early in the nineties Dr. Charlie began to report his operations as tonsillectomies, though during that decade the operation most generally used was tonsillotomy, the slicing off of the readily accessible, protruding portion of the tonsil. Not until experience had shown how often the remainder grew again to bring a return of the symptoms were methods and instruments devised for complete removal.

That development, coming after the turn of the century, received a tremendous impetus from the theory of focal infection, the idea that infection in the tonsils or the teeth may be a focus from which the bacteria pass to other parts of the body. In time the tonsils were blamed for everything from rheumatism to pneumonia, and they were shelled out on a breath of suspicion. That fad passed, but tonsillectomies still number one third of all the operations performed.

In comparison with that, the round hundred removals that Dr. Charlie was doing annually by 1905 were a bagatelle, but they were a noteworthy increase over the five or ten he had been doing in 1890.

## 16

Scrofula was a disease of ancient lineage. For centuries it had been known and called the "king's evil" because the touch of a royal hand was thought to be the only unfailing cure for it. As late as the end of the seventeenth century medical practitioners little gullible in other matters referred their scrofulous patients to the reigning monarch and credulously passed along the tales of his finger cures.

In one of its most common forms scrofula was marked by an enlargement of the lymph glands of the neck, followed by a cheesy degeneration and the formation of sinuses discharging to the surface. The cause of the malady was a mystery, but because of the loathsomeness of the sores and swellings and because the disease was most common among street waifs or the children of the very poor, affliction with scrofula was considered cause for reproach, the mark of poverty and uncleanness.

Then came Pasteur and Koch and the discovery of the tubercle bacillus, and scrofula was found to be a tubercular infection of the glands.

The Mayos saw an unusual amount of this disease in their practice, and thought it was because they lived in an agricultural community that drank raw milk. Somewhere they had picked up the fact, not yet generally accepted, that tuberculosis could be transferred from cattle to men through milk.

Dr. Charlie adopted surgical treatment for this glandular affection early in the nineties, when such treatment was very new, after he had seen the operation done a few times, perhaps by Dr. Ochsner, who was an early exponent of it. At first he cut out only the enlarged glands and was proud of the small incision through which he could accomplish the task, but when patient after patient came back to him showing an extension of the infection that necessitated a second or even a third or fourth operation, he knew he must take out more in the first place. Soon he was making the incision as large as he could in order to remove every lymph gland he could find between the ear and the clavicle, and not only the glands but the fascia, or muscular sheaths, in which they lie. That was an extensive operation, but not a dangerous one, and it seemed to increase his percentage of permanent cures, so he continued to practice it.

And to defend it. For he found himself in conflict with some of his fellow Minnesota surgeons on the matter. Several of the best of them had been so discouraged by the results of operation that they had turned against it entirely. You don't cut out enough, Dr. Charlie told them. And John B. Murphy backed him up, saying only the thorough extirpation of every lymph node would check the spread of the infection.

But the others insisted that no matter how complete an operation they did, the trouble came back. Besides, they said, just look at the unsightly scar that big S-shaped incision leaves on the child's neck.

It's not half so unsightly as the scars made by the glands themselves if they aren't removed, replied the advocates of excision, but they quickly learned how to operate through an incision along the natural creases of the neck so the scar would not be so noticeable.

The opponents were not won over. In 1900 Dr. Charles Wheaton of Minneapolis declared the removal of tubercular glands of the neck to be on a par with the indiscriminate castration of women that surgeons had engaged in a few years before. Dr. Charlie, firmly, did not think so; on the basis of experience in about four hundred cases he was sure that thorough extirpation would cure in the majority of cases.

Drs. Boeckmann, MacLaren, and Dunn agreed with Dr. Wheaton, and Drs. Dunsmoor and Moore sided with Dr. Charlie. The argument was heated. Dr. Wheaton described the lymph glands as the policemen of the body, standing at its portals to prevent the entrance of infection; to remove them was almost malpractice. Dr. Dunsmoor retorted that when a cop was tired or sick he was no protection and might as well be removed.

Four years later young Dr. Dennis, a former assistant of Wheaton's, brought the question up again by reading a paper pleading for complete removal of the glands. Immediately someone reminded the audience of what Dr. Wheaton had said on that earlier occasion, and Dr. Dennis replied: Dr. Wheaton's views on the matter were based on an incomplete operation, for he was not accustomed to remove the fascia as well as the glands. "I never saw elsewhere such a complete and fine dissection as that of Dr. Mayo, made at Rochester, and when that is universally done I think the statistics will be much better. His operation is better than any I have found in the literature on the subject."

## 17

The Mayos had learned to treat various forms of acute bone infection, often tubercular in nature, by cutting into the affected area, cleaning out the septic material, providing free drainage for any further accumulation, and packing the wound with antiseptic powder or gauze. Done in time this procedure would check the infection and

# Applying the New Surgery

save life and limb. But it was not always done in time, not even in accident or fracture cases, and then to avoid death amputation was necessary as of old.

Dr. Charlie scored one of his earliest triumphs when he was called to see a patient with acute suppuration of the knee joint. It was too late for mild measures; the patient was already showing all the constitutional signs of dangerously active infection. Yet Dr. Charlie hesitated. He hated to amputate. If only he could get at the inner cavities of the joint, to clean them out and drain them thoroughly.

Well, why not lay the knee joint wide open by a sweeping transverse incision so he *could* get at them freely? He might yet check the infection. Of course the motion of the joint would be gone, but a stiff leg would be better than no leg at all. If it did not work, there would be time enough for amputation. So he made the incision, drained all the recesses of the joint, and packed it full of antiseptic gauze.

The effect was astonishing. In a few hours the symptoms of active inflammation subsided and the patient was obviously on the road to recovery. Then Dr. Charlie put the joint in position and allowed the parts to unite. Soon the patient was up and about again, his leg stiff but useful, and his own.

Feeling that this outcome was no lucky accident, Dr. Charlie wrote a report of the case and the method he had used for publication in the *Annals of Surgery.* And a few months later he was pleased as Punch to read in that same journal a communication from Dr. Arpad Gerster of New York calling attention to this "Mayo operation" and testifying from his own experience to its worth.

## 18

By 1890 Von Bergmann of Germany could write a whole book about *Surgical Treatment of Diseases of the Brain.* Although this branch of surgery was still in its infancy, it was already possible to remove blood clots and certain kinds of tumors, drain cysts, and do a much better job than formerly of repairing damage to the tissues in compound fractures of the skull.

Dr. Charlie kept step with developments in this field and achieved some of the most dramatic of the Mayo cures in it, among them several cases of epilepsy resulting from old head injuries. He found many cases of this sort in the state hospitals for the insane, and for a time he hoped that surgery might prove effective in all kinds of epilepsy, but he had finally to accept the fact that only where the "fits" were the result of an accident to the brain could the knife help.

He also learned to treat surgically such nervous disorders as spasmodic wry-neck and various forms of facial neuralgia, often with brilliant success to the patient's way of thinking. His major triumph was the cure of a case of the frightfully intense neuralgia accompanied by tic that occurs when something goes wrong with the cranial nerve cluster known as the gasserian ganglion. The removal of the ganglion was an operation of surpassing difficulty and uncertain results, even in the improved form devised by Hartley of New York and Krause of Germany. So the Rochester editor was right in thinking it worth reporting when Dr. Charlie performed it successfully in 1899.

One of the rarest operations was performed Friday on a man at St. Mary's Hospital, it being the removal of the gasserian ganglion, which is located inside of the skull under the brain, midway between the eye and ear. It was taken out because it had become diseased and caused neuralgia in the face. The moment the troublesome ganglion was gone, the pain in the face of the patient ceased. The operation is an exceedingly delicate one, for it was necessary to lift up the skull and then enter the dura-mater, the inner covering of the brain, and cut the nerve center off.

## 19

Varicose veins occurred frequently among the hard-working farmers of the Rochester community. Often they caused no discomfort or so little that it was not thought worth complaining about in this vale of woes, and the condition dragged on for years before the doctor's help was sought. Dr. Charlie once told how casually these patients came to him. Sometimes, in the spring of the year perhaps, a farmer would come into the office, apologizing for his appearance. "I've just put in my crop," he would say. "I've been following the drag and I'm all dirty, but I don't like the looks of this old ulcer." Then he would pull off the faded bandana he had wrapped around his leg to keep his overalls from rubbing the sore, and Dr. Charlie would see a varicose ulcer, as big as the palm of his hand sometimes, raw and ugly. The man might have had it for eight or nine years, open that way most of the time.

# Applying the New Surgery

"How sore that must be," Dr. Charlie said to one patient.

"No, it isn't sore," the man answered. "But it doesn't look so good. I thought maybe I'd better have you see it."

Or perhaps there would be some soreness or cramps and aching in the muscles, enough at last to make the man send for Dr. Charlie, who would find him sitting by the kitchen stove, foot in the oven maybe, trying to keep the bad leg hot.

If the condition was not too old or too extensive, rest in bed and strapping the legs with elastic bandages, with antiseptic salves and dressings for the ulcer, would work the healing. Otherwise operation was necessary.

Surgical treatment of sorts for varicose veins was very old, but it was the Germans, Trendelenburg and Schede, who had devised practicable procedures for removing the offending saphenous vein through an incision stretching from the thigh to several inches below the knee. The operation was not difficult, but it was tedious because of the time it took to close the long incision, the scar was almost certain to break open later at the knee through motion of the leg, and the extensive exposure was risky because of the peculiar susceptibility of the veins to infection. All in all, most surgeons did not like to do the operation and would just as soon patients with varicose veins went elsewhere.

Putting his mechanical bent to work, Dr. Charlie designed some long-handled forceps that formed a ring at the end when closed. Inserted through a short crosswise incision and closed around the vein, these forceps were pushed along for several inches underneath the skin, stripping the vein from its sheath and cutting off its lateral feeders as they went. When the end of their length was reached, another crosswise incision was made, the forceps reintroduced and pushed on as before. The entire length of vein could be removed with from three to five incisions, easily and quickly closed. This cut the required time in half and made the operation a relatively minor procedure.

In 1904 Dr. Archibald MacLaren of St. Paul told the state medical society he had seen Dr. Mayo use his new method a short time before, and "The next day I saw another surgeon do the same operation, where he himself and four assistants, all at work, did about the same amount of work in four times the length of time, using the old method."

Where the varicose ulcer was large in extent or persistently refused to heal, it had to be cut out and new skin grafted onto the wound. That too was practicable because of a recent development.

Skin-grafting was first tried in 1854 and the use of it spread with antisepsis, but the methods available were tiresomely slow. The grafts used were tiny and time for healing was allowed after each one before the next was applied, so that it might take three or four thousand grafts and from six months to three years to cover a scalp or a thigh with new skin.

Karl Thiersch of Munich proposed a new method in the middle seventies, but it was not generally adopted until after he described it a second time in 1886. Thin shavings of skin, each about an inch and a half wide and several inches long, were cut with a razor from the source area, applied at once to the wound, and fastened in place with sutures of absorbable catgut. By this method an area from one to twenty-four inches square could be covered with new skin at one operation, with healing in from ten days to two weeks. Dr. Charlie was using it expertly and frequently by 1893.

Among the uses for skin-grafting was the covering of the large denuded area left by the new radical operation for breast cancer, one of the most malignant forms of that malignant disease and then considered hopeless. Surgeons were cutting out the cancer when they found it, but to no avail. A quick and fatal recurrence was apparently inevitable.

Then in 1888 Halsted conceived the idea of complete amputation. Not just the growth itself but the entire breast must be removed, and to such an extent that the knife would not at any point cut through tissue already affected by the cancer. The enormous wound left by the amputation made it such a formidable-looking procedure that surgeons as well as laymen shuddered away from the mutilation. But by 1894 Halsted could announce that in fifty such operations there had been only three recurrences. Well, it was surely better for a woman to live with one breast gone than to die intact. So the use of the radical operation spread.

The Mayos adopted it promptly, having learned it firsthand by watching Halsted himself perform it. That they found it good may be assumed from the increase in the number of breast operations they performed, from eleven in 1895 to fifty-nine in 1905, all but five of the latter being amputations by the Halsted method.

## 21

James Strain of Fillmore Co., has been at St. Mary's Hospital for several months, under the treatment of the Drs. Mayo for a swelling of the throat. When he came here the swelling was of immense proportions, but under the skillful treatment he will be all right in about a month, and will be able to assume the management of his farm.

So reported the Rochester *Record and Union* on March 14, 1890.

The Drs. Mayo were nonplused when Mr. Strain, a brawny Scotsman of some sixty years, walked into their office. They knew his "swelling of the throat" for what it was, a goiter, and large goiters were no rarity, but they had never seen such an enormous growth as this man had. It hung far down onto his chest, and forced his head up and back as far as it could go. He had come to them because the tumor was interfering seriously with his breathing.

What could they do? Dr. Will remembered having heard that injecting iodine into these thyroid tumors would make them shrink, so he tried it in several places. But the skin had literally had the life stretched out of it, and it broke open at the points of puncture, discharging large amounts of pus and blood.

The brothers talked over the possibilities. Perhaps they ought to make an incision connecting the open places, so the tumor could drain more freely. But when they did that the huge growth began to bulge through the opening. The man's condition was desperate; whatever happened, that goiter had to come out.

They knew one big danger in removing it would be that of hemorrhage, and remembering that their father always used turpentine to check bleeding, they saturated a big abdominal sponge with turpentine and put it in a bowl handy to the operating table. Then they got Mr. Strain onto the table, gave him a little anesthetic—he could not take much—incised the skin and superficial tissues freely, and quickly scooped the tumor out with their hands. The bleeding was terrific, for they could take time to tie off only the largest vessels. The minute the goiter was out they stuffed the sponge filled with turpentine into the cavity, sewed the skin and flesh together across it, and bandaged the wound as tightly as they dared.

They had no real hope that the man would live, but he fooled them. He recovered slowly, but he recovered. Why, only nature knew. In a few days they reopened the incision and removed the sponge, and a few months later Mr. Strain was able to return to his farm, where he lived for many years, a willing witness to what those Mayos could do.

That was the beginning and the end of Dr. Will's work in the goiter field, but it was only the beginning of Dr. Charlie's. The case awakened his interest in that mysterious little body, the thyroid gland, and he began learning what he could about it and about goiters.

Mr. Strain's tumor was what is called simple goiter, an enlargement of the thyroid gland that is not ordinarily attended with disturbing complications. At that time it was thought to be only an inconvenience and disfigurement, unless it grew so large or in such a direction as to press upon the trachea and cause distress in breathing. Removal of the growth for this complication had been practiced, crudely to be sure, in the Middle Ages, but the modern development of the practice began in 1878, when Theodor Kocher, the pupil of Billroth at work in Switzerland, where goiter was endemic, began to remove enlarged thyroid glands. By the 1890's the treatment of this kind of goiter, where necessary, was recognized as a job for the surgeon.

Not that the operation was simple or safe. There was first the difficulty of controlling hemorrhage and second the vexing problem of removing just enough of the gland. If the surgeon cut away too little of it the goiter might grow again; if he took away too much—as Kocher learned from sad experience when he at first tried to get out every shred of the offending gland—the patient suffered a grievous change. She (it was most often a woman) swelled in bulk, her features coarsened, her skin got dry and rough, her hair thin and brittle, and mentally and physically she slowed down.

This condition was known as myxedema, and its developing after total thyroidectomy helped doctors reach the conclusion that it was somehow the result of atrophy or loss of the thyroid. An analogous disease called cretinism was known to occur among children, and whether congenital or acquired, it made itself evident in a marked retardation of mental and physical development.

# Applying the New Surgery

The administration of thyroid extract made from the glands of sheep to overcome the insufficiency in myxedema and cretinism was first tried in 1891, but it did not immediately enter the ken of the practitioner, for in 1892 even the alert William Osler knew of no effective remedy for these maladies.

But within five years at the most thyroid extract was available, for it was being used in Rochester. On June 9, 1897 a little boy was brought to the Mayo offices. He was five years old, but he could neither walk nor talk, and he had the heavy, short body, broad, flat nose, thick lips, and moronic expression characteristic of the cretin. Thyroid extract was prescribed—in small doses to be safe, because the family lived too far away for the boy to be kept under close observation.

The effects were swift and amazing. The boy brightened up, learned to say a few words and to walk a little, and his body thinned out and lengthened. Then bad weather set in so the parents could not get to Rochester for more medicine, and slowly, disappointingly, the child relapsed to his former state. But with spring and more of the pills, growth began again and continued steadily and rapidly until the boy had caught up with his years. The pathetically happy mother fumbled for words: "John was always so bloated; now he is like other children."

Clearly, knowledge of the functions and diseases of the thyroid was still toddling and would take years to mature. Meanwhile the surgical treatment of goiter groped forward empirically, with Dr. Halsted, Dr. George Crile of Cleveland, and Dr. C. H. Mayo leading the way in the United States. The major problems of thyroidectomy were solved, and the use of the procedure increased slowly until by 1904 Dr. Mayo could report a total of sixty-eight operations for simple goiter, with only two deaths among them.

Yet he was then doing only a score of such operations a year, in spite of the fact that there were plenty of goiters roundabout, since Rochester lay well within the principal American goiter belt, which stretched roughly from southeast to northwest across the Middle West. Persons afflicted with the terribly disfiguring "big neck" were familiar sights throughout the area. The explanation for the slow pickup in surgery may be that the people and their doctors had to be educated to accept operation for what seemed more a humiliation than a danger. Or, more probably, they did not distinguish between the operative results in simple goiter and those in exophthalmic goiter, for the latter was a horse of far different mettle—in action capricious, unpredictable, often vicious.

Exophthalmic goiter is the familiar and descriptive name for a disorder known to doctors also as Grave's disease or Basedow's disease, after the men who first described it. It is characterized by a number of severe symptoms: unnatural thinness, great nervousness, rapid pulse, quick and extreme changes of mood, vomiting, diarrhea, and the two from which it was named, a goiter and protruding eyeballs (exophthalmos). The goiter was then considered merely one of many symptoms, and the disease was not associated primarily with the thyroid gland. Dr. Osler, writing in 1892, said the best guess as to the cause of Grave's disease made it an affection of the medulla oblongata, a part of the brain, but that no theory proposed thus far could account for all the diverse symptoms.

After listing the drugs thought to be specifics for Grave's disease, Osler added that in his experience rest in bed with the occasional application of an ice bag over the heart had proved the most satisfactory remedy. Operating on the thyroid gland had been tried but was not successful, he said.

A decade later some progress had been made, but real success in the treatment of exophthalmic goiter was still to be achieved.

## 22

Repetition in disease after disease emphasizes the essence of that story: The omissions and errors of medicine had accumulated a vast reservoir of uncured illness of long standing, to which the new surgery made it possible for qualified practitioners to bring relief. And the Mayo brothers began practice at just the right moment to be the first to tap that reservoir in a wide area surrounding Rochester. No wonder Dr. Will once musingly remarked to a friend, "As I look back over those early years, I am impressed with the fact that much of our success, if not most of it, was due to the time at which we entered medicine." The time *and* the place—assuming always the men able to grasp the exceptional opportunity they presented.

# CHAPTER THIRTEEN

# The Radius Lengthens

Today's doctors, most of them, impatiently shrug away any tendency to dwell upon the romance and drama of their work. It is the solid science that counts, they say. Granted, but even they admit to wonder at the achievements on the frontiers of their profession—at the incision and repair of an injured heart, or the quick and far-reaching effects of a newly discovered chemical formula or a lately synthesized vitamin. Much of what the Mayos were doing from 1890 to 1905 was achievement on just such a frontier.

For the purposes of medical science the patient they worked on might be only a set of initials identifying a group of anatomic and physiologic facts, but "H. W., male, white, aged 46" was a husband and father, a brother, a friend, a member of the community. And the new life-saving, health-giving operations were miracles to those to whom they brought hope and happiness. Unless that fact is taken well into account, there is no explaining the amazing increase in the Mayos' surgical practice.

Something of all this is distilled in the recollection of a Nebraska doctor, born and raised in the vicinity of Rochester, where a certain Irishman was one of the sights of the little community. Natives would point him out: "There is Pat Glynn," they would say. "Will Mayo cut a piece out of his stomach, and he lived!"

Because people felt and talked that way, a deep and comforting faith in the marvelous powers of the brother surgeons in Rochester spread through the countryside like fingers of water in thirsty sand.

## 2

A Rochester doctor has reported that when Dr. Will first began to do major surgery, to remove the appendix or the dead portion of the bowel in strangulated hernia, the bewhiskered elder physicians of the neighboring villages shook their heads and said something ought to be done about that rash young man. They allowed it was malpractice to cut up a patient like that. But not for long; they too soon saw that "he lived," and their disapproval turned to incredulity, then to admiration and confidence.

Some of the older men might resent the claims of the new surgery, but they were all fascinated by it, and dazzled by what one of them called "the glare of that marvelous brilliancy" it attained. They might walk out on a lecture about dyspepsia, with which they had to deal almost daily, but they crowded the hall to hear about the new operations, which most of them would never perform. For as they learned to accept surgical treatment for one ailment after another, they referred their patients to men they knew were experienced in operating.

Ordinarily one looks to the big city for the specialists, not to a country town as small as one's own. So it would have been natural for Minnesota practitioners to look to Minneapolis and St. Paul for their surgeons, as many of them did. But there were others like the old doctor in Dodge Center. Mrs. Robertson, a patient of his, must have a major operation, and he told her so. But to whom should she go? Some surgeon in the Twin Cities? The old doctor shook his head. He didn't know those men in the Cities, and he wouldn't know which one of them to recommend. But he did know that old Dr. Mayo over in Rochester was an honest man and a good surgeon. So Mrs. Robertson went to St. Mary's Hospital in Rochester for her operation.

Starting on the foundation of their father's reputation among his colleagues, the brothers laid their bricks well. They continued his activity in the Olmsted County Medical Society, and for several years the meetings of the group were held in the Mayo offices, with the two Mayos taking turns with the others in holding office and contributing papers. Occasionally they invited the members over to St. Mary's to watch a series of operations instead of listening to the usual essays.

In 1892 they took a leading part in the organization of the Southern Minnesota Medical Society, a regional association for the southeastern counties of the state. The annual meetings of this group, alternating between Winona and Rochester most of the time, were gala affairs, complete with full-dress banquet and many addresses, and they were always well attended.

# The Radius Lengthens

The Minnesota Valley Medical Society, organized in the days of the Civil War, was still active, and the Old Doctor maintained his membership in it. He often journeyed over to Mankato or St. Peter to attend one of its meetings, visit with his old friends, participate in the program, or even preside, and not infrequently one of his sons went along to read a paper. As settlement thickened to the west, the Minnesota Valley group voted to merge with the Southern Minnesota Medical Society, and the privileges of membership were extended to all doctors in the southern half of the state.

In that company the Mayo brothers stood out as surgeons; their growing knowledge and experience made its impression, and many members came to feel about the sons as the old doctor of Dodge Center had felt about their father. They might not be able to pick wisely among the Twin City surgeons, but they knew the Mayo brothers personally.

Gradually a few of them learned to do for themselves some of the less radical operations, particularly those of an emergency nature. But even those who went furthest in adding surgery to their general practice tried little more than a simple appendectomy or the removal of stones from a gallbladder. For anything more serious they continued to rely upon the Mayos. Dr. Andrews of Mankato illustrated the general situation when he rose at a state society meeting to thank Dr. C. H. Mayo for a description of the methods he used to remove foreign bodies from the trachea and esophagus.

This is a very helpful paper for us general practitioners, said Dr. Andrews, because it deals with cases in which we must act at once, in which there is no time to send the patient over to Rochester or up to Minneapolis.

In this matter of referred cases St. Mary's was of signal importance because it stood out as the only hospital in the district. If a doctor had a patient who must be hospitalized there was only St. Mary's in Rochester to take him to, and if he was to enter St. Mary's he must be referred to the Mayos.

After a while other hospitals were built in the towns roundabout, often with the success of St. Mary's as the spur to action. The editor of the *Owatonna Journal* pointed out that the fares paid by Owatonnans going to the hospital at Rochester over a period of five years

341

would build a hospital of their own. But when Owatonna got its hospital it learned, as had Winona and other towns before it, that such facilities at home could no longer keep patients from going to Rochester. Even when the local doctor was willing to operate himself, the patient often decided against it, for operations were new and frightening; even appendectomy was a major ordeal that the patient faced with great apprehension. Was his family doctor competent for this? Was it safe to let him do this cutting? If the ailing man could afford it he preferred to go over to Rochester to the surgeons of whose prowess he had heard so many tales.

### 3

Not always did the doctor send or take his patient to Rochester; frequently he summoned one of the Mayos to come to a patient who was unable or unwilling to leave home. And time and again the operation that Dr. Will or Dr. Charlie performed on such an occasion was the first instance of major surgery in that community. In 1893 a physician from Faribault, a town of eight thousand inhabitants to the northwest of Rochester, defended himself for not using surgery in appendicitis by saying there had never been an operation in his town and he could not induce anyone to submit to one!

When someone in a neighborhood like that at last got desperate enough to say all right, call a surgeon, the operation was an event. The doctors for miles around assembled to witness the visitor's performance and afterward perhaps to break bread with him in the local doctor's home. Each success in such circumstances meant return calls and more patients referred to Rochester.

But this journeyman surgery was time-consuming and wearing. Dr. Will long remembered one day he had of it. Early in the morning he started out for Plainview to the east to operate on the wife of the president of the bank for extra-uterine pregnancy, or so Dr. Slocum had said. And no doubt Dr. Slocum felt proud of himself for having been able to make that diagnosis. Extra-uterine or ectopic pregnancy is an accident of nature in which the development of the impregnated ovum occurs outside the uterus, usually in the fallopian tube. It was one of the medical mysteries Lawson Tait cleared up, and Dr. Will had learned the surgical handling of it from Joseph Price, but very rarely indeed could the accident be diagnosed correctly before the tube ruptured.

When Dr. Will arrived at the patient's home he found some fifteen doctors assembled, at Dr. Slocum's invitation. The rug had been taken up and the curtains down, the floor and the walls had been scrubbed, and a quantity of hot water and clean towels were at hand. Everything was ready and waiting for the surgeon.

But when Dr. Will examined the patient he disagreed with the diagnosis. The woman had merely a lateral pregnancy, which occurs in one horn of the uterus, and he refused to operate. Some of the doctors thought he ought to open the abdomen anyway, perhaps to make sure of the diagnosis, but he knew there would be nothing he could do once he got in, so he said no and left.

It was a twelve-mile drive to the nearest railroad station, and Dr. Will got back to Rochester about noon—and found a call waiting for him to come over to Aurora to do an appendectomy. He took the next train west, but it was early evening when he reached there, only to learn that the patient lived in Blooming Prairie, some ten miles farther on. It was nearly eight o'clock when he reached the bedside.

Again a group of doctors and a room in readiness. This time the diagnosis was correct, but the patient's condition was such that Dr. Will decided it would be unwise to operate. Her father got angry about it, insisting that they had called Dr. Mayo to operate and he ought to go ahead. Dr. Will flatly refused.

As he turned to go he felt tired and discouraged; such a futile, wasted day! Then a neighbor standing near by spoke to him. "Doctor, you have an old friend here in town who would like to see you. Do you remember the girl from Blooming Prairie you operated on a year or two ago?"

When he gave the name Dr. Will did remember. She was the patient a German doctor had brought to Rochester, a little girl eight or nine years old, "the thinnest creature you ever saw, about half an inch thick." Yes, Dr. Will remembered her very well, for she was one of the first persons he had operated on for stomach ulcers. He remembered how frightened she was, how her father hung onto her while she took the anesthetic, and how her mother stood outside in the corridor crying loudly while he did the operation.

He drove over with the neighbor and was welcomed quite without reserve. The father hugged him, the mother kissed him, and the little girl, healthy and robust-looking now, kissed him too. Then they got out a bottle of wine to celebrate his visit.

Dr. Will was deeply touched, and felt a warmth that was not of wine. The day had been hard and disappointing, but this was reward enough.

4

The business of referred cases was loaded with dynamite. Sometimes of course the reference was made reluctantly and the referring doctor was not happy when the Mayos did what he could not do, especially if the remedy was a simple one requiring ingenuity rather than surgical skill. Here are two such instances, as Dr. Will told them:

One night a man came to the house accompanied by his two brothers. He was nearly exsanguinated from a bleeding tooth. We carried him in and I made an examination. There was nothing to be done at that time of night except to plug the cavity, so I took the cork from a peppermint bottle and drove it well up between the teeth and told him to hold it. The doctor who had sent him never forgave me.

Another time a doctor brought a man in who had lost a great deal of blood from persistent nose-bleeding. He had burst a vein in the nose, and was becoming exsanguinated. I noted that the man was doing a great deal of coughing and spitting of blood, and I said to him, "Catch your nose between your thumb and finger and let it bleed back into the throat and then spit the blood out." Of course, all that was required was to give the blood a chance to clot a little so that healing could take place. The man promptly got well and the doctor was much less friendly to me.

But the Mayos handled referred cases tactfully and never showed up a local doctor's mistakes or incompetency if they could help it. A doctor in a town not far from Rochester was leaving for California and sold his practice to a young man just graduated from medical school. Among the young doctor's first patients was a girl with a broken leg. He put the leg in a plaster cast, but when he examined it next day he found he had made the cast too tight and the leg was already gangrenous.

Quickly he discovered that he had received an urgent call from out of town and suggested that the family consult another physician. The doctor they called, whose name may be Smith, was a fine old man, one of the pioneer doctors of Minnesota, and a highly respected practitioner in the community. There was nothing for him to do but amputate the child's leg, and he did. The family hunted for the young doctor with a shotgun, but they never caught up with him.

Some time afterward an uncle of the girl came to Dr. Smith with a badly injured hand, and the good doctor prepared again to amputate. But the injured man's brother interfered. There would be no cutting and sawing done there because he was going to take his brother over to the hospital in Rochester.

When the Mayos examined the hand they saw there was no need for amputation; it was already getting better. But they gave a thought to old Dr. Smith. Redressing the wounded member, they told the patient that since Dr. Smith had seen the hand the previous day they would have to call him in for his opinion. So Dr. Smith came over, and in the end was credited with having helped to save the hand. He was pathetically grateful to Dr. Will and Dr. Charlie, saying they had saved him from ruin in his community.

Dr. Smith, and others who fared similarly at the brothers' hands, naturally did not hesitate to refer their patients to the Mayos. The brothers' policy was determined partly by their realization that keeping the friendship and the confidence of their colleagues was to their own advantage, partly by the memory of an instance or two in their own early practice when they had been spared humiliation in like fashion, but mostly by the lesson in professional solidarity they had learned from their positive father: "I did it for the profession, not for him, damn him."

5

The Mayos never bought a patient, and it would be interesting to know whether they were ever asked to bid for one. The despicable practice of selling cases to the highest bidder, known as fee-splitting, grew up with specialization, when the general practitioner began sending his patients, not to the most competent specialist he knew, but to the man who paid him the biggest commission.

In 1900 two members of the Chicago Medical Society, wishing to expose the extent of the racket in their city, drew up and sent to all its leading surgeons a letter that purported to come from a country doctor and asked what share of his fee the specialist would give for a patient. When the answers, with names attached, were published in the newspapers, the scandal shook the city, and the society's members were particularly annoyed because John B. Murphy, whom they were accusing of all the unethical practices in the medical calendar, was among those who had peremptorily refused to make any proposition. In the end the society, to its discredit, disciplined the two men who had concocted the hoax and let those who had revealed themselves as fee-splitters go scot free.

That episode brought the problem into the open throughout the country, and it got a thorough airing at the annual session of the Minnesota State Medical Society that year. Who was to blame for the pernicious practice? The general practitioner said it was the fault of the specialist, who charged so much that the patient had no money left to pay the family doctor. The specialist retorted that it was the other way round; the local doctor bled his patient white without doing him any good, so that the specialist had to give his services free of charge. The younger men blamed the older for setting a bad example, and the older men accused the younger of splitting fees because they were unwilling to work up a practice slowly, as their elders had done.

Finally Dr. A. S. Adams of Rochester got the floor. He was bewildered by all this argument that took the existence of fee-splitting for granted. He had practiced medicine next door to surgical specialists for fifteen years, he said, and never once had they so much as intimated that they would give him a commission of any sort for placing a patient in their hands. He did refer to them the cases he felt himself incompetent to handle, but not because they had ever suggested it or solicited the work.

Dr. Adams was speaking of the Mayos of course. They considered the barter in sick men a damnable business and never hesitated to say so or to fight it in professional circles. But Dr. Will once pointed out that they could not claim uncommon virtue for abstaining. They had never lacked patients, had never been forced to struggle with competitors for enough cases to get started on, and so "we were never tempted into the unfair practices that competitive medicine sometimes appears to force on very excellent men."

# The Radius Lengthens

The practitioners in Olmsted and adjoining counties who had formed the habit of going to Rochester to watch Dr. Mayo operate when the Old Doctor began his work in surgery kept it up after the sons took over the operating, and they were always made welcome. In fact, in the early years the brothers sent out postcards to the doctors roundabout whenever some operation or morning's schedule of unusual interest was in prospect. That was not necessary for long; the doctors began dropping in whenever they wanted to, and items like these became frequent in the Rochester papers:

Drs. Dixon and Holoran of Chatfield and Dr. Bigelow of Dodge Center were in the city yesterday to attend a clinic at St. Mary's Hospital.

Doctors Wright of Kasson, Adams of Elgin, Chamberlain of St. Charles, and Dugan of Eyota attended a clinic at St. Mary's Hospital yesterday.

Sometimes the younger men would go for a week or two of clinics, and the operating room at St. Mary's became a kind of school in which the doctors of the district could learn the uses and techniques of the new surgery.

Because the Mayos themselves were moving rapidly away from medical practice to concentration on surgery and the medical men were attempting little of that as yet, the brothers were not dangerous competitors of the doctors with whom they dealt, except in the near vicinity of Rochester. Later, when the brothers' partnership became the Clinic and swung back to medicine, and when surgeons had become more common among doctors, there would be more reason for friction and resentment.

But during this period the Mayos were a comfort and a bulwark for their fellows. The doctors of southern Minnesota were glad rather than annoyed that the Mayos were within easy reach, grateful for the presence of so fine a school as the Mayos' operating room, proud that these colleagues of theirs were achieving so mightily and so worthily. Their attitude was nobly summarized in a letter written years later by the son of one of them.

To Doctors Will and Charley Mayo:
My father died yesterday, ten days after a fall on the ice. He was 78 years old and had practiced over 50 years in this community.

# The Mayo Brothers

I am writing you because during all these years he valued your friendship so highly. He often spoke of your father, whom he saw and knew in the early years of your practice. For over twenty years now I have daily stood at his side as we operated in the best way we knew how, and I believe he hardly ever did an operation that he did not say, "This is the way Dr. Charley does this," or make some reference to you or to what he saw at his last visit to you.

Your great success was to him a great source of personal pride. He watched every step in your progress as though he were personally interested in it. What he saw there was, I believe, responsible for keeping him the student of medicine he was up to the last. He often told of the visit of Dr. Will to Blue Earth in the early nineties and the operation on Mrs. Charley Pride. It was the first abdominal operation ever done in the community, an ovarian cyst as I recall it. I recall your visit at our home at the time.

I write this letter with only the one thought in mind, that of indicating something of the love and interest that some of these "old men of the prairie" had in you and your work. I doubt whether there will ever be a more loyal group in American medicine.       Roscoe C. Hunt

## 7

It would have taken a greater attraction than even the Mayos possessed to build more than a local medical practice on the motive power of horseflesh moving over narrow, rutted wagon roads. The successive developments in transportation have been essential in the Mayo rise, and the first of these was the railroad. When the Mayos were ready for expansion beyond the radius of team-and-wagon travel, the rails were ready to provide transportation to carry the surgeons out and the patients in.

Until late in the century there was only one railroad through Rochester, the Winona and St. Peter division of the Chicago and Northwestern Railroad, but that ran in the right direction, east and west through southern Minnesota into the Dakotas, with extensive branches south into Iowa. The train connections left something to be desired, and the feeder lines could hardly be said to form a network in the hinterland, but "the cars" to Rochester were within reasonable reach of anyone willing to juggle timetables and spend a few tedious hours between trains at the junctions.

Even within horse-and-buggy reach of Rochester, the trains permitted some feats of transporting patients that would not have been

# The Radius Lengthens

possible without them. Carrie Brown, a farmer's daughter, seventeen years old, was severely burned in the explosion of a kerosene lamp. Physicians were called and did all they could to alleviate her suffering, but she grew worse, and at the end of three months her condition was desperate.

The parents had heard of Rochester's famous hospital and determined, as a last resort, to bring her here. Their home is just twenty-five miles from St. Charles, the nearest railroad station. It was planned to take their injured daughter by team to St. Charles, and thence by the cars to Rochester. It was found, however, that she could not stand the jarring incident to a trip with a team, so Mr. Brown consulted with his neighbors and three of them volunteered to assist him and carry his daughter to the station. Accordingly a cot was made, provided with handles.

Last night when darkness had settled over the land, the party started out for their destination. Early this morning they arrived at St. Charles, having been on the road for fully ten hours. Their progress was necessarily very slow, as they had to proceed with extreme care, lest the least jar should injure the charge intrusted to them. . . . The morning passenger west was taken, and a sorrowful yet withal hopeful party arrived here at ten o'clock. After resting at the depot for an hour, the cot bearing the frightfully burned young lady was taken to St. Mary's Hospital, where she is now in charge of the best nurses and will receive the most careful attention."

But the railway played more than a facilitating role. Every western line of any size maintained its own surgical service and in many cases its own hospitals. Providing care for injured employees and passengers had been no great problem in the well-populated East, but when the rails plunged into the wide open West the companies found themselves faced with the task of providing their own medical services. So they equipped each train with an emergency chest of medical supplies and taught their trainmen how to check hemorrhage, administer opiates for pain and stimulants for shock, and apply temporary antiseptic dressings.

And they named a railway surgeon at each station to whom accident victims could be taken or who could be summoned to the scene of a disaster. Since they could find few local men competent to handle major surgical problems, they appointed district surgeons to be called for serious cases on each division and hired a full-time chief surgeon to keep a supervisory eye on the entire network.

The companies built their own hospitals where necessary, but they preferred to pay for accommodations in existing institutions wherever there were such. The building of St. Mary's Hospital quickly brought to Dr. W. J. Mayo an appointment as local surgeon for the Chicago and Northwestern road. He was required by his contract to provide a competent substitute whenever he himself was not available, and where could William James find a more competent substitute for himself than Charles Horace?

The fees allowed for the work were low, but payment was certain and prompt, and the appointment carried the valuable perquisite of an annual pass on any company line. That greatly reduced the costs of the brothers' many trips for professional study and gave them free transportation in their daily practice, on passenger train, freight car, or caboose, whichever was going their way first.

While the Mayos remained local surgeons, the railroad work was an unimportant element of their practice. They examined local applicants for railway positions, to eliminate the risk of entrusting a train to an engineer with a weak heart or defective hearing or vision; occasionally an injured brakeman or fireman was brought to the office; and once an unidentified stranger was seized with a fit in the Rochester depot. But only once in the three years did a serious accident occur near Rochester.

On a night in September 1892 a Chicago and Northwestern train struck a carriage in which two women were riding, one of them a visitor from New York state, Mrs. William Bennett. She was badly injured, unconscious, suffering from severe shock, and bleeding freely from the nose, mouth, and ear. The conductor got her on board at once and headed at full speed for Rochester, where she was taken to St. Mary's Hospital.

Both of the Mayo brothers were on the job immediately, but the injury was obviously to the skull and brain, so Dr. Charlie took charge. He opened the line of fissure in the skull with gouge and bone forceps, exposed the severed meningeal artery, and tied it. At once the bleeding ceased, and Mrs. Bennett soon regained consciousness and began to mend. Reporting the accident and the excitement of the train's arrival, the editor congratulated Rochester on having in its midst physicians who could deal successfully with so serious a case.

# The Radius Lengthens

Back in Buffalo, New York, Mr. William Bennett knew nothing about that. His feelings when he received word of the accident may be imagined. His wife seriously injured—in a hick western town and at the mercy of god-knew-what kind of a doctor! As soon as the trains could get him there Mr. Bennett arrived in Rochester.

Before he left to take his wife home, he expressed his sentiments in a letter to the paper:

I wish to express my heartfelt gratitude to the good Sisters of St. Mary's Hospital and also to the corps of physicians in that institution for their kind and skillful care of my wife. . . . It seems a miracle indeed that she recovered, and nothing but the most skillful surgery and the most attentive care could have accomplished the result. I further desire to express my gratitude to Conductor Manley, of the Northwestern railroad, for his discriminating judgment in bringing her to this city and to · St. Mary's Hospital, for I feel assured that had not such been done she would not have been spared to me.

In conclusion I desire to recommend St. Mary's Hospital to all sufferers and Conductor Manley to promotion by his company.

## 8

The earlier trickle of Dakotans back to their Rochester doctors became a stream in the nineties, fed at the beginning of the decade by hard times in the Dakotas, when the boom of the eighties that populated the territory collapsed. The railroad companies, as the center of their interest moved farther west, ceased to advertise and colonize; the bonanza farms went downward with the price of wheat; the ranchers were forced into bankruptcy when thousands of their cattle perished in the hard winter of 1886–87; and the homesteading farmers were stripped to poverty by three successive seasons of killing drouth. Once again those who had trekked westward with high hopes saw their dreams in ruin at their feet.

With famine rode pestilence, and with destitution came worry and illness. More and more of those who were ill remembered the Mayos back in Rochester and made every effort to get to them for treatment. So many and so insistent were they that the railroad officials must have wondered what manner of men these Mayos were, that sick folk should want to travel hundreds of miles to consult them and should be so certain that if they could just get back to Rochester

Dr. Will and Dr. Charlie would take care of them whether they could pay the fees or not.

But if they felt that way about it the railroad men would help them. Alexander C. Johnson, the special agent who was managing the company's philanthropies, authorized free transportation and food on the way for those who wanted to go to Rochester but could not scrape together the price of a ticket. To some who had heard of the Mayos but did not know them he gave letters of introduction, and often from his own pocket a few dollars to see them through. The Mayos had never met Mr. Johnson, but they came to respect him through the tales they heard of his generosity and humanity.

The hard times passed, but the procession of patients from the Dakotas, especially South Dakota, did not lessen. Going to the Mayos had become a habit, particularly with those needing surgery. Scarcely an issue of the Rochester paper appeared without an item or two about Dakota patients. When the superintendent of the Dakota division of the Chicago and Northwestern road felt ill, he boarded his private car and ordered the engineer to take him to Rochester, where his appendix was removed. When the son of South Dakota's governor developed appendicitis Pierre doctors sent for one of the Mayos to perform the operation.

Meanwhile Dr. Will had become district surgeon for the Minnesota division of the railroad, and two years later for the Dakota division as well. He, or his brother substitute, was called to the scene of any major accident along the line in either state, and though such occasions were not numerous they were dramatic. The message would come in: *Tornado derailed passenger train at Owatonna; five killed and twenty injured. Dr. Mayo at once.* And away he would go, on a special train or riding in the cab of a detached engine, with all tracks cleared for him.

Special trains and the right-of-way were soon given him for any emergency trip, whether on a company case or not. Just as the liverymen used to turn aside into snowdrifts to clear the road for the Old Doctor, so now passenger trains waited in the station and freights took to the sidings to keep the tracks clear for the sons on their errands of healing. Traffic was not yet too heavy or complex for that.

Mr. Johnson had finished his work in South Dakota and was now the company's general agent at Winona, where he witnessed again the widespread faith in the Mayo brothers. So when his wife was seized with acute appendicitis he too wanted Dr. Mayo. Since the next train was not due at Winona for several hours, he wired an engineer and a fireman at Dodge Center to detach the engine from a special train standing there, proceed with all speed to Rochester, pick up Dr. Mayo, and bring him to Winona.

Dr. Will was waiting at the station when the locomotive with caboose attached pulled in. He swung aboard, and

At 11:04 p. m. the train plunged out into the night, wound its way down among the hills and arrived in Winona at ten minutes past the hour of midnight, having made the entire run of fifty miles over heavy grades and around sharp curves in just one hour and four [sic] minutes. This is twenty-six minutes faster than the quickest time made by the lightflyer, the fastest train on the line.

That was a story for the trainmen to tell in the yards or at home when the day's run was over. There were many such: the time they carried that girl so badly burned, or the young woman who shot her little brother by accident and then turned the gun on herself in remorse, or that helpless paralytic, Sister Martha, who came on a cot all the way from Ironton, Ohio, where not even the Cincinnati doctors had been able to find out what was wrong with her, though the Mayos located her trouble and had her getting better within a week. For many who rode the trains to Rochester St. Mary's was the "gleam of hope," the "last resort."

Mr. W. E. Magandy returned to Tyler, Minn., this morning. He took with him his wife, who came to this city several days ago prepared to die. St. Mary's Hospital was in the last resort for the dying woman. An operation was performed, and Mrs. Magandy began to improve at once. She was little more than a skeleton before the operation. She began to gain in flesh, and by splendid treatment is now as well as she ever has been in her life.

J. O. Otterness of Rio, Wis., died in the waiting room of the depot at Winona Wednesday. He was on his way to this city to undergo an operation at St. Mary's hospital. He had been taken to Milwaukee and other cities and pronounced beyond hope, but had decided to come to Rochester. He passed away suddenly while waiting for the train.

[A Mr. Scanlan of Tyler, Minnesota, was injured in a fall from a wagon. His family found him almost completely paralyzed by an injury to the spinal cord.] It did not take them long to decide what to do. It looked to them as if their brother must die, but there was yet one gleam of hope, Rochester physicians. Spurred with this hope . . . they started . . . for this city. . . . The ambulance awaited them at the depot, and Mr. Scanlan was taken to the hospital. The case was at once pronounced hopeless. Paralysis seemed almost complete, and the hospital staff of physicians could give no hope whatever. At eleven o'clock . . . Mr. Scanlan passed from this life.

John Ingleby Lewis . . . a boy [of] about nine summers, left Saturday for Butte, Mont. Master John came here a year ago on a pillow. He was so thin and wasted and so sick that it was not expected he would live, but today he is as well and lively as a cricket. John was taken to St. Mary's hospital as a last resort. He had been operated on twice at Butte without any good results. Two operations were performed here, and the little lad stood it like a major. He recovered rapidly. John became a great favorite with the doctors. . . . He remarked to his grandfather just as he was leaving: "I came here on one pillow, but I guess it would take two or three now."

And there was the time a young mother in Mountain Lake, one of the German Mennonites from Russia who settled there, put her little boy on the train and asked the trainmen to take him to Rochester. The little fellow was almost blind, only six years old, and couldn't speak a word of English. His mother couldn't afford to go with him, but she fixed him a basket of food, and across his front she pinned a big sign, "Take me to St. Mary's Hospital."

When the conductor set him off at Rochester, the people at the depot couldn't believe he'd come all that distance alone. A hackman took care of him, and drove him right out to the hospital.

With incidents like those for the trainmen to talk about, it was not mere coincidence that there soon began to appear on the Mayo records patients identified as "engineer from Omaha," "railroad man from La Crosse," "dispatcher at Dubuque."

Nor were trainmen the only ones from beyond the state. As early as 1893 St. Mary's was admitting patients from Illinois, Kansas, Missouri, Nebraska, New York, and Ohio as well as the nearer Iowa, Wisconsin, Dakota, and Montana. Those from the more distant states were mostly members of the nationwide Catholic church or relatives and friends of pleased Minnesota patients.

# The Radius Lengthens

The Mayo brothers might be willing to treat the poor without charge, but it was not by so doing that they were able to expand their facilities and activities. For that there had to be men and women who not merely *would* go to Rochester but who also *could,* people who could afford to pay the surgeons' fees as well as the costs of the trip and the expenses of residence and hospitalization. If agriculture in the Middle West had not got out of the doldrums it was in during the 1870's and 1880's, the development at Rochester could not have occurred on the scale it did.

Solutions of the farmer's problems took time, but they were under way in the southeastern counties of Minnesota by 1890. At Rochester blooded livestock was rapidly taking the place of primary importance, which wheat had surrendered. The breeding of stock, especially of fine horses, became the leading enterprise of Olmsted County, and Rochester became the port of call for buyers from Chicago and eastern centers. It was called "the Lexington of the Northwest," and Mr. Blickle, the town jeweler, designed for sale to visitors a souvenir spoon on which was engraved a horse's head within a horseshoe.

Unfortunately the panic of 1893 came along, and Olmsted County horse-raising never recovered from the body blow. But the panic and subsequent depression only interrupted the general improvement in agricultural conditions, and by 1900 the hard times were entirely forgotten. In that year Rochester was jubilant about its need for more laborers, about its many new stores and busy old ones, and its lack of vacant storerooms. "The last five years have been a period of uninterrupted progress," reported the newspaper contentedly, prophesying that the coming year would be the busiest and most prosperous in Rochester's history.

The Mayo practice was already large enough to be responsible for some of this unwonted activity, but not for all of it. In great measure it was a reflection of improving economic conditions in the country roundabout. The census of 1900 showed Olmsted County to be one of the richest agricultural counties in the United States, flourishing on its production of cattle, pigs, sheep, butter, flax, and small grains.

That was a remarkable change from the conditions that had aroused the wrath and sympathy of the Old Doctor a few decades before. The developments responsible for it were occurring in varying degree throughout the Middle West. The value of farm land was rising steadily, so that the acres the farmer had got for nothing but living and working on them were worth one hundred dollars or more each and were still appreciating. The western farmer was entering upon a period of prosperity.

In Minnesota itself the timber counties to the north were still basking in the glow of lumbering's golden age, an illusory glow and soon to fade, leaving a cheerless aftermath of desolation and unrewarding drudgery. But for the present the lumbermen went exuberantly on their stripping, slashing way, excusing the destruction they wrought by pointing to the taxes and wages they paid, the market they provided for agriculture and industry, and the useful houses and barns, boxes and barrels their lumber built.

In the north also the richest iron ore deposits of the American continent were being uncovered, to pour wealth into the coffers of eastern financiers but in the process to bring new communities into being with phenomenal rapidity. Towns sprang up on the iron ranges like mushrooms, and the entire northeast of Minnesota was turned from wilderness into settled territory almost overnight. The population of Duluth jumped from three thousand to thirty-three thousand in a single decade.

In Minneapolis and St. Paul commercial, industrial, and financial activity was humming. As the result of a revolution in milling machinery and methods and of the quantity of excellent hard spring wheat at its door, Minneapolis was attaining preeminence as the flour-milling center of the world, from which Pillsbury's Best and Gold Medal flours were being advertised into every kitchen, and the slogan "Eventually, Why Not Now" was being added to the parlance of the nation.

Only at first glance do such developments seem far from the story of medicine, far from the work of two doctors in a small town in the southeastern corner of the state. For it was those developments that enabled thrifty farmers, laborers, and professional men to build better homes, buy better furniture and clothes, and send their sons to high school and the state university—and finance a trip to Rochester for themselves or their wives for expedient physical repairs.

All these factors may serve to explain how the Mayos developed at Rochester a second center of surgery in Minnesota. But it was a *second* center, for patients from all over the state went or were sent to consultants in the Twin Cities too, and the growth of the new surgery, the presence of railway transportation, and economic betterment in the surrounding community worked to the benefit of Minneapolis and St. Paul practitioners as well as for the Mayos.

Why then was it not one or two of the Twin City surgeons who developed a national and international reputation? Why was it not Minneapolis or St. Paul that drew the nation's doctors and the nation's sick to Minnesota? Why did Rochester become America's surgical mecca?

Individual ability is not the whole answer, for there were men of commanding intellect and skill in Minneapolis and St. Paul too. Perhaps they lacked the drive, the unwearying energy, the single-minded application to the task of the moment that went hand in hand with ability in the Mayo brothers, but certain other differences mattered quite as much.

Each of those men worked alone. If he had a partner it was only for the convenience of sharing an office; his practice remained his own. The partnership was never a close-knit working team, with each member an alter ego, a second brain and pair of hands, an equally able and acceptable substitute for the other.

Not only that, but each of the Minneapolis or St. Paul men was just one among half a dozen good surgeons and a dozen more whose claims to excellence did not admit of immediate disproof. The patients going to the Twin Cities were distributed among many practitioners who were competing among themselves, in friendly fashion perhaps, but competing nonetheless. No one of the surgeons, no two of them, stood out on the horizon as the one spreading, sheltering tree on a broad, level landscape.

Then too, the hospitals at which those men worked were public institutions maintained by the city or by one of the medical schools, and many of the patients came to the institution rather than to some one doctor. Each man shared its work and the direction of its policies with others and enjoyed its privileges on sufferance.

Almost all of the good Twin City men were teachers as well as practitioners, and though teaching might help to keep them alert and abreast of developments in surgery, it was done under conditions that took their time and divided their interests. There were always lectures to prepare and classes to meet.

So the Mayos came abreast and then pulled ahead. No longer did Dr. Will rise in medical meetings to ask the men of the metropolis to instruct him out of their greater learning and experience; no longer did he apologize because Rochester had nothing comparable to offer. Instead, Dr. James E. Moore of Minneapolis admitted that whereas Will Mayo used to come to him for pointers, now he went to Dr. Mayo, and Dr. Dunsmoor confessed that he felt complimented when a patient from the country came to him instead of going to Rochester. And patients from the Twin Cities themselves took to going down to Rochester.

Working together and without nearby competitors, the Mayos piled up an experience of hundreds, for some operations thousands, of cases while each of their Twin City colleagues was accumulating scores or a few hundreds. And it was the volume of their work that enabled the Mayos, even forced them, to secure assistance and expand their activities; it was the volume of their experience, given their unexcelled use of it, that sent them soaring into national prominence.

# . . . and Company

The nearly four thousand operations Dr. Will and Dr. Charlie performed at St. Mary's Hospital in 1905 represented the surgical culmination of about ten thousand office examinations. Obviously they did not handle all of them alone. They early faced the question of whether to restrict their practice to what they could do alone or to delegate some of the work to others, and they decided on the latter, partly because they were not willing to forego their time for study and travel.

Their need for assistance first made itself felt in the early nineties. Dr. W. W. Mayo was then preoccupied with his duties as state senator, which took him away from Rochester for several months at a time during the sessions of the legislature. In 1893 Governor Nelson named him state surgeon for the Minnesota building at the World's Fair in Chicago, and he was away for most of that summer and fall. He was called frequently to testify as a medical expert in court; he was busying himself with several schemes for securing additional railroad connections to the north and northwest for Rochester; and he was beginning to show the wanderlust that so strongly marked his declining years.

All in all, though the Old Doctor answered calls, assisted at operations, and paid daily visits to the patients in the hospital when he was in Rochester, he was too concerned with other activities to give dependable assistance to his sons. And they felt he had earned the freedom to come and go as he liked.

But whom should they ask to take his place? In making that decision the Mayo brothers showed the stuff they were made of. They rejected the customary solution of taking into the office some fledgling just out of medical school who was looking for a little practical experience before opening an office of his own. It was not a lackey they wanted, not an odd-job man, but a responsible partner who could carry his own weight and contribute positively to the practice. And, seeing themselves as others saw them, they felt they needed the presence of an older man to take the edge off their own appearance of inexperienced youth.

With unerring judgment and entire lack of fear for their own security, they chose the ablest neighboring practitioner they knew. For some time they had remarked that they were seldom called to see a patient in the vicinity of Eyota and Dover unless the doctor there called them in consultation. Apparently Dr. Stinchfield was able to cure his patients and retain their confidence. That was the sort of man the Mayos wanted—and they were not unmindful of the possibility that some of Dr. Stinchfield's patients might follow him to new connections in Rochester.

Dr. Augustus W. Stinchfield was then fifty years old, a man of short, spare figure, with the soft voice, courtly manner, and distinctive costume of the practitioner of the old school. Born in Maine and graduated from Bowdoin College in 1868, he had gone west to practice, opening an office in southern Missouri first, then in Dundas, Minnesota, and finally in Eyota, where he had been practicing for eighteen years. He had built up a large local practice and a reputation throughout Olmsted County second only to that of the Mayos. Like them, he was given to continued study and had taken courses at both the New York and the Chicago polyclinics. From his papers and contributions to discussions in both local and state medical societies the Mayos knew him to be able and sound. So early in 1892 they asked him to become their partner and he accepted.

In preparation for his coming the Mayos enlarged the offices they had been occupying on the ground floor of the Cook Block ever since Dr. Will's graduation. They built in a stairway and rented additional space on the second floor, where they set up quarters for the minor surgery they did in the office, leaving the downstairs rooms for the reception and examination of patients. To their own names on the entrance door they added "Dr. A. W. Stinchfield," and the partnership quickly became known as Drs. Mayo and Stinchfield.

2

Edith Graham was still serving the Mayos as anesthetist, office nurse, and general bookkeeper and secretary. She did not pretend to business experience or efficiency, but their method of keeping accounts was simple, and when she made mistakes, "they did not scold." They left most of their letter-writing to her too, taking time only to jot down an outline of the proposed answer or just a brief "say no" or "tell him yes" or "write up a good answer to this one."

Miss Graham was a small, sprightly, attractive young woman—so attractive in fact that the doctor to whom she was assigned on her first case in Chicago refused to accept her because she was too young and beautiful for a nurse. Dr. Charlie found her a good and gay companion outside as well as in the office, and soon his heart fell captive to her charms.

His favorite pastime at the moment was bicycling. He had been among the first in Rochester to learn the new art, using the empty lot adjoining the house on Franklin Street for his trial efforts, so much to the entertainment of the congregation in the church next door that the pastor had to close the windows one Sunday morning to shut out the counterattraction to his sermon. Edith Graham learned to ride too, and part of their courtship took place on bicycle trips for two.

They were married in April 1893 in a simple ceremony at the Graham home south of Rochester. Hurrying out to the house on foot, Dr. Charlie tried to leap across a rivulet in his path and fell into it, so the ceremony had to wait until his clothes were dried out. But the mishap was no omen, for the marriage of Charles Mayo and Edith Graham was a great success, "made in heaven," according to their friends.

Mrs. Mayo shared her husband's professional interests fully enough to join happily and intelligently in his activities. Their wedding trip was a round of eastern medical centers, and often thereafter Mrs. Mayo accompanied her husband to conventions and on his observation jaunts. Nor did she spend her time in shopping or at the theater; she went with him to visit hospitals and clinics, met his doctor friends, and quickly made them hers.

At the time of his marriage Dr. Charlie was living with Dr. Will and his wife in their home on College Street, though he spent the week ends with his father and mother at the farm home. Will insisted that Charlie and Edith live with him and Hattie, but the newlyweds said they would share a home only until their own was built.

361

They were willing though to build it as near as possible, and they bought the property next door, tore down the old house on the lot, and built themselves a fine new one, the one so long known affectionately to Rochester as "the red house." Enthusiastically the brothers planned to take advantage of the adjacency of their homes. The architect was told to draw up plans for a covered passageway connecting the two houses and broadening into a one-room, one-story building halfway between, which they could use for a joint study and library.

But the two wives united firmly against that idea. Will and Charlie spent all their days together and if they had a joint workroom they would spend all their evenings together too. When would their families see them? So the passageway and library were not built, and Will and Charlie contented themselves with a speaking tube between their houses. When either was ready to start out for the office or the hospital in the morning, he whistled through to the house next door and the two went off together.

3

At the hospital the immediate result of Dr. Charlie's marriage was a need for a new anesthetist, and the brothers chose Alice Magaw, a good friend of Mrs. C. H. Mayo's, who, perhaps in anticipation of this very vacancy, had taken a course in nursing at the Women's Hospital in Chicago. In order that she might also help with the examination of pathologic specimens the doctors sent her to Chicago the following summer to take a special course in the use of the microscope. Dinah Graham, a sister of Mrs. C. H. Mayo's, was taken on to do the office work.

There were thirteen children in the Graham family. The parents, both English born, had come from Cortland County, New York, to pioneer in Minnesota in 1856. Mrs. Graham had long been one of the community's midwives and boasted a record that put many doctors to shame, for she had brought two hundred and forty children into the world without losing one of them. Life in the big Graham family was not easy, and the children were reared to hard work and early responsibility.

Christopher Graham, one of the sons, was now thirty-seven, but he had yet to find a niche that fitted him. When he was twenty-six he decided he did not want to be a farmer and, his nerve bolstered by the companionship of a friend of like circumstances and convictions, he left the farm and went to study at the state university. Overcoming the handicap of haphazard preparatory schooling, he received a bachelor of science degree in 1887. Then two years of academy teaching convinced him that he did not want to be a schoolmaster either, so, again in company with a like-minded friend, he entered the school of veterinary medicine at the University of Pennsylvania and received his degree in 1892.

At the time of his sister's marriage to Charles Mayo he was teaching veterinary science in the small school of agriculture at the University of Minnesota. But he was not happy, for ever since he struck the course in physiology at the University of Pennsylvania he had been sure he wanted to be a doctor of human medicine.

Presumably he said as much to his new brother-in-law, who passed the word on to Dr. Will, for the Mayos told "Kit" that if he would go back to Pennsylvania and take the additional year of work needed for the medical degree, he could work with them when he was through. He jumped at the chance, spent the summer studying bacteriology in Dr. Hewitt's laboratory at Red Wing, reentered the University of Pennsylvania in the fall, and was graduated the following June a full-fledged doctor of medicine.

When he began practice with the Mayos some patients objected to being treated by a "horse doctor." That must have cut Christopher Graham to the quick, for he was a sensitive person without overmuch self-confidence, too conscious and ashamed of the late start he was getting. He worked hard and conscientiously, feeling to the full the doctor's responsibility and never being able to regard a sick man impersonally. That attitude made practice a strain for him, but "his patients just loved him," according to a nurse who took care of many of his cases, and the first distrust was soon dispelled by his own successes and the continued backing of the Mayos.

They pushed him as their father had pushed them, because the time had come to resign the country practice to other hands. Their days were full with the work at St. Mary's Hospital, at the offices, and on calls for consultation, so as fast as their patients would permit they turned the local daily ride over to Drs. Stinchfield and Graham.

Most of the pregnancy cases fell to Graham, which was all right with him; he liked obstetrical work. He worried about each case, however, and could never, like more experienced men, let the comfort of his presence suffice and go off to sleep upstairs while the neighbor women delivered the child. The birth was almost as much of an ordeal for him as for the mother, but there was a tangible accomplishment in seeing a woman through labor that gave him deep satisfaction. Dr. Graham would have liked to become a specialist in obstetrics, but developments turned him into a specialist in differential diagnosis instead.

4

*Graham* was added to the firm's name, popularly at least, in the early summer of 1894, but Christopher seems not to have been taken formally into the partnership until August 1895, when he was given an examining room of his own on the second floor and next door to it a new laboratory.

The Mayo brothers had long appreciated the fundamental importance of diagnosis in medical practice; that was one of the lessons their father had taught them, and the point was being driven home hard at every step of their advance into surgery. So often they had to grope and explore because they could not tell exactly what was wrong with a patient. How, *how,* could they distinguish between inflammation of the gallbladder and duodenal ulcer, cancer of the stomach and ulcer of the stomach, appendicitis and typhoid fever in the beginning phases?

Feeling so, they would not willingly miss any development that promised better diagnosis, and promising instruments and laboratory procedures were beginning to appear. The Mayos saw them in use here and there, read and heard claims for them everywhere, and felt they must try them in Rochester. But where were *they* going to find time to learn how to use them, or time to apply them?

They probably had this need in mind when they told Christopher Graham they would have work for him when he got his medical degree, and they no doubt suggested the extra summer course in bacteriology with Dr. Hewitt. At any rate Dr. Graham did learn some of the new techniques and began at once to apply them.

# . . . and Company

He took over the work in urinalysis and began to make a few simple blood analyses too, especially leukocyte counts. An abnormal increase in the number of leukocytes, or white cells, in the blood was thought to indicate the presence of an infection in the body, since the white cells were recognized as nature's defense against invading organisms. Dr. Graham and Dr. Will Mayo had great faith in this test for a time and used it often to help in diagnosing appendicitis. But with growing experience came doubt, and eventually they lost all faith in the leukocyte count. Hematologists had yet to learn that a straight count of all the white cells does not tell the whole story, that a differential count of a certain type of white cell is necessary.

The most important beginning Dr. Graham made was in gastric analysis. By numerous experiments medical scientists had determined the chemical state to which a normal digestion will reduce a prescribed amount of food in a specified number of hours, and certain variations from that normal state were supposed to have diagnostic significance. The presence of free hydrochloric acid was said to mean ulcer and the absence of it cancer, for instance, and that differential diagnosis was one Dr. Will was especially eager to be able to make. So patients with serious stomach symptoms were sent to Dr. Graham, who fed them the prescribed rolls and water after a night of fasting, then in a few hours gave them a tube to swallow and pumped out their stomach contents for analysis.

Eagerly at first he and Dr. Will compared the results with the clinical and surgical findings, but as the number of such examinations mounted to a thousand and beyond, Dr. Will's hope waned. The acid sign was not dependable even as confirmatory evidence, certainly not in the early surgical stages of cancer. It seemed to increase in value with the progress of the disease and to become most reliable when the case was hopeless. He let Dr. Graham continue the work in gastric analysis, hoping that more precise determinations could be developed, but he turned back to reliance on his clinical hunches and the exploratory incision.

Those were the meager beginnings of clinical pathology in the Mayo practice. Since the laboratory work was necessarily incidental in Dr. Graham's day, he never became expert at it and in a few years resigned it to other hands. But he had started it.

# The Mayo Brothers

The most useful of all aids to diagnosis made its appearance in the world at about this same time. In December 1895 Wilhelm Conrad Roentgen, a German physicist, announced to his scientific brethren "a new kind of ray" that he had discovered by accident in his laboratory a month before. He knew so little about it that he called it the X ray, but he did know it could penetrate some kinds of matter, including clothes and flesh, and sensitize a photographic plate to make a picture of the internal structures of the body.

The news of Roentgen's discovery spread rapidly. "The public response was magnificent. Morality brigades were formed overnight to resist to the death the destruction of all decency and privacy. A London firm rose to the occasion, and made a small fortune from the sale of X-ray-proof underwear. New York was also in the van, with a determined attempt to obtain legislation against the 'use of X rays in opera-glasses in theatres.' " And in Rochester the public was warned that the salesman and the merchant would soon be using x-rays to pry out the minds and habits of prospective customers.

Sheepishly, and with a measure of disappointment, people learned the limitations of the x-ray, and although for years the new device was a curiosity that attracted unbelievably long queues at fairs and exhibitions, the practical use of it was left to the physician and the surgeon.

Just two months after Roentgen's announcement an x-ray machine made its appearance in Rochester. Dr. J. Grosvenor Cross, the son of E. C. Cross, bought one for his office in February 1896. For a time it was merely a new toy, but in August he demonstrated his pictures and their uses at the annual meeting of the Southern Minnesota Medical Association, and early in 1897 he repeated the demonstration for the Olmsted County society.

A week later the Mayo brothers had an occasion to test the machine for themselves. A little boy who had swallowed a vest buckle was brought to the office. It would help in deciding how best to remove it if the doctors could know just where in the esophagus it was lodged, whether it was open or closed, and if open in what direction its prongs were pointing, so they went over to see whether Cross's x-ray machine could tell them.

Dr. Cross made two pictures, one of which showed the buckle in remarkably clear outline, with the prongs pointing upward, so that drawing it out through the mouth would punch them into the esophagus walls. Consequently Dr. Charlie made an incision into the esophagus and pulled the buckle out blunt end first. His subsequent report of the case, written quite uncharacteristically without any reference to Dr. Cross's part in it, was one of the first on the use of the skiagraph, as an x-ray picture was called, to appear in the Northwest.

During the next three years Dr. Cross did a considerable amount of x-ray diagnosis for the Mayos, most of it to locate foreign bodies such as needles, bullets, and bits of glass or steel so the surgeons could remove them more easily. In defining the position and extent of fractures also they found the Roentgen ray a marvel, but it was still of little use in the diagnosis of organic disease, for techniques and substances to render the organs of the body opaque to the ray had yet to be found.

In those early stages the x-ray could be dangerous. Manufacturers, eager to make the apparatus as simple as possible, did not provide sufficient protection and enthusiastic operators did not exercise sufficient care, so that severe burns and skin affections, often degenerating into cancer, created an honor roll of martyrs to the x-ray. Word of this possibility spread among laymen, and unscrupulous persons found a new racket in suing the x-ray specialist for damages.

One of the patients Dr. Cross handled for the Mayos sued him for ten thousand dollars, claiming severe injury as the result of the x-ray. His bill of particulars set forth a convincing case, and Burt Eaton, the lawyer defending Dr. Cross, was worried and went to Dr. Will for advice. When he finished reading the particulars Dr. Will said the man had listed the very same complaints in a letter he wrote them before he ever appeared for examination. A long search finally turned up the letter, and that was the end of the case against Dr. Cross.

Before long even Twin City doctors were referring patients to Dr. Cross for x-ray diagnosis, and early in the 1900's he moved to Minneapolis to continue his practice there. Meanwhile the Mayo brothers had got a machine of their own. In 1900 Dr. Charlie, while attending a national medical convention, saw a demonstration of a new kind of x-ray machine the two young Wagner brothers of Chicago were putting on the market. It was said to be better, faster, and less dangerous than the older models, so Dr. Charlie ordered one. It was an imposing apparatus fitted with a number of connections that served no purpose except to flash lights and throw off sparks calculated to impress the patient—a concession to charlatans, who were making much of the novelty. Such theatrical "hooey," as he called it, filled Dr. Will with contempt, and after he and Dr. Charlie had experimented to find out what was essential and what was added merely for dramatic action, they called in an electrician to replace the latter with wooden plugs.

For a short time Dr. Charlie did most of the x-raying, and to the end of his life he carried the scars of minor burns he got in the process. Dr. Graham also operated the machine on occasion and ventured a little into the x-ray diagnosis of lung disease, but his brief records show how uncertain and experimental his attempts were. Afraid that what he found in physical examination might color his reading of the skiagraph, he tried making the x-ray first and noted with pleasure that the "phys. ex. and x-ray coincide fine."

## 6

Along with the enlargement of the medical partnership went the expansion of St. Mary's Hospital, wing by wing. At the dedication of the first addition in 1893 the speakers talked much of the phenomenal success of the hospital and its great prospects, but many of them were privately of the opinion, as one of them confessed later, that the Sisters of St. Francis had been too ambitious. They had made the hospital too large, and they would never be able to keep it full of patients. Yet in little more than five months the hospital was again so crowded it was necessary to turn the new smoking and lounging rooms into wards and move the smokers to the attic.

One of the highest compliments visitors could pay the sisters was to tell them how utterly unlike a hospital St. Mary's looked. They tried hard to make the rooms pleasant and homelike by the use of stiffly starched and ruffled curtains, quantities of decorative sofa pillows on the beds, and shirred and pleated cloth screens to shut from sight the pitchers and basins and medicine stands.

And they tried to match the homelike appointments with the kindliness and personal nature of their service. Not merely because they had to beat the competition of home care, but because nursing was more than a job to them, more than a profession with standardized duties and codified ideals; it was a mission, a truly religious offering.

Good testimony to how well they succeeded in their purpose is this little story that the Rochester editor copied from the *DeSmet* (South Dakota) *News*.

Along last spring Solon Putnam sent his six-year-old girl to the Rochester hospital for treatment for a deformed foot. After her return the little one confided to her sister on numerous occasions the fact that life at the hospital was simply an every-day and all-day-long siesta, with princely food and royal attendance, and so impressed the eleven-year-old daughter with the joys of hospital life, that the two little girls determined to remove thence permanently.

Accordingly they helped themselves to the common family fund, to the extent of ten dollars, and on the evening of circus day, when everybody's attention was otherwise engaged, the little tots secured a half-fare ticket and boarded the passenger for Rochester. Mr. Putnam soon missed his children and instituted an immediate search for them. For some time it seemed hopeless and he could find no clue to their whereabouts, but at length, with the assistance of Officer Dow, learned the facts stated above. A telegram intercepted them at Volga and on the next train they were returned home.

In view of St. Mary's conspicuous success it is hard to guess what put so quick an end to the training school for nurses the sisters opened with high hopes and much fanfare in the fall of 1894. Two young women were already enrolled when the announcement was made, but apparently the beginning was also the end, for no further news of the project appeared, and it was twelve years before they tried it again.

In 1894 too the Sisters of St. Francis decided to move their academy to Winona and keep only the day school at Rochester. In order to finance the new buildings at Winona the corporation voted to borrow fifty thousand dollars, using St. Mary's Hospital as security. But Dr. Will Mayo objected; he did not wish to work in a mortgaged hospital. He preferred to furnish the collateral himself, and did so.

That little story throws into high relief for a moment the close relationship existing between the Mayos and the sisterhood, and also, less pleasantly, a potential insecurity in the doctors' position. The terms of the relationship had not yet been set down in a formal contract, for Dr. Will and Dr. Charlie never bothered to legalize anything until they were forced to.

As the brothers' experience grew and their work got heavier, it became an unnecessary and impracticable expenditure of time and ability for them to serve as each other's assistant. Dr. Will in particular needed the extra time to look after the growing business affairs of the partnership. So they combined their efforts in fewer and fewer instances, until finally the separation of their schedules was complete, except for operations like excision of the rectum for cancer that required close surgical teamwork.

That it was Sister Joseph the *nurse* who stepped into the place of regular first assistant to Dr. Will bespeaks the easy, informal atmosphere that prevailed. But why should she not? She was an exceptional woman, highly intelligent, spirited and positive in personality, and possessed of executive ability of an unusual order, as she was demonstrating in her management of the hospital. Once she had got over that first shock at the personal nature of nursing, she showed a natural aptitude for the work, especially in the operating room. She soon acquired a remarkable understanding of surgical procedures, worked quickly and quietly, could guess the surgeon's intentions before he voiced them. Her fingers were nimble, their touch light, and her hands were so tiny that she could often get them into parts of the body the surgeon could not reach. Dr. Will never hesitated to credit Sister Joseph with a share in his success. He always ranked her an easy first among his assistants, though he later had many good ones with medical degrees.

At first Dr. Charlie shared Sister Joseph's services, and also Miss Magaw's as anesthetist, or when for any reason they were not available, as when the two brothers were operating simultaneously, he called upon his father or Dr. Stinchfield to assist him. Male orderlies had been added to the hospital staff by this time, but there were as yet no regularly appointed interns, only the medical students who spent their vacations serving as volunteer interns, giving what assistance they could in return for experience.

## 7

After 1894 activity leveled off for two or three years—coinciding, surely not by accident, with years of depression. No need was felt for more men or more space. The number of patients at St. Mary's increased by only a hundred or so a year and in one year actually dropped back a hundred.

Then the pace began to quicken. In the summer of 1897 the Mayos hired T. R. Spillane, formerly the head of the male nursing staff at the state hospital for the insane, to relieve them of some of the routine tasks in pathology—such as counting gallstones!—and in surgical dressings. A few months later when it became necessary for Dr. Charlie to have help with his work at the office, he chose Dr. Gertrude Booker, a recent graduate of the University of Minnesota practicing in neighboring Dover. He sent her to Chicago for a period of study in the clinics there, then taught her himself how to test eyes and fit glasses, and she soon took off his hands all the work of refracting.

Once again having to say "no more room" too often, the hospital sisters ordered the building of a second addition, a four-story wing to the west of the original unit. When done, this brought the capacity of the hospital to one hundred and thirty-four beds, which the good sisters thought would surely take care of all demands for some time to come. But before the carpenters had gone the new rooms were filling so rapidly that their delusion vanished.

Orderlies and flitting summertime interns were no longer help enough in the hospital; someone was needed in permanent residence, and the right man might also take over the work of gastric analysis, now assuming proportions beyond the time Dr. Graham could spare. Fortunately the Mayos thought they knew the right man.

Melvin C. Millet, a schoolteacher turned doctor with a degree from the University of Minnesota, had practiced for several years at Dover and was now in partnership with Dr. Hart of LeRoy. In both locations he had called the Mayos to do his surgery and had often given Dr. Will able assistance in the operations performed on his patients. Moreover, his papers before the Olmsted County Medical Society had shown him to be interested in physiological chemistry and well versed in the techniques of gastric analysis. He seemed made to order for the Mayos' job, and the job for him. With pleasure he accepted the invitation to join them.

He took up residence at St. Mary's Hospital in November 1898 and made himself generally useful, relieving the Mayos of the need to answer night calls and acting as Dr. Charlie's first assistant in the operating room. After a laboratory had been fitted up for him in the basement of the hospital, patients with stomach symptoms were sent there to eat and surrender the test meals. Dr. Millet had too investigative a turn of mind to stop with routine analysis, however; he began to study the whole problem of gastric ulcer, attempting to marshal ways of telling the acute from the chronic form and both from appendiceal or biliary colic.

But he did not go far on that road. He turned off to open up a newer one. Dr. W. J. Mayo was doing the partners' surgery of the kidney and ureters and knew that their work was weak in that field, weaker than it need be. The possibilities of exact diagnosis in renal disease had been greatly increased by several inventions, chief among them the cystoscope, an instrument that enables the physician to see into the urinary bladder and even to do some kinds of direct treatment through its tube. Though available since 1877, the cystoscope was not widely used because it took considerable skill and experience to use it profitably, and most general practitioners had neither the time nor the occasion to become expert. Besides, there were several different cystoscopes on the market, some of which worked so badly that many doctors had been led to question the value of cystoscopy.

It is a likely guess that Dr. Will pointed out to Dr. Millet the possibilities of development along this line, for that was a habit of his, but in any case before long Dr. Millet was deep in the mysteries of urinary disease. He studied, watched, and worked, mastered the use of the cystoscope, and even made some important improvements in it. He learned other new techniques of diagnosis, such as the "separation of the urines," by which the secretion of each kidney was examined separately to determine which organ was diseased.

As his proficiency increased and made itself felt in better practice the Mayos gave him every encouragement, even sending him to London for a year's study of methods in use there. And they were rewarded by seeing diseases of the kidney climb gradually into place alongside gastric ulcer, gallstones, and goiter as a field in which the Rochester doctors were known to be especially proficient.

Not long after Dr. Millet's coming the Mayos began looking for someone who could act as anesthetist for Dr. Charlie and also take over the important work in pathology, which was in danger of being neglected in the rush. That was a queer combination of duties, for the pathology would require a graduate in medicine, and graduates in medicine who were willing to specialize in anesthesia were rare indeed. But Dr. Ochsner knew a person who would qualify—Dr. Isabella Herb, a young woman with considerable experience in hospital work who had made a special study of anesthesia in his operating room the year before. Terms were agreed upon and Dr. Herb took up her duties in Rochester in November 1899.

Dr. Millet remained in charge of gastric analysis, but since he obviously had no intention of becoming a surgeon, he was anxious to be released from his work in the operating room. He wanted to give up residence at the hospital too, because he was planning to be married. Consequently in 1901 he was promoted from resident physician to attending physician, and his place at the hospital was taken by the first regular intern. Thereafter two or more interns were appointed each year, to serve as Dr. Charlie's assistants among other duties, while Sister Joseph continued to work with Dr. Will.

8

It was at about this time that the Mayo brothers paused to take stock of their position and make some decisions for the future.

It is hard to believe but undeniably true that the two men had only one pocketbook, one bank account, between them. All they earned went into it, and whatever either wanted—for travel, home-building, clothes, food, fun, everything—he took from it without any accounting to the other. What was left over at the end of the year they divided equally.

That single pocketbook supplied them well. Their homes were among the largest and most comfortably appointed in Rochester, jointly a center of the community's social life. The two men and their wives had become members of a gay, sociable crowd, and they went out often for dinner and an evening of dancing or card-playing. But such activity has a way of multiplying by geometric progression, and the brothers found it a drain on time and strength, conflicting with the demands of their work. If they were to have any home life at all, any leisure for pleasures within the family circle, something had to be given up. And it was not their work.

# The Mayo Brothers

Their wives agreeing, reluctantly perhaps, the Mayos withdrew from the social round that occupied their friends. "We knew they wouldn't mind much," said Mrs. C. H. Mayo. "We were so often late for their dinners or had to leave in the middle of an evening, because Charlie would get a call. And Charlie never cared much about playing cards. He wasn't as bad a player as he let on, but he wouldn't bother to put his mind to it."

However, the Mayos continued to entertain in lavish style, with parties that were the highlights of the Rochester social season. Two or three times a year, often in successive weeks, one or the other of the two houses was thrown open to seventy-five, a hundred, or even as many as three hundred guests, for a reception, a musicale, or an evening of dancing. Those were the formal occasions; a "dinner for fifty intimate friends" was informal.

For recreation at home there was a well-equipped game room in each house. Dr. Will first, then Dr. Charlie, bought one of the celebrated Brunswick-Balke-Collender billiard tables, elaborate in design and fitted with "Monarch match cushions." Dr. Charlie, having injured his arm one season in a fall from a bicycle, gave up cycling as too dangerous for a surgeon, but he found a new plaything in the horseless carriage. He bought the first one, steam-driven, and the second one, gasoline-powered, to appear in town. Dr. Will still preferred the horse and buggy and treated himself to the finest that money could buy.

The finest but not the most ornate. On one occasion when a new surrey was delivered he called his driver aside and pointing to two ornamental lamps that flanked the dashboard, said, "Jack, I wish that sometime when you're crossing the river you might in some mysterious way lose those fancy lamps." Jack understood, and a few days later the lamps had disappeared.

Summers found the Mayos at their lake cottages near Oronoco, but the men drove back and forth to Rochester every day. On the lake they had a sailboat named *Ariel*, a steam launch, and a motorboat —for Dr. Charlie to tinker with and Dr. Will to ride in, for the elder brother was already feeling some of that need for motion while resting that was characteristic of him in later years.

Their families were coming along too. Dr. and Mrs. W. J. Mayo had lost several of their babies, two boys among them, but they had two fine daughters, the elder soon to enter finishing school at Bryn Mawr and then go on to Wellesley College. Dr. Charlie's family numbered two girls and a boy and was still growing. But that single pocketbook held ample money for anything the parents wished to provide for their children.

From the same pocketbook the Old Doctor and his wife were enjoying comforts and pleasures they had not previously been able to afford. They still owned the farm home and occasionally went out there for a day or two, but they were living with their daughter, Mrs. Berkman, in one of the three modern houses the boys had built on the site of the rambling old homestead on Franklin Street.

The Doctor was still a popular speaker at civic and political functions in Rochester, and his age and a strong loyalty to party of the kind he had deplored in his younger and more flexible years made him the beloved mentor of younger Democrats in the district. In 1904 he was elected a Minnesota delegate to the Democratic convention in St. Louis, and was named to the committee appointed to notify Alton B. Parker of his nomination. Although Parker lost to Theodore Roosevelt, in the Minnesota gubernatorial campaign the popular John A. Johnson of St. Peter brought victory to the Democrats for the first time since the Civil War. Dr. Mayo was overjoyed. With youthful high spirits he made the trip to St. Peter to ride as a guest of honor in the victory parade.

Despite his more than eighty years, he had become a veritable vagabond—off to Florida, Cuba, and the Bahamas one year, the Atlantic Coast another, the American Southwest and Mexico the next, and the American Northwest and Canada the year following, with shorter trips down the Mississippi or up along the North Shore of Lake Superior in between. Reports of his travels written back to the newspapers while he was away and told to audiences in church and lodge when he returned kept Rochester entertained. His energy and endurance, his insatiable curiosity about everything he saw amazed his less venturesome fellows.

Sometimes he was accompanied on his trips by his longtime personal and political friend, Charles C. Willson the lawyer, who was forced to admit that Dr. Mayo had more endurance than he when it came to hiking two or three miles down the trail to the edge of a glacier or a canyon they wanted to see. It was a standing joke in Rochester that these two good friends simply could not remain on thoroughly amicable terms long enough to complete a journey together. They always parted company in a spat somewhere on the way and returned singly by different routes.

The letters he wrote while on a tour of southern Europe breathe an almost childish delight in new sights and sounds. "I wish you could get from my letters what I feel and dream," he wrote. "I am in the land and sea of fable and strange myths. . . . This trip to me is fairy land and sea." He described the "procession of beauty" at a fancy dress ball on the boat, and immediately thereafter the homely details of how the crew swabbed down the decks, the awful beauty of the towering Rock of Gibraltar, the motley of human kinds in the Spanish market places, and the lot of the poor peasants who had to pay taxes on everything they took to or from Gibraltar.

Italian money and the Italian language were too much for him. The porters and hackmen were pests; they got the best of him in every dealing he had with them. "They smile at you with the sweetness of angels and cheat like pickpockets."

One afternoon in Rome he cut free from the party and hired a hack to himself for two hours because he wanted to see the graves of Shelley and Trelawny in the cemetery of the Protestants. He had someone give the driver careful directions before he started, but in vain. The man drove where he pleased, and to Dr. Mayo's flurry of protest in English he turned a happy and blandly unheeding smile. Giving up at last, the Old Doctor in sheer exasperation curled up on the carriage seat and went to sleep. When they got back to the hotel he had to pay the man for five hours instead of two!

The old gentleman, so dapper and precise, inclined to get choleric when crossed but so alive and eager about everything, was the darling of the party. "Have no fear for me," he told his friends. "Everyone wants to take care of me." And again, "I am well, perfectly. The ladies all look after my interests."

On the Old Doctor's eighty-fifth birthday, May 31, 1904, the business and professional men of Rochester gave a big banquet at the Cook House in his honor, and presented him with a solid silver loving cup as a tangible token of their admiration for his "sterling worth."

## 9

Yes, the Mayos had done well for themselves in ten years. They had all that their idea of abundant living demanded and they had started a substantial life insurance program to take care of the future. Yet they had a sizable surplus on hand, and their income was increasing rapidly. They wondered what they ought to do about it?

The father, called a radical by his contemporaries, had so developed his sons' social conscience, so filled them with the idea that no man has a right to great wealth while others are suffering in poverty, that they regarded their growing bank balance with uneasy minds.

They could not and would not reduce their fees. The size of their income was due to the volume of their business, not to exorbitant charges, for they kept to the schedule of fees customary among their colleagues. To cut fees for the purpose of attracting patients was forbidden by the medical code of ethics, and who would believe that anyone could be so quixotic as to cut them to reduce his income?

Moreover, the Mayos did not approve of lowering the customary charges. They were willing to adjust them for any patient who could not afford to pay them, even to the point of making no charge at all, for they were men of warmly sympathetic natures. As they went through the day collecting from the patients they examined or treated they merely stuffed the money into their pockets, and when they came to the bedside of a person worried and worn with the struggle to make ends meet, they dipped into those pockets to leave a bill or two in the hand or under the pillow. If they were convinced of a man's need they were as likely as not to send him away with the amount of their fee, or more, having changed hands in reverse. They lost surprisingly little money that way, they found, for what they gave came back after a while; men would come in to repay them long after they had forgotten the giving. The tales of their generosity spread through the countryside, multiplying with the years.

But if the Mayos were not shylocks, they were certainly not suckers either. They saw no reason why a man who could afford it should not pay a reasonable amount for their services. Surely his life and

377

health were worth as much to him as a new horse or an extra suit or a hunting trip! That the doctor should sell his services cheaply was not to the advantage of the profession, nor in the long run of the patient either. The doctor had to earn enough to pay for good equipment and finance study and travel if he hoped to keep up with medicine and be able to give the patient the best medical care available. In most cases the customary fees allowed no more than that.

The brothers talked about this problem a great deal that year, 1898 Dr. Will thought it was. And from their talking emerged certain policies, not new, most of them, but crystallized and definite.

They would make no charge to other doctors, nurses, ministers, and missionaries, and none to educators or state employees whose salaries were small. They would collect the usual fee from those who could pay it and from others in accordance with their ability to pay, but never would they knowingly let their bill become an economic burden to any patient. They would never sue to collect a fee or accept in payment a note or a mortgage or money raised by a mortgage. They would rest their case with the honesty and conscience of men, believing, as Dr. Will once expressed it, that "if a man can pay, he will. . . . The variations from fundamental decency and honor are too rare to be taken into calculation."

Above all, they would never let financial considerations influence the degree or kind of care they gave. A man's income should determine only what he paid; it should have nothing whatever to do with the quality of the medicine and surgery he got.

In the use of their earnings they would always put the improvement of facilities and personnel first. The professional men who worked with them, either as partners or as employees, should be generously paid, and there should be enough of them to allow each man time for self-improvement. They would finance observation journeys for the others as well as for themselves, because it was a necessary and legitimate investment in the betterment of the practice.

As to their growing personal income, solemnly they vowed to set aside one half of it that year and as much each year thereafter as they could. One half or less would suffice for themselves and their families; of the remainder they would consider themselves only the trustees. They would invest it and increase it to the best of their ability, and someday they would find a way to return it to the people, from whom it came.

Perhaps the decision was not taken so formally or so exactly as Dr. Will remembered it, but those policies did prevail in the Mayo practice, and with modifications only in details, none in principle, they still prevail in the Mayo Clinic. The Mayo brothers actually lived on much less than one half of their incomes, and they turned the accumulated surplus into a great trust for the public benefit—not only the surplus but eventually the properties and assets of the practice too, which amounted to much more.

## 10

For a time the brothers managed their own investments, and did not do it too well. Casual, impulsive, and naive about it, they suffered some heavy losses. If a Rochester friend could make a venture sound reasonably good, he could count on the Mayos to invest in it. And sometimes they got into company they did not like.

One time Dr. Will put some money into a chain of banks a Rochester man was establishing to serve the new communities in western Minnesota and the Dakotas. In due time the stockholders assembled for the annual meeting, and the banker with satisfaction reported a wonderfully successful year. He had earned them twenty-two per cent on their investment. Those westerners needed money so badly they were willing to pay any rate of interest to get it.

That had an unpleasantly familiar sound to Dr. Will. It had been true in Olmsted County when he was a boy, and he had seen the effects of it in the lives of the borrowers. Abruptly he announced that he was turning in his stock and would take just six per cent on his investment for the year, not one penny more.

At last, and not too long a last, the brothers admitted to themselves that they were not cut out to be businessmen and decided to ask Burt Eaton, who was doing considerable investment business for his clients, to handle their savings for them. Eaton hesitated a little but finally agreed to take the job. He never forgot how Dr. Will then walked over to the office safe, took out a bundle of papers, tossed them over to him, and said, "For God's sake, take them."

There was no inventory, no record of the interest paid or due, just the certificates, and it took Eaton a year to weed out the poor choices and assemble a list of gilt-edged securities. He made it his business to watch the Mayos' personal account, and when it got up to twenty-five thousand dollars, he would "swipe it for the investment account" and buy more securities. At his urging the brothers signed an agreement that each of them would own half of the total investments.

They never asked for an accounting but Eaton thought they ought to have one, so he sent them a copy of the inventory each year, until some clerk in the office opened the letter by mistake and spread all over town the news of how much the Mayos were worth. After that he merely jotted down the results of the inventory on a slip of paper and gave it to Dr. Will personally. With a glance and a nod so indifferently brief as to exasperate the lawyer, who was proud of the job he was doing, Dr. Will would put the slip into his pocket and forget it. Mr. Eaton once saw him take it out again nearly a year later.

That is hardly a picture of men who were either money-mad or money-shrewd. Perhaps Dr. Will could have been so had it been necessary, but there was always enough for anything they wanted to do, so why bother to pinch pennies or multiply odd dollars?

## 11

Not long after Mr. Eaton had taken over the financial affairs of the brothers the Old Doctor fell sick, seriously so, and though he recovered, the anxiety of the moment had given the lawyer cause for thought. If W. W. Mayo should die, what would become of the partnership? Unless there was a prearranged settlement it would be possible for anyone so minded to make trouble for the surviving partners in probate court. Eaton raised the question with Dr. Will, and made him see the possibility of an arbitrary distribution of the practice by the probate judge if the affairs of the partnership ever got into court. Consequently, with the amicable consent of all concerned, the lawyer eliminated Dr. W. W. Mayo legally from the partnership, although there was actually no change in his participation in the activities and income of the firm.

Then Dr. Will began to think about the other partners. The terms on which Drs. Stinchfield and Graham entered the partnership are not available, but there is the lawyer's word for it that they were verbal only. Thinking over the situation in the light of the legal aspects Eaton had explained to him, Dr. Will decided they were all living in a fool's paradise. The men themselves might have complete confidence in each other's good faith, but families and heirs are an uncertain quantity.

Together he and Charlie worked out a general outline of their wishes. They did not want their practice to be looked upon as a property, like a grocery store; they did not want it to be disrupted by the death of any one of the partners; they wanted the survivors always to have unhampered control, so that the practice might continue intact. But they wanted some provision made for fair payment to a partner's heirs. They left it to Mr. Eaton to put these principles into legal terms.

He therefore drew up a contract limiting the partnership to participation in income. A retiring partner or a deceased partner's heirs should receive in liquidation of his full share in the partnership and its profits a sum equal to the amount of his income in the year preceding his retirement or death, and the survivors should continue the practice without further obligation to him or his estate. That was fine. Dr. Will and Dr. Charlie signed the document and then presented it to Dr. Stinchfield and Dr. Graham.

It was an arbitrary procedure, no matter how noble the motives or admirable the arrangement for realizing them. There could have been no objection had it come when the men joined the firm, but apparently they had understood that their share, whatever it was, applied to properties and assets as well as to income. To ask them now to sign away this share in the ownership was too much, and they balked. For two years and more they refused to sign.

Then the steel in Dr. Will came out. Flatly he named the alternatives: Either you sign this contract or we dissolve the partnership now. You can then open separate offices for yourselves and we'll send you what business we can.

There was no question who held the whip hand. Dr. Stinchfield signed first, and after a time Dr. Graham followed protestingly. Thereafter each man joining the firm signed the contract and understood that his partnership meant only a stipulated share in the income and not in the ownership.

## 12

At the turn of the century the Mayos were pushing hard against the walls of their offices; they needed more room. It occurred to Dr. Charlie that he and his brother could help the Masons finance a new building and in return secure the use of its first floor for their offices. The lodge agreed to the proposal with alacrity, and within a month the plans had been drawn, those for the first floor in accordance with the Mayos' specifications, and the work of construction was under way. On January 1, 1901, or thereabouts, Drs. Mayo, Stinchfield, and Graham moved into their new quarters, on the corner of Main and Zumbro streets, diagonally across from the Cook Block.

A young druggist who had been a friend of the Mayos since their boyhood and for several years had been copartner in the drug store adjoining their offices moved with them to the Masonic Temple, taking possession of one half of the first floor. He had a bonanza there, and he was inclined to work it to the limit by charging the highest prices he could get. That angered Dr. Will, who hated to see the patients exploited so heartlessly, and he remonstrated with his friend again and again, but without effect.

Then one day the druggist came to him with a proposition. The Masons were about to raise his rent and he wanted to avoid paying the added sum. Knowing that under the circumstances the Mayos would be able to secure much better terms than he could, he proposed that they rent the space from the lodge, as if for more office room, and then rerent it to him.

Dr. Will saw his chance. He leased the space from the lodge, then informed the druggist that the room was not for rent—to him. Bested, the man sold out his share in the drug store and took himself eventually to California. But when misfortune laid him low many years later, it was to Dr. Will he turned for help, and he got it.

That deal and the contract episode were early instances in which Dr. W. J. Mayo showed the impersonality of action that later made some people call him ruthless. When a course of action seemed right to him, that is, for the good of the practice and its patients, neither friendship nor family ties could turn him from it. Personal likes or dislikes had remarkably little effect on his decisions, and as far as he was concerned the decisions need not disrupt friendship.

# . . . and Company

## 13

The name Masonic *Temple* and contemporary descriptions of the "handsome, three-story structure" lead a reader to think the new quarters of "Drs. Mayo and Company" were something de luxe. But that mental picture goes glimmering at first sight of real pictures of the ordinary-looking brick building, misshapenly top-heavy with fire escapes on the second-story walls, surrounded by mud streets, and fronted by a row of horse-drawn hacks. As a matter of fact, that very unpretentiousness, the unmistakable country-town surroundings, and the informality of the office methods helped to catch the fancy of the world in the end, for this was where the world made the acquaintance of the Drs. Mayo.

The entrance led into a wide hallway lined with straight wooden chairs to make a waiting room, off which opened three rooms on each side. The first on the left was the library and general office, and the two behind it and the three across the hall were the examination rooms. Off to the right in an L-shaped extension behind the drug store were rooms for minor surgery and the laboratory work.

There was a homely bustle about the place and anything but system in the way of doing things. When patients arrived they simply took chairs in the hallway and waited their turns to see one of the doctors, for there was as yet no formal receptionist, only gruff Jay Neville sometimes, when he was not off driving Dr. Will's carriage or back in one of the offices helping Dr. Graham set a broken finger or down in the cellar firing the furnace.

Jay had begun working for the Old Doctor when he was a young man lately returned from the Civil War, in which he was with Sherman on his march to the sea. He managed the Mayo farm for many years. When Dr. and Mrs. Will moved into their home on College Street they hired a Swedish immigrant to look after the place for them, but one day Jay appeared at the door and told them he had fired the Swede and was going to run things himself. He moved in and lived with Dr. Will for twenty-four years. When the offices were established in the Masonic Temple he became janitor and general handy man there.

He was a familiar character to many of the patients, as to all Rochester, and a lovable comic relief for the members of the staff.

"The many laughs we got out of him were worth much to us," said one of them. Short and pudgy and bald-headed, with a little fringe of hair around the edges, Jay was given to chewing tobacco, eating onions, and swearing, not offensively, just easily and constantly. He loved Dr. Will and Dr. Charlie, was proud of them and fiercely loyal, but he still thought of them as the boys he had bossed on the farm. That he need take their orders seriously or fear their firing him was unthinkable. Dr. Will did fire him, often, but Jay never paid any attention and Dr. Will did not enforce his hasty decisions.

Stories of Jay's doings are many, most of them illustrating his proprietary interest in the offices and his bullheaded independence. There was the time, for instance, when he put on the storm windows before the fall was well begun. Storm windows at this time of year! Dr. Will was outraged and ordered Jay to take them off. "Those windows are going to stay on," said Jay. And they did. And so did Jay.

One of his many duties was to file the correspondence, and he was fabulous at the job. He simply pasted the letters end to end—as they came, alphabetically or chronologically only by chance—and rolled them into a cylinder. To find a letter he unrolled it like a scroll. Then someone must have shown him how druggists filed their prescriptions, for he suddenly began stringing the letters one upon another on a length of wire or heavy twine. A far cry from the precise folders and files of the Mayo Clinic division of correspondence!

The partners might get along still without a registration and reception clerk, but the business side of the practice was becoming far too heavy for Dr. Will to handle it as an incidental job. Someone was needed to take over the collecting, bookkeeping, banking, and payroll. Shortly after moving to the Masonic Temple the Mayos installed a business manager, and they named a layman to the post, William Graham, brother to Dr. Graham and Mrs. C. H. Mayo. His experience as a cheese and butter maker in the village of Byron, then as overseer of the cheese factories of a large St. Paul creamery, and finally as a grocer in Rochester may seem queer training for the job of business manager in a medical practice, but such a job was something new in the world; it was unique and actually set a precedent.

Mr. Graham's coming made little change in the method of collecting, which was highly informal. Each doctor set his own fees and took the money from those who paid on the spot, putting it in his pocket or in a table drawer to be turned over to Mr. Graham at the end of the day, together with the scrap of paper or old envelope on which he had jotted down the names of those who had not paid. Occasionally he also penciled a brief "no pay" or "could pay nothing" alongside the case history in his ledger.

## 14

Those old case ledgers are a mutely eloquent record. There they stand, shelves of them, tall, gray, cloth-bound volumes, rarely opened nowadays except when some patient of their day seeks to prove his right to an old-age pension by their entries. The pages filled with dimming script, much of it in pencil, evoke for the imaginative reader a picture of those busy offices with the endless stream of sick folk, worried, weary, querulous, moving through them, and the doctors listening, pondering, and deciding.

The collection covers the years from 1885 to 1907. There is a series for each doctor, because each man kept his own ledger, filling it with three, four, five case histories to the page until the book was full and he called for a new one. At first a thinnish volume would last him two years or more; then it took a thicker one for a single year; and at last the thickest that could be bought was enough for only a few months, so much did the practice grow.

No reliable statistical study could be made from these volumes; the records in them are too meager. There is no uniformity in the terms used, little description of physical findings, and half the time not even the diagnosis or treatment prescribed. Only rarely is there such a direct statement as "Goes to the hospital" or "Operated on next week"; more often the fact that the patient came to surgery is learned, if at all, on indirect evidence such as a note in the margin, "Died six months after operation" or "It was appendix." For many cases the record includes only the name, date, age, place of residence, and phrases like "Complains of sciatic rheumatism," "Wants to know the cause of her sterility," "Gas on the stomach and poor sleep," or "Night terrors—wetting bad." Indications of the laboratory tests used are incomplete, such as "Sent to the hospital for test meal" without any record of what the test meal showed.

# The Mayo Brothers

The comments that sometimes escaped the doctor's pencil lift the curtain briefly on comedy or near-tragedy. Dr. Graham, for instance, listed carefully the complaints detailed by a man from Sleepy Eye, then added, "Well as ever he was, so says his wife." A man from South Dakota "Thinks has been poisoned by his daughter-in-law. Bad in bowels and can't sleep. Diag.—Insane." And a patient from Canton "Feels weak, pain no particular place, some water trouble, constipated. Full of witchcraft nonsense."

In many cases it was hard to get the story. Dr. Graham "pumped hard for little information" from a woman from Green Isle. Of one from Hayfield he wrote, "Can't get much out of her. Seems to be neurasthenic and dumb." And of another, from Butternut, "All complaints hard to get, she unable to speak or understand English and interpreter poor." A woman from River Point was "Bohemian, can't speak or understand English." Others talked too much; a patient from Summit, South Dakota, was "Indefinite. A long-winded Dutchman."

Unnumbered were the patients classed neurasthenic or neurotic. A woman from Woodstock complained of spells of crying and screaming and "Gave me a sample of her scream," while another, from Le Sueur, was "Such a hopeless neurotic difficult to give her credit for any ailment." And a man from Lemond told a story of many fears: "Mind off—says can't tell good from bad. The cold weather makes him feel better."

To the brief account of a woman from Elkton, South Dakota, who was pregnant and so worried about it that she feared she was losing her mind, Dr. Graham added, "C. H. saw her with me." Was that an early instance of the way the Mayos' associates turned to Dr. Charlie for help with patients who needed reassurance more than medicine? He had a way with such persons that was beyond price, a gentle, natural, homely way that eased tense nerves and distrait minds. Fully aware of the importance of emotional and mental factors in physical disease, he did not worry overmuch about scientific justification for his methods of dealing with them, accepting instead the great Sydenham's rule of practice: "Whatever is useful is good."

From these years comes the story of a girl who insisted to Dr. Charlie that there was something wrong inside her head. He knew there was no physical lesion, but he knew too it would do no good to tell her that.

So he took her to the hospital, gave her some anesthetic, and wrapped a bandage around her head. When she "recovered" the quirk was gone and she was happy.

## 15

Now the Mayo offices stayed open all day instead of for the carefully specified hours of earlier and less busy years. The doctors' day began at seven-thirty in the morning and even then they found patients waiting, for the farmers rose early and the first train arrived in Rochester at six-thirty. Work went on without pause until seven or eight o'clock at night. The offices were open on Sunday forenoons too, for the convenience of the country folk who drove into town for church and liked to look after their souls and their bodies on the same trip so as to have the rest of the week free for farming.

As the numbers increased the Mayo brothers found their mornings filled by work at the hospital. The afternoons they spent at the offices, but no longer in the work of general diagnosing and prescribing; they had time now only for examining the patients their partners found in need of operation. Dr. Will and Dr. Charlie thus became wholly surgeons and surgical consultants.

As a result of the same press of numbers, Drs. Stinchfield and Graham were becoming wholly diagnosticians. The medical side of the practice was decreasing fast. There was literally no room and no time for it. In the early years approximately one third of the hundreds of patients admitted to St. Mary's Hospital were medical cases; now only ten or twelve out of three or four thousand a year were medical. That was partly because more ailments were treated surgically, but mostly because rooms at the hospital were too few for all who came and preference was naturally given to surgical cases. The others could more easily be taken care of elsewhere, at home if the patient was a resident or at one of the hotels or boardinghouses if he came from out of town.

But it was growing harder for the doctors to find time to visit such patients. Often they could go only after the office closed at night. Dr. Graham's son remembers how his father used to come home from the office, have a bite of supper, then hitch up the horse and go out to make some country calls. Frequently he would be called out for a confinement and would have only an hour or two of sleep before returning to the office to begin another day.

That could not continue for long. Although no local call was ever refused, gradually most of the patients from a distance who were found to need only medical care were referred back to their home-town doctor with a report of the diagnosis made and the treatment recommended.

The medical men of the firm surrendered to this necessity reluctantly. They would have liked to follow up the diagnoses themselves, especially in unusual cases, and they knew the patient did not appreciate a diagnosis alone; he had come not just to be told what ailed him but to be cured of it. However, they had time for no more than a sigh of regret, for the next man was already in the chair and outside the room more people were waiting.

This growth of specialization in diagnosis, unplanned, forced only by the demands of circumstances, brought excellent results. Spending all their time in sifting, weighing, interpreting the signs and symptoms of various diseases, the Mayo partners naturally became more expert at differential diagnosis than practitioners who saw fewer patients and divided their time between examining and treating. As Dr. Graham put it, "How could we help being good in diagnosis, with all the cases we saw?" It was Dr. Graham who, working with Dr. Will, began through cumulative experience to detect the distinguishing symptoms of duodenal ulcer, and who became aware through hearing many case histories that an unusual number of stomach cancer victims had suffered from stomach ulcer at some previous time.

The Mayo brothers realized the importance of this development in diagnosis, but they, like Dr. Graham and Dr. Stinchfield themselves, saw it only in its relation to the improvement of their surgery. None of them yet thought of diagnosis as an independently worthwhile function of their firm. It was surgery that patients came for, and the work in diagnosis developed as, and continued to be, the handmaid of surgery. The primary function of the diagnosticians was to pick from the procession of patients passing before them those whom the Mayo brothers as surgeons could benefit.

# ... and Company

## 16

One day early in 1901 Dr. Albert Plummer of Racine, Minnesota, called Dr. W. W. Mayo to see a patient of his in consultation, as he had been doing on occasion for years. The Old Doctor was away at the time, so Dr. Will decided to make the trip in his stead. When he arrived he found Dr. Plummer in bed with a cold and unable to keep the appointment. But Henry would go with Dr. Mayo to see the patient, said Dr. Plummer, referring to his son, who was in practice with him.

Soon Henry appeared, with a microscope in his hand, and he and Dr. Will got into a little buckboard behind an old gray team and started on the hour's drive to the patient's house. "A slender, eager boy, dreamy appearing, full of ideas and ideals, his thought rushing ahead of his language, which one or two sentences behind, was attempting to keep up." So Henry Plummer seemed to Dr. Will that day. He must have known the boy before, for Plummer had spent several summer vacations at St. Mary's Hospital during his schooldays, first at the University of Minnesota and then at the Northwestern University Medical School, from which he had graduated in 1898. But not until that day did Dr. Mayo learn what young Plummer was really like.

The patient they were going to see was suffering from leukemia, and during the ride they discussed the chemistry and physiology of the blood. Dr. Will was amazed at Plummer's knowledge of the subject. When they reached the bedside the young man took a drop of blood from the ear of the patient and another from the ear of the hired man and demonstrated to Dr. Will the microscopic differences between them. On the way back to Racine he continued to talk about the blood.

"I was overcome that this gangling boy should know so much about the blood, and I so little," confessed Dr. Will later. He knew enough about it to realize that much of what Henry Plummer was telling him was not yet to be found in print, and he had long been convinced that the condition of the blood was a vital factor in the success of an operation and that analysis of the blood would soon be as routine as urinalysis in diagnosis.

When he got home that night he said to Dr. Charlie, "That son of Dr. Plummer's is an extraordinary young man. He knows more about the blood than any man I have ever met. I believe we ought to get him up here to take charge of our laboratories; he would do us a lot of good." Dr. Charlie agreed, the invitation was extended, and a few weeks later Henry Plummer joined the staff in the Masonic Temple offices.

That event must be red-starred in any history of the Mayo Clinic. Dr. Will Mayo himself said the hiring of Henry Plummer was the best day's work he ever did for the Clinic. There was genius in the man, with the eccentricity that so often accompanies it, and both contributed mightily to the development at Rochester.

Dr. Plummer addressed himself first to the task for which he had been employed. He took over the supervision of the clinical laboratories, which had been sadly neglected, and quickly brought their methods and apparatus up to date. He also took charge of the x-ray work, and was amused but approving when the Mayos, rather shamefacedly, explained the presence of those wooden plugs on the machine. Keeping carefully abreast of advances in roentgenology and contributing several original refinements in technique and equipment, he gradually built x-ray diagnosis solidly into the structure of the practice. But he steadfastly refused to publish any account of his work in that field or in the clinical laboratories, so strong was his determination not to become known in the slightest degree as an x-ray or laboratory technician.

When he assumed a share of the work in general diagnosis he held out against the pressure of circumstances. He would not content himself with a small piece of medicine and would not subordinate medicine to surgery, because he could not. He was a congenital perfectionist, to the despair and sometimes the exasperation of those who worked with him. When his interest settled on any subject, be it French painting or the chemistry of the blood, he dug into it from every angle, reading, thinking, questioning, experimenting, until he had mastered it to his satisfaction.

He faced his patients in the same spirit. Each one presented a problem to be solved, and he insisted upon his right, his obligation, to stick with it until he had solved it or had satisfied himself that it could not be solved in the present state of knowledge. Diagnosis was only the beginning; that merely unlocked the door to treatment, and treatment should be catholic, making use of *all* available methods, of which surgery was but one.

With such ideas, which in practice at least were a generation ahead of the time, Henry Plummer did not fit easily into the division of labor that had developed in Rochester. Nor did he try to. Except for the modifications forced upon him by the lack of facilities for medical treatment, he went his own way in his own time. And the Mayo brothers not only suffered him to do so; they encouraged him.

Dr. Charlie had good reason, for Henry Plummer's chief and most enduring interest was the thyroid gland. As a boy he had known Mr. Strain, the Mayos' first goiter patient, and the course of events in that case so impressed him that he had given particular attention to the thyroid in all his medical studies and experiments since. Now his interest coincided neatly with Dr. Charlie's, even though to Plummer the thyroid was not just a surgical problem but a broad question of physiology, including the gland's function, its secretion, and its total relation to health and disease.

To that Dr. Plummer added a problem that Dr. Will put into his hands. Success in treating esophageal stricture caused by the swallowing of lye brought to Rochester some patients, adults, who had all the symptoms of stricture though none could be found. To discover what really was wrong with them would take more time than Dr. Mayo had to give. Plummer was the man for the job, but what he made of it must be left for later telling.

17

Another medical student who haunted the operating rooms of St. Mary's during the summer was Edward Starr Judd, the son of a Rochester businessman who had got his start as a grain dealer in the heyday of wheat. Starr, as he was called, had begun to work at the hospital during his high school days. He must have been employed for odd jobs of some sort by the sisters, for informal as the Mayo brothers were, they would not have hired a high school youngster to assist them.

However that was, Starr Judd made the acquaintance of surgery, promptly fell in love with it, and took Dr. W. J. Mayo for his hero. Talking over the events of the day, he would say, "Why mother, I'd rather be a Dr. Will than be president of the United States."

He made an excellent record in his medical course at the University of Minnesota, and when he graduated in 1902 he was appointed to an internship at St. Mary's, where he quickly attracted Dr. Charlie's special notice. Starr was a quiet chap, with little to say, but he was an untiring worker, utterly absorbed in surgery. And he had the gift. Although he did not sparkle with originality, one showing was all he needed to get the hang of any procedure, and he would be doing it with great skill in an amazingly short time. With proper training and experience he would make a superb surgical craftsman.

Up to this time the Mayos had chosen partners and assistants who could relieve them of the nonsurgical phases of the practice, while they kept the operating entirely in their own hands. But if the present increase of patients continued they would shortly face the necessity of employing an associate surgeon. Young Judd appealed to them as a possibility. He could be trained in their methods and be trusted to apply them skillfully. If he continued to work with Dr. Charlie he would be quite able to take over a share of the operating a few years hence when the need arose.

So when his year's internship ended Dr. Judd was made a member of the staff, serving as Dr. Charlie's first assistant in the mornings and helping with diagnosis at the offices in the afternoons. He developed according to their expectations and the next year was encouraged with the title of junior surgeon. Though he continued to act principally as Dr. Charlie's assistant for several years longer, he began to do some operating on his own and before long was giving Dr. Charlie reason to be proud of his pupil.

Dr. Judd's appointment as junior surgeon coincided with a further enlargement of St. Mary's Hospital. The overcrowding had again become insupportable. Patients sometimes had to wait days for their operations because there was no hospital bed available for them. So the Sisters of St. Francis once more called in the architect and the contractor, and the third addition to the hospital was completed in 1904.

The new four-story east wing brought the capacity up to one hundred and seventy-five beds, made space again for more kitchens, boiler rooms, and the like, and provided spacious new quarters for the surgeons. Two operating rooms connected by a small dressing and sterilizing room were fitted out on the fourth floor, and near them a cheery, comfortable lounge for the accommodation of visiting physicians. The old third-floor room that Dr. Charlie had been using was turned into a ward, but the original second-floor room was kept for Dr. Millet's use in cystoscopy and for surgical dressings.

## 18

About that time a local wag looked about him and added cripples to retired farmers and lunatics as the chief components of Rochester's population, for the Mayo firm and its patients had become an inescapable feature of the scene. The practice had long been an invitation to druggists, and now that men and women were coming from farther afield it offered golden opportunities in other lines as well.

Transportation, for instance. The mile that lay between St. Mary's Hospital and downtown Rochester called for means of conveyance, and independent hackmen prospered in providing it. One of them had enough initiative to inaugurate an ambulance service in 1897. While the special vehicle was in process of construction in a Rochester carriage shop it attracted much attention from curious visitors. "A large covered body rests on a perfectly adjusted gearing provided with a series of easily moving springs, that reduce the possibility of jarring to the minimum. It is a model of convenience and even graceful in its proportions." It was considered a great improvement on the "ungainly looking dray" that had apparently served in emergencies until then.

A similar concession to special needs was made by the Chicago and Northwestern station master. To supplement the rough benches that sufficed for able-bodied travelers he ordered "two fine hard wood rocking chairs . . . the personification of comfort . . . to be placed in the ladies' waiting room for the use of invalid passengers."

Almost every patient who came to Rochester was accompanied by one or more relatives or friends to stand by him during the possible surgical ordeal. These people had to have a place to eat and sleep, and as their numbers increased the restaurant and hotel business boomed. Old hostelries took on new life and new ones appeared like mushrooms, bringing forward names that are still familiar in the hotel world of Rochester.

The Cook House, which had been such a white elephant on its

owners' hands in the depression of the early 70's, was taken over in the late 90's by a Mr. Kahler and his son, formerly the managers of the Archer House in Northfield. Young John Kahler was an able hotel man, and aided by Rochester's prosperity he soon put the Cook House on its feet. He redecorated, refurnished, remodeled, and expanded until the original forty-five rooms had grown to a hundred," the accommodations taxed every night."

The Cook House was entirely a hotel, but most of its smaller competitors became in part nursing or convalescent homes, keeping a nurse or two on the premises and catering to the sick, those waiting to enter St. Mary's, those discharged from the hospital but not yet able to go home, and those receiving medical treatment only. Hotels were too few, however, and too expensive for most of those whose stay must be long. "Rooms for rent" signs began to dot the streets and boarding-houses flourished, especially in the vicinity of St. Mary's Hospital.

The growth of business possibilities in Rochester required a decision from the Mayo brothers. They were vitally interested, for it was essential that all necessary services be provided for their patients and those who came with them. Investments there promised good returns, which after all would accrue indirectly from their practice. Should they participate?

They decided not. No profits from a drug store, a hotel, or a real estate deal made in the knowledge of events to come should pay their rent or buy their cars. "We felt that our position should be one above suspicion of selfish purpose and that neither directly nor indirectly ought we to profit from the sick who came to Rochester, except through professional fees."

## 19

In spite of indications to the contrary in this talk of restaurants and hotels, Rochester was still a small country town. Its population had grown little during the last three decades and in 1900 it stood between five and six thousand. The trade of the farmers was still the town's chief reason for being; no industry of any importance had established itself, and there was nothing of urban smartness about the place, either in manner or in appearance.

The best of its stores were small and cluttered, lamp-lighted and stove-heated. In any of them on almost any afternoon could be found a farmer's wife or two hanging forlornly about while their husbands topped off the trading trip to town with a spell of sociable drinking. Her shopping done, there was nothing for the wife to do but wait in some store, sitting on a packing case near the stove perhaps, trying to hush a crying baby or keep track of the restless older children, who roamed the store, getting generally underfoot, curiously fingering the goods within reach, and poking dirty little fingers into open barrels of crackers or brown sugar.

When the newly organized women's club resolved to alleviate this situation and opened a women's rest room furnished with chairs, cradles, cots, picture books and magazines, and a cookstove (for warming over the lunches brought along), the number of visitors from the country who made use of it rose quickly to the surprising total of between five and six hundred a month.

Private enterprise had given Rochester the pure water supply the Old Doctor had worked for so long, and also a city telephone system. Electricity was available through a municipal plant, but only at night. Dr. Charlie was doing his best to persuade the city fathers to provide a daytime service, but they doubted that there would be enough call for it to justify the added expense.

In street-paving the progress was slow. Except for half a dozen blocks of the main business street, the roadways were lanes of ruts and dust or mud, Zumbro Street from town out to St. Mary's Hospital as well as the others. The need for improving the "execrable condition" of that important artery was often the subject of editorial comment.

At present it is a mass of nasty, sticky mud and filth, through which vehicles and horses are compelled to plow, and pedestrians wade through water and mud on the crossings at the expense of footwear and cleanliness. . . . It is traveled more than any street in the city. Visitors go over it, and their comments are emphatically uncomplimentary to the enterprise of our city. We might better go without many other things than let this street remain as it is . . . a crying evidence of our lack of appreciation of the benefits accruing from St. Mary's Hospital.

But paving waited while factions bickered about costs, the proper width, and the best wearing material. Not until well beyond 1905 was the approach to St. Mary's Hospital made smooth.

If pavements were hard to get, any sort of park or beautification project was impossible. The Old Doctor had never stopped talking about his Bear Creek improvement project, but his dream merely amused his fellow townsmen, who dubbed the proposed lake "Mayo's frog pond." Adopting the designation with great good humor, Dr. Mayo kept right on with his persistent campaign, and on one occasion he was able to stir the city council to such a flush of enthusiasm that they voted to buy the Bear Creek site and chose a name for the park. It should be Mayo Park:

Dr. W. W. Mayo has been a resident of Rochester for many years. Much of her material progress is due to him directly or indirectly. Energetic, progressive, thoroughly convinced of the possibilities of the city, he has never let an opportunity pass to aid in its advancement. And now in his declining years the city remembers his public-spiritedness, and tenders what little of recognition it can for his untiring efforts in her behalf by naming what should prove to be the beauty spot of Rochester after him.

Unfortunately the enthusiasm spent itself in words. The name stuck but the park did not materialize. The resolution to buy the site went the way of many good intentions, and occasional attempts to revive the project came to nothing.

## 20

The Mayo brothers shook their heads at such communal shortsightedness, for they had lately been looking at Rochester with critical eyes. So far all their partners and assistants, with the exception of Dr. Herb, had come from southern Minnesota and like themselves were used to small towns and rural surroundings, but the Mayos knew that if they went on adding men to their staff they would soon have to look for them farther afield. Could they hope to persuade the kind of men they wanted—well-trained, capable men, able to practice successfully wherever they chose—to settle in Rochester? How would the town appear to them as a home? How did it appear to patients coming from other places, and to visiting physicians?

A little thinking along those lines convinced the Mayos that it would be to their own advantage to provide for Rochester some of the improvements and advantages its citizens seemed unlikely to provide for themselves. Deciding they could afford to spend about one tenth of their income in that way, they had next to consider what sort of project they should finance. Dr. Will described their reasoning thus:

Too often charity debauches persons who receive, and it is as easy to debauch a community as it is an individual. It is as much the duty of the community to give attention to its sick and poor as it is to its pavements and sewers. To relieve taxable citizens of their just burdens tends to break down public spirit, and the sense of communal responsibility. But however much we may make the citizens responsible for the immediate care of their own community, experience shows that little can be expected of them in anticipating future needs. Their attitude is that of the congressman who after listening to a lot of talk on conservation for the future which interfered with the division of political spoils said, "I'm sick of all this talk of posterity; what the hell has posterity ever done for us?" It seemed to us that efforts to advance local and general public welfare should be made along the line of anticipating future needs and developing methods of meeting them.

They made their first gift to the city in 1904. One evening in July the Commercial Club sponsored a lecture by Charles Loring of Minneapolis, a crusader for city beautification whose work earned him the title of Minnesota's "apostle of parks and playgrounds." He spoke enthusiastically of the possibilities he saw in Rochester—in the park site along Bear Creek, the lengths of riverbank winding through the town, and the hilltop behind St. Mary's Hospital.

At the close of the address it was announced that Drs. W. J. and C. H. Mayo had given five thousand dollars and John R. Cook one thousand "for the purpose of buying a park or otherwise improving or adorning the city."

At last the Old Doctor's dream was realized, for the money was used to buy the Bear Creek land. But it took the city two years to obtain title to it, because the owners suddenly discovered the value of their land and their asking price went up. Condemnation proceedings and a long series of appeals to the courts were the wearisome result.

Meanwhile the Mayos had decided on a second gift, and this time they bought the land themselves, a tract two blocks long on the hilltop Mr. Loring liked so well. They presented it to the city, along with a thousand dollars, to which Mr. Cook again added a thousand, to be used in making it into another park. This with a later addition or two became the St. Mary's Park of today, Rochester's miniature "sky-line drive."

That policy systematically continued and expanded was the chief means of giving to Rochester physical features and facilities for recreation, education, music, and art that are unusual, if not unique, in American cities of its size. And the practical purpose was achieved— that good men who were otherwise willing to join the Mayos should not be deterred by the disadvantages of Rochester as a home.

# CHAPTER FIFTEEN

# Recognition Won

The medical code of ethics does not sanction a doctor's reporting his achievements to the world at large, but it requires him to make them known to the profession, in order that "the experience of one may contribute to the instruction of all." And of course it may also contribute to the reputation of the one. From the beginning the Mayo brothers gave serious and intelligent attention to reporting their work in professional circles. Writing and speaking were hard for both of them at first, and time for the preparation of papers had to be found at odd hours, which were few and mostly at night. But appreciating the tremendous importance of this phase of their activity, they forced themselves to the task.

They began with participation in local societies, where their father's reputation secured them a ready hearing. Their papers, printed in the state society *Transactions,* were reprinted or abstracted in the *Northwestern Lancet,* owned and edited by Dr. A. J. Stone, the Old Doctor's good friend. To that journal the brothers also sent clinical reports of their unusual cases and some of the papers they read before the Southern Minnesota Medical Society. Thus word of what they were doing reached men who had not heard it in person.

Statewide recognition of their ability was swift. They were elected to one office after another in the state society, were appointed in turn to membership on the state board of health, where they served with men of their father's generation like Dr. Staples and Dr. Hewitt, and were elected to coveted memberships in the Minnesota Academy of Medicine, an exclusive fifty of the state's medical elite. That provided another outlet for their reports and occasioned two more papers a year to be published.

At the convention of the state society in 1893 Dr. Charlie presided as chairman at the session of the section on surgery, for which he arranged the program. Nicholas Senn was unable to accept his invitation to be present, but John B. Murphy was there to lend fiery eloquence to the inevitable battle over the merits of appendectomy. A paper on the radical cure of hernia precipitated another heated discussion, in which Dr. Will took a notable part. All in all it was a good session, full of spirit.

The next morning the society proceeded to the business of electing officers. Although nomination was still from the floor rather than by committee, the custom of a three-year rotation in the presidency had been well established; a St. Paul man was elected one year, a Minneapolis man the next, and a downstate member the third. This was the year for a downstate man, and Dr. Richard O. Beard, a young Minneapolis practitioner, offered the name of William J. Mayo. The election was unanimous.

There was a just-think-of-it tone in the *Minneapolis Tribune's* announcement of the choice: surgeon to St. Mary's at Rochester, "one of the largest and best-equipped hospitals in the state," member of the state board of health, and district surgeon for the Chicago and Northwestern Railroad—and only thirty-one years old, the youngest man yet elected to the presidency of the state medical society.

In the afternoon Dr. Will read a paper before the section on gynecology dealing with the functions and surgical uses of the great omentum, the double fold of peritoneum that hangs from the stomach like a protective apron in front of the abdominal viscera. His discussion was based largely on his own observations during operations, and the society members were warm in their expressions of admiration. Dr. A. W. Abbott, a Minneapolis surgeon to whom Dr. Will owed his knowledge of more than one useful surgical trick, thanked the young author for his excellent work, adding, "He always gives us that kind of a paper, but because we always expect it is no reason why we should not thank him for it." And Dr. Dunsmoor said:

After hearing Dr. Mayo's paper, I feel that it is useless for me to attempt to criticize it or discuss it, when it is apparent on first presentation that it is the best paper yet written on this subject, and merits only remarks of commendation.

The paper, all the way through, is original; the topic is one that has certainly not been worn threadbare, and I am glad now that we have another evidence of the wisdom of our selection of Dr. Mayo as President of this Society.

# Recognition Won

## 2

Throughout the 1890's Dr. Will confined his formal papers to the section on gynecology, while Dr. Charlie did the team's reporting to the general surgeons. That worked out too well to have merely happened; it must have been a deliberate division of effort. There were two of them; so let them make the most of the fact.

Dr. Will was doing enough pelvic surgery to rank with the specialists, though he denied that he was a gynecologist; he was a general surgeon. But so were most of the others in the section. His experience and results were fully equal to theirs, and in many instances he could give them pointers on the latest techniques. Before the decade ended even the best of them were deferring to Dr. Mayo's opinion.

As he moved into the newer fields of gallbladder and stomach surgery he described his work to the Minnesota Academy of Medicine, whose members might be expected to be the most able to appreciate its worth, but even they got left behind. When Dr. Will reported his first operations for obstruction of the pylorus, all the excellent Dr. Dunsmoor could find to say was that the procedure was at least novel.

One has only to read the published *Transactions* of these medical groups to understand why the young Mayos made such an impression on their fellows. Time and again after a paper full of fumbling, rambling surmise, one of the brothers rose to explain simply and quietly, but with a breathtaking barrage of names, facts, and figures, just where this procedure would work and where that, to what extent, and precisely why. Their own papers were chock-full of references to the work of other men, and of the details of anatomy, physiology, and pathology on which their opinions and conclusions rested.

They knew everything, it seemed, though they were still such boys! They looked utterly unlike successful professional men, with their earnest, intent young faces above suits that were obviously from a small-town store and hung loose and ill-fitting on their slender frames. The fair-haired, blue-eyed Will had a natural dignity of manner and an erect, assured bearing that saved him from any appearance of naiveté, but Charlie always looked like the farmer's son come to town, uneasy in his dress-up suit and his attempts at dress-up deportment. His dark hair would not stay down, his tie was soon awry, and if his suit had a press when he left home it always lost it on the way.

But there was nothing in the least small-town or immature about their knowledge; that was really amazing. Yet they were always modest and deferential toward the older members of the society, whose practical suggestions they gratefully accepted and publicly acknowledged.

Dr. Will's papers almost always started a discussion, in the course of which he seldom failed to get a nice compliment or two, but Dr. Charlie was not so fortunate. Often a dead silence would greet the end of his remarks; no one had anything to say. The reason is not hard to find. On one occasion the doctor called on to open the discussion said that Dr. Mayo's paper was undoubtedly very valuable but he could not discuss it because he knew nothing about the subject.

Dr. Charlie talked for the most part about surgery of the eye, the brain, and the nerves, whereas the profession's attention was focused upon abdominal and pelvic surgery, and only there were interest and experience widespread enough to engender differences of opinion and strong feeling. Not until later, on the subject of goiter surgery, did Dr. Charlie move up from the outer rim to the center of the medical spotlight.

Then too, in those earlier years Dr. Will was the better speaker, making the same determined effort to improve his speaking ability as to improve his surgery. Gradually he evolved a formula for his papers: Begin with an arresting sentence; close with a strong summary; in between speak simply, clearly, and always to the point; and above all be brief. He heeded the maxim of the old minister to the effect that few souls are saved after the first fifteen minutes of the sermon, and he acquired a gift for compact sentences and a piquant turn of phrase well suited to his own dry humor.

In delivery he was unassuming, completely devoid of anything pompous or affected, but crisply direct and assured for so young a man. Obviously he was a fellow with something to say and an effective way of saying it. The Rochester newspapers were soon happily reporting that Dr. Will Mayo was considered one of the best public speakers in the state.

Nonetheless they showed more than a little surprise when he was invited to give the commencement address for the medical school of the University of Minnesota in 1895. That invitation usually went to some big name from the East, and it was a remarkable honor for a

The College Street homes had a speaking tube between.

Summer found the Mayos
at their lake cottages near
Oronoco.

Will and his daughters,
Carrie and Phoebe

Charlie and the boys,
Charles, Jr., and Joseph

Mrs. Charlie with Edith,
Charles, Jr., Joseph, and
Dorothy

The Mayo cars, 1910

For several years the Will Mayos entertained summertime guests at their home at Lake Allis near Oronoco.

Charlie found a new plaything in the horseless carriage.

"The biggest thing Will and I ever did was to pick the father and mother we had."

This was where the world made the acquaintance of the Drs. Mayo, the Masonic Temple offices, between 1901 and 1914.

Jay Neville,
caretaker extraordinary

Burt W. Eaton and Frank B. Kellogg were law partners in Rochester in the 1870's.

Dr. W.W.Mayo, with J.F. Van Dooser and C. C. Willson, longtime personal and political friends

Dr. Will's new residence on College Street. He asked only that it have a tower like his mother's.

Mayowood—the site Charlie chose was in the midst of rolling hills, still wooded and wild.

Up the Mississippi

The first two Mayo boats were sternwheelers.

Mrs. Will and Dr. Ochsner

*At the Keokuk dam*

*Front row*, Philip Heintz, J. H. Kahler, Dr. W. J. Mayo, Dr. H. S. Plummer, and Hugh Cooper, famous hydraulic engineer. *Back row*, Mrs. Kahler, Mrs. Mellish, Miss Melita Roberts, Mrs. Plummer, and Mrs. Heintz

*European travel pictures*

Dr. Will and his family, Dr.
Graham, and the Kahlers on
the *S. S. Amerika,* bound
for Russia

Dr. and Mrs. Charlie on the right

Dr. and Mrs. Will with Mrs. Balfour and the Kahlers

Sir William Wheeler of Dublin,
Dr. Franklin Martin of Chicago,
and Dr. Charlie at Mayowood

Dr. Charlie and Dr. William D. Haggard
of Nashville

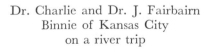

Dr. Charlie and Dr. J. Fairbairn
Binnie of Kansas City
on a river trip

The hospitality of Mayowood

Dr. Charlie
duck-hunting

*A meeting of famous surgeons in London*
*Front row,* John B. Murphy of the U.S.A., Körte of Germany, Hartmann of Germany, Fuchs of Austria, von Eiselsberg of Austria, Kocher of Switzerland, Tuffier of France. *Back row,* Nicolaysen of Norway, George Crile of the U.S.A., *unidentified,* Sheppard of England, Bastianelli of Italy, William J. Mayo and Harvey Cushing of the U.S.A.

Visiting doctors in Rochester—the International Society of Surgery

The library, 1909

Mrs. Maud Mellish Wilson,
pioneer medical editor

Dr. Louis B. Wilson, a man of
boundless intellectual curiosity

With the reorganization and
the new building of 1914 the
Mayo Clinic emerged as a
distinct institution.

local man, one from downstate at that. The president of the graduating class, who extended the official invitation, may have had some influence in the selection, for he was one of the medical students who spent the summer working at St. Mary's, but the final choice was made by a unanimous vote of the class and the faculty.

That commencement address must be one of the shortest on record. Dr. Will, in words at least, was a bit diffident. "It is customary to give some practical advice . . . but I fear that my age and limited experience do not qualify me for the task." He essayed it all the same.

I wish to call your attention to . . . the necessity of a broad culture upon your part to enable you to sympathize with all classes and all people in the hour of their need. . . . The medical profession has, of necessity, always exercised a great liberality of spirit and thought toward those individuals and classes of society with whose opinions they may differ, whose actions they may condemn. . . . Whatever our individual beliefs may be, let us . . . put aside all bigotry and intolerance, which would defeat the very object of our convictions by putting us out of touch with men of different views. . . .

Your study of exact methods and detail work, which has occupied your time until now, must be supplemented by a general knowledge of the lives and the work of people in other walks of life, in order that you can meet them as patients with a certain degree of sympathy and understanding. . . . The whole tendency of modern life is toward the amplification of purely technical work. . . . It is incumbent upon you to develop a broad culture as the only means whereby you can obtain and maintain a proper appreciation of social conditions.

3

About this time Dr. Franklin H. Martin, professor of gynecology in the Chicago Postgraduate Medical School and one of its proprietors, attended a meeting of the Minnesota State Medical Society. As he recalled it:

A young man modestly stepped forward, was recognized by the presiding officer, and began his discussion of a paper that had been presented. His talk was very much to the point, and notwithstanding his boyish appearance, his words and manner were most impressive. He did not indulge in the usual complimentary references, and the wisdom he dispensed was too good to be true. The entire audience, including the older wheelhorses of the profession, listened with rapt attention, and applauded appreciatively as the speaker finished his terse, interesting, and definite discussion and took his seat.

A second young man, a boy in stature and appearance, addressed the audience. There was the same direct discussion with pertinent references to distinguished men whose operations he had watched, and to recent scientific articles he had perused. An occasional humorous observation brought smiles and chuckles from his attentive listeners. I was profoundly attracted to these young men, their simplicity, and their unconventional appearance.

"Who are these youngsters?" I asked of the doctor who was seated next to me. He looked surprised. "Don't you know the Mayo boys? They are two surgeons practicing in the little country town of Rochester."

My conversation with this man convinced me that the two country surgeons had already won the respect of their elder confrères in their state medical association.

So they had. But outside Minnesota the name of Mayo meant nothing except to a few who knew the two young doctors from the West as frequent and earnest observers in the nation's chief surgical clinics.

The brothers had been subscribing to the *Annals of Surgery*, the organ of the American Surgical Association, since it first appeared in the middle 1880's, and the immediate height of their ambition was to have a paper published in its sacred pages. Dr. Will Mayo tells the story:

In 1895 my brother and I sent to the *Annals* our earliest joint contribution. For the first time we believed we had something sufficiently valuable not to seem a profanation of its pages. My brother's contribution was the report of a case in which an open injury of the knee-joint was accompanied by extreme sepsis. . . . My contribution was the report of a case of accidental traumatic division of the vas deferens, in which I made an end-to-end union. . . .

That was our unimpressive advent into the surgical high light. Previously we had each written four or five papers a year, but had confined our contributions, or perhaps more accurately, they had been confined to where they belonged, county, district, and state societies. Occasionally, we sent our little papers to some good eastern medical journal, hoping that they would enter the current of the stream, only to have them rejected, and restored to us in the eddy. That was the beginning of almost yearly contributions to the *Annals*. . . . Many of those papers, as they appeared in the *Annals*, were wonderfully improved in English and sometimes in fact, by the kindly, friendly, helpful corrections of the editor. These I noted with care and profit, and to few men do I owe so much as I do to Lewis Stephen Pilcher . . . the editor of the *Annals of Surgery*.

# Recognition Won

Dr. Mayo's memory was slightly at fault there; the brothers' first publication in the *Annals* was a joint case report in 1893, and, recommended by his position as president of the state society, Dr. Will in 1894 had made the pages of the *Journal of the American Medical Association* and the *New York Medical Record*. But the ambitious young men were especially jubilant over the 1895 paper because it attracted the notice of the great Dr. Gerster of New York, who subsequently published a hearty recommendation of the Mayo method of treating infection of the knee joint.

The brothers had been attending the conventions of the national societies regularly, sometimes as official delegates from the state group, but only once had either of them found courage to participate. Dr. Will loved to tell the story of that once. It was one of the first meetings of the American Medical Association he attended, and the *pièce de résistance* of the program was a paper on the incidence of cancer presented by the surgeon general of the army. The speaker appeared, pompous and paunchy, stiff from head to toe in official regalia, with two assistants to handle his statistical charts.

The gist of his remarks was that cancer was increasing in the United States. Though it was growing more prevalent even in such a new state as Minnesota, the larger percentage was in the older communities, and there seemed to be more of it among residents in old houses than in new dwellings. The inevitable conclusion, he thought—with the theory of infection newly in the air— was that cancer is an infectious disease. The learned men of medicine who discussed the paper agreed that it was a remarkable and thoughtful contribution to its important subject.

In the intensity of his disagreement Dr. Will forgot his shyness and rose to his feet, protesting that there was another way of explaining those facts. When the audience became aware of what was happening —a beardless, unknown youth daring to challenge such eminent authorities—they were delighted and began to shout "Platform! Platform!" The president invited Dr. Will to the rostrum and, as he recalled it, he spoke to this effect:

I am from Minnesota. It seems to me that this is the way it is. Cancer is preeminently a disease of forty and beyond. Only the young people who were in good enough health to struggle with the development of a new

405

country came to Minnesota from the East, leaving the people of cancer age behind. There was therefore greater freedom from cancer in the new state. Now Minnesota is older. The young people are moving on, leaving behind a larger percentage of people in the cancer age, and we note an increase in cases of cancer just as happened in New England and the older states. As to the old houses, they are more likely to be inhabited by old people of cancer age. And anyway the question of coincidence must play a part. I am not a poker player, but I am told that a perfectly honest man may sometimes hold four aces.

The crowd laughed and applauded heartily, and for many years thereafter Dr. Will was told by men he met, "The first time I remember seeing you was when you challenged the surgeon general of the army on cancer."

That was an isolated instance, however. A biographical dictionary of the physicians and surgeons of the United States published in 1896 made no mention of either William or Charles Mayo. But then, that volume was compiled by a New Englander, and it probably never occurred to him that anyone worth including might be at work in the West.

4

It was wise of the Mayos not to rush their debut in the national arena. "When the opportunity came we were ready," ready with experience and ability to take a place at once among the leaders, ready to rise, not slowly and therefore unimpressively, but like rockets.

In 1896 Dr. Wheaton of St. Paul was chairman of the surgical section of the American Medical Association, and he invited Dr. W. J. Mayo to appear on the program. That was the opportunity. With faultless judgment Dr. Will chose his topic in the youngest field of surgery, the stomach, and with admirable restraint he stuck to his formula, even to the old minister's fifteen minutes.

Whatever the audience may have expected when it came time for Dr. Mayo to speak and they saw he was a mere youth—he looked much younger than his thirty-five years—what they got was obviously one of the best papers of the entire session. In frank wonder Dr. Alexander H. Ferguson of Chicago observed that the young man's talk was a really remarkable presentation of its subject. "I do not think that I have ever heard so much condensed into a paper occupying but fifteen minutes to read, and I congratulate the author upon the mature opinions expressed and the manner in which he states the case."

That paper and participation in other discussions of the session set Dr. Will's feet on the ladder, and he went up fast. Each year he gave a paper, usually on gallbladder or stomach surgery, and contributed to the discussions in other fields. It was the story of the Minnesota state society all over again: The men who heard him were profoundly impressed by the extent of his knowledge and experience, in such astounding contrast to his youthful appearance and modest manner.

Take the matter of gastroenterostomy. Probably not half the men attending the section meetings had yet seen that operation performed, and hardly more than a score had actually tried it for themselves. Yet here stood this youngster, talking with quiet authority about gastroenterostomy on the basis of *his personal experience* in twenty-five, fifty, one hundred cases—with results that not one of his listeners could equal. Men listened in amazement and turned to ask their neighbors, Who *is* this Dr. Mayo?

Early in 1899 Dr. Will prepared a report of the one hundred and five operations he had done to date on the gallbladder and its ducts. Carefully he tabulated the statistics, computed the mortality rate in the several types of cases, and set down his observations and conclusions. Then he submitted the paper to the exclusive *American Journal of the Medical Sciences,* probably the best of the medical monthlies.

The manuscript came to the Philadelphia office of the editor, Dr. Alfred Stengel. One hundred and five gallbladder operations? Amazing, this Dr. Mayo. And just where is Rochester, Minnesota? Dr. Stengel looked up the town and learned that it had less than six thousand inhabitants. Was it possible that a doctor in so small a western town had done so many operations in so new a field?

When he inquired into the records of some of the leading Philadelphia surgeons, he found that not one of them had done anything like that amount of work on the gallbladder, while a survey made in Louisville the year before showed that all the surgeons of that outstanding southern center together had performed just one hundred and six gallbladder operations.

And this country doctor claimed he and his brother had done one hundred and five themselves! The man must be a knave. Without further ado Dr. Stengel put the manuscript in an envelope and addressed it back to its author, with "regrets."

5

Dr. Stengel did not stand alone in his disbelief; others too found the Mayos' experience and results utterly incredible.

Dr. Carl Beck of Chicago was a Czech by birth and by training in medicine. After graduation from the German University of Prague, a considerable period of postgraduate study at other European universities, and a turn at teaching on the Prague faculty of medicine, he moved to the United States in 1886. In the middle 1890's he began his long career as professor of surgical pathology at the University of Illinois College of Medicine and professor of surgery at the Chicago Postgraduate School.

One morning he was conducting a clinic for the benefit of practitioners attending the latter school. The principal case was a stricture of the common duct, and in the course of the operation Dr. Beck attempted to use a Murphy button to effect the union between the gallbladder and the intestines. He had such difficulty in placing the button that he finally had to give up altogether and resort to suture anastomosis.

When the clinic was over, a short, stocky young man came up to discuss the case with Dr. Beck, who soon saw that this fellow knew an uncommon lot about the operation he had been trying to do. A little sharply perhaps, Dr. Beck inquired who he was and how he came to know so much about it. Why—with an engaging smile—he was Charles Mayo. He and his brother were surgeons in Rochester, Minnesota, and they had had occasion several times to use the button in gallbladder surgery.

In Dr. Beck's own words: "I was naturally more than surprised that he should have ever attempted to operate on a gallbladder," let alone his having had "an experience much wider than my own."

Beck reported the incident to Nicholas Senn, whose assistant and protégé he had been. "Senn was astonished." He had just returned from a meeting of the American Medical Association at which this man's brother had reported cases and results "such as only very progressive surgeons with large practices could have." He did not believe the stories these chaps were telling; they must be stretching the truth, and it was high time someone checked up on their tales. He advised Dr. Beck to accept the invitation Dr. Charlie had given him, visit Rochester, and investigate. Dr. Beck did so, within the week.

It took me about a day and a half to make the trip, and when Í arrived I saw the most interesting conditions. I stopped at the Cook House, a very antiquated hotel in front of which was a large square with dozens of buggies and carts with their horses tied to the hitching posts. There was a large building in the square, in the basement [on the first floor?] of which were the offices of Doctors Mayo, Stinchfield, and Graham.
As I entered the office, I saw an old gentleman behind a desk covered with large books. I introduced myself to him, and with a smile he turned to a lady who was present (Mrs. Mayo) and said, "This is the man Charlie saw in Chicago."

The "boys" were not there at the moment but Dr. Beck was invited to meet them at supper at the Old Doctor's home. The cordial informality of the reception surprised Dr. Beck, and pleased him.

The next day he made his investigation. He watched the brothers do several major operations, with a skill the like of which he had seldom seen, was shown over the hospital, and met the partners in the office. The number of patients thronging the waiting rooms would have done credit to a Chicago outpatient clinic. By the end of the day Dr. Beck was a convert.

When he got back to Chicago he told Dr. Senn he was mistaken about the Mayo brothers; they were doing all they claimed and much more. They could teach a man many things and he, for one, intended to visit them often. He did, became one of their good friends, and aided materially in spreading their reputation throughout the United States and Europe.

6

Believing waited upon seeing for many, but though they might doubt Dr. Will's figures they could hardly deny the excellence of his ideas. His papers drew the warmest kind of commendation from men whose opinions everyone respected, and tangible recognition followed.

In 1897 he was elected vice-president of the American Association of Railway Surgeons, in 1898 chairman of the surgical section of the American Medical Association, in 1899 vice-chairman of the section's

# The Mayo Brothers

executive council, and in 1900 chairman. In 1899 he also received the accolade of which he had dreamed, which above all else he had labored to deserve. Despite the honors that came to him in later years, Dr. Will always said the proudest day of his life was the day he was elected to membership in the American Surgical Association. Only fourteen years before, as a youth just out of medical college, he had asked himself whether a small-town man could possibly achieve fellowship in that company of the surgical mighty. The small-town man had done so, even in advance of big-town men like Drs. Ochsner and Murphy.

Dr. Donald Maclean once told the American Medical Association, "I have watched with the intense and critical observation of a father watching his son the work of my former pupil, Dr. Mayo, and I admire it very much indeed." Perhaps partly as a result of that admiration and at Dr. Maclean's instigation, Dr. Will was granted the honorary degree of master of arts by his alma mater in 1900, "in recognition of his labors for the advancement of the science and art of surgery," and he was invited to address the university medical school in the fall of 1900.

Other invitations to speak followed: from the surgical section of the Suffolk District Medical Society in Boston in February 1902, the Chicago Medical Society the next month, the New York Surgical Association the following October, and the New York Academy of Medicine in December.

The invitation to Boston may have been the result, indirectly at least, of the experience of two prominent surgeons in that metropolis, Drs. John C. Munro and Fred B. Lund, who visited Rochester and returned singing the praises of the Mayos. Said Dr. Munro, "We were truly inspired by what we saw and learned, and related the story of the accomplishments of these brothers to our confrères at home. To our embarrassment, we were looked upon as a couple of fanatics who had been 'taken in.'"

There was no hint of that attitude in the proceedings when Dr. Will addressed the society. The president's introduction was highly complimentary.

There is something in the atmosphere of our Western States, and in the freedom of their communities in matters of thought, that breeds men of strong purpose and peculiarly favors original methods of work. Among the men of this stamp is one of our profession, whose achievements deserve to

410

stand high in the list of the best that have come from the minds and the hands of American surgeons. Six years' study of his surgical work, as it has appeared in publications, and the application of such of his procedures as I have had the opportunity to put into practice, convinced me that there was no greater satisfaction that I could give to this society than that of seeing and hearing him personally. Dr. William J. Mayo of Rochester, Minnesota.

## 7

Early in their travels to learn from others the Mayo brothers had decided that when a man was called a liar for his reports of success it might be worth their while to see his work. When in their turn their word was questioned, they logically reversed the process. They said to their doubting brethren, Come and see.

Men who went to satisfy their curiosity returned again and again to learn. Their enthusiasm for what they saw sent others "to see what it was all about," and to the doctors of southern Minnesota reported to be attending clinics at St. Mary's Hospital were added national names. Sometimes the list was long. On one day in 1901, for example:

A number of the eminent surgeons of the country were in the city Friday. They attended clinics at St. Mary's Hospital, where several operations were performed. The gentlemen are Drs. J. B. Murphy of Chicago, one of the greatest surgeons of the United States; Robt. Weir, Professor of Surgery, College of Physicians and Surgeons, New York City; C. A. Powers, Professor of Surgery, University of Washington, Seattle; [Arthur Dean] Bevan, Professor of Surgery, Rush Medical College, Chicago; Dr. Christy, Professor of Surgery at Omaha college; and Drs. Vance of Omaha and Dredge of Mille Lacs, Minn. The unanimous opinion of these famous surgeons is that St. Mary's is one of the best hospitals in the country, and all were delighted with their visit.

Although American medicine was nearing the age of self-reliance, Europe was still its great postgraduate school. Even in surgery, then indisputably cock of the walk in medicine, the universally acknowledged masters were Europeans. But they were beginning to watch developments in American surgery, reading its literature and marking its rising stars, sometimes before Americans themselves had done so.

In the spring of 1901 Arthur Mayo Robson was guest of honor at the convention of the American Surgical Association. Chief of staff at the Leeds General Infirmary, Robson was Great Britain's brightest surgical light, and his record and original contributions in abdominal surgery, especially that of the gallbladder and the stomach, were known and acclaimed the world over. After attending the convention for which he had come, Mayo Robson took the train west to spend a week with William and Charles Mayo before returning to England.

Then on May 1, 1903, to quote the *Rochester Post and Record,*

Dr. W. J. Mayo, with several physicians who are visiting here, went to Dodge Center in Superintendent Goetzman's private car to meet Prof. Mikulicz of Breslau, Germany, the leading surgeon of Europe, and accompany him to this city, where he has come to attend clinics and witness the work of the surgeons at St. Mary's hospital. . . . The fact that Prof. Mikulicz came to Rochester to attend clinics speaks in the highest possible manner of the skill of the surgeons at St. Mary's hospital.

It did indeed. "Prof. Mikulicz" was Johann von Mikulicz-Radecki, the brilliant Pole who had been a pupil and assistant of the great Billroth and was now preeminent in visceral surgery on the Continent. He too had come to the United States by invitation, to be the featured speaker at one session of the triennial assembly of the Congress of American Physicians and Surgeons, which was shortly to convene in Washington. The names of both Robson and Mikulicz were sure to appear in any paper on abdominal surgery that cited authorities.

American jaws dropped when these titans from abroad merely nodded to the Eastern centers and passed on across the continent to Rochester, and Robson and Mikulicz were only the first of a procession. Of course the Europeans did not find it so surprising that an outstanding surgical center should be located in the provinces, for they were accustomed to a greater dispersion of first-class work than was then a fact in the United States. But even they must have lifted an eyebrow when they saw the small and completely rural town in which the Mayos were working.

8

The weeks immediately after Mikulicz' visit provide a good illustration of the way Dr. Will sometimes scuttled around the country when it was medical convention season. On May 4 he went to New Orleans for the meeting of the American Medical Association, where, having other uses in prospect for his usual topics, he talked about the operation he had literally stumbled onto for the repair of umbilical hernia. He had described it briefly to the association of railroad surgeons in 1898 and in greater detail to the American Surgical Association in 1901, but now he could report further experience, all highly satisfactory.

The discussion was a contest in enthusiasm. The procedure was so excellent and, once learned, so natural that others claimed to have used it first, but Dr. Ferguson of Chicago made short work of them; this boon to surgery was "the Mayo operation." Yes, said Dr. Ochsner, Dr. Mayo had told him about it even before he published his first paper on it. And what a splendid operation it seemed to be. Why, it made such perfect use of anatomical structures that the more strain the patient put upon the repaired abdominal wall the more firmly it seemed to hold!

Then Dr. Murphy pointed up the magnitude of Dr. Mayo's achievement by recalling the futility and frequent fatality of the old techniques. One day while he was doing the old operation in his clinic one of the spectators remarked that every patient he had seen so treated had died. When Murphy's patient died too he began to inquire into the experience of others, and heard (perhaps from Ochsner) about the Mayo operation. So he went to Rochester to learn it from Dr. Mayo himself. Now he could repair umbilical hernia safely and lastingly.

The warmth of the praise embarrassed Dr. Will and for once he sounded a little flustered as he closed the discussion.

I feel somewhat overcome by the remarks of Drs. Ochsner and Murphy, and I think we must all take them as a joke. Dr. Ferguson has insisted that this is the Mayo operation. My own feeling is that all this stuff about priority is bosh. I have no doubt that this operation was done by Hippocrates; he was a very sensible old fellow; and quite likely, as they get deeper into the Egyptian ruins, they will find that this operation was performed by the inhabitants several thousand years ago.

The enthusiasm of the surgeons apparently communicated itself to the convention as a whole, for to Dr. Mayo they voted the association's crowning distinction in surgery; he was chosen to deliver the oration on surgery to the general convention the following year.

Apparently at this same session Dr. Will was called on to speak at the association banquet. Mayo was a miracle worker, said Dr. Frank Billings, the great Chicago internist who was acting as toastmaster, and

not the least of the miracles he worked was that of making Chicago a
stopping-off place on the way to Rochester, Minnesota.

9

That convention ended on May 8, and on May 11 Dr. Will gave
"A Review of 303 Operations upon the Stomach and the First Portion
of the Duodenum" before the Philadelphia Academy of Surgery. It
was a real honor to be the speaker of the evening for that august body,
especially when the men invited to discuss the paper included Dr. John
M. T. Finney, second only to Halsted in the surgical clinic of the Johns
Hopkins Hospital, Dr. Murphy, and "Mr. B. G. A. Moynihan."

Plain Berkeley Moynihan he was then, not yet Lord Moynihan,
"one of the greatest surgeons of this century," but he was already sufficiently challenging company to keep. He had lately succeeded to the
position of his former teacher Mayo Robson at the Leeds infirmary,
and his writings ranked him easily among the pioneers in gastric surgery, so that he had been called across the Atlantic to address the convention of the American Surgical Association. He was a surgeon
without a superior in craftsmanship, and a speaker whose poise, polish,
and grace in diction were the despair of even John B. Murphy.

Mayo and Moynihan had met three years before when Dr. Will was
in Europe, and they were to meet again in a few weeks when Moynihan
in his turn made his way out to Rochester before returning to England.
This was the first of many visits, which Dr. Will returned at Leeds, and
the two men became mutually admiring professional friends.

Next day the American Surgical Association and the Congress of
American Physicians and Surgeons convened simultaneously in Washington, and at the congress Dr. Will scored a triumph. His version of
it, given many years later, is a good story.

At this meeting the guest of honor was a German authority on gallbladder disease. He was to give a lecture on the gallbladder, and I was the
American surgeon chosen to open the discussion.

While Mikulicz, Murphy and I were walking in a park before the meeting, we chanced to meet the lecturer. Mikulicz introduced me, said some
nice things about me, and told the lecturer that I had done much work on
the gallbladder. He snorted, "I never heard of him."

Mikulicz was embarrassed and very indignant. Murphy could hardly
keep from laughing; he had to turn his face away. As we walked on,

Mikulicz raged, "He is a boor, a peasant." The incident was amusing; it was not strange that he had not heard of me but it was strange that he should have said so.

In his paper the German authority reported a large number of cases with a mortality of sixteen per cent; I reported several hundred more cases, with a mortality of two per cent.

After my discussion, the lecturer was very disagreeable, said such a report could not be true. But I had another chance. In closing, I said, "We are greatly indebted to the Professor, for he has given us a knowledge of mortality in these cases which we, with our much smaller death rate in this field of surgery, could not obtain." He thought he was being complimented, looked friendly, and gave me his stiff German bow.

Unfortunately the published *Transactions* tell a more prosaic story. The second day of the congress was given over to a formal symposium on "The Medical and Surgical Aspects of the Diseases of the Gallbladder and Bile Ducts." The surgical aspects were treated in papers by Hans Kehr of Halberstadt, Germany, and William J. Mayo of Rochester, Minnesota.

Kehr had been imported because he was the foremost authority on the subject. In his private clinic in Halberstadt he had confined his attention almost entirely to gallbladder surgery for several years, had made many original contributions to the technique of it, and had amassed the largest series of cases on record. He was quite obviously capable of the disagreeable deportment Dr. Will attributed to him, for even in cold print his every sentence oozes arrogant conceit about his clinic and his record. He would not have taken kindly to any report of an achievement that surpassed his own. But Dr. Will's did not. Kehr's record was "some 800 cases," Mayo's a tabulated 547, and their mortality was about the same, three per cent in uncomplicated cases.

Kehr must have heard of Mayo previously, for he included him in the list of American surgeons to whom he paid perfunctory tribute— unless he inserted the *Mayo* after his encounter with Mikulicz. And the "discussion" as printed consisted merely of half a dozen brief supplementary papers by other American practitioners; it was all stodgily cut and dried, leaving no room for such a retort ideal as Dr. Will remembered.

Yet his story cannot be dismissed as mere wishful wit. More happened on that occasion than the published records reveal, something that caught the fancy of those present, because the episode was referred to in subsequent medical meetings and formed the core of the first layman's article on the Mayo brothers. Despite Dr. Will's previous reputation in the gallbladder field, attested by the place accorded him at this very congress, the profession's full realization that the American Mayo could match experience and results with Europe's best dated from this occasion.

Thereafter Dr. Mayo's words on gallbladder surgery were accepted virtually as *ex cathedra* pronouncements. When Dr. Joseph C. Bloodgood, distinguished surgeon on the staff of the Johns Hopkins Hospital, was called on to discuss a paper on that subject the next year, he voiced the hope, a little petulantly, that in the future the chairman would allow him to speak before Dr. Mayo. "After him there is nothing left to say but ditto."

## 10

Returning from Washington, Dr. Mayo went to Milwaukee on June 4 to give the annual address on surgery for the State Medical Society of Wisconsin, and on June 17 he appeared as usual with a paper for his own Minnesota group.

His activity there had not slackened in the least as his national labors developed. The Minnesota men watched his rise with mingled surprise, pleasure, envy, and inevitably in some cases with jealous resentment, though that last was kept to a minimum by Dr. Will's behavior. As with travel, observation, and the services of a good tailor his appearance had taken on the trimness that always characterized it later, so with wider experience and success his manner became more assured and his opinions more authoritative. But he moved among his local brethren as simply and quietly as before.

There is not the least hint of boasting in his remarks, and references to his new acquaintances and experiences are so entirely lacking that one suspects a deliberate effort not to give offense. Only once, in the heat of an argument with Dr. Dunsmoor, did he so far forget himself as to cite the practice of his Chicago friends in a way that implied the greater worth of their opinions. Whereupon Dr. Dunsmoor retorted that he didn't care what the Chicago men did or said; there were still good surgeons in St. Paul, thank God.

Men who had given up, or had never had, aspirations to more than local reputation gloried vicariously in their young neighbor's success. At this 1903 session Dr. Charles Hill of Pine Island, the Old Doctor's erstwhile partner, expressed his pleasure:

Near me is a great hospital that was scarcely known fifteen years ago, that has now a national and, I might say, an international reputation, and it is presided over and is the work of young men. The Mayos are geniuses. I live within fifteen miles of Rochester and a good many people go there that might otherwise come to me, but I have no feeling in the matter. I have nothing against such men; I am proud to know them, and I am glad to live near them. I think the profession of the whole state is feeling the same way in regard to that institution.

From appearances at that session the profession of the state *was* feeling that way. Dr. A. W. Abbott spoke of the honor they shared in having Dr. Mayo named orator on surgery by the national association, and Dr. J. Warren Little said, to the accompaniment of "much laughter and applause":

I have been treated so splendidly by Dr. Mayo when I have been to see him, I have received so many good points from him, that I feel like complimenting him because he has done me so much good. It reminds me of what a Chinaman said to me in a chop suey house a few days ago. . . . I saw on the bill of fare, "Best Dinner, $5.00." I said to the Chinaman, "What does the best dinner consist of?" He replied, "Everything better."
I was praising [Dr. Mayo's] work to a man the other day and he asked me what Mayo did that I did not do. I told him that I could tell him in no better way than to say what the Chinaman said to me, "Everything better."

Quietly though he took them, words like those were sweet to Dr. Will. They were wine to stimulate his energies, but never to befuddle his head.

## 11

And what was Dr. Charlie doing all this while? Just holding the fort at home? Not a bit of it; he was merely traveling in different directions. Though he would derive no less pleasure from recognition than Dr. Will, he was less impelled to strive for it. He was more easygoing, and alone would perhaps have been content with local acclaim. But he was no more given to lying late abed than his brother, and he pushed forward as steadily toward the goals the other set.

He had willingly agreed that Dr. Will should represent the team before the national groups, because he knew he was not so good a speaker and it would be to their mutual advantage for Will to do the talking. He did not like public speaking anyway. Put him among a group of farmers or hackmen, at the bedside of a patient, or in a small group of close friends and his tongue moved easily and well. But before a crowd he felt shy and awkward, and his low, soft voice was not good for platform talking. His natural way of speaking was a slow, comfortable drawl that seemed hesitant when stiffness before strangers deprived it of personal intimacy.

Dr. Charlie knew as many facts as Dr. Will, but he did not marshal them so well. His mind did not walk straight from this point to that, but proceeded by a kind of hippety-hop from side to side, turning off into picturesque bypaths, exploring this lane and that, covering a lot of extra territory before it reached its destination. All in all, it was obviously best that Dr. Will give the important papers.

But it soon became apparent that this was going to work an injustice. The older brother got an unfair share of the traveling, and of the recognition as well. He was careful to say "we" and not "I," and whenever the facts were so, he said "my brother C. H. Mayo" has done this or that, but that was a poor substitute for Dr. Charlie's appearing personally to give his own reports. Furthermore, it was a pity to waste the abilities and energies of half the team. Dr. Charlie had an unmistakable gift for making friends, and he had contributions to report in fields of surgery that Dr. Will could not adequately cover in discussion alone.

So Dr. Charlie set doggedly to work to make himself a better speaker, with his wife's encouragement and active help. Together they worked over his speeches, pruning away the luxuriance of Charlie's ideas and straightening some of the crooked paths his mind persistently followed. Then Dr. Charlie practiced his delivery before his wife, giving the speech over and over until she knew it as well as he. Many an evening they worked till midnight and after.

Then Mrs. Mayo would go along to the meeting and take her place in a rear seat, to tell him how he was doing by signals they had agreed upon. If he must speak louder, she would hold her handkerchief so; if faster, then this way. That worked all right, but poor Mrs. Mayo was always disconcerted. She never heard the speech they had so carefully prepared and rehearsed, because Dr. Charlie simply could not stick to his manuscript. He would think of something extra to say or some story he wanted to tell and would soon be so far from the prepared speech that there was no use trying to get back to it. So he would just talk.

It was much better that way of course, for then he spoke with the engaging spontaneity, the homely analogies, and rich humor that constituted his own peculiar gift. Once he had conquered his voice difficulties and got used to the platform spotlight, he became as good a speaker as Dr. Will, though in a very different way. His forte was not to impress but to win, not to enunciate fundamental principles but to describe what he called the "wrinkles and recipes" of surgery, the little details of technique that make the difference between good surgery and bad, within the framework of a few big principles.

Dr. Charlie's charm as a speaker is still a byword with all who knew him. His chuckle-raising humor and his droll stories are legendary in Rochester and in medical circles the country over, but one looks for them in vain in his early published papers. The explanation lies either in the fact that the prepared speeches and not those he delivered were published, or in the misguided blue pencil of some editor.

## 12

When Dr. Charlie was ready for speaking on a larger stage, where should he go? Was he merely to second his brother's efforts in the national associations?

Those groups included the professional leaders of the entire country, but the bulk of the doctors in attendance at most of the meetings were from the East and the eastern Middle West. The other sections were more fully represented in the two great regional societies, the Western and the Southern Surgical and Gynecological associations, of which Dr. Charlie became a member in 1899 and 1902 respectively.

In both of them membership was presumably honorary, that is, a man had to be recommended by two or more members, be approved by the governing council, and then be elected by a two-thirds or a unanimous vote of the group. But it overstrains credulity to believe that anything so perfectly designed for the widest possible dissemination of the Mayos' reports should have come about by chance. Probably it was just another evidence of Dr. Will's power to plan. At any rate, Dr. Charlie concentrated his efforts on the two regional societies.

His papers covered a wide range of topics. One year he would talk about the surgical treatment of tic douloureux and the next describe his operation for the removal of bunions. Or he would speak to the southerners about the surgical physiology of the lymph glands and then tell the westerners about a plastic procedure he had worked out for the correction of congenital deformities of the male urethra and penis.

More immediately important than his papers, however, was his continual participation in discussion. From the society *Transactions* it would be hard to guess that Dr. Charlie had ever been loath to speak in public, for he talked on any and every subject and always had a supplementary experience or a differing opinion to contribute. The truth is that he had come to enjoy speaking and to derive a natural pleasure from the attention and approval given him. And he might as well get up and talk of his own accord, because if he did not someone was sure to ask him what the Mayos thought or did about the matter under consideration. He always responded, usually at length and with such a wealth of technical detail that it is easy to understand why he was so often called upon.

Sometimes his willingness led him to speak when he should not have done so, to offer an opinion his experience did not warrant. Then if he was talking to the westerners he was sure to be caught up on his statement, for when they took exception to a remark they said so, bluntly. They were less likely than the southerners or the easterners to cloak their disagreement in tactful wonderings or supposings.

Meeting everyone with a simple friendliness that inspired genuine liking in return, Dr. Charlie was soon personally popular with the men of the profession. Impulsively he would invite all and sundry to visit him and Will in Rochester, and in increasing numbers the men accepted the invitations. The first visit was seldom the last. Doctors from widely scattered points were soon referring in medical discussions to their "annual pilgrimages to the mecca of surgeons the country over." Said Dr. Tait of San Francisco to the American Surgical Association:

Like many others, I have journeyed to Rochester (Minnesota), to that great surgical shrine where dominate two masters, and on each occasion of my pilgrimage to that shrine I have come away bewildered with a knowledge of what I saw there. I have carried that knowledge to my masters in Europe, and they shared my enthusiasm for the work done at Rochester.

# Recognition Won

Soon such men were giving Dr. Charlie a generous measure of assistance in reporting the Mayos' work. This speaker would describe C. H. Mayo's method of correcting harelip and cleft palate; that one would tell how C. H. Mayo performed prostatectomy. Dr. Bernays of St. Louis had seen the Mayos do excision of the rectum for cancer and marveled at the exhibition of perfect teamwork. "The operation was beautifully planned, and I need scarcely say that it was executed in a masterly manner."

Dr. Haggard of Nashville described the fishtail drainage tube he had seen the Mayos using; it was of their own invention and it worked like a charm. Dr. Ransohoff had not seen the tube but "I can see that it is a very bright and excellent idea, and . . . like many other ideas that have emanated from Rochester, Minnesota, it is good."

Sometimes the comments took a wistful turn. Dr. Robert Carothers was much excited about the new method and instruments that C. H. Mayo had devised for stripping out varicose veins. Yes, said Dr. Stuart McGuire of Richmond, Virginia, they are a tremendous improvement on the old ways; "I have never seen more brilliant results more quickly accomplished." But that was in the hands of Dr. Mayo. Dr. McGuire feared the operation was not for the likes of him; he would be afraid to try it.

Again, Dr. Hugh Young, genito-urinary specialist at Johns Hopkins, complimented Dr. Mayo on his contribution to the surgery of tumors of the bladder, but Dr. Stone of Washington thought, sadly, that "the surgery he has described is so difficult that many of us would hardly undertake it."

So the tokens of recognition came to Dr. Charlie in his turn, usually four or five years after Dr. Will had received them. In 1900 he was invited to give the commencement address for the state university medical school, and in 1903, while his brother was picking up bouquets all over the country, he was elected to the presidency of the Western Surgical and Gynecological Association, and to membership in the American Surgical Association.

## 13

"Today the surgical borderland lies in the upper region of the abdomen, a locality until recently considered almost purely medical." So said Dr. Will in his oration on surgery in 1904.

# The Mayo Brothers

The earlier battles between the physicians and the surgeons over pelvic surgery and appendectomy might be considered won, and the surgeons were busy consolidating their position. But a vanguard had moved on to begin the struggle for surgical treatment of diseases of the gallbladder and bile ducts. As may be surmised from the foregoing story, the Mayos—Dr. Will chiefly but with Dr. Charlie as an able lieutenant—were in the thick of this current conflict. They were taking the part that men like Price and Kelly, Murphy and McBurney had taken in the earlier campaigns.

Having learned from experience that in more than half the patients who came to them with some vague kind of stomach trouble the gastric symptoms were reflex warnings of trouble elsewhere, they were trying to pass that knowledge on to the profession. They told their colleagues that in many cases of so-called indigestion or dyspepsia "the stomach is merely acting as a mouthpiece to call attention to the disturbance elsewhere in the digestive tract. Treatment directed to the stomach in these cases is about as effectual as it would be to deluge a fire-alarm box with water because it is sounding the alarm of fire." Look for the fire, they urged, in those supposedly slumbering gallstones that turn up in postmortems as innocent findings.

At one meeting of the Southern Surgical Association a member asked Dr. C. H. Mayo what he should do about a troublesome case of "neuralgia of the stomach." Dr. Charlie listened carefully to a description of the patient's symptoms, his head characteristically cocked to one side, dark eyes intent but gradually taking on a twinkle. When the man had done, Dr. Charlie smilingly advised him to remove the patient's gallbladder.

But Dr. Will did the bulk of the teaching in formal statements of the case, and his early papers often led to long arguments. On one occasion Nicholas Senn was chief among those who disagreed. He still thought medical treatment would do for many cases of gallstones—and surely there was no justification for operation if the stones were not causing trouble.

The stones *were* causing trouble. But Dr. Will did not have to say so again. Dr. Ochsner took the floor:

Two years ago, while visiting Dr. Mayo's hospital, I asked the Doctor how he explained the great number of gall-stone cases which came under his care for operation. His answer was exceedingly simple and undoubtedly correct. He said: "We make a diagnosis in these cases."

Since that time . . . I have operated on more than thirty cases of gall-stones which had been treated for a long time for gastritis, no diagnosis of gall-stones having been made previously. . . . We constantly find these patients at autopsies and imagine that the gall-stones gave rise to no symptoms because no diagnosis had been made before death.

Diagnosis was the point, but the doctors did not get it. As Dr. Mayo reported more and more gallbladder operations, the men of the profession tried to find an explanation for the phenomenon in some peculiarity of climate or living conditions in the Northwest. Dr. Will warned them that was not the reason: The patients in question had come from twenty-six states and Canada; less than twenty per cent of them lived in Minnesota. And Dr. Moore of Minneapolis repeated the point: The Mayos did so many operations not because the Minnesota climate produced gallstones but because the Mayos could diagnose gallstones.

To emphasis on diagnosis the Mayos added the doctrine of early operation, and it was chiefly to make the latter point that they poured their statistics into the ears of their colleagues. The figures made it abundantly clear that the risk of operation rose in proportion to the extent of complication. Mortality was slight when the disease and the stones were confined to the gallbladder, but it was appreciable when the bile passages, pancreas, or duodenum had become involved.

## 14

Surgeons did not invade the gastric ulcer field, any more than the gallstone field, without doing battle with the medical men who held it. The operators had to marshal a host of statistics to prove that medicine did not cure all the ulcers it was thought to cure and that a goodly percentage of the cases treated medically were fatal. Then they had to accumulate data to prove that surgery could do a better job of healing with less mortality. The opposing forces are still skirmishing on the borders of the field.

To the early victories for surgery the Mayos' statistics and their refinements of operative techniques contributed immeasurably. They were willing to yield acute ulcer to the physician, at least until they were called in to operate for one of its complications, and they recommended a fair trial of medical treatment in chronic ulcer. But where the cycle of apparent cure, relapse, cure, and relapse attested the failure of medicine they advised operation. They well knew that many an individual was dragging out an existence made miserable with stomach pain that surgery could relieve.

With almost a crusader's zeal Dr. Will championed early operation as a possibility, and the only one, for curing cancer of the stomach. Since early diagnosis was difficult, physicians must be won to accept the principle of exploratory operation upon suspicion of malignant disease, and Dr. Will preached the necessity at every chance. In a typical "strong close" he once said:

Let us put this question to the practitioner of medicine: Can you cure a case of cancer of the stomach? If not, why withhold the only known means of effecting such a cure—a surgical operation? Again let us ask, Can you diagnosticate cancer of the stomach early enough for surgical relief? If not, why withhold an exploration, the only certain means of diagnosis?

It aroused his wrath to visit hospital after hospital and in all of them find the stomach cancer patients in the medical wards. The examiners in the outpatient clinics would send suspected cancer of the breast, the uterus, or the rectum straight to the surgeons, but cancer of the stomach they turned over to the physicians—in spite of the fact that in all medical history there was not a single instance of a medical cure of stomach cancer. "It is worse than a blunder; it is a crime," declared Dr. Will.

He knew that physicians held off from surgery because the appalling mortality of the early operations on the stomach had made them afraid. "The physician . . . has continued the 'sins of medical omission,' having the results of 'surgical commission' before his eyes." But, he said:

The medical man must discard the older statistics as to technic and mortality which have become merely venerable relics, and do not at all represent advanced thought on the subject. It is certainly discouraging to turn to the newer works on medicine and find not the slightest attempt made to show the advance in surgery, and the question of surgical relief being arbitrarily determined by the achievements of a decade ago.

Dr. Charlie put a name to what the brothers were advocating—it was preventive surgery, akin to preventive medicine. They considered the physician who congratulated himself upon curing recurrent attacks of gallstones or gastric ulcer, the physician who waited to make sure of the presence of cancer while his patient drifted into a dangerous or wholly inoperable condition, every bit as culpable as though he had let his patient drink water from a well thought to be infected.

Yet the Mayos were known to be among the most conservative leaders in the field. Although they practiced and urged operation they believed in weighing the results against the risk before deciding what procedure should be used. They accepted the more radical operations only when the mortality of the procedures dropped into balance with increased permanence of cure.

### 15

What the Mayos had to say of laboratory procedures was in essence a warning to "Slow Down." Many practitioners were taking the highway to the laboratory at high speed, joyously, incautiously, because in the new hematological, bacteriological, and chemical tests they saw promise of exactness to replace the old empirical uncertainty. Count the white blood cells and *know* whether or not the patient has appendicitis; use the serum test prescribed by Fernand Widal and *know* whether or not the patient has typhoid fever. What a relief, such certainty!

But trial of the new procedures brought disappointment to the Mayos, and their disillusionment was not wholly due to the fact that their hopes had been highest in cancer, a disease that has proved one of the slowest to yield its secret to science. Some of the new tests being announced were actually invalid; others needed perfecting. Dr. Louis B. Wilson, assistant bacteriologist to the Minnesota state board of health, told the state's doctors in 1898, apropos of the Widal reaction test for typhoid fever, that "the implicit faith sometimes placed in the test by the clinician is enough to make the laboratory man's blood run cold, knowing as he does the many chances for error."

Under those circumstances Dr. Will and Dr. Charlie viewed with real concern the doctors' apparent inclination to forsake the old methods for the new. And they raised their voices against it.

The general tendency is to rely too much upon the results of laboratory analysis and too little on the ordinary clinical examination. While not wishing to minimize the importance of such analysis as confirmatory evidence I would emphasize the fact that the history and clinical course are of first consideration. The laboratory must go hand in hand with clinical observation.

The tendency they decried was as nothing to what it has since become. Presently the Mayos themselves were encompassed with laboratories and technicians of their own supporting, but they never ceased to warn against the danger of "laboratory diagnosis," to insist that laboratory findings ought to be only supplementary to the clinician's personal study of the patient.

As might be expected, the brothers often expressed their disapproval of the therapeutic nihilism engendered by too much reliance on "deadhouse pathology." They were quite ready to concede the unrivaled advantages of the postmortem for study of the groundwork of medicine and to give credit to pathologist physicians like Fitz and Fenger for the knowledge upon which surgery had made its start. But, they asked, in all its years as an institution how much did the postmortem advance the treatment of appendicitis, or gallstones, or gastric ulcer? Of necessity, necropsy reveals the facts of disease in its fatal stages. The postmortem furnishes "a hundred pages of pathology and two meager lines of treatment."

Again and again Dr. Will and Dr. Charlie urged the need for more of the "living pathology" that the new surgery had made possible.

The medical man must haunt the operating theater as he has haunted the autopsy room and the pathologic laboratory. The times have changed; we must have more treatment and less pathology. It is here that surgery wins its triumphs. . . . It is in the union of the internist and the surgeon that progress is most rapidly made, and in the readjustment of science the former will be the architect and the latter the master builder.

The Mayos did not say "we" when reporting the use of scientific procedures, and did not even stop with "the men working with us" or "our diagnosticians." What they said was "Christopher Graham has made a study . . ." or "in gastric analyses in 1500 cases Graham and Millet have found . . ." They cited the work of their partners and employees as they would that of any independent authority. There was more than literary formality or scientific impersonality in that; there was an attitude of mind that promised to able and ambitious men scope for independent development in association with the Mayos.

# Recognition Won

As yet none of the Rochester group other than the two brothers had ventured beyond the state either in speaking or in publication, though several of them were doing good service on the home front and special interests were beginning to appear among them. Dr. Stinchfield spoke most often on the diseases of the heart and lungs, while Dr. Graham was reporting his conclusions on various clinical phases of gastric ulcer and cancer.

Dr. Millet's papers on urological diagnosis and treatment were remarkably precise and comprehensive evaluations of the latest instruments and laboratory methods available in that field, perhaps the most *scientific* papers to come out of Rochester at that time. One of them moved a St. Paul doctor to comment:

The paper has a ring of exactness about it. It is not quite so easy as it sounds for those without experience to accomplish the results as outlined in Dr. Millet's paper. . . . The difficulty is that the general practitioner has not the time or opportunity to make frequent enough examination to become expert.

Yes, that was the difficulty. Medicine was developing beyond the ability of any one man to be expert in all its phases. Specialization must come.

## 16

Because surgeons were awakening to an intense interest in the problem of anesthesia, the work of Alice Magaw won more widespread notice than that of any other member of the Rochester group apart from the brothers.

Early methods of administering anesthetics were dangerously crude. Ether was given by saturating a sponge and holding it over the patient's nose and mouth until he became unconscious. The stuff might burn his face, or, since little air could pass through the wet sponge, the patient, inhaling nearly pure ether vapor, might get "ether pneumonia" and die. In any case he was likely to fight violently against the suffocation.

Consequently most surgeons preferred to use chloroform. Its after-effects were less unpleasant and it put the patient to sleep more quickly and easily. Just drench a cloth—a large handkerchief would do—and clap it over the man's nose for a few minutes; even the office boy could do it if necessary. Of course if the patient inhaled too deeply and got too big a whiff, the fumes might overwhelm his heart and his sleep would suddenly become profound and eternal. But that was just one of the day's risks.

Under such circumstances anesthesia deaths were frequent, but when the mortality from sepsis and poor technique was so high these were lost in the general sum of fatalities. When the new surgery found itself on the defensive, however, and surgeons were seeking to achieve the lowest possible death rate, they became more conscious of the danger of anesthesia.

In 1885 Dr. James E. Moore of Minneapolis went abroad for a year's study. Accustomed to pouring chloroform "by the hatfuls" on the accident victims the patrol wagon brought to his office, he was impressed by the different way they did things in the clinics of Berlin. The bottle of chloroform he would have used up in one busy morning lasted the German surgeons an entire week, because they poured the stuff drop by drop onto a few thicknesses of gauze laid over a piece of wire netting stretched on a frame above the patient's nose.

Dr. Moore was so struck by the merit of this method that when he returned to the United States he brought with him an anesthetist from one of the German clinics. He kept the man in his employ for a year to teach the open-drop method to him and any of his surgeon friends who wanted to learn it. Among these were the Old Doctor Mayo and his sons. They promptly applied the method in the use of ether too, and since slow administration with a generous admixture of air helped to overcome the most objectionable and dangerous phases of ether anesthesia, that soon became the Mayos' favorite.

The drop method spread slowly. They were still using the old ways in the Massachusetts General Hospital in Boston in 1890 and at the Johns Hopkins Hospital in 1895. The sponge had been replaced by a cardboard cone wrapped with toweling and fitted with gauze stuffed into its apex, but it was still drenched with ether and the patient was nearly asphyxiated with the fumes. His consequent violent struggles were so generally expected that it was routine to strap the patient firmly to the stretcher before anesthetizing was begun, and even then it sometimes took two or more orderlies to hold him down. As late as 1906 a Massachusetts surgeon visiting the Mayos was surprised to find them using "the newest method" of giving ether.

Naturally the Mayo brothers themselves directed the development of anything so intimately related to their success in surgery, and they were principally responsible for the methods and system adopted at Rochester, as Miss Magaw was always the first to concede. But she proved herself an able adjutant, capable of independent observation and judgment, so that Dr. Will and Dr. Charlie were soon able to leave the immediate responsibility to her and give their undivided attention to the operation.

In employing a permanent, full-time anesthetist, and that a nurse, the Mayos were very unusual if not unique in the United States. In other hospitals anesthetizing was one of the duties of the interns. Coming to the task untrained and inexperienced, having seen it done only at a distance, the intern was often scared and inept at first, and by the time he had gained a reasonable facility in the work he moved on to other duties and another novice took his place.

The Mayos had given the job to Miss Graham and then to Miss Magaw in the first place through necessity; they had no interns. And when the interns came, the brothers decided that a nurse was better suited to the task because she was more likely to keep her mind strictly on it, whereas the intern was naturally more interested in what the surgeon was doing. As Miss Magaw put it in one of her pleas for the use of nurses as anesthetists, "No one can learn to be a surgeon while giving the anesthetic."

In other hospitals the anesthetic was administered in an adjoining room and the patient was not taken into the operating room until he was unconscious, a practice adopted, or at least defended, on the grounds that he would be less nervous and more manageable if he had not seen all the paraphernalia to be used in the operation. The Mayos seem to have begun with this idea, but they soon came to the conclusion that moving the person in a state of relaxation from one room to another of possibly differing temperature sometimes contributed to the development of a cold, bronchitis, or some other respiratory complication. So they inaugurated the practice of anesthetizing in the operating room.

To their surprise and pleasure they discovered that this procedure had all sorts of advantages. The psychological effect was good. The patient was less disturbed by the actuality than by what he imagined, and he went to sleep more readily in the presence of the surgeon than in that of some strange and untrusted assistant. Also if the preparation of the operative site was going on at the same time as the anesthetizing, it helped to divert the patient's attention, so that it took much less anesthetic and less effort, to say nothing of less time, to produce surgical narcosis.

The Mayos emphasized those psychological factors. Miss Magaw maintained that an anesthetist's first job was to size up the patient's mental and emotional state and then "adjust her firmness of manner," as well as the anesthetic, to it. With characteristic insight into the ways of the human mind, Dr. Charlie contributed the principle of positive suggestion. He had noticed that when the anesthetist got rough and kept saying, "Don't do that" or "Hold still now," the patient just got more obstreperous. It was like antagonizing a drunk man, Dr. Charlie decided. If instead the nurse gently explained what she was doing and said, "You're all right; your pulse is good; your breathing is fine," the patient was much more likely to go under easily and quietly.

## 17

That was the sort of thing Miss Magaw discussed in her papers, together with a hundred and one details as to signs of sufficient anesthesia, ways of recognizing and preventing impending disaster, and the like. Since she could not be a member of any medical society, she gave her first talks by invitation before the Olmsted County group and they were then accepted for publication in the state medical journals. In 1904 she was asked to address the state society and gave a review of what she had learned from *eleven thousand* anesthesias.

To such experience and knowledge they must all bow, commented Dr. Moore when she finished; if he could have Miss Magaw to give his anesthetics he would never worry about the patient. He could not agree, however, that ether was safer than chloroform. In a sentence to be remembered Miss Magaw had said, "Ether kills slowly, giving plenty of warning, but with chloroform there is not even time to say good-bye." Dr. Moore had found chloroform as safe as anything else, and besides, it was so much quicker. Miss Magaw was sharp on that subject. Time ought not to be a primary consideration. The anesthetist ought never to feel hurried. "The surgeon's time may be precious, but the patient's life is more so."

# Recognition Won

By this time the search for more nearly ideal anesthetics was in full swing throughout the country. The Mayos tried out the more promising of those suggested and Miss Magaw reported their results, but they always returned to ether as their preferred anesthetic. They had little sympathy with all the to-do. When Dr. Will on a trip to New York saw a furniture van unload the anesthetist's equipment for a home operation his surgeon host was to do next day, he thought it silly. A vanful of stuff, when all that was necessary was an inhaler, a couple of cans of ether or chloroform fitted with grooved corks, and a head of brains that knew how to use them properly.

"Useless fussiness" was Miss Magaw's term for the elaborate prescriptions and precautions being advised. She considered even the oxygen tank and the tongue forceps unnecessary; anesthetists ought to spend less time in surrounding themselves with gadgets to help them out of emergencies, and more time in learning how to avoid them.

At every opportunity Dr. Charlie harped on the idea that all the hunting for some new anesthetic was due less to an actual need for one than to the inexperience and idiosyncrasies of many who tried to use the old ones. What was really needed, he insisted, was a good professional anesthetist in every hospital in the country, and the medical schools ought to be training people for the jobs.

Often in such discussions other doctors would refer to what they had heard or seen in Rochester. On one occasion an Iowa doctor, in reporting a decrease of anesthesia fatalities in that state, remarked that "Many of us have had the pleasure of seeing that peerless anesthetist, Alice Magaw . . . 'talk her patients to sleep.'" The things she is teaching about the administration of anesthetics, he added, "are practiced by the men throughout Iowa and many other states." A few years later a German surgeon reported to his countrymen that anesthetists from all parts of the United States were going to Rochester to learn their craft from the Mayos' expert nurses.

## 18

In 1904 it was Dr. Charlie's turn to receive an honorary master of arts from his alma mater, Northwestern University, and shortly thereafter he made his first appearance before the American Surgical Association. He spoke on the removal of the thyroid gland as a treatment for exophthalmic goiter and was able to report forty cases in which he had performed the operation, a hint to those who heard it that the Mayos were pioneering in another field of surgery.

It had taken the Mayos twelve years to accumulate their first five hundred operations on the gallbladder and ducts, but their second five hundred came in eighteen months, and in December 1904 Dr. Charlie read to the Southern Surgical Association his and his brother's joint report of one thousand operations for gallbladder disease.

The listeners were overwhelmed. One after another rose to express his pleasure in being present to hear the report of such an achievement. Said Dr. Haggard of Nashville:

I think the Fellows of the Association should feel greatly honored to have had the pleasure and privilege of listening to this admirable contribution. When we stop to reflect that it is the largest group of gall-bladder cases operated on in the world, it is not difficult to draw the conclusion of the value of this paper.

And Dr. Finney of Baltimore continued:

It gives me great pleasure to congratulate the Association on being the vehicle of giving to the world this report of the Mayo brothers, which, as Dr. Haggard has said, is surely unequalled in the annals of surgery. I am sure that we are all proud to have as members these two men who have done so much for surgery not only in this country, but in the world. We are all impressed with the special characteristic of their work—its honesty. . . . because of the limited personal experience I have had as compared with the Mayos I can only say that our experience at the Johns Hopkins Hospital has borne out every point that Dr. Mayo has made regarding drainage and operations on the gallbladder.

The paper was published in the *Transactions* of the association and was promptly reprinted in a number of medical periodicals, including the *American Journal of the Medical Sciences*, whose editor only five years before had found it impossible to believe Dr. Will's report of a hundred and five operations on the gallbladder.

There was reason for Dr. Finney's remark about the Mayos' honesty. The different ideas of what constituted success in surgery were one of the stumbling blocks in evaluating techniques from printed reports. Reputable surgeons no longer counted mere recovery from the operation as success, without regard for the degree or permanence of the improvement. But how was one to decide whether or not a given death had resulted from the operation? There were as yet no accepted standards for reckoning mortality from operation.

Many surgeons when using their own judgment in the matter did not resist the temptation to prejudice the figures in favor of whatever fact they were trying to establish. Some were suspected of remembering only their successes and forgetting to record their failures. That charge had been leveled against John B. Murphy in his campaign to put over the Murphy button, and he admitted that he did not report every death that followed the use of the button. Why blame the button for the death of a patient when the fool surgeon had not known any better than to leave the gangrenous portion of the bowel in the man's insides? But no one ever charged the Mayos with concealing their failures. They reported plenty of them. One of Dr. Will's addresses to the American Surgical Association was entirely an analysis of cases in which he had failed.

In this review of their thousand gallbladder operations the Mayo brothers made an unequivocal statement of the basis on which they reckoned mortality from operation. They took the position of the layman: If the patient goes into the hospital alive and comes out dead, the death should be charged to the operation, no matter how many months have elapsed or what other disorders have developed to be the actual cause of death.

That was hard on the statistics. "A percentage of the deaths could be fairly excluded, but since our object is to show the relative curability of gall-stone disease rather than good statistics, we have adopted this method, as it is at least unprejudiced." Even so, their mortality for the entire series, including the operations done in the years of inexperience, was only five per cent, and for cases of simple gallstones it was just above two per cent.

## 19

In the spring of 1905 Dr. Charlie was elected president of the Minnesota State Medical Society, and shortly afterward Dr. Will was notified that he had been awarded fellowship in the Royal College of Surgeons of Edinburgh. The honor was enhanced by the fact that the only other American surgeons to be so acclaimed were William W. Keen of Philadelphia and William S. Halsted of Johns Hopkins. But

Dr. Mayo decided not to make the trip abroad to receive the honor in person, choosing instead to attend as usual the annual conventions of the American Surgical and American Medical associations. He had probably been warned of what was in the offing at the latter meeting.

For years Dr. Will had held the nation's best record in the performance of gastroenterostomy. Repeatedly he had described the method he was finding best at the moment, but more than once someone among his hearers, even a pioneer in stomach surgery like Dr. Maurice Richardson of Boston, complained that he had tried Dr. Mayo's method after hearing him describe it but simply could not duplicate his results; he would give a great deal to get at the secret of Mayo's success. As Dr. Ochsner once explained, the peerless technique that made Dr. Mayo successful had to be seen; it could not be adequately described.

At this 1905 session of the American Surgical Association Dr. Will read "A Review of Five Hundred Cases of Gastroenterostomy," in which he described clearly, step by step, the evolution in his performance of the operation, announcing as the climax the method he and his brother had determined to be the most nearly ideal—the thereafter famous "no-loop" operation.

Once again the audience declared their profound respect for the Mayos' accomplishment. Dr. Weir of New York said that while of course the final step in perfecting gastroenterostomy had not been taken, Dr. Mayo's paper announced so big an advance that he could not digest it all at once; Dr. Munro of Boston wished to acknowledge publicly his "everlasting gratitude to the Mayos for what they have taught me in stomach surgery"; Dr. Ochsner thought "There is no doubt but what the advance in stomach surgery in this country today is largely due to Dr. Mayo's teachings"; and Dr. Moore of Minneapolis generously added:

We often notice the evolution of an operation, and it generally comes to us through the experience of a large number of men. Today we have had something which is almost anomalous in the history of surgery. We have been given the whole evolution of surgery within the experience of one man. Dr. Mayo is a neighbor of mine. He used to come to me for pointers, and now I am pleased to reverse the order of things. I wish to thank him for the good he has done for suffering mankind, for the honor he has done this Association. I wish to thank him for one particular thing, and that is the elimination of the loop.

# Recognition Won

When the no-loop operation was accepted as good, other American surgeons claimed they had used it before Dr. Mayo announced his approval of it, and perhaps they had. But Dr. Will was the first to describe it for the American profession, and he did so with all the authority of his extensive experience. Although he said explicitly that he and his brother learned this step from Peterson, that from Mikulicz, and these from Moynihan, Americans were soon referring to the no-loop method as the "Mayo operation." But to that Dr. Will quickly called a halt. He said all he and Charlie had done was gather up good ideas from many men, assemble them as a whole, and tie a string around them, so that all they could claim credit for was the string.

Because they did so often make up the bundles and provide the string the Mayos could have had their name attached to many more operations than bear it now, but they were scrupulous about giving credit where it was due—and as Dr. Will had said earlier, all the priority stuff is bosh anyway. Only once did either of them publicly make a claim to credit. At the session of the Western Surgical Association in 1907 a Dr. Summers presented a paper describing the open-incision method of treating infection of the knee joint and reported some cases in which he had used it with gratifying success—all without a mention of the name of Mayo. That operation, his first youthful success, had long been Dr. Charlie's pride, and he could not refrain from saying that if the speaker had known the literature he would have called the method the "Hippocrates-Mayo operation." Dr. Witherspoon of Butte, Montana, rose at once to say with asperity that it was Schede who first proposed the operation. (If Schede had proposed it Dr. Charlie was not aware of the fact, nor was Dr. Arpad Gerster.)

It was unquestionably gastroenterostomy that brought Dr. Will the most recognition during this period, but even as he announced his success with that operation he was moving on to the refinement and greater use of the more radical gastrectomy. And there again he was arranging the bundle and braiding the string, as some of his fellow surgeons were well aware. In the course of the discussion in 1905 Dr. Munro said, "We all owe a debt of gratitude to the Mayos for their gastrectomy operation. This operation, as they have perfected it, has robbed that procedure of almost all its terrors, and the results are, I think, almost phenomenal."

435

## 20

A week later the American Medical Association convened in Portland, Oregon. It was pleased to learn that a large section of the New York profession which had strayed away a number of years earlier during a dispute over the ethics of consulting with homeopaths was about to return to the fold. Dr. Joseph Bryant of New York City had done much to effect the reconciliation, and the New York delegates wished to celebrate it by having him elected president of the association.

But when the nominations were opened Dr. William L. Rodman of Philadelphia secured the floor:

Mr. President. . . . The profession of the great west have ever been most loyal to the American Medical Association. . . . Recognizing this loyalty . . . I wish on behalf of Pennsylvania . . . to place in nomination one of the ablest, one of the cleanest, one of the best loved of the western profession. Living in a small town, he has made it the surgical Mecca of America. If we delegates were all asked to make a list of the leading five American surgeons, we should doubtless differ as to all the names and as to the order in which we would write them down. But I am very sure that every list would contain, and many of them would place at the head, the name of William J. Mayo.

. . . Therefore, Mr. President, in view of the fact that the great trans-Mississippi country has not been recognized with the presidency for the last eleven years, it seems to me that it would be a graceful thing to tender this able, this clean, this popular representative of American medicine and surgery the unanimous election to the presidency.

When Dr. Harris of New York, in behalf of Dr. Bryant and the New York delegates, graciously concurred in the nomination, it was mere routine to instruct the secretary to cast a unanimous vote for William James Mayo as president for the ensuing year.

Rochester was elated when it heard the news. To Will Mayo first among Minnesota's doctors had come "the highest honor within the power of the medical profession to bestow"! Nothing, not even the appearance of European masters of surgery on their streets, had made Rochester folk so aware of the heights to which these Mayo boys of theirs had climbed. At once the leading townsmen laid plans to greet the return of their triumphant son with a banquet, the biggest and most impressive celebration they could arrange.

On the sultry evening of July 24 the guests, some hundred and fifty of them, gathered in the parlors of the Cook House. Among them were many state officials, come to bear witness that by this honor to Dr. Mayo Minnesota too was honored, and present also were a dozen or so doctors from as many states who had stopped off for a few clinics at St. Mary's on their way home from the West Coast.

No women were allowed of course, but a committeee of them had spent the day making things ready. At nine-thirty John Kahler threw open the doors to the dining room and the guests moved into a chamber transformed. The walls were screened with great banks of ferns and flowers; festoons of asparagus fronds and colored lights swung from the ceiling; the name of the honor guest was everywhere, spelled out by lighted letters among the leaves and by strands of sweet peas and smilax in the center of each table.

When the caviar, fried chicken, champagne, and ice cream had come and gone, the speechmaking began. Rochester men eulogized their famous neighbors: "Where in the history of the world do we find such a trinity as in this family—the father and his two sons—great doctors, great men, and the father the noblest Roman of them all." Visiting doctors told the home folks they really had little idea of the renown the Mayo brothers had won in the medical world. Yes, both brothers, said Dr. C. H. Rosser of Texas, for "We of the medical world find it hard to separate the two men, Will and Charlie. We wish that it could have been possible to have elected them both to the honored position which the elder brother now holds."

Then United States Senator Moses Clapp suitably reminded the men that while acclaiming the sons and their worthy sire they ought not to forget the tribute due to her at home, the mother of these brothers, and Governor John A. Johnson added the proper note of the patient's pleasure in "my doctor's" success, for having undergone three operations in Rochester, he considered himself "a living example of the Mayos' skill."

It was Frank B. Kellogg, then an eminent lawyer in St. Paul, who pointed the moral of the occasion. He would have the young men present take note that the Mayos had achieved their position by working for something more worthy than financial gain. They had never made the dollar sign their standard of success, but had sought instead the satisfaction of work well done.

437

After Dr. Charlie had been presented with a "handsome cut glass vase" to assure him that his worth too was appreciated, Dr. Will was called to the toastmaster's side to receive a silver loving cup as a memento of the evening. The emotional imperturbability William Mayo always showed the world cracked a little that night as he spoke his thanks. At the end he said he wanted everyone to understand that he felt the honor which had come to him was as much his brother's as his own. They had labored side by side and the achievements of one were the achievements of both.

So ended "the grandest occasion, the greatest social event ever held in Rochester . . . one which the tide of years will never efface from the memories of those who were present"!

## 21

Conspicuous and inexplicable is the absence from the celebration of any representative of the Minnesota State Medical Association. Dr. Mayo's election to the national presidency was given only a casual mention, and the Rochester banquet none at all, in the *Northwestern Lancet,* which had lately become the official organ of the state association. Publicly at least, the Minnesota profession was not overly impressed by these events.

It paid more attention when the list was announced of the honorary degrees conferred by the University of Toronto during a meeting of the British Medical Association in the Canadian capital. The degree of doctor of laws was given to men from England, from Germany, from France, and to one man from America—William J. Mayo.

American physicians knew that Dr. Mayo's office in the American Medical Association would not alone have placed him on that list with men of the caliber of Sir Thomas Clifford Albutt of Cambridge University and Sir Victor Horsley of London. The Britishers must think very highly of Dr. Mayo's work, commented the *Northwestern Lancet* editorially, to number so young a man among those older men who had been famous for many years.

Dr. Will was inducted into office at the 1906 convention in Boston, in a brief ceremony performed by the retiring president, Lewis S. McMurtry of Louisville—the man who almost fifteen years before had interfered to prevent Joseph Price from rudely dismissing the very young doctor from the West who had come to watch him operate. Dr. McMurtry told the assembly:

I have exceptional pleasure in presenting to you your President-elect this morning, a gentleman of national and international reputation . . . won simply and alone by individual merit, without the aid of great institutional environment; a gentleman comparatively young for the position to which he has attained, and whose claim on the recognition of the medical profession of America . . . is that of high scientific achievements, to which there is joined a superb and pure professional character.

As Dr. Mayo stepped forward the crowd broke into a long and unwontedly wild ovation. The entire five thousand rose to their feet, cheering, clapping, stamping, waving hats and papers in the air.

"It must be a psychological moment in any man's career to receive such honor and homage," remarked the *Northwestern Lancet*. "Yet in the face of this enthusiasm and in the presence of the governor of the state of Massachusetts, President Eliot of Harvard, Mayor Fitzgerald of Boston, and many prominent foreign physicians, Dr. Mayo maintained the calm, dignified, and unassuming manner that is so characteristic of him."

When quiet returned Dr. Mayo gave his presidential address, on "The Medical Profession and the Issues Which Confront It." Several of the points he made foreshadowed developments to come or already under way at Rochester. He urged the profession to educate the public to an understanding of the new spirit in medicine. How could laymen be expected to accept legislation for public health and the regulation of medical practice when most of the information they received about medical matters came to them from the advertisements of patent-medicine vendors and voluble charlatans? "The time has come for the public to be taken into our confidence; if we wish better results, we must enlighten the people, for with them lies the final word."

Adding his voice to the chorus demanding improvement in standards of medical education, he observed that young men ought not to be encouraged in "wanton assaults on major surgical diseases. . . . *The future will demand schools for advanced training for those who desire to do special work.*"

Doctors must curb the widespread abuse of medical charities. Throughout Europe and America the services of free hospitals and clinics were given to thousands who were well able to pay for medical care, because no attempt was made to investigate the financial condition of those who applied. That was not commendable charity of spirit, said Dr. Will; it was foolish negligence. "All hospitals should have competent individuals whose business it is to see that no one secures free treatment who is able to pay."

Not that any sensible man entered upon the calling of medicine expecting to get rich, or that any physician ought to adopt the money standard of success. Unworthy of their title were the doctors so tainted with the demoralizing commercialism of the age as to engage in the pernicious traffic in referred cases (that is, fee-splitting). The very secrecy with which they sought to shroud their bargaining showed that they recognized its "moral obliquity," even while attempting to justify it.

And what was the reward of the doctor's laborious life?

To realize that one has devoted himself to the most holy of all callings, that without thought of reward he has alleviated the sufferings of the sick and added to the length and usefulness of human life, is a source of satisfaction that money cannot buy. I know many a man, grown gray in the profession, with little of a tangible nature to show as a result of his work, but who is not only contented with his lot, but proud to have served in the ranks, and who looks back on a life of privation and hardship for the benefit of humanity as a privilege which he is thankful has been vouchsafed him.

That evening Dr. Will was again the guest of honor at a social function, but this time at a brilliant and sophisticated affair, the association's formal reception for its president. "The costumes of the ladies, the enormous throng of dancers, and the music of a military band made a spectacle long to be remembered." If he had time to think as he moved through it, Dr. Will must have reflected that the "green Western boy" of medical school days had come a long, long way.

# CHAPTER SIXTEEN

# The Surgeons Club

We are "fortunate in hearing the reports of Dr. Mayo's cases, because he is situated where he can have an enormous amount of material," Dr. Ochsner told the audience in a discussion of one of Dr. Will's early papers, but he was unusual in his perception. Most others, even while exclaiming over the volume of the Mayos' experience, began urging them to leave Rochester and transfer their labors to some big city where they would have more scope for their abilities. Some even offered them specific appointments to the staffs of metropolitan hospitals.

But the brothers were never tempted. They had become too firmly established in, and attached to, Rochester, and Dr. Will was of the opinion that they could not have won the recognition they had if they had been lost in a crowd of surgeons in a large city.

He knew though that the town had disadvantages to be overcome, among which was the distance from adequate laboratory facilities. Ninety miles to Minneapolis was too far to permit regular resort to the laboratories and scientists of the University of Minnesota. The Mayos and their partners already had laboratories superior to those generally available in a private practice, even to those in most hospitals not connected with a medical school, but that was saying little. Dr. Millet had a laboratory bench in the basement at St. Mary's where he examined gastric contents after tubing them from the patients' stomachs in a room upstairs. In one of the office rooms downtown Helen Berkman, a niece of the Mayos', made routine analyses of urine, blood, and sputum under Dr. Plummer's supervision, and across the hall was the small room, little more than a closet really, that Plummer used as a dark room for his x-ray work. That was all. The last addition to St. Mary's Hospital provided a possible laboratory near the operating rooms, but it stood empty except for a large porcelain sink.

Dr. Plummer had long been urging that it was time for the partners to make laboratories something more than a stepchild in their practice.

# The Mayo Brothers

Believing that scientific procedures were becoming an aid to diagnosis worth more than incidental use, he was sometimes impatient with the Mayos' cautious conservatism in adopting them and once told Dr. Will, more forcefully than elegantly, "You still think laboratory men are just a lot of pee-boilers." On the other hand, Plummer considered surgeons just high-class technicians skilled in only one branch of the healing art.

Fortunately both Plummer and Mayo possessed to an exceptional degree the ability to differ radically in opinion without becoming emotionally involved. Arguments between them were frequent and vehement but never entailed any suggestion that they part company. Both left the decision in any disagreement to time and circumstances.

And here these were on Plummer's side. When Dr. Herb's leaving in 1904 made it necessary to hire someone for the work in general pathology, and more of it than she had found time for in the odd moments not taken up with anesthetizing patients, the Mayos decided to employ a competent, well-trained pathologist to give his full time to the task of organizing and developing adequate laboratories. Having made that pregnant decision, they aimed high in picking a man for the job. They chose Dr. Louis B. Wilson, assistant director of the bacteriological laboratory of the Minnesota State Board of Health and assistant professor of bacteriology and pathology in the University of Minnesota.

Going to Minnesota from Pennsylvania in 1886, Wilson taught biology in a St. Paul high school for several years before entering the university medical school, from which he received his degree in 1896. The Mayos knew him to be a man of pleasing personality and boundless intellectual curiosity who had repeatedly demonstrated his scientific abilities in investigations undertaken for the state board of health. That very summer he had quickly located the source of a typhoid infection in Rochester and put an end to an incipient epidemic. Furthermore, he was closely associated at the university with Dr. Clark Stewart, a mighty evangelist for more and better postmortems to check the results of clinical diagnoses and operative procedures.

So in the fall of 1904 Dr. Will invited Wilson to come down and discuss the possibilities of the Rochester job. He was dubious. The Mayos were offering a bigger salary than the state paid him, but independence in his work and opportunities for research meant more to Dr. Wilson than money. Dr. Mayo's description of the job promised plenty of freedom. . . . Still, there must be a profit motive in private practice. What fetters would it impose? Would he have to account for every test tube and slide he used?

"What would be my budget?" he asked.

"You won't have any."

"Then that settles it. I won't come."

Dr. Will hastily explained that he meant there would be no fixed budget. "When you want something ask for it and we'll get it for you."

There wasn't much evidence of the profit motive in that. One could hardly ask more—*if* the man kept his word. After a discussion of the advantages and disadvantages of living in Rochester, during which Dr. Mayo probably described his and his brother's plan to spend ten per cent of their earnings in improving the city, Dr. Wilson agreed to take the job, beginning January 1, 1905.

The university officials were reluctant to let him go, but they finally accepted his resignation, sure that he would quickly repent of his bargain to exchange a berth with the state for employment in a private practice. Dean Frank F. Wesbrook told a man who applied for the vacant position that he was keeping it for Wilson, who would soon be back and would be the next dean of the medical school.

2

When Dr. Wilson began his work in Rochester his pathologist's soul, full of faith in the value of preserving specimens for subsequent study and reference, was distressed to find that in spite of the great amount of surgery done by the Mayos in the preceding fifteen years only a few specimens had been saved, in Henry Plummer's closet downtown. The rest had been thrown away or lost except for a few that had been sent for examination to Stewart at the university or to Le Count in Chicago.

Dr. Wilson soon had that empty room at St. Mary's well equipped and began the systematic examination, cataloging, and preservation of all the specimens removed at the operating and autopsy tables. The Mayos had been hiring an artist to illustrate their medical papers, but Dr. Wilson was convinced that sketches of pathological conditions were likely to be misleading, because the artist drew what he saw or thought the surgeons saw, which might be very different from what was really there. Good photographs would constitute a more accurate record, so Dr. Wilson, himself an expert with the camera, asked permission to employ a photographer to assist him.

Dr. Will hesitated a minute, then said, "Well, I told you we'd get you whatever you wanted and we'll get you that, but I've never thought pictures worth a damn."

After Dr. Wilson and the photographer he hired devised new apparatus and techniques for photographing both gross specimens and microscopic sections, Dr. Mayo made an occasion for admitting that he had been wrong. The photographer's salary was a good investment, he told Dr. Wilson; the pictures were a big help.

Autopsies were performed in twenty-two per cent of the deaths that occurred at St. Mary's Hospital in 1904, a record considerably above the average at that time, but it was not good enough for a man who had worked with Clark Stewart. In his first year with the firm Dr. Wilson raised the percentage to seventy. He never requested permission from the relatives as a favor; he put it squarely on the basis that the family and descendants ought to know the exact cause of death and everything possible about the processes of disease in their dead. And laymen responded with a readier understanding than Dr. Wilson had expected.

Being an intensely sympathetic man, he often found it hard to make his request of a family when their grief was fresh. But on one occasion he found he was unnecessarily distressed, for his gentle, tactful sentences were suddenly interrupted by one of the relatives. "Of course we want you to do a postmortem. We want everything we're paying for."

After that Dr. Wilson included this idea among his arguments, though he put it in less sharply mercenary terms.

### 3

Shortly after Dr. Wilson began his work at St. Mary's, Dr. Will remarked to him, "I wish you pathologists would find a way to tell us surgeons whether a growth is cancer or not while the patient is still on the table."

Among the questions surgeons had to answer most often were:

# The Surgeons Club

Is this tumor benign? Is it malignant? Is it tuberculosis or some other infection? Which of them it was determined the operative procedure to be used, but frequently it was impossible to tell from the gross appearance, and by the methods then in use it took hours, sometimes days, to prepare the tissues for microscopic diagnosis. If the pathologist was busy it might even be a week or two before he made his report to the surgeon, who, acting on his best judgment, might have done too much cutting or too little. Perhaps he had removed a breast where the lump itself would have been enough, or worse, perhaps he had taken just the lump and left an organ sprinkled with cancer cells.

The problem immediately engaged Dr. Wilson's active mind. The essence of it was to find a satisfactory method for handling fresh tissues. The early histologists had done their work on such tissues, but it was so hard to cut sections of these sufficiently thin for use under the microscope that the practice of hardening them in alcohol had been universally adopted when that technique was developed, and almost all the later work in microscopic pathology was based upon the use of "fixed" tissues. Consequently, when methods of freezing instead of fixing the tissues began to appear pathologists were inclined to view them askance.

Dr. Wilson shared this distrust of frozen sections, but he would have to use them if he was to solve the problem Dr. Mayo had set. So one by one he tried out the various methods that had been described. The chief objection to all of them was that they gave poor differential staining; the stains in general use for fixed tissues would not work for fresh tissues. A new one was needed.

It was natural that Dr. Wilson should soon think of trying methylene blue, an aniline dye whose affinity for living cells had been discovered by Paul Ehrlich and his uncle, the first man to stain bacteria. As a boy dabbling in botany Dr. Wilson used methylene blue to stain fresh sections of such things as May apple roots, and he used it again in bacteriology to make the living organisms visible. Just before he left the university he had been using it to stain nerve endings in living bodies to trace the path of the nervous system.

Now he decided to see what methylene blue would do to sections of fresh tissue. Drawing again upon his experience in botany, he fastened the bit of tissue between layers of elder pith, sliced off his sections by hand with a razor, and—it was January in Minnesota—froze them by putting them outside the window for a few minutes. Then he dipped them into methylene blue, washed them in salt solution, and mounted them in a glucose mixture that he had also learned about in botany.

The result was a good clear microscopic picture with well-differentiated details. But it was a picture in red, purple, and dark blue instead of in the browns and pinks with which pathologists were accustomed to deal, and it was a picture of living cells, not dead ones. For weeks Dr. Wilson examined every bit of fresh tissue he could get his hands on, normal and abnormal, so as to make himself familiar with the new microscopic patterns, and he checked every fresh-tissue diagnosis by later examinations of sections prepared in the usual way. Simultaneously he standardized each step of his staining method and bought a microtome to freeze and cut the sections automatically.

By the end of April 1905 he was able to give the Drs. Mayo his report within five minutes at most and often within two minutes of the time they handed him a bit of tissue just removed from the patient!

The Mayos were quick to recognize the revolutionary possibilities of this development. As Dr. Will put it, "The quick examination of sections of living tissue . . . enables the miscroscope to guide the operating surgeon's knife for the benefit of the patient in a manner as fundamentally different from the examination of mummified dead tissue, several days after the operation, as the work of the operating surgeon differs from the anatomist's dissection of the cadaver."

Fresh-tissue diagnosis quickly became the scientific mainstay of Mayo surgery and one of its distinctions.

4

For this new kind of surgical diagnosis the pathologist must be constantly at the service of the surgeon, and Dr. Wilson soon found himself needing more help than intern assistants could give him. Another full-time pathologist must be added to the staff. So Wilson wrote to Dr. William Welch asking him to recommend some good Johns Hopkins graduate.

The same mail brought Dr. Welch a letter from William C. MacCarty, a graduate of the Baltimore school in 1904. Just returned from a year's service as assistant pathologist in the Königin Augusta Hospital in Berlin, he was entering private practice in St. Louis in addition to a job teaching pathology at Washington University, and he wrote to tell Dr. Welch he was back in the United States—and perhaps to say he was disappointed in conditions at Washington, where the hospital facilities were in prospect rather than existence.

Mating the two letters Dr. Welch suggested to Dr. MacCarty that he apply for the position with the Mayos. He did so promptly, thinking to get a little more experience while he was waiting for the hospital to materialize at Washington University.

But after a few weeks' work at Rochester Dr. MacCarty was completely absorbed in fresh-tissue diagnosis. He too had a background of interest in botany, had even taught the subject for a year at Kentucky State University, and he found it a joy to work with delicate living cells again instead of with tissues pickled in alcohol. The possibilities fascinated him: at first the possibility of pathology's being a practical and immediate aid in surgical diagnosis, and then increasingly the possibility of revising and adding to knowledge of cell structure and function by studies of living cells.

No one seemed to object to his spending time in these studies. The Mayos never interfered. On the contrary, they were interested in what he was doing and encouraged him to go ahead. When Dr. Will brought visiting doctors in to see the laboratory he introduced Dr. MacCarty as one of his associates and told the guests about the promising research he was doing. The young man warmed with pride on such occasions and set to work harder than ever. The idea of returning to Washington University and general practice faded farther and farther from his mind.

5

Visiting doctors had become a regular feature of the Rochester scene, partly because of a growing tendency among surgeons to travel for observation. For some time they had been dissatisfied with the work of their medical societies; the programs seemed theoretic and academic, of little help in the solution of practical problems. Most men wanted to see a fellow operator demonstrate his work, instead of listening to him talk about it.

They envied the members of the exclusive Society of Clinical

Surgery, that peripatetic association conceived by W. J. Mayo, Ochsner, and Cushing in Paris and brought to birth by Mumford and Crile. Their idea seemed such a brilliant answer to the general problem that William Osler sponsored the formation of a similar group among medical men and Berkeley Moynihan organized a "chirurgical society" of similar purposes in England. Those who had no such society to join took to traveling on their own, as the Mayo brothers had been doing since their first years in practice.

By now Rochester was unquestionably one place to be included on every surgeon's itinerary. The Society of Clinical Surgery itself held its fall meeting there in 1905, and its members, all men whose word carried weight among surgeons, went away enthusiastic about "the grand display of surgical work" the Mayos had given them, as John B. Murphy, himself a frequent visitor to Rochester, reported in a letter to Moynihan of Leeds.

Early in 1906 there was published in Boston a description by Dr. George N. P. Mead of a trip he had just made to the little Minnesota town. On the train he found himself one of eight doctors bound for Rochester, from California, Texas, Iowa, Kentucky, New York, and Massachusetts. Going directly to the hospital upon their arrival, they were conducted into a moderately large, well-lighted operating room, where Dr. W. J. Mayo was performing a resection of the stomach. When he had finished the major part of the procedure, he suggested that the visitors go into the next room where his brother was doing some work he was sure they would wish to see. They went reluctantly, feeling sure they could not possibly see anything as fine as what they had just witnessed.

But they were quickly disabused of that notion. The younger brother was doing a thyroidectomy for exophthalmic goiter "with remarkable skill." The men watched in fascination, for the patient was stirring so restlessly that most surgeons would have stopped operating, "and would have sworn too. Not so Dr. Charles Mayo. He went right on, where a single false cut might have meant a bad case of bleeding, or the severing of a nerve and possible paralysis; he cut true, with a marvelous sureness and dexterity of touch, and the job was soon done."

The visitors spent the morning that way, passing back and forth between the two operating theaters. Dr. Will alone did ten operations, and Dr. Mead reported that together the two brothers were doing four thousand operations a year, "a total that is simply staggering."

Describing the Mayos' habit of traveling to learn any method they heard of that sounded good, which made Rochester "an almost automatic clearing house for the best work of the world's hospitals," and adding to it the thorough work of diagnosis carried on at "the Shop," the brothers' offices, Dr. Mead concluded, "It is no wonder that foreign surgeons count Rochester one of the places in America that simply must be seen."

At about the same time Dr. A. C. Bernays of St. Louis, not one of the day's surgical great but a man well known in professional circles, published in the *New York Medical Journal* an account of "A Visit to the Mayos at Rochester, Minnesota." The remarkable papers published by the two brothers "on some of the most difficult chapters of surgery" had attracted his attention, and he began sending his pupils and assistants to Rochester to observe what was being done there. What these young men had to tell when they returned convinced him that it would be well worth his while to make the journey himself. He found it to be truly so. In six days he saw one hundred and four operations, ranging through all branches of the surgical art, and he was convinced that surgery was being done more artistically and scientifically at Rochester than anywhere else in America.

I have learned by observation that patients operated on by the Mayos scarcely ever die, and I know that the mortality following their work is getting lower every year, until now it seems almost impossible to reduce it further. . . .

Among the many physicians and surgeons who visit the Mayos are all kinds, from the most expert and renowned metropolitan surgeon to the plain country doctor who has brought in a case for operation. There were usually from twenty to thirty spectators every day.

In such accounts by doctors the anomaly of the "clinic in the cornfields" was first described, for in them the Rochester setup was first called a clinic—not yet the "Mayo Clinic" but the "Mayo clinic at St. Mary's Hospital." The name was natural, for the visitors saw in the Mayos' private practice a form of organization apparently similar to institutional groups like the Osler clinic and the Halsted clinic at Johns Hopkins Hospital.

On June 7, 1906 seven of the visiting doctors present in Rochester met in a room of the Cook House and organized the International Surgeons Club. The purpose of the organization as stated in the minutes was to provide a means "whereby the many physicians who come here to see the work done at St. Mary's Hospital by the Mayo Brothers may be enabled to meet together and discuss the work of the day and other matters of mutual interest."

According to the plan of organization any visiting physician could become a member of the club by paying a nominal registration fee (at first fifty cents, later a dollar, and finally two dollars). Officers were to be elected each Monday afternoon, and two reporters were to be appointed daily to take notes on the next morning's clinics and present them as an aid to discussion at the afternoon meeting of the club. Dr. J. L. Wiggins of East St. Louis, Illinois, with whom the idea seems to have originated, was elected the first president and Dr. M. H. Blackburn of Princeton, Illinois, the first secretary.

Amid the distractions and amusements of a large city such a club might have failed to take hold, but in Rochester, where the transient doctors lacked occupation for their late afternoon and evening hours, it filled a real social need as well as an educational one. Within a month it had become an integral and important part of the visitors' activity. A room had been rented and furnished to accommodate the group, the daily attendance had risen to an average of twenty-five, and a third daily reporter had been added to make the rounds at the hospital with the interns and report on the postoperative progress of the patients whose operations the club members witnessed. The custom developed of rounding off the discussion with an informal talk by some visitor of repute or some member of the local staff.

All this activity was carried on by the visitors themselves. The Mayo brothers took no part in it. Although they were named honorary members of the club, they attended its meetings only when they were asked to speak, because they wanted the discussions to be frank and free from any possible embarrassment of their presence.

Only once did Dr. W. J. Mayo interfere. When it became quite apparent that the club was to be a lasting thing, he informed the members through their secretary that he did not like their name and wished they would adopt something less pretentious. To oblige him they voted to drop the *International* and become simply the Surgeons Club.

Actually the charter members had not been unreasonably optimistic. During the six months preceding their first meeting the list of foreign visitors to Rochester included such still familiar names as Trendelenburg of Leipzig, Samuel Pozzi and Jean Louis Faure of Paris, and young Alexis Carrel of Lyons, who despite his scant thirty-two years had already begun his revolutionary work in visceral transplantation. He went to Rochester with Dr. Carl Beck of Chicago, who was proclaiming his unbounded admiration of the Mayo brothers to all his many European friends.

When it was only three weeks old the Surgeons Club admitted to membership on one day Alexis Thompson of Edinburgh, Henry Stokes of Dublin, W. H. Parkes of New Zealand, and Baron Kamhiro Takaki, surgeon general of the Japanese navy. By the end of its first summer the group numbered more than three hundred members, the roster of whom reads like a medical roll call of the American states, the Canadian provinces, and many foreign lands.

As the number of spectators at the clinics had risen to forty and more a day, keeping order was becoming a problem, so the Surgeons Club prepared rules of conduct, copies of which were given to visitors when they arrived, and assigned to the daily reporters the added task of enforcing them. Larger club quarters having become a necessity, the entire second floor of the building next door to the Mayo offices was rented, redecorated, and furnished with tables, chairs, and a blackboard. Dr. J. E. Crewe, the Rochester physician who had taken over the practice of Dr. Grosvenor Cross when the latter moved to Minneapolis, was hired to act as permanent secretary for the group, and acting on instructions he wrote to numerous publishers of both medical books and periodicals to suggest that copies of their publications on the tables of the Surgeons Club in Rochester would be good advertising. When enough responded with free copies and subscriptions to give the club a start toward a library, a librarian stenographer was employed to assist Dr. Crewe.

Since there were so many members taking part, the afternoon sessions were proving too short for all that was to be said, and the informal talks were postponed to evening meetings and organized into a regular course of lectures. With the Mayos to teach surgery in the operating room, their associates to teach the several phases of scientific diagnosis, and some of the biggest figures in the world of surgery to add comment and different points of view, the Surgeons Club of Rochester became a postgraduate school of surgery without equal elsewhere in America. Indeed, one Canadian doctor, writing about the Mayos for the *Canada Lancet,* declared,

The rush of medical visitors is unabated, many fresh from continental clinics who are most enthusiastic in their expressions of pleasure with this clinic, which they say far surpasses anything they saw upon the other side of the Atlantic. . . . The little western town [is] slowly becoming the greatest post-graduate centre of the century, with possibilities practically illimitable.

In September 1906 Harold J. Stiles, the noted orthopedic surgeon of Edinburgh, spent several weeks in Rochester. Deeply impressed with the educational value of the clinics, he told the Surgeons Club he thought they ought to do something to express their appreciation of the remarkable opportunity the Mayos were giving them without charge. The committee appointed forthwith to recommend ways and means pointed out that the daily clinic was growing so large it must bring about its own destruction unless some provision was made for the increasing number of spectators. Therefore they proposed that the club show its "appreciation of the Mayos' work and its gratitude for the privilege of coming here" by building a surgical amphitheater, "to be paid for by the club or by voluntary contributions taken up among the surgeons who admire the Drs. Mayo."

For the spirit of the proposal Dr. Will and Dr. Charlie were grateful, but they would not permit its letter to be carried out. They and the Sisters of St. Francis had always financed their own expansion and they would continue to do so.

On their own visits to other clinics the brothers were sometimes irritated because the surgeon exerted no effort to make the trip worth their while. He made no explanation of what he was doing, and he was surrounded by such a flock of assistants that the visitor could see nothing of the operation. As Dr. Charlie said, "It looked as if you weren't wanted." Early in their traveling experience he and Will had vowed that if they ever had anything to show visitors they would make them welcome, arrange things so they could really see, and explain the operations to them. And never would they charge a doctor a fee for admission to any surgical clinic of theirs.

Now mindful of that early vow, they recognized their obligation to arrange things so the visitors could see all they had to show. For the time being they solved the problem by having built to their order— and probably Dr. Charlie's design—a number of metal platforms mounted on wheels and topped with handrails on which people could lean. These stands, each carrying a number of men, could be rolled into positions from which the occupants could see what the surgeon was doing, and they were high enough to permit the spectators to look over the operator's shoulder without getting in his way. The brothers also had slanting mirrors installed above the operating tables in such a way as to make the work visible at a considerable distance from the table.

## 7

There was as much to be heard as seen in a Mayo clinic, for the brothers accompanied their operations with a running clinical commentary, reviewing the case history and the diagnosis, describing the conditions they found, and explaining what they did and why. In these talks they ranged through the whole of medical science, literature, and history, giving freely the convictions born of their wide reading and experience and, according to one listener, bringing out "points in surgical anatomy and physiology in a way so plain and forceful that one marvels at the barrenness of textbook literature on such matters."

At the operating table they illustrated with unforgettable object lessons the principles of differential diagnosis, antemortem pathology, and early surgery that filled their formal papers. No man could attend Dr. Will's clinics very often without witnessing such a demonstration as this: The history, read by the assistant while the anesthetic was given, was a classic one of "stomach trouble"—years of treatment for indigestion without relief—yet when incision brought the stomach into view it looked perfectly normal.

"You have heard the history, gentlemen, but you see this stomach. In my opinion there is nothing wrong with it; the trouble is somewhere else. If I am right in a few minutes you will notice a spasm of the pylorus." Shortly a spasm of the pyloric muscles was evident to all.

"That does not tell us where the trouble is, but it is not in the stomach. I will see if it is in the appendix." And he pulled into view a badly diseased appendix.

Then as he proceeded to remove the appendix and close the abdomen he told them of his own experience. Thinking that the pylorospasm in connection with a history of stomach pain meant something functionally wrong with the stomach, he had performed gastroenterostomy in several cases with no relief of symptoms, but when he reoperated and took out a bad appendix or gallbladder the symptoms vanished. He had learned the lesson, but he was still undoing many a gastroenterostomy some other surgeon had lately done for stomach trouble that was not in the stomach. The next day the men might watch him undo just such a gastroenterostomy, or they might see him operate on a "dyspeptic" who had a normal stomach but a gallbladder full of stones.

Such lessons went home as they would in no amount of public speaking without demonstration, so that soon a paper on stomach or gallbladder disease at any medical meeting was likely to call forth a flock of stories beginning "The first time I understood . . . was when I saw Dr. Will Mayo in his clinic . . ." Dr. Ernest Hall of British Columbia did not exaggerate when he wrote:

We are enjoying at the Mayos' clinic the third revelation within the history of the present generation of surgeons. Thirty years ago Birmingham dispelled the fallacy of pelvic cellulitis, and in its place gave us a new pathology of pus tubes. Twenty years ago America put inflammation of the bowels out of business, and gave us the interesting appendix to juggle with; and to-day catarrh of the stomach and chronic dyspepsia, through the genius of Dr. Will Mayo, are fast becoming matters of history, and in their place he is giving us a pathology of organic stomach, liver, and duodenal disease as definite and accurate as that which we possess of the lower abdomen. What Lawson Tait was to the pelvis, Will Mayo is to the upper abdomen.

8

Dr. Charlie was working in too many fields to have yet attained such an outstanding position in any one, but he was fast rising to the fore in thyroid surgery, and visitors noted it. Dr. Andrew Smith of Portland, Oregon, vice-president of the American Medical Association, reported to the Surgeons Club one day that Dr. C. H. Mayo had that morning "dissected and shelled out two cysts of the thyroid with such ease that it seemed very simple. The cysts seemed to *roll out*," in great contrast, said Dr. Smith, to a similar case he had seen elsewhere not long before, in which the patient had almost bled to death. Dr. Will saw what was coming and once remarked to Dr. William D. Haggard, professor of surgery at Vanderbilt University in Nashville, "Charlie is going to be the Kocher of America."

As a clinical speaker Dr. Charlie was surely unique. He "kept his audience in a bubble of anticipation. During the morning's work of anything from ten to fifteen major cases he might discuss the number of nails and match-heads, the weight of charcoal and gunpowder which could be made from the constituents of the human body; he might philosophize about the gall-bladder of the pocket gopher, the pineal eye of the tuatara lizard, the galls on his oak trees, the tuberculous lesions of turkey's livers, or a hundred other odd subjects, and between these divagations introduce sound clinical teaching drawn from the accumulated wisdom of his vast experience. Those who listened . . . fascinated by his extraordinary discourse never knew what curious information his wide reading and shrewd observation would bring to light."

Both brothers had a gift for putting things so they stuck in the hearer's mind and he went away quoting the "maxims" of the Mayos. Dr. Charlie's forte was description through homely analogy. "Don't remove the parathyroid. It looks like a piece of fat, somewhat harder, and is about the size of a lima bean," he would say. Or, "When the hatchet-sharp edge of the liver is gone, you had better take out the gallbladder." Those who heard that had seen the normal liver many times, but they had never seen its edge as hatchet-sharp until Dr. Charlie saw it for them.

Dr. Will's gift was for an almost epigrammatic conciseness. "Don't monkey with the ovary; either remove it or leave it alone." "In obstruction a silent belly is a septic belly. The bowels are paralyzed and the case is inoperable." "Forty per cent of 'gastric' ulcers are in the duodenum." "Draw your conclusions before your experience is large. . . . Those of large experience are wary of conclusions." "Always report the postmortem findings; for if there is a lesson to be taught it is right that it should travel as far as possible."

Grateful as they were for the instruction, many visitors wondered how the surgeons stood the strain of giving it. A verbatim report of either brother's daily clinical talk runs to fifteen or twenty printed pages, and all the while they talked they were "working placidly yet rapidly . . . cutting, sewing, ligating, and performing all the manipulations of surgical technique."

The Mayos were not brilliant surgeons in the sense in which that term had been applied in earlier years; they did not dazzle their audience with a display of speed, daring, and flourish. But surgeons no longer asked to be thrilled by a spectacular performance. The principles of Halsted were coming into their own, and sureness, soundness, and thoroughness were now more generally respected than brilliance. Of these saner qualities the Mayos had a large share, with the added polish and mastery of technique they had acquired with long practice.

One day an onlooker asked Dr. Will how he had done the operation he had just finished. After thinking a few seconds Dr. Will replied, "Well, I hardly know myself until I go home and look it up in Binnie." Dr. J. Fairbairn Binnie, a Scotsman who had transferred his practice from Aberdeen to Kansas City, had just published a manual of surgery in which the technique of operation after operation was described precisely as the author had seen it done in one of the Mayos' clinics. So the audience that morning greeted Dr. Will's remark with delight, thinking it a sally at Binnie, who was in the group. But it may not have been so. Like all skilled craftsmen, the Mayos had mastered their techniques till they could use them almost without thinking, leaving their minds free for the more important questions of which to use and when.

Their surgery was, in the words of one who studied it, "the essence of the techniques of all masters of surgery, enriched with the original ideas of the Mayo brothers." They did not claim to be original very often; they were more concerned that they should know and practice the very best methods available, no matter who had discovered them. To repeat Dr. Will's fine figure of speech, they were gathering good ideas from every source, tying them into practical bundles for which they provided the string, and demonstrating the use of the bundle to all who wished to learn it. Those functions they rightly considered about as important for the advance of surgery and the better care of the sick as the function of discovery itself.

Both men were perfectly frank about their role, constantly telling visitors where they had picked up this good thing or that. Sometimes it was from their father, often from Joseph Price, Ochsner, Murphy, or Halsted. "I used to do this differently, but Moynihan showed me his method when he was here and it was better, so I use it now," Dr. Will would say. And Dr. Charlie, "The first time I tried this operation I got stuck at this point, but Dr. George Monk of Boston was here and he told me what to do."

Many of their listeners, more used to the kind of man who "invented" some good method or instrument he had seen used in Europe, were humbled by the Mayos' simple honesty. When they spoke to the brothers about it or complimented them on their constant efforts to keep on learning from other surgeons, the answer was merely an echo from the Old Doctor: "No man is big enough to be independent of others." Or Dr. Charlie would cite the European surgeon who was doing several hundred abdominal operations a year but who never bothered to see or read what others were doing, so that he was proud of a mortality of sixteen per cent when others had reduced it to three.

## 10

Dr. Will and Dr. Charlie pretended to infallibility no more than they did to originality. In some American clinics the morning schedule would list several "abdominal operations," a vagueness that permitted the surgeon to make sure of his diagnosis while the assistant was reading the case history. The Mayos always listed a specific diagnosis, or if they had been unable to reach one they admitted it with "Explore stomach, duodenum, and gallbladder." If their diagnosis proved wrong they called for a rereading of the history and in the presence of their visitors, and sometimes with their aid, tried to discover what had led them astray.

Some surgeons, notably John B. Murphy, saved the difficult operations for doing in private, but every visitor was welcome to see any operation the Mayos did and learn from the hard luck as well as the good. Often the master was most fully revealed when things went wrong. Among Dr. W. J. Mayo's outstanding characteristics as a surgeon, next to his remarkable judgment as to how far he could go in an operation—when to go in and when to get out—was his imperturbability in a crisis.

One day he was removing a tumor of the kidney. As an upheaval of the ocean floor might render useless the navigator's charts, so the huge growth had pushed all the familiar surgical landmarks out of place and attached itself to the adjoining body parts. As Dr. Will lifted it to the surface, the largest vein in the body was ruptured; blood welled forth in a horrifying flow that would have ended life in a few minutes.

With one flash of his finger Dr. Mayo found and plugged the rent, entirely by his trained sense of touch, for the blood shut everything else from sight.

Then he said quietly to the tense watchers, "Gentlemen, I have torn the *vena cava* and it will be necessary to make another incision to repair the vein."

He stitched up the tear, made sure it was tight, and then went calmly on with the task of cutting the growth away from the tissues to which it was attached. Suddenly the tumor came loose, making a long tear in the bowel. Dr. Mayo continued talking: "This, gentlemen, is a much more serious accident than the injury to the vein. I have torn a long rent in the duodenum and if it is not made intact, the contents will leak out and the patient will live but a few days." Then slowly and carefully he sutured the torn bowel before he went on to complete the work on the kidney.

The operation took three and a half hours. At the end the spectators were exhausted by the strain and stared in awe at the outwardly unperturbed man who had carried the responsibility.

Either accident would have meant death in the hands of the average surgeon, so the men naturally watched the postoperative course of the case with great interest. There were no complications, no signs of shock, and the patient progressed smoothly to a complete recovery.

Asked one time to compare the two Mayos as surgeons, Dr. Haggard replied, "Dr. Will is a wonderful surgeon; Dr. Charlie is a surgical wonder." The amazing characteristics in Dr. Charlie were his versatility and ingenuity. Other surgeons could not get over the ease with which he turned from removing a thyroid in one case to taking out a prostate or a varicose vein in the next, always with admirable skill. To him was due the range of surgery at Rochester, which made it possible for one man to say, "If you stay here long enough you can see every operation known to surgery."

His ingenuity in devising operative procedures for the unusual case became a byword in the profession. The fellows of the American Surgical Association met in Rochester one year and, wanting to see Dr. Charlie's peculiar talent in action, they asked Dr. Will to select some difficult case that Charlie had not examined and let them see what he did with it. As Dr. Will told the story:

I chose the case of a woman who had been operated on seven times before coming here, and whose condition was apparently hopeless of surgical repair, and had the Fellows examine her. They all agreed that it was a case hopeless of relief, and so the whole crowd was prepared to see Charlie floored. The patient was placed before him, and when he looked at the ghastly postoperative results he whistled. Then, without apparent effort, he outlined an entirely new plan of operative treatment, which was successful, and the crowd of doctors was simply dazed.

## 11

From the very beginning the Mayos were determined to bring back from every trip away some specific improvement that could be applied in Rochester—even if it was only a new kind of soap or antiseptic. Sister Joseph used to say to her aides, "Dr. Will is back; now there will be lots of things to change." Consequently the members of the Surgeons Club could pick up many pointers about hospital and operating-room procedure, and in both they found the cardinal principle was the utmost simplicity consistent with good work: "The central thought at St. Mary's Hospital is to get the patient well with as little loss of time as possible; whatever contributes to this end is adopted; whatever does not is eliminated."

By working with as few assistants as possible Dr. Will and Dr. Charlie went far toward realizing their early vow, and the visitors were grateful. Said one of them:

A phase of the work which is particularly gratifying . . . is the absence here of the vast horde of assistants that one sees in the majority of surgical clinics, both at home and abroad. The onlooker . . . has a beautiful view of the tops of the heads of the assistants and occasionally sees a bloody sponge or a gaping wound, but he seldom really sees the various steps of an operative procedure. Here at Rochester, however, things are different. Each brother has but one assistant or actual helper at the table. The other assistant or nurse stands back and only comes forward to exchange instruments, bring up suture material, etc. The Mayos have apparently found that one highly-trained assistant is better than a half dozen poorly-trained ones.

So "highly-trained," indeed, was Sister Joseph that sometimes when Dr. Will turned to answer a question from the gallery she automatically went on with the operation!

The visitors were impressed too by the work in pathology, especially in fresh-tissue diagnosis. For the pathologist to receive tissue at the operating table, hurry away to the laboratory, and return with a report in time to determine the surgeon's procedure was an innovation no one could fail to remark. The chief surgeon of the Samaritan Hospital in Montreal declared that his wavering faith in the value of pathology had been restored by seeing what practical use the Mayos made of it.

Immediate microscopic diagnosis had been in use in Rochester for many months when Dr. Wilson, on one of the study trips the Mayos financed for their associates, visited Halsted's operating room in Baltimore. He saw the surgeon take a bit of tissue from his patient and then, leaving the woman on the table, work in the laboratory for more than an hour to determine the exact nature of the growth. Knowing how much better his own procedure was for the patient, Dr. Wilson told Halsted about it and invited him to come to Rochester and see it in use. Halsted accepted, and his unwonted enthusiasm at the sight of Wilson's fresh-tissue preparations was heart-warming to the pathologist.

The Mayos considered the visit of the Baltimore surgeon a signal honor, and they were pleased by his unexpected friendliness. They had always thought him so reserved and unapproachable that they could scarcely believe it when they heard he was entering whole-heartedly into the activities of the Surgeons Club, contributing his great wisdom and experience to its discussions.

For surgeons to be impressed with the value of fresh-tissue diagnosis was one thing; for pathologists to adopt it was another. At Dr. Will's urging, Dr. Wilson had published a description of his rapid-staining method in the *Journal of the American Medical Association,* but pathologists shrugged it away as just another technique for handling the distrusted frozen sections. Even when they could be persuaded that it was reliable, few hospitals could afford the extra pathologist needed to practice it and few pathologists had time enough to specialize in it. Besides, in many cases the pathology laboratory was located far from the hospital, so that when the surgeon removed the specimen in the morning the pathologist did not get it until afternoon or the next day, much too late for fresh-tissue diagnosis.

## 12

The Mayo "system" of diagnosis was one of the most discussed features of their work, and the visitors usually went to the offices in the afternoon with considerable anticipation. There was certainly nothing impressive at first glance about the Masonic Temple and its rather dark hallway, furnished only with wooden benches and a framed copy of "The House By the Side of the Road" by Sam Walter Foss.

*I would not sit in the scorner's seat, or hurl the cynic's ban,*
*Let me live in a house by the side of the road and be a friend to man.*

But through that hallway and the examining rooms that flanked it passed a hundred and fifty or two hundred patients daily. While the Mayo brothers were busy at the hospital throughout the morning their associates carried on the work of diagnosis downtown, and patients who seemed likely candidates for surgery were asked to return in the afternoon for examination and a final verdict by the Mayos themselves.

When a diagnostician had a patient for one of the Mayos to see he stepped into the hall and stuck a piece of colored cardboard above the door frame, a red card for Dr. Charlie, a green card for Dr. Will. All afternoon the Mayos went back and forth from one room to the next, pausing often to exchange a pleasantry or word of greeting with some new arrival waiting his turn in the hallway.

Such an arrangement was a revelation to private practitioners. Most surgeons, working alone, were too busy to make a really thorough examination and unable to afford the facilities needed for it, and they looked with envy upon the division of labor that had developed through the Mayos' efforts to achieve the most accurate diagnosis possible to medicine without curtailing their own time for surgery. "Specialization and cooperation, with the best that can be had in each department, is here the motto. Cannot these principles be tried elsewhere?" asked one of the guests from Canada.

Only Henry Plummer had anything unusual in the way of medical treatment to show the visitors. The cases of esophageal stricture of obscure origin that Dr. Will turned over to Plummer soon after his coming to Rochester constituted the sort of problem in clinical investigation he excelled in. Characteristically he "went into a trance as far as the workaday world was concerned." He read, examined, reexamined, pondered, and soon he was able to treat with dramatic success many cases of ordinary stricture that previously would have been subjected to surgery. A cousin of Dr. Wilson's was one such patient. He was a man of thirty-five, but puny and wizened because he had lived on a liquid diet ever since he swallowed lye as a child of three. After two weeks of treatment by Henry Plummer he was able to eat a steak dinner without difficulty, and, needless to say, with relish.

Many of the instruments with which Dr. Plummer worked such wonders he made himself, turning them on a lathe in his office workshop, sometimes according to a design he had worked out to fit the needs of the individual.

In many cases he found the trouble was not caused by stricture but by diverticula, bulges in the esophagus wall that formed little pockets in which the food lodged instead of passing on into the stomach. He could not repair these defects himself, but he worked out highly ingenious ways of determining by x-ray and measuring devices of his own invention just where the diverticula lay, in what direction they extended, and how large they were, and then with this precise information he turned the patients over to the surgeons.

It was of this work Plummer talked when it was his turn to address the Surgeons Club, and the members were impressed with its originality and possibilities. Naturally when they got home and were confronted with a difficult case of esophageal derangement they advised the patient to see what Henry Plummer could do for him. So people from many states were soon going to Rochester for treatment by Dr. Plummer.

Here and there in the lot appeared a type of case he had not yet solved. The patient was unable to eat anything but liquids, yet there was no stricture of the esophagus, for the probes could be passed readily into the stomach. There was no diverticulum either, but often there was a marked dilatation of the lower esophagus. He was unable to help these patients, so they returned, disappointed, to their homes.

But Dr. Plummer did not forget them. He knew their difficulty to be caused by cardiospasm. For some unknown reason the cardiac muscle contracted to obstruct the passage of food into the stomach, and after a while the esophageal muscles, tired out by the extra effort necessary to force the food along, gave up the struggle and dilatation occurred.

In the literature Dr. Plummer found descriptions of attempts to overcome this difficulty by introducing a rubber balloon and inflating it to stretch the cardiac muscle, but the attempts had not been very successful and in some cases had resulted in rupture of the esophagus. However, the method seemed logical to Dr. Plummer, so he analyzed the reasons for its failure and then fashioned a dilator free of those defects. The results were sensational. Even Dr. Plummer, given to understatement as he was, was moved to say, "The immediate results are most striking. The patients are almost invariably able to take any kind of food at the following meal."

Reporting this development at a meeting of the Surgeons Club, he took one of his patients along as a demonstration. In the midst of his unemotional, scientific presentation of the case, the patient, unable to restrain himself, interrupted. "I was dying, and he saved my life," he shouted. Embarrassed by the outburst, Dr. Plummer hustled the man from the room, but some in the audience knew how truly he had spoken, for two weeks before they had seen him carried from the train on a cot, comatose and apparently within a few hours of death from starvation.

Now that he had solved the problem of those patients he had been unable to help, Dr. Plummer could not rest until he got them all back and cured them. One by one they came until finally there was only one left, a washerwoman from a small town in Ohio. She had paid the costs of her first trip with the lodge insurance she had received upon the death of her husband, but she had no way of financing a return trip. Although the treatment would cost her nothing, there were the expenses of transportation and lodging.

Dr. Plummer's associates had been following his work with great interest, so he told them about this case. "Men, we've just *got* to get that woman back and fix her up." They agreed, and all chipped in to pay the woman's way to and from Rochester.

## 13

The story of Henry Plummer's work provides a good illustration of one highly important by-product of the Surgeons Club. Men who had visited Rochester and seen for themselves what the brothers and their associates could do thought of the Mayos when they were faced with a case beyond their own skill. It was cases referred by other doctors that first extended the scope of the Mayo practice beyond the Northwest, to include American states from Maine to California and Canadian provinces from Quebec to British Columbia, and boosted the number of operations at the rate of about one thousand annually.

Not only did the doctors send their patients to the Mayos; when they themselves required surgical treatment they too took the train for Rochester. "And we always bought a round-trip ticket," said one of them. So general was this that Dr. Will and Dr. Charlie were often called the "surgeons' surgeons," and the following anecdote gained wide currency.

A story is told of a Southern practitioner of some note who, finding himself compelled to undergo a serious abdominal operation, went to New Orleans to put himself in the hands of a celebrated specialist. He found the specialist's office closed on account of illness. There was a fine operator at Memphis. Thither the patient went only to be confronted with the announcement: "Away for a month." Cincinnati was his next stop. The man he wanted to see there was in Europe. He telegraphed to the Mayos and took a train for Rochester.

"You've come quite a distance, Doctor," said the superintendent of the hospital, who greeted him.

"Yes, but not direct," replied the Southerner. "Frankly, I intended to go to Dr. M . . . of New Orleans, but failed to find him."

"Yes," said the superintendent. "He's been here for ten days and is convalescent now."

"Then," pursued the patient, "I tried Dr. S . . . of Memphis, but . . ."

"He'll be able to see you by the time you're able to see him," said the smiling superintendent. "He's in the second room down the hall."

# The Surgeons Club

"You haven't got Dr. L . . . of Cincinnati here, have you?" asked the other, looking at her suspiciously. "They told me he was in Europe."

"He is by this time. We shipped him off last week to recuperate after a gastrotomy operation."

Although fiction has probably enhanced fact there, many American surgeons, and some of the greatest of them, did become patients of the Mayos. In less than two years Dr. Will operated on three nationally known professors of surgery in three Philadelphia medical colleges, J. William White, Charles H. Frazier, and William W. Keen.

When Dr. White arrived he was so sure he had cancer of the bowel that he told Dr. Will he almost hoped he wouldn't recover from the operation. He didn't want to live "with that thing inside of me." As incision brought the sigmoid flexure of the colon into view the surgeon pathologist who had accompanied Dr. White took one look at the hard nodular mass and turned away. Yes, it was cancer.

But Dr. Mayo and Dr. Wilson were not so sure. A few months before they had had a patient, also named White strangely enough, whose colon presented a very similar appearance, but Dr. Wilson had been unable to find any evidences of cancer. The mass had proved to be an intestinal diverticulum, a protrusion of the inner lining through the outer wall of the bowel.

In Dr. White's case too Dr. Wilson reported the condition to be diverticulitis and not cancer. White's pathologist friend and the watching surgeons were strongly inclined to doubt Wilson's diagnosis, but when they examined fixed-tissue preparations later they were forced to admit that he had been right. Within two weeks Dr. White was serving as president of the Surgeons Club, and he lived for some thirty years longer.

Discussing the incident with Dr. Wilson, Dr. Will remarked that a few years before he had operated on a Rochester man for what he was sure then was cancer of the bowel, and he had been wondering ever since why the man was not dead. Now he wondered whether the "cancer" had been a case of this diverticulitis. Shaking his head to think that the specimen had gone so long unstudied, Dr. Wilson dug into the old records and discovered it was one of those that had been sent to the state university. He had it sent back to Rochester and found that it *was* a mass of diverticula.

Thereafter the Rochester men were on the lookout for this condition. Dr. Will learned to recognize it from the gross appearance, and the diagnosticians tried to find clinical signs by which they could make a differential diagnosis between diverticulitis and cancer. They felt a distinct sense of triumph the first time Henry Plummer suggested the possibility of diverticulitis and operation proved him right.

When they had accumulated enough cases to suggest that the condition was fairly common, they made a joint report of their experience to the American Surgical Association. Dr. Reginald Fitz, the pathologist who had described and named appendicitis, was present at the meeting and congratulated the Rochester men on their report of "what must be recognized as a new disease of the lower abdomen." Such diverticula of the bowel had often been observed at postmortem, he said, but so far as he knew, the fact that they gave rise to symptoms simulating malignant tumors was altogether new.

## 14

The Mayos were courtesy itself to their visitors. When operations did not follow each other too rapidly the brothers spent the intervals conducting guests through the hospital or chatting with them in the waiting room. Nor was their consideration reserved for men of fame. Dr. J. E. Crewe was a young man fresh from medical school practicing in a small Minnesota town, and when he was taken to the home of his wife's parents in Rochester to convalesce from a serious illness, he was anxious to take advantage of the clinics at St. Mary's. When word of that got to Dr. Charlie he sent a carriage each morning to take Dr. Crewe to the hospital. Between operations he helped the invalid out to a couch in the doctors' waiting room to rest until the next patient was ready, and he never forgot to call him back in time.

In the earlier days, when visitors from a distance were an event, the Mayos celebrated their presence by serving refreshments at the conclusion of the clinic. They had long since outgrown that custom, but newcomers in the gallery were quite likely to be invited to the home of one of the brothers for lunch.

Because the hotel accommodations of Rochester fell somewhat short of metropolitan standards, the Mayos turned their homes into virtual inns, and the demands thus made upon their wives would have tried the good nature of angels. Their larders must always be stocked, their kitchens staffed, and their menus arranged to accommodate from two to ten extra guests at a moment's notice, but they rose nobly to the task, and the simple but gracious hospitality they dispensed has become legendary in medical circles the world over.

Hattie Damon had not bargained for renown when she married Will Mayo, and she would have preferred a quiet life and simple good times with the home-town folks. But she adjusted herself without complaint to the way of life her husband's position required, seeking satisfaction in achieving a smooth-running, efficient household.

One day she planned to serve at the evening meal two wild ducks a friend had given her, and when Dr. Will arrived with two unannounced guests just at dinnertime, there was not an oversupply of fowl. During the task of carving, which Mrs. Mayo had assumed to relieve her husband, one of the ducks slid to the floor. Calmly she rang for the maid and, with a barely perceptible lowering of one eyelid, said, "Bring in another duck, Bessie." So Bessie took the fallen duck to the kitchen, wiped it off, and brought it back to the table.

Mrs. Mayo was a quiet woman who never lost her shyness despite long experience in meeting people. To make conversation with the men of medicine who were her husband's guests was hard for her, yet the burden of conversation at the noontime meal fell upon her shoulders, for Dr. Will took that occasion to deal with his voluminous correspondence. His secretary sat at a table near by, and he dictated the answers to his letters while he ate.

## 15

There was no chance for any such occupation at mealtime in Dr. Charlie's home, for his house was filling up with children who adored their father. They greeted his arrival with squeals of delight and raced to be the first to reach his side, and after lunch they struggled noisily with each other for the best position on his knee.

Watching that contest one day, Dr. Haggard remarked to Mrs. Mayo, "Charlie has done a day's work this morning, and will do another this afternoon. He ought to be resting now, but how can he with those children clambering all over him?" Smilingly Mrs. Mayo advised him to look a little closer, and he saw that Dr. Charlie was asleep! It was his habit to nap for fifteen or twenty minutes after lunch each day, and he had trained himself to do so in spite of the children's bedlam.

Although Dr. and Mrs. Charlie never pretended to anything other than their normal informality of living, visitors to the "red house" did not always take the full measure of it. On one occasion a visitor from England was entertained overnight and in the British fashion left his boots standing outside the door when he retired. Finding them there when they went up to bed, Dr. and Mrs. Mayo knew the Englishman expected the servants to polish them before morning, but the Mayos' help were not of that kind, and besides they had all gone to bed. Chuckling softly at his wife's dismay, Dr. Charlie carried the boots to the kitchen and polished them himself.

Conversation at Dr. Charlie's always roamed through many topics and was certain to be punctuated by the delightfully funny stories the host collected or invented. But sooner or later the talk would turn to automobiles, Dr. Charlie's favorite hobby. Mrs. Mayo was sure she knew every hill in the vicinity of Rochester, for she had at some time or other walked up each one, taking the children out of the car at different levels to make it lighter so it could get to the top.

Since there were as yet no garages or automobile dealers, Dr. Charlie took on the agencies for several of the various makes, to be sure of getting all the new models. They were shipped to him in pieces, and it was relaxation for him after a hard day of surgery to take the parts from their crates and assemble them into a car. He made the process seem so simple that some of his doctor friends were persuaded to buy an auto for themselves, but they seldom found a mechanic at home who could put the thing together and make it go.

Inner tubes had not yet been invented, so the whole tire was inflated with air. Characteristically Dr. Charlie attempted an improvement, filling the tires on one of his cars with a mixture of molasses and glue that in wintertime stayed hard as rubber. But when he sold the car to an Olmsted County farmer early in the spring he forgot to take the molasses and mucilage out of the tires. On Easter Sunday the farmer and his wife started for church in their new Easter finery, the wife bright and beribboned in stiff taffeta. Presently the air was full of floating threads of gluey molasses that spun from the tires at every revolution of the wheels, and the farmer and his wife were beating about madly, trying to keep the sticky stuff away from their faces and clothes.

Dr. Charlie had to buy them a new set of tires, a new suit, and a new taffeta dress, but it was well worth it for the many hearty laughs he got and gave as he told the story on himself.

## 16

Dr. Will was slower than his brother to succumb to the fascination of the motor car, but he too got one at last, "a handsome machine of the Pierce make, styled the 'Great Arrow.' It is two-seated, the front being arranged for two, and the rear seat being capable of holding three."

Dr. Carl Beck arrived in Rochester for one of his periodic visits while the car was still new, and the Old Doctor showed him the Pierce Arrow with pride. Warming to Beck's admiration, he impulsively suggested they take a ride. The guest agreed, they got in, and Dr. Mayo started the motor. But at this point Dr. Will came running from the office calling to his father to stop. Breathlessly he explained to Dr. Beck that his father had never driven a car.

The visiting surgeons found the Old Doctor very entertaining, and they often asked him to talk to the club about the early days, the education of his sons, and the building of St. Mary's Hospital. Some of them would stop to chat with him a while in his little room at the hospital, and to one of them at least it seemed that "a visit to Rochester is not complete without making the acquaintance of this most interesting man."

When he walked around the corner to the offices he did not always bother to don formal attire, but went without a collar, just putting a button through the fastening of his shirt. He was dressed that way one day when the brothers received word that a group of European doctors were to arrive on the next train, then almost due, and Dr. Charlie rushed to the drygoods store a few doors down the street to buy a collar and tie for his father. While he fussed around to get the old man spruced up for presentation to the visitors, the office staff stood by and laughed, because Dr. Charlie was so entirely unconscious of the fact that he himself needed sprucing up fully as much as his father did.

One afternoon when the Old Doctor took some visitors for an automobile ride—with a chauffeur this time—the car broke down on the outskirts and the men had to hire a team to take them back to the office. That was a humiliation the Old Doctor could not endure, and there was determination in his eye as he walked into the office, rapped the table with his cane, and told one of the assistants he wanted to see Will. When Dr. Will sent the young man back to say he would come as soon as he got through with his patient, the Old Doctor struck the table again with his cane. "I want to see Will *now.*" The assistant reported this to Dr. Will, who said quietly, "I guess father means *now*," and excused himself to his patient.

The Old Doctor declared emphatically that he wanted a new car. All right, they'd see about getting him one, said Dr. Will. "Damn it," cried the old man with another blow at the table, "I want a new car *now.*"

That was the Old Doctor as the associates of the Mayo brothers knew him—sometimes amusingly, sometimes irritatingly headstrong, irascible, past his days of active participation in the work. Consequently they have never been able to appreciate the extent of his contribution to the origins of the Mayo Clinic.

And yet there were many indications still of the remarkable man he was. In a note to the Sisters of St. Francis thanking them for a gift they had sent him he wrote,

The gracious privilege is not often accorded mortal man to live to witness the accomplishment, the culmination of his best wishes, his ideals. That this happiness has come to me after many days, fills my heart with deepest gratitude and peace. Of me it can be truly said:

> Every yesterday was a vision of hope,
> Every today is a dream of content.

But the content did not efface the hope. When the Methodist Episcopal Church of Rochester celebrated its semicentennial he was invited to give one of the addresses. The audience expected him to dwell upon the history of the church and the town, for the subject assigned him was one on which he at eighty-seven was well qualified to speak, "The Changes of Half a Century." But Dr. Mayo brushed the topic impatiently aside and chose instead to describe the marvels of three industrial plants he had recently visited, concluding with the hope that

Rochester would soon make use of its water power instead of coal for operating its electric light plant.

The next year he set off in January with his friend C. C. Willson for a tour of the Southwest and Mexico. The doctors of Salt Lake City sent a committee to meet him at the station, and since of the two elderly gentlemen who got off the train one was tall and distinguished in appearance and the other short and old-fashioned in a long-tailed coat and top hat, the committee picked their man unhesitatingly and addressed their speech of greeting for Dr. Mayo to Mr. Willson.

The Old Doctor was offended and would not be mollified by the committee's apologies, until some reporter asked him his opinion of the state of the nation. His answer shows how well he had kept up with current affairs.

Never before have I seen such a tremendous sentiment for honesty in both public and private life as that which exists at the present time. . . . I can plainly see that the people pay little attention to party lines nowadays and are becoming what we used to call "mugwumps." This condition may not last but it is a move in the right direction, as it will teach dishonest political bosses that they must either mend their ways or be ousted from control. . . . I look for a radical change in the personnel of the national senate and house within a few years as a result of this sentiment.

After two months on the road he returned to Rochester for two weeks and then set off for the Orient. James J. Hill had learned that his old friend, "the little doctor coming up the river," wanted to visit China and Japan, and invited him to make the journey as a guest on one of Hill's boats. He sailed from Seattle in March, and for more than five months his family and friends heard nothing from him. Then he returned in good health and full of tales, proud because he had gone on around the world and had celebrated his eighty-eighth birthday on board the ship with a party and cake provided by the officers.

But when anyone asked him a question he could not answer about the Orient he referred them to his wife. Mrs. Mayo had refused Mr. Hill's invitation to accompany the Doctor on his journey, but she had sent for all the books on China and Japan she could get and knew more about those countries than her husband by the time he returned.

"Madam Mayo," as she was called to distinguish her from her daughters-in-law, had lost none of her forthright vigor in spite of her snowy hair and comfortable grandmotherly appearance. She had her own car and chauffeur and enjoyed riding, often with a friend or two as guests. One day she suddenly called to the driver to stop the car because she had caught sight of a patch of pumpkins and wanted to steal one. Since there was a barbed wire fence protecting them, the chauffeur offered to get it for her. "No," said Mrs. Mayo, "you have to steal it yourself; then it brings you luck." So she climbed over the fence and got the pumpkin.

When an errand took Mrs. Mayo to the offices she often spent an hour or two talking to the patients, many of whom she knew from the days when she helped take care of them as babies. One day she walked into the waiting room to find Dr. Will trying to comfort a woman who was sobbing violently. She walked right up to them and asked what was the matter. Blessing the fate that sent her over at that moment, Dr. Will explained that he had just had to tell the woman she had a hopeless case of cancer. Mrs. Mayo sat down beside her, hauled her fear into the open, and talked about it in a matter-of-fact way. Death like birth was just a natural process, she said. She had seen many people die, and most of them were contented when the time came; they accepted death as a release and just dropped off to sleep. As she talked the woman stopped crying and was soon able to go her way with something like calm.

## 17

When he was past ninety Dr. Mayo began experimenting with a process for extracting alcohol from animal and vegetable wastes. While he was supervising an experiment one day the mechanism got stuck, and he impatiently thrust his hand in to see what was wrong. It had only seemed to stick. His hand and lower forearm were badly crushed.

Not liking the way his sons dressed them he got the hired man to help him rearrange the bandages and splints to his own satisfaction. The injury was so severe, however, that within the next year three operations were necessary, the last to amputate the hand and forearm. The nerves had been so bruised that Dr. Mayo suffered intense pain much of the time, and his general health failed rapidly under the strain. His life closed on March 6, 1911, just a few months before his ninety-second birthday.

The funeral was held next day under the auspices of the Olmsted County Medical Society, and by proclamation of the mayor flags were flown at half-mast, the schools closed, and all business suspended in Rochester during the service, which was a simple one without eulogy and without music, as Dr. Mayo had requested. An epitaph was pronounced privately by Sister Joseph, who was not given to loose praise of men: "He was an alert, able, earnest humanitarian, worthy of all the glory his sons have added to his name."

A few months later the William Worrall Mayo Memorial Association was organized, with Burt W. Eaton as president, for the purpose of raising funds to erect a monument to Rochester's foremost pioneer. Although at the Mayos' request contributions were limited to one dollar each, five thousand dollars poured in, and Leonard Grunelle of Chicago, assistant to Lorado Taft, was commissioned to execute in bronze the statue of the Old Doctor that stands in Mayo Park.

It was Dr. Will who, in providing the inscription for the base of the statue, hit squarely upon his father's salient characteristic: "A man of hope and forward-looking mind."

Mrs. Mayo was present at the ceremony of unveiling, but in a wheel chair. Going to the door one night to call in her cat before going to bed she had slipped off the step and broken her hip. The long confinement to bed while the bones knit sapped her strength, and less than two months after this last public appearance she passed quietly away, on July 15, 1915.

The true memorial to Dr. and Mrs. Mayo was a living one, the minds and characters of their famous sons.

## 18

For a number of years Dr. Will and his wife entertained summertime guests at Lake Allis near Oronoco, but after a while Dr. Will got bored with the lake cottage; it was too stationary and afforded too little variety to give him recreation. So he exchanged it for an old river towboat, which he had remodeled into a comfortable pleasure craft that he named the *Oronoco*. A week-end cruise down the Mississippi with a party of professional friends refreshed him as nothing else could do.

He took over the boat's captain with the boat, and when failing eyesight compelled Captain Cassidy to retire from his post he said he had ended his career as a riverman in "one of the nicest situations on the Mississippi River or any other river in the world." He was consoled in his retirement by the fact that Dr. Mayo placed one of the *Oronoco's* staterooms at his and his wife's disposal whenever they wished to occupy it.

Dr. Charlie shared in the ownership and use of the *Oronoco*, but he was beginning to find his principal recreation in farming. Mrs. Mayo, feeling that the two boys, Charles William and Joseph Graham, were getting too old to spend all their summer vacations at play, one day suggested a farm home for the summertime. The idea met with Dr. Charlie's approval, and within a month the place was chosen and bought.

Although the house was to be just a cottage, Dr. Charlie took a keen interest in the plans for it and persuaded the contractor to use walls of poured concrete with an intervening air space for insulation. That was his own idea, long before it came into general use, and it worked so well that when the family decided to live in the country the year round, Dr. Charlie used it again in the much bigger house he built near by.

The site he chose was in the midst of rolling hills, still wooded and wild, and he wanted to keep it that way, so whenever he heard that the owner of some view or walk he particularly liked was about to cut down the trees, he bought the plot to preserve them. As his interest in various phases of practical farming grew he acquired other acres for fields and pasture lands, and almost before he knew it the little farm had become an estate of two thousand, then three thousand, acres. He named it Mayowood.

His knowledge of and love for plant and animal life remain one of his children's most vivid memories of him. Sunday afternoon rambles or picnic suppers with him in the woods or along the banks of the Zumbro were never dull, because he had a bit of nature lore to tell about everything they saw. Each year when spring came the bird chart went up on the dining-room wall, and the whole family entered into the game of seeing who could find each bird first.

A new one seen before breakfast counted an extra point, for Dr. Charlie abhorred laziness and was distressed by his children's inclination to lie abed in the mornings. He did not try to get them up by exercising parental authority, however. Instead he played the bird game, or stood beneath the boys' window and talked to their parrot about sleepyheads.

Ingenious little economies were characteristic of Dr. Charlie. Visitors shown through the Mayowood greenhouses were always astonished when they came to an ell in which dark glass had been used to shut out the burning southern sunlight, for looking up they saw a grotesque array of bones and other body parts; Dr. Charlie had salvaged some old x-ray plates to shield his flowers. Chided for such thriftiness, he said he had got the habit of making every bit of material do double duty when he was a boy and in those early years when he and Will were trying so hard to make St. Mary's pay its own way.

An Australian surgeon who enjoyed the hospitality of Mayowood in 1914 has left a happy little sketch of the house and the host and hostess.

Charles Mayo . . . called for me in his car, with a doctor from China, and another from some other distant part. . . . It was a lovely frosty moonlight night. We drove up to a fine "cement" house in the centre of two thousand acres . . . on the side of a hill overlooking a valley, in which there is a winding river looking very beautiful in the moonlight. We entered the house by steps leading up to a porch and a "cloak room," up some more steps to a large hall with a tremendous old-fashioned fireplace, in which logs were burning, surrounded by seats. The floor of wood, covered with rugs. Under the house was the garage. In the side of the hill a garbage destructor, fuel house, ice house, and engine for generating his own electricity; several living rooms and bathrooms, a billiard room; and on top a large ballroom for the children, of whom he has seven.

His wife is a charming lady. We had an old-fashioned tea-dinner . . . all very plain and homely; no "frills" and no "side."

His wife joked him about the farm, especially about a flock of geese, of which he was proud, but which had—so she said—that day flown away. So he told us about his farm experiences.

He got trout and put them in the stream. As soon as they were doing well, a cloudburst was sure to come and sweep them all high and dry. . . . He bought a fine herd of Guernseys, and claimed to have the finest dairy in the State. . . . They all became tubercular, or rather, were so when he bought them. He could, of course, have taken action against the man who sold them, but he did not "squeak," as he did not wish to proclaim to the whole State that he was a "sucker."

His poultry was the talk of the neighborhood—all the best broods—but they would not lay. One day one did, and all the countryside came to see the egg.

His pet desire—his wife told me this tale—was to have at the farm some Chinese pheasants, but he did not know how to get them. However, a friend sent him a pair from Portland, and he was very anxious that they should breed. While at dinner one night, a servant came in and whispered quietly to him. He said, "All right; I'll see after dinner." His family asked him what it was, but he only gave a self-satisfied chuckle and went on with his meal. . . . At last his son burst out laughing, and his father asked him what *he* was laughing at, and he replied . . . "That egg under the pheasant is an 'Easter egg.' "

"And now to cap everything . . . my wife tells me of that flock of geese. I was right proud of those geese; raised them myself; they were doing well; fed themselves on the bank of the river and cost nothing; and now they have followed a flock of wild geese and left.

"Farming is the finest thing for a busy professional man. I guess when I leave town and get in the car all thought of work goes and I concentrate on this farm."

His wife joked him about being a farmer, but he said: "I am not a farmer. . . . I am an agriculturist." "And what's the difference?" says she. . . . "In the first place an agriculturist makes his money in town and spends it on the farm; while a farmer makes his money on the farm, and spends some of it in town. Also, a farmer eats all he can't sell, while an agriculturist sells all he can't eat." . . .

His is a charmingly simple home and household—he a delightful personality.

Dr. Will felt not a prickle of his brother's interest in farming. He had had all of farm life he wanted when he was a boy. Ironically enough, he inherited the old farm homestead, but an occasional visit to look over the premises was quite enough to satisfy him.

When Dr. and Mrs. Charlie decided to make their home permanently at Mayowood and gave the old "red house" to the Rochester YWCA, Dr. Will and his wife built a new house too. They chose a lot a few blocks farther up College Street and erected a large, impressive residence of cut stone. In this instance it was the wife who worked with the architects, for it was of this house that Dr. Will asked only that it have a tower like the one from which he had watched the stars with his mother.

In that tower, on the fourth floor, he established a "hideout" to which he could retire from the guests and distractions downstairs. The little room was simply furnished, with books and pictures, a large flat-topped desk, and the view from the windows. There in the few hours he could spare to be alone Dr. Will made his plans and decisions and dreamed his dreams.

## 19

Behind the dairy and the tubercular cows of which Dr. Charlie spoke so jokingly to his guests lay an earnest purpose and a new professional interest of considerable importance.

Neither brother ever showed any inclination to imitate his father in political activity. Both, though mainly Dr. Charlie, attended and addressed numerous public meetings called to advocate better streets and roads or other civic improvements, but they steadfastly refused to run for office. When an earnest citizen proposed to the assembled businessmen that they start to clean up the city government by nominating Charles H. Mayo for mayor, Dr. Charlie rose to protest, and as soon as he could make himself heard above the cries of "Mayo for mayor! Mayo for mayor!" he said, "I will do anything I can for the good of Rochester. It is the place I was born in; it's the place I want to live in and die in. I thank you for this apparent appreciation, but I want to stay out of politics."

Four years later, in 1912, scarlet fever appeared in Rochester. After reporting the first twenty-nine cases the newspapers applied voluntary censorship, lest they frighten away prospective customers and patients, but the disease rapidly assumed epidemic proportions and several visiting surgeons contracted it, much to the Mayos' chagrin. As Dr. Charlie said, "That's a fine report about Rochester to have spread all over the country." When the state health authorities threatened to close the town to traffic if the epidemic continued, he felt it was time he take some action, since Dr. Will was out of town at the moment.

A short while before, the Civic League, which was the Rochester women's club, had offered to contribute two thousand dollars toward the salary of a full-time health officer to be appointed by the state board, but the city fathers refused the offer, saying they were afraid to take such a step in the dark, and elected a local physician, Dr. A. S. Adams, as part-time officer at a salary of one hundred and fifty dollars a year. Now Dr. Charlie rounded up the angry members of the Civic League and appeared with them before a joint meeting of the city council and the Commercial Club to demand that something be done about the public health administration. The session was long and stormy. Dr. Adams defended himself by saying that whenever he tried to enforce any regulations about milk or meat the dairymen and the butchers threatened to have him fired. To which Dr. Charlie replied, "Give me the job. They won't try to fire me."

At midnight Dr. Charlie withdrew and went home to bed. But about one-thirty he was awakened by a loud knocking at the door downstairs. "Who's there?" he called out the window.

"The city council," was the reply. "Dr. Adams says he'll resign if you'll take the job and take it tonight." So Dr. Charlie went downstairs in his nightshirt and dressing gown to be sworn in as health officer. He asked one of his associates to act as his deputy for a few weeks, and together they soon put an end to the epidemic by enforcing strict measures of quarantine.

It was obviously impossible for Dr. Charlie to perform the duties of the office himself, and equally impossible for him to secure a competent deputy for one hundred and fifty dollars a year, so he and Dr. Will decided to pay the salary of the deputy themselves. To what better use could they put a share of their yearly contribution to Rochester?

Dr. Charlie had long been convinced that many of the humped backs, crippled limbs, and scarred necks he saw were due to the drinking of infected milk, and a state inspector had declared Rochester's milk to be the dirtiest in the state for a town of its size, so the milk supply was the first problem he tackled—after organizing a health service in the schools to provide periodic examination and vaccination against smallpox. With the authority of his new office he persuaded the city council to pass, over the mayor's veto, an ordinance providing for the inspection of dairies to secure the most elementary cleanliness. More than that was impossible in the face of the dairymen's protest that they could not afford to institute a lot of falderal.

It was to see for himself exactly what they could afford that Dr. Charlie established a dairy farm at Mayowood. Step by step he made it into one of the model dairies of the state, producing pure, clean milk that could be sold at a reasonable price.

But experience taught him that the best efforts, the most scientific precautions, could not guarantee a herd of cattle free from tuberculosis, and once convinced that only compulsory pasteurization could assure the consumer safe milk, he set out to secure a city ordinance requiring Rochester dairymen to pasteurize their milk. The bill he proposed was sensationally advanced for the time. Imagine it, commented the Twin City newspapers, Dr. Mayo wanted to make Rochester dairy farms observe rules almost as strict as those in force in his own operating room. He wanted the milkmen to wash their hands with antiseptic soap before entering their cow barns, to wear spotless clothing, handle the milk in special cooling rooms, pasteurize every drop of it, and have it graded regularly by an employee of the city health department.

The inevitable battle took place at a meeting of the city council, where twenty milk distributors led by the one woman among them fought Dr. Charlie's bill, insisting that its provisions would drive them out of business. Besides, they said, this pasteurization nonsense spoils the taste of the milk. Dr. Charlie cited the statistics of his own farm to prove that the measures of the bill were not financially impossible and said that if pasteurized milk tasted different from raw milk it had been cooked too long.

The debate dragged on until Dr. Charlie's patience was exhausted. In a burst of heated eloquence he told the aldermen their primary job was to safeguard the health of the city, not the pocketbooks of the dairymen, and dared them to defeat the ordinance. When the count was finally taken, long after midnight, the bill passed by one vote. Dr. Charlie and his friends considered that the biggest victory of his official career.

But he promptly astonished everyone by naming as milk inspector the woman who had led the opposition—and she did a good job of enforcing the new regulations.

## 20

When Dr. Charlie took charge of the health office there was no provision for garbage collection in Rochester. About twenty families in the town were paying a dollar a week each to have their kitchen waste hauled away, and the same man performed a like service for the hotels and hospitals, but throughout the rest of the city the garbage lay scattered about in the back yards and alleys until it was hauled away with ashes and rubbish at irregular intervals.

# The Mayo Brothers

Dr. Charlie was sure that feeding the garbage to pigs would be a profitable enterprise. So, prodding the city council into requiring immediate disposal of garbage, he rented from John R. Cook thirty acres of sandy land and turned it into a feeding farm thoroughly equipped and stocked with purebred hogs. The garbage was collected from each house three times a week, scientifically treated to eliminate any possible source of infection, and then fed to the pigs.

Here too Dr. Charlie had to learn from experience. He lost more pigs than he sold until he learned to vaccinate them against cholera and to buy them when they were about ten months old instead of breeding them. Meat packers refused to buy his garbage-fed pigs until they had been inveigled into visiting the farm and seeing the methods in use, and then some of them refused to buy anything else. The farmers of the neighborhood complained of the competition and went so far as to institute court action, declaring the hog farm to be a public nuisance. But Dr. Charlie went serenely on his way.

When the income from the farm had repaid the investment in it, John R. Cook deeded the land to Dr. Mayo, who then turned the enterprise over to the city on condition that the proceeds thereafter be used to finance public health activities. By that time the farm with its equipment was valued at more than ten thousand dollars, was stocked with hogs worth five thousand dollars, and had more than two thousand dollars cash on hand. During the preceding year it had shown a profit of over seven thousand dollars. Dr. Charlie had certainly proved his point, to say nothing of having rid Rochester of one source of infection.

# CHAPTER SEVENTEEN

# Target and Magnet

It was a source of wonder to the members of the Surgeons Club that the Drs. Mayo with a worldwide reputation in medical circles should be so little known outside of them. As late as 1905 a *Minnesota* newspaperman could report that "Dr. C. H. Mayo of *Duluth*" had been elected president of the state medical society!

But early that year Samuel Hopkins Adams published in *McClure's Magazine*, for which he was then a staff writer, a popular account of contemporary surgery, in the course of which he told how medical men had awakened to the competence of American surgeons when a country doctor from Minnesota was able to match the figures of Hans Kehr, the greatest European authority on gallbladder surgery. Then briefly but dramatically he recounted the story of that country doctor and his brother, and of St. Mary's Hospital, the most remarkable institution of its kind in the country, handling more surgical cases annually than any other hospital in the United States, more even than the great Johns Hopkins.

*McClure's Magazine* was then at the peak of its popularity and influence because of such coups as Ida Tarbell's exposé of the Standard Oil Company and Lincoln Steffens' unmasking of the "shame of the cities." Naming medical names in such a spot was a violation of the profession's ethics, but the blame could hardly attach to the Mayos; they kept too good a company in Adams' article. John B. Murphy was there of course, but so were the irreproachable William W. Keen, Howard Kelly, and Maurice B. Richardson.

Then when Dr. Will was elected president of the American Medical Association the seemingly sudden elevation of a young man from an unknown western town to that position caught the attention of journalists, who smelled a story and followed the scent. The *Boston Transcript* skimmed the cream from Adams' article and from the accounts written by members of the Surgeons Club for a feature story, which was reprinted in other papers, including the *St. Paul Dispatch*. And a few months later a newspaper syndicate supplied its clients with a Sunday-supplement feature about the two "mischievous country lads" who had been "swift to rise" to the pinnacle of success.

Whereupon the doctors who had never been persuaded that the Mayos were anything but liars began to mutter about unethical advertising.

The boy-wonder tone of the newspaper accounts was offensive to Dr. Will, but quite apart from his personal reaction, enlightened self-interest demanded that the Mayos do what they could to head off this development. Such publicity might bring them more patients, but if they lost the respect and support of the medical profession the patients who came would be the credulous souls who formed the clientele of the quacks. The mere possibility of that filled the brothers with alarm. So they issued a brief statement, which was published in both state and national medical journals, disclaiming any responsibility for the newspaper articles, and they sought the advice of their lawyers as to possible legal redress. Somewhat amused, the lawyers informed them that such laudatory accounts could not be considered libel by any stretch of imagination.

2

The Mayos and their associates might refuse to talk, but they could not bottle up the enthusiasm of Rochester townsfolk or pleased patients or the members of the Surgeons Club. Their next appearance in the lay press was authored by Wilfred T. Grenfell, "the Labrador doctor," who paid a long visit to Rochester in February 1907 and then wrote the story of what he had seen and heard there for publication in the *Outlook* four months later. Naturally the humanity of the two brothers interested Grenfell quite as much as their surgical skill and astonishing reputation, and for the use of the writers to follow him he added another appealing story to the already familiar tale of the southern doctor who finally found in Rochester all the great specialists he had tried to consult.

A patient, after a most successful operation, was asked if he could afford to pay. He replied in the affirmative.

"What is the source of your income?"

"I mortgaged my farm to raise the money."

The check was accepted and the good faith thereby proved. But on returning home the man received a letter which contained not only his returned check, but one of a similar amount, as "a trifling help" towards the losses that had accrued to him and his family through his unfortunate illness.

Grenfell was already well known in America. He had published several books describing his missionary work among the deep-sea fisherfolk of Labrador, he was being decorated by the king of England that very year, and he was engaged in an extended lecture tour for the purpose of raising money for his medical mission. The *Outlook* was a popular weekly magazine among the educated classes. So the effect of the article was in nowise lessened by the editor's prefatory statement that "neither of the famous surgeons whose work and spirit it interprets had any knowledge that it was in preparation. . . . They are distinguished by their avoidance of public distinction."

The publisher of *Human Life*, a ten-cent monthly devoted to American success stories, was less thoughtful. His issue for April 1909 carried the stories of " 'Bill White' of Kansas," "James Stillman, Banker," "Samuel Gompers, Labor Leader"—and "The Mayos, Father and Sons, America's Most Remarkable Surgeons." The Mayo story began:

How would you feel if you were a millionaire, one of the richest men in the world, with an income almost too big to estimate, and with this great wealth you had a disease that baffled the physicians of this country; if in despair you had sought relief from the surgeons and physicians of France and England; if failing to find it you had finally gone to the greatest medical men in Germany, only to be told, after a thorough investigation, that your only chance of living for even a few months was to return to your own country and travel out into the West to the little town of Rochester, Minnesota.

You would be surprised, wouldn't you? . . .

And you would hasten homeward and speed across the country to that little town, and offer your fortune to those wonderful men, plural it is, who could save you when all other earthly beings could not, wouldn't you?

Well, this was the recent experience of one of America's financial masters, and it has been the fortune of a number of other famous men who have sought abroad in vain for cures for their ills, and returned to find the remedy here.

For several pages more the author raved about "those wonderful men." Not a single patient had ever died under their knife. They knew more than any other living surgeon, and their diagnosis was almost never wrong. They had been offered alluring titles and untold wealth from every quarter, the German government, even the Kaiser himself, having sought strenuously to persuade them to take up residence in Germany. They were wizards of surgery, the court of last appeal for the sick of all the world. And yet they gave as freely of their services to the poor who could pay nothing as to the rich who could pay well. "Here humanity reaches a common level. . . . You belong to the democracy of pain and you have come to the most democratic place imaginable."

That was quite enough in itself to raise a howl from the Mayos' critics, but to make matters still worse the publisher mailed marked copies to many of the nation's doctors and followed them up with letters soliciting subscriptions. Undoubtedly he meant only to suggest that *Human Life* sometimes carried items of interest to the medical profession, but by some weird process of reasoning many doctors took the free copies to mean that the Mayo brothers had authorized the story. The mail carried to the Masonic Temple offices a flood of accusations and quotations from the medical code about the bad ethics of advertising.

Once again the Mayos sought advice from their lawyers, but to no avail. The law could not help them. One of the attorneys said to them, "Do you suppose for a moment that the wizards of oil and finance would allow themselves to be commented on by the press in the way they are if they could prevent it? If they with all their money and influence cannot stop it, how can you expect to do so?"

So Dr. Will and Dr. Charlie did what they could. They prepared a statement of their case, including the written opinion of the lawyers verbatim, for publication in the *Journal of the American Medical Association* and sent reprints of it to as many doctors as they could. After reviewing their experience with journalists and denying any responsibility whatever for the disgusting exaggerations and untruths of the article in *Human Life,* they said:

It seems incredible that any fair-minded man in the medical profession could read this article and believe that we had anything to do with its production. . . . We consider any such supposition in regard to our integrity . . . an affront to our intelligence. . . . It is incomprehensible how anyone could suppose that two men over forty years of age and one at the age of ninety would deliberately take measures to discredit the work of a lifetime.

### 3

A dispassionate view of the matter finds sufficient explanation for the publicity without resorting to the belief that the Mayos had suddenly lost all regard for professional ethics. No magazine or newspaper editor could be expected to forego the use of such a Horatio Alger formula in the flesh, full of the honesty and humanity that appealed to readers in that markedly idealistic age, and of drama enhanced by the intriguing paradox of a country town that had become a foremost capital in the medical world.

Reasonable men in the medical profession understood and sympathized. In the midst of the furor over the article in *Human Life* Dr. Maurice Richardson expressed his understanding in striking fashion by sending the Mayos a copy of a Boston newspaper with his picture and a eulogy of his work sprawled full across the front page. But many men who could not make page one would not understand, and the Mayos became a bone of contention in medical circles.

Those who had grown hostile sneered that they were not great surgeons; there was nothing original in their work. They were just two more quacks out to get all the business they could, through advertising or any other means, however unethical. By adding so many partners and employees and hiring a layman as business manager they were commercializing the practice of medicine. Their adaptation of fees to income was nothing but cutting rates, and the provisions they made for the visiting surgeons, such as the mirrors above their operating tables, were only instances of their cheap showmanship.

According to these critics the Mayos padded their figures or got them by soliciting patients. Whenever they wanted to impress the profession by the number of their cases in some new field of surgery, they offered low rates in that field to entice patients away from "the country surgeons who were just as able to operate on them." One neighboring physician told a story about a railroad porter he was treating for kidney trouble. Deciding the kidney was tuberculous, he told the man he must have an operation, which would cost him one hundred dollars. The porter went away to think it over, and the next time the doctor saw him was when he came to report how fine he was feeling since he had had the kidney removed—in Rochester.

"You see what happened," said the doctor. "He met Charlie Mayo on the train and Mayo told him if he would come to Rochester for the operation they would do it for fifty dollars."

Another explanation rather more plausible is that when the porter told his fellow trainmen he must have an operation *they* advised him to go to Rochester for it. Of course, the opposition said the railway men of the Northwest were such enthusiastic boosters for the Mayos because the brothers conducted deliberate propaganda among them— ignoring the fact that with the things the trainmen saw and heard daily among their passengers they needed no coaching.

To all these charges the brothers' admiring friends simply answered, Go and see. The Mayos carry on their work with about as much privacy as goldfish in an aquarium, and if there is anything off-color in their practice members of the Surgeons Club ought to have found it out long since. As for the originality of their work, they do not *claim* to be original, though they might seem more so if they were not so uncompromisingly honest.

In that connection Dr. Haggard often told the story of the Polya operation for resection of the stomach, which Dr. Will was populariz- ing as the procedure of choice for stomach cancer. He devised and perfected it himself and had it all written up for publication, even had the illustrations drawn, when he discovered that a similar procedure had been described several years before in an obscure Hungarian medical journal. The author, an unknown surgeon, had tried it only a few times and his account had gone unnoticed, but Dr. Mayo im- mediately revised his article to give the operation the name of the Hungarian surgeon.

Naturally criticism of the Mayos increased in intensity in inverse proportion to the doctors' distance from them. It was most bitter in Minnesota, where the competition of Rochester was still strongest. It was humiliating for a St. Paul doctor, say, in introducing himself to some European surgeon to be met invariably with the question, "St. Paul, Minnesota. Is that anywhere near Rochester?" And it was irri- tating to watch one's patients take the train for Rochester the instant they were told they needed an operation. Resentment was only human, and but little less so was the tendency to put the worst construction upon the facts.

One unfortunate result of the increasing hostility was the stifling of unprejudiced criticism. Men who disapproved of some phase of the Mayos' work or differed from them on some point of technique were reluctant to say so openly lest they be classed with those who were jealous of the brothers' success.

After several years of worried efforts to prevent the publication of articles in newspapers and magazines and to counteract their untoward effects among doctors—to which Dr. Will once attributed his first gray hairs—the Mayo brothers decided to ignore it all. They would walk as circumspectly as possible, keep everything they did open for inspection, and let men say what they pleased. After all, as Dr. Will once said, "A target must arrest attention to be a target."

4

Two episodes for which the Mayos were clearly not to blame gave momentum to the rolling ball of publicity. The first derived its effect largely from a political situation of the moment. John A. Johnson was the most popular governor Minnesota had yet had. Although he was a Democrat and Minnesota was persistently Republican, he was elected to the office three times, once despite an overwhelming landslide for Theodore Roosevelt on the national ticket, and that feat had attracted the attention of national Democratic leaders, some of whom saw in the Minnesotan a hope of breaking the rule of Bryan and winning victory for the party. Johnson was persuaded to try for the nomination in 1908, and though the Bryan machine proved too strong for him he inspired such a demonstration of personal popularity that it was pretty generally believed he would be the Democratic candidate in 1912.

During the 1908 campaign the Republicans promised a downward revision of the tariff, but the Payne-Aldrich Act of 1909 was in effect just the opposite. In a speech at Seattle in September Governor Johnson, an advocate of tariff for revenue only, charged President Taft with violation of his campaign pledges in supporting the objectionable act, and the President, even then on a speaking tour to defend himself for his vastly unpopular action, replied with an attack on Johnson.

In the midst of that exchange, which aroused unusual interest because of the possibility that the two men might be opponents in the next election, the nation was surprised to learn that Governor Johnson was undergoing a major operation at St. Mary's Hospital in Rochester, Minnesota.

Several attacks of severe pain had warned him that no matter how crucial the political moment he dared no longer postpone a fourth resort to surgery. Dr. Will had already operated on him three times for an intestinal disorder stemming from a nearly fatal case of typhoid fever contracted when he was a country editor in St. Peter, and he and the Mayos were such warm friends that he was considered "one of the family" in Rochester. In 1907 he had appointed Dr. Will a member of the board of regents of the University of Minnesota, perhaps in the extent of its consequences the most important act of his gubernatorial career.

So naturally the governor went to Rochester for his fourth operation. He anticipated no trouble and confidently assured his associates that he would be back at his desk in the capitol in four weeks' time.

The two brothers joined forces to perform the operation, but they encountered unsuspected complications and were apprehensive about the outcome. So were those who witnessed the operation. Said Raffaele Bastianelli, personal physician to the king of Italy, "It was one of the most difficult and dangerous operations I have ever seen . . . a brilliant success, but I did not believe that the patient would recover."

For several days the issue hung in the balance, and the eyes of the nation were on Rochester. The case was front-page stuff for New York and Chicago papers as well as those of the Twin Cities, for President Taft had reached Minnesota and was paying tactful tribute to Governor Johnson every time he spoke. The people of the state were clamoring for news so constantly that the twenty telephone lines of the *St. Paul Pioneer Press* were busy all day long answering the inquiries.

Twin City and Chicago newspapers sent special reporters, their "brightest and brainiest," to Rochester, and those worthies hounded everyone for news, the Drs. Mayo, their associates, their friends and Governor Johnson's, even Mrs. Johnson herself. They sought out the members of the Surgeons Club who had watched the operation and sent back to their papers a succession of professional opinions, always including that of Signor Bastianelli. When they lacked personal news of Governor Johnson, they filled in with stories of the town, the hospital, the Mayos, and their other patients, and one of the St. Paul papers ran these separately as front-page spreads about Minnesota's "celebrated surgical specialists."

All this was a new experience for Rochester, and the local residents gaped at the tactics of the big-time gentlemen of the press, who paid the hackmen fancy prices to speed the tiniest bit of news from the hospital to the telegraph office and fought among themselves for control of the town's limited facilities for communication, paying some local man a dollar an hour to talk nonsense or read the Bible over the telephone so the line would be open whenever they had news to report.

For four days the doctors hoped for the governor's recovery, but on the afternoon of the fifth day he suddenly collapsed, and although Dr. Will, Dr. Charlie, and Dr. Judd worked desperately to rally his strength he sank rapidly to a point past hope. At two o'clock in the morning Dr. Charlie withdrew and went home. Mrs. Mayo was waiting up for him, and she never forgot the occasion.

Charlie came home in an awful state, saying that Governor Johnson couldn't live more than an hour longer. We were both just sick. I tried to tell Charlie he had done his best, all that he could, but that didn't help when the best hadn't been good enough. We had had an awful time with the newspapermen too; there were lots of them here and they would climb trees to look in the windows, and other annoying things like that. It was our first experience with them, and it was terrible.

While we sat talking the bell downtown began to toll. We both shook with a nervous chill. That was one of our bad times.

## 5

The Mayo brothers themselves were the central figures in the second episode. Late in 1911 on the way home from a meeting of the Southern Surgical Association in Washington, Dr. Charlie was taken suddenly and acutely ill in New York. He diagnosed his own trouble as gallstones, but the physicians called in to attend him said it was appendicitis, and Dr. Joseph Blake operated to remove the appendix.

The idea of the great surgeon himself in need of an operation caught the public fancy, and throughout the nation newspapers carried the story in detail. For a few days after the operation they printed the brief daily bulletins from the hospital announcing that Dr. Mayo's convalescence was progressing nicely.

Then came a sudden flurry of headlines: "Famous Surgeon Takes Turn for the Worse." "Condition of Dr. Mayo Alarming." "Dr. Charles Mayo Dying in the East." When the relapse occurred it was decided that Dr. Charlie did have gallstones after all and that he must undergo a second operation.

The news reached Dr. Will about four o'clock one morning, and he decided to go at once to New York, taking Florence Henderson, Dr. Charlie's anesthetist, with him. They left Rochester at four-thirty, riding a locomotive engine to Winona to catch the morning train for Chicago. Word of their journey preceded them and when they reached Winona a special train was waiting. The railroad men set themselves the task of breaking all existing records to get Dr. Will to his brother's bedside, and freight cars were shunted onto sidings and other passengers were made to wait while "Dr. Mayo's train" sped through on a cleared track.

The story had everything, or could be made to have it—irony, drama, sentiment, suspense—and the newspapers made the most of it. Dramatic headlines pictured the great surgeon lying at death's door, his anxious wife waiting in the next room, his loving brother racing with a nurse to his bedside. They traced the record-breaking journey mile by mile, even the last wild ride from the station to the hospital in the car of Dr. Raymond P. Sullivan, one of New York's great surgeons.

The only thing they missed was Dr. Will's wry comment that during the train trip he was afraid Dr. Charlie would not live until he arrived, but after Ray Sullivan began that mad dash to the hospital he feared *he* would not live to get there.

The journalists took this occasion to tell once more, on a wider scale than ever, the whole story of the Mayos and their hospital. They reminded their readers of Robert Herrick's novel *The Healer,* the story of a backwoods physician whose great skill and kindness drew so many patients to his humble abode that he had to build a hospital for them. Here was that very story come to life. Those efforts of "trainmen and railroad workmen along the line of steel stretching halfway across the continent to facilitate the lightning-like trip from Rochester" were not inspired by the surgeons' fame but by their heart-warming humanity. The railwaymen knew, sang the newspapermen, that the Mayos were doctors to whom the life of the laborer meant as much as that of the banker.

They repeated again the anecdotes made familiar by writers like Adams and Grenfell, said the Rochester clinic was the biggest in the country, and compared the crowds in its waiting rooms to those standing in line to get football tickets at a university stadium. They told their great lay audience that surgeons crossed oceans and continents to consult the Mayo brothers "about operations they had not the skill or courage to perform themselves." Said the *Mining Gazette* of Houghton, Michigan,

This all sounds like patent medicine advertising, does it? Well, it isn't. The Mayos are as adverse to advertising as the rest of their brethren profess to be, but we have heard too many stories of the kindness of the Mayos, have heard of too many cases where sufferers have been cured of their bodily ills, and where the Mayos failed to make the raid of their pocketbooks that is the usual accompaniment of surgery. We have heard too much of that to pass up this opportunity to say something about the Mayos.

When daily bulletins had traced Dr. Charlie's second convalescence, his removal from the hospital to a hotel, and finally his journey back to Rochester, the newspapers concluded the incident by voicing the thanks to Providence of "thousands and thousands who owe their lives and health to Charles Mayo."

6

That all the publicity did not prejudice the Mayos' standing with the leaders of their profession is apparent from the society officerships accorded them. Dr. Will became president of the American Surgical Association and Dr. Charlie of the surgical section of the International Society on Tuberculosis. Jointly they were elected president of the Society of Clinical Surgery and in succession president of the Clinical Congress of Surgeons of North America.

That Clinical Congress, initiated in 1910, was the brain child of Dr. Franklin H. Martin of Chicago, who planned it to give all American surgeons something analogous to the opportunity for clinical observation enjoyed by the exclusive Society of Clinical Surgery. The response was enthusiastic, and the numbers registering for the annual program of clinics soon mounted into the thousands. But it took only two sessions of the congress to reveal to all and sundry the chaotic state of American surgery. Knowledge and technique had advanced to the point of demanding special training or experience, but there were no requirements for a surgeon other than the M.D. degree. So no other qualifications had been set up for membership in the Clinical Congress, with the result that many unqualified surgeons registered for its sessions, causing many an embarrassing situation and violent disagreement over the acceptability of members and clinics.

Considering this state of affairs, Dr. Martin conceived the idea of organizing an American College of Surgeons like the royal colleges of England, Scotland, and Ireland. The purpose of the organization would be to establish such qualifications for election to its fellowship that the designation *F.A.C.S.* would signify to profession and public alike a competent practitioner of surgery.

The idea met with determined opposition from politicians in the established medical societies who were afraid of the possible competition, and from some sincere but misguided individuals who actually thought the formation of a group of specially qualified men was improper in a democracy. But with wholehearted support from the men of vision in the profession Dr. Martin put over his idea, and the American College of Surgeons became a fact in 1913.

Both the Mayos were among the active supporters of Dr. Martin's plan and both were included in the original body of fellows of the college. As a member of the committee on organization, Dr. Charlie became a member of the first board of regents and served in that capacity for many years.

It was probably their growing reputation among laymen that brought more honorary degrees—to both brothers from the University of Maryland and to the elder from the University of Michigan and Columbia University. But more to be valued than any degree was an enduring friendship that began when Dr. Will received the last of those. The other party to it tells the story:

We were standing in line at Columbia University in the City of New York at commencement in June, 1916, wearing borrowed academic gowns and about to receive degrees. Around us were a lot of notables whose faces we recognized. But we were put side by side and we looked at each other like a couple of dogs for a minute. Finally Dr. Mayo said to me, "I don't know what I'm doing here," and I said, "You've got nothing on me, neither do I." Then we both grinned and he said, "Who are you?" And I said, "To tell you the truth, I am just a country editor from a little town in Kansas called Emporia and my name's White." He grinned again and said, "Well, all right, I am just a country doctor from a little town in Minnesota called Rochester and my name's Mayo."

## 7

The publicity that made the Mayo brothers a target for the darts of resentful doctors made them also a magnet drawing patients to Rochester from all over the country. To this the brothers' many speeches contributed, for now that they were becoming known to laymen the newspapers found it worthwhile to publish what they said to medical societies, especially on subjects of general interest like Dr. Will's favorite topic, the curability of cancer of the stomach in its early stages.

The two brothers were speaking more often than ever. They sometimes appeared together on the programs of the American Surgical Association, but for the most part they kept to their established spheres of activity. To topics in the field of the upper abdomen and the intestines Dr. Will was beginning to add discussions of surgery of the kidney and the spleen, the latter a new field in which he was again pioneering for American surgeons.

Dr. Charlie continued to talk about everything from bunions to bladder tumors, but the subject rising rapidly to monopolize his bibliography and the one of most interest to laymen was surgery of the thyroid. By the end of 1908 he was able to report the results of one thousand operations for goiter. The period of trial and error in the field was over, and the major problems of surgical technique had been solved. Surgeons had learned how to control hemorrhage, how to avoid myxedema, how to escape tetany by leaving the parathyroid bodies intact—in short what to do and what not to do. Operation for simple goiter was now relatively safe in competent hands.

But nearly half of Dr. Mayo's thousand cases were operations for *exophthalmic* goiter, with a mortality of about five per cent. Only Kocher of Switzerland had a better record in that disease, and the usual record in the United States was a score or two of cases with a death rate often as high as twenty-five per cent.

Exophthalmic goiter was one of the most treacherous and perplexing maladies the surgeon had to deal with. Success in treating it did not depend on perfection of surgical technique alone, for no matter how flawless the operation, within a few hours an acute postoperative crisis might develop marked by high fever, vomiting, prostration, delirium, or coma. The patient might die in the crisis, or if not he was likely to be extraordinarily susceptible to complicating infections. This tendency to postoperative crisis was the principal cause of operative mortality in exophthalmic goiter, and there seemed to be no way of telling which patients would develop it; a rosy-cheeked, healthy-looking girl might die while a thin, sickly woman pulled through safely.

Because of that uncertainty a surgeon with a limited local practice did not dare to operate for exophthalmic goiter. He could not risk his reputation on an operation in which the death rate was so high, and his cases were too few for him to learn how to reduce it.

To improve his own results Dr. Charlie in 1908 adopted Kocher's graduated, or multiple-stage, operation, in which the removal of the gland was accomplished by degrees. The surgeon might begin by injecting hot water into the gland. If that produced too violent a reaction nothing more would be attempted, but if the patient responded fairly well the surgeon might in a day or two tie off the vessels on one side or both and then send the patient home. Or he might perform the ligation and a week later remove both lobes of the gland, or remove one lobe and later the second.

The extent of each installment and the interval between was determined by the condition of the individual patient. Feeling their way carefully, Dr. Mayo and Dr. Plummer slowly learned by experience to recognize little warning signs in the patient's appearance that told them how far it was safe to go at the moment, and gradually their mortality of operation dropped to about three per cent.

Reports of these results brought other surgeons to Rochester to see how Charles Mayo did it, but they were bewildered by the array of procedures he used. Why did he do this in one case and that in the next? Dr. Charlie and Dr. Plummer could not tell them. There was just something about the look of the patient that they had learned to recognize, but what it was not even Dr. Plummer could put into words. Consequently the method seemed very mysterious, and instead of trying it for themselves most of the men simply sent their patients to Rochester.

8

With refinement of the multiple-stage procedure, surgery had advanced about as far as it could without more knowledge of the pathologic processes involved in exophthalmic goiter. Dr. Plummer had been working on this problem from the beginning and had enlisted the essential aid of the pathologists. The theory that exophthalmic goiter is a disease of the thyroid gland had been demonstrated empirically by the relief of the symptoms following surgical removal of the gland, but it had not been proved pathologically, because no one had had more than a score or two of specimens to study. So Dr. Wilson began a systematic examination of every thyroid gland Dr. Mayo removed.

It was generally accepted that the function of the thyroid is to regulate the rate of metabolism, that is, the rate at which the body burns its food. Reasoning physiologically from that theory, Dr. Wilson was able by the time he had studied three hundred glands to tell from the appearance of the gland itself what the patient's symptoms had been. His guesses were so usually and precisely correct that Dr. Plummer's scientific conscience was satisfied that the thyroid was the mischief-maker in exophthalmic goiter.

Dr. MacCarty carried the work on from there, refining and standardizing Dr. Wilson's classification until he was able to give a routine pathologic diagnosis that Dr. Plummer could correlate with the clinical diagnosis. On the basis of such a correlation made systematically each year and his own astute observations in thousands of cases Dr. Plummer gradually came to a pregnant conclusion: The group of cases generally labeled exophthalmic goiter actually included two distinct diseases. One was an advanced stage of simple goiter, in which the thyroid was secreting too much of its normal product, and the other was true exophthalmic goiter, in which there was present not only too much thyroid secretion but in addition some abnormal product which by its toxic action produced the tendency to gastro-intestinal crises that complicated the surgical problem.

495

Other workers who had less clinical experience or whose practice lay outside the goiter belt, so that they saw relatively few cases of *simple* goiter, could not distinguish between those two groups, but Dr. Plummer could pick one from the other correctly in ninety per cent of the cases, his accuracy being determined by the differential pathologic diagnosis.

But there he stuck for the moment. To verify and expand his two-product theory he had to know what the normal product of the thyroid is and be able to measure it, and that was a problem for a specialist in biochemistry.

## 9

Because of those developments in Rochester Dr. Charlie was in great demand as a speaker on the thyroid. He was invited to address many state medical societies on the subject, particularly in the South and the Middle West, and the local newspapers always reported the substance of his remarks, adding the fact of his remarkable record in the removal of goiter.

Although family doctors no longer told a woman with goiter that she would die if she was operated on or would have a horrible skin disease or be "foolish" (myxedema) if she recovered, those ideas still lingered among laymen and they were desperately afraid of operations for goiter. Consequently the newspaper reports of Dr. Charlie's work and the increasing number of living examples of his skill intensified the magnetic properties of the Mayo name. "Mayo Brothers" and safety in a goiter operation became synonymous in the lay mind.

The adolescent daughter of a middle-class family in Fort Wayne, Indiana, began to display symptoms of an abnormal physical condition, and her mother took her to see a doctor one afternoon. When they returned and the father asked, "Well, what did the doctor say?" the mother began to cry.

"He says it's goiter. What will we do? It means an operation and that's so dangerous."

"Yes, it is. But never mind. We'll see some other doctors and if they agree the girl has goiter we'll put her right on the train and take her out to the Mayo brothers."

The mother's tears stopped short. "Oh, *could* we do that? Could we *afford* it?"

"If our girl has a goiter we *will* afford it."

That was the sentiment which sent such a stream of goiter patients to the Mayo brothers that pregnant women in Rochester were afraid to go downtown lest they mark their babies by their repugnance at the sight of the many big necks and protruding eyeballs. Operations on the thyroid mounted from a total of one thousand to five thousand in four years, and took the place of appendectomies as the most frequent operation in Rochester. Beginning in 1911 and for ten years thereafter thyroidectomies made up more than one tenth of the total number of operations performed by the Mayos and their associates.

## 10

The ripeness of time that is a leitmotiv in the story of the Mayos appeared in this spread of their reputation among laymen, for it coincided with a period of national prosperity. The rising values of farm lands, still a broad jump ahead of rising taxes, and the expansion of industry and commerce in the cities provided money for improving the comforts and conveniences of homes, for multiplying churches, colleges, and public libraries, for beautifying cities with parks and playgrounds and imposing buildings—*and* money for journeying halfway across the continent if necessary to see the doctor of one's choice.

Equally important was the increasing mobility of the population. The automobile was beginning to carry men's minds and bodies beyond their own back yards, even though low-powered models and unspeakably bad roads made a hundred miles a good day's journey. The railroads were adding to their established trunk lines a vast system of feeder rails and were improving their roadbeds and rolling stock to make train travel more comfortable and safe. Train wrecks were growing fewer, and long-distance travel by rail was becoming a matter of course.

So the people and the money came. The number of persons registering annually at the Mayo offices rose steadily to fifteen thousand in 1912 and then more than doubled in the next two years—the beginning of what those who experienced it can describe only as "an avalanche of patients." The office force found it exciting, never knowing what wealth or fame or far-distant place might be represented in the rush that followed each train's arrival.

All but one of them, that is. While Dr. Will was away one time his wife and Mrs. C. H. Mayo persuaded Dr. Charlie to discontinue the Sunday morning office hours, and when Dr. Will returned they talked him into approving the accomplished fact. Only Jay Neville refused to be reconciled to the change. While the rest of the staff scattered for the Sunday holiday he remained gloomily at his post in the office, and so received an eminent personage who arrived in a private railway car to consult the Drs. Mayo. Jay told him grumpily that "Will and Charlie" had gone to the country for the day, whereupon the personage declared that if one of them was not called back to attend to him he would return immediately to Chicago.

That was too much for Jay. He poured a torrent of wrath into the ears of the astonished would-be patient, ending with, "Take your goddamned private car and go to hell if you want to; we've got more patients now than we want."

The influx turned Rochester into a camp whose transient population annually exceeded by many thousands the number of its permanent residents, though that too was spurting upward. More and more the life of the town came to reflect the dominance of the Mayo practice. Cab drivers greeted new arrivals with the query, "Are you a patient or a doctor?" Restaurants put up signs requesting their patrons not to talk about their ailments at table. And wags made jokes like the one about a visitor who stopped to pet a kitten on the street. "Who do you belong to, kitty?" he asked. And kitty in true Rochester fashion replied, "May-ow, May-ow."

## 11

More registrations meant more work at St. Mary's, too much for the sisters to cope with alone. Nor was it right that the remarkable opportunities for training nurses should go unused, for the organization of the Minnesota State Nurses Association in 1905 showed that the direction of the wind was toward professional standards and licensing for nurses. Foreseeing a day not far distant when a staff of formally trained and registered nurses would be necessary to maintain the standing of the hospital, Sister Joseph decided it was time to institute a school for nurses.

The Drs. Mayo did not welcome the idea, for a reason Dr. Will gave some years later:

# Target and Magnet

Dr. Charlie and I had always done our surgical work with the Sisters' help, and we were much concerned as to whether anyone could be taught, even by the Sisters themselves, to perform the duties of the nurse as well as they. We had absolute confidence, then as now, in this group of women who have no thought outside their duty to the sick.

Through intelligence and devotion some of the sisters had acquired a truly astonishing facility in their work. Sister Joseph was the outstanding example, but Sister Fabian, who was in charge of postoperative dressings in the hospital, had developed an inexplicable sixth sense that told her better than the doctors' ordinary senses whether a patient was going to get well or not, and her wizardry at prognosis was a kind of last hope to which the Drs. Mayo and Judd clung when things were going wrong. Sometimes Dr. Charlie would go home much worried about a patient and say to his wife, "Things look bad for him, but Sister Fabian says he'll pull through all right and she's not often wrong."

Sister Joseph did not share the doctors' doubts about nursing care by lay women students; she thought the results would depend on the kind of person selected to superintend the school. One day, favorably impressed by the appearance and manner of a young woman in the gallery at Dr. Will's clinic, she was pleased to learn that the visitor was a Catholic and a nurse. Anna C. Jammé was her name, and she had just graduated from the new Johns Hopkins Training School for Nurses. Taking Miss Jammé on a tour of the hospital, Sister Joseph found her first impression confirmed by the young woman's intelligent questions and her reverence when shown into the sisters' chapel. The good sister thought she had found the proper head for a St. Mary's school of nursing, and Miss Jammé was not long on the job before the Mayos and their associates thought so too.

The school opened with a class of two, chosen from five applicants, on November 19, 1906. Three others were admitted four months later and eleven the following year, with applications already coming in from states as distant as New York and Oregon. The young women were given a two-year course that included two or three hours of classroom instruction a week, much of it from members of the Mayo staff, and all the nursing sisters, even Sister Joseph, took the first full course under Miss Jammé's supervision.

A maxim of the Mayo brothers much remarked upon by the members of the Surgeons Club was that good surgery kept a man in bed no longer than absolutely necessary, but the most rapid turnover they could achieve did not empty the beds at St. Mary's fast enough. Often several of the operations scheduled for a given morning had to be postponed simply because there were no beds available. The sisters were reluctant though to incur again the debt necessary to build an addition. Discussing the matter with the Drs. Mayo one day, someone suggested that a percentage of the fees received by the surgeons might properly be allocated to the hospital.

Under the circumstances the idea was not unreasonable. In the absence of a distinct organization bearing the name of Mayo, St. Mary's was the institution to which the brothers' fame attached. Many tributes directed to the Mayos were given publicly in terms of St. Mary's Hospital, and when any member of the Rochester group, including the Drs. Mayo themselves, published a paper, the author was always identified as "surgeon [or physician] to St. Mary's Hospital." It was quite natural, therefore, that some of the sisters should have an exaggerated notion of the part played by the hospital, important as that was.

But whoever made the suggestion was certainly not aware of the Mayos' views on fee-splitting. Dr. Will rejected the idea peremptorily and nothing more was heard of it.

It had given the Mayos food for thought, however. Thoroughly satisfied though they were with the nursing care provided for them at St. Mary's, they possessed no guarantee of security in their position there. Although it was largely their work that had given the hospital its worldwide reputation, there was nothing but a sense of moral obligation to keep the sisters from capitalizing on that reputation through the medium of other surgeons imported for the purpose. Dr. Will and Dr. Charlie did not anticipate any such eventuality, but they thought it might be wise to add another string to their bow.

They had just passed through a season marked by such a rush of tonsillectomies that neither offices nor hospital could furnish facilities for them. In the emergency Dr. Will appealed to his friend John Kahler, and one floor of the Cook House was turned into temporary hospital quarters, including a small operating room. The rooms were restored to hotel uses when the emergency passed, but the idea of a downtown hospital had been born.

It was nourished by the urgent need for additional hotel accommodations. A member of the Surgeons Club observed that every second house in Rochester had two or three of its rooms occupied by convalescent patients, their friends, or visiting surgeons. Even so there were not rooms enough, and the newspapers were reporting with pleasure that they got anxious inquiries every day from persons unable to find suitable lodgings.

Knowing such a situation could not long endure, Dr. Will suggested to John Kahler that he build a high-class convalescent hotel that could be turned into a hospital if the need arose. Kahler agreed and announced his intention of doing so, but he backed out when he learned that the building would cost much more than the forty thousand dollars he was willing to invest. (The location he had chosen was immediately taken over for the new YMCA building, which was the tangible result of a revival lately conducted by the Reverend "Billy" Sunday and toward which Drs. W. J. and C. H. Mayo had contributed a thousand dollars.)

Unwilling to give up the idea of a big hotel-hospital downtown, the Mayos decided to break their rule of not participating in Rochester business developments and invested ten thousand dollars in the venture to demonstrate their faith in it. F. A. Knowlton, the local drygoods merchant, then put in his residence on the corner across from the old Mayo home on Franklin Street and other Rochester businessmen contributed additional capital. The Rochester Sanatorium Company was organized and plans for the Kahler House went forward.

Meanwhile Mr. and Mrs. Charles Chute, finding their boarding-house filled to overflowing all the time, tore it down and built a sanatorium twice the size, but within six months that too was so overcrowded that the rooms were engaged as much as a week in advance. So the proprietors again doubled the size of the Chute Sanatorium, and in the new wing set apart a small "operating room" for the postoperative care of their patrons. Dr. Judd entered into residence as the house physician.

The Kahler House was opened two months later, in May 1907.

Sixty of its beds were set aside for hospital purposes and Dr. J. E. Crewe, the secretary of the Surgeons Club, and Dr. E. H. Beckman of the Mayo staff became the resident house physicians. Members of the Surgeons Club found the accommodations at the Kahler splendid, but the Cook House was still good enough for most of them, and much less expensive. Nevertheless it was soon necessary to enlarge the Kahler and add fifty hospital beds.

Although the facilities of the hotel included a completely equipped operating room, for the time being it was used only for dressing wounds; the Mayos continued to do all their operating at St. Mary's and their relations with the sisters remained unruffled. But the sisters did not miss the meaning of the operating rooms provided in the new sanatoriums, and plans were immediately prepared for a new wing to St. Mary's, which was opened the following year. It increased the capacity by a hundred beds, added several new laboratory rooms, and made available a third operating room to be used by Dr. Judd. The stringency in space was relieved—for the moment.

# CHAPTER EIGHTEEN

# The Clinic Takes Shape

The outstanding result of the tremendous increase in patients was the swift expansion of personnel in every phase of the practice. There was little of plan or fixed policy about it; the group just grew, as one man after another was added to keep pace with the work to be done.

Dr. Stinchfield was forced by ill health to retire in July 1906, and though he remained on call as a consultant in diseases of the heart and lungs it was necessary to get a new man in his place at the office. Dr. Herbert Z. Giffin, a graduate of Princeton University and of the Johns Hopkins Medical School who had served two years of internship, one at Johns Hopkins and one at the Children's Hospital in Philadelphia, was the Mayos' choice. After spending a month as assistant to Dr. Graham, Dr. Giffin was given an office of his own. He shared the work in general diagnosis with Drs. Graham and Plummer, but much of the examination of children fell to his lot because of his training, and most of the incidental local practice was left to him as the latest comer.

When Dr. Stinchfield's retirement occasioned a change in the partnership, Drs. Plummer, Millet, and Judd were taken into the firm as "participating partners," sharing to a specified extent in the income but not in the ownership of the practice; that remained vested in the Mayo brothers as the "principal partners."

For Dr. Millet the sharing was not long. The Bright's disease from which he had suffered for several years became suddenly acute early in 1907, and he was stricken blind one day while he was on duty in the hospital. His death soon afterward cut short a promising career and was a severe loss to the firm, for he had made a splendid beginning in the specialty of urology.

To succeed him the Mayos employed Dr. William F. Braasch of Minneapolis. Despite his record of graduation from the University of Minnesota Medical School, a year's internship in the Minneapolis City

Hospital, two years as assistant city physician in Minneapolis, and a year's study of diagnosis in Vienna, Dr. Braasch was still so young-looking that patients were reluctant to trust him. But the Mayos had been through that themselves and, being sure of his ability, they were unwontedly ostentatious in their demonstration of confidence. Presently they sent him on an extensive tour of eastern clinics to make a special study of methods in urology, and he was soon carrying Dr. Millet's work forward so successfully that two associate urologists had to be added to the group, Dr. Gilbert J. Thomas and Dr. John L. Crenshaw, each of whom had spent one year as intern or surgical assistant in Rochester before joining the permanent staff.

By 1909 there was need for another general clinician. One of the surgical assistants, Dr. J. Fletcher Robinson, himself an exceptionally able man of considerable experience beyond his internship, carried word of the opening to his friend, Dr. Arch H. Logan, who had been an intern when Robinson was a pathologist at Mercy Hospital in Pittsburgh. Dr. Logan, then teaching medicine at the University of Pittsburgh with the usual private practice on the side, was willing to change positions but not to join the Mayos, because from what he had heard he thought they and their associates were a disreputable bunch. Dr. Robinson soon disabused him of that notion, but by the time he had decided to apply for the position it was filled. Two months later he got a wire from Dr. Will asking him to report on January 1, 1910; the other man had not liked the job. Logan worked under Dr. Graham's supervision for a year and then set up the fourth diagnostic office.

The fifth was opened three years later in charge of a Twin City practitioner, Dr. Walter D. Shelden, who held his medical degree from Rush Medical College, had interned in the Cook County Hospital in Chicago, studied in Vienna for two years, and practiced medicine for fourteen years, the last ten of them in Minneapolis.

Around those five senior diagnosticians moved a growing group of clinical assistants and associates, some like the hospital interns on annual appointments and others in lesser positions on the permanent staff. They came from many places and with widely varying backgrounds. Dr. Leda J. Stacy, for instance, was a Rochester girl who after taking her degree at Rush and interning at a San Francisco hospital returned home to engage in private practice. The Mayos employed her as an anesthetist early in 1908, but within a few months Dr. Graham was so in need of help that she was transferred to the position of his assistant.

Dr. George B. Eusterman was a Minnesota graduate. After serving a year's internship in St. Mary's Hospital, another year as clinical assistant to Dr. Plummer, and another with Dr. Graham, he was named an associate in Dr. Graham's office. His place as clinical assistant to Dr. Plummer was taken by the latter's younger brother, Dr. William A. Plummer, fresh from the Northwestern University Medical School.

About the same time Dr. Alexander Archibald, a native of Ireland who had received his medical degree from the University of Edinburgh and taken his internship at an infirmary in England, and Dr. Harry G. Wood, a graduate of McGill University who had served two years' internship at the Montreal General Hospital and had been engaged in private practice for six years, were named full-time assistants to Dr. Giffin.

Dr. Robert D. Mussey came from Ohio, where he took his M.D. at the University of Cincinnati and served two years' internship at the Cincinnati Hospital. After another year as intern at St. Mary's Hospital and one in charge of postoperative dressings, he became assistant and then associate to Dr. Graham. And about a year later Dr. Lee Pollock, another graduate of the University of Minnesota, was employed as Dr. Logan's first full-time assistant.

2

So it went. By 1914 the permanent diagnostic staff numbered seventeen, and the clinical assistants were eleven. These men were all engaged in general diagnosis, each of them seeing all kinds of cases in whatever order they chanced to come. But a measure of specialization was developing among them as each found a field of special appeal to him. Dr. Graham's in gastro-intestinal disorders and Dr. Plummer's in diseases of the thyroid and the esophagus were already well defined; Dr. Giffin was beginning to give special attention to diseases of the blood and the spleen in addition to his work in pediatrics; Dr. Logan had carried over from his year with Dr. Graham a major interest in intestinal complaints, particularly of the colon; and Dr. Shelden was especially well versed in neurologic and psychiatric disorders. Although there was as yet little system for referring patients from one clinician to another, those with ailments in any of the above fields tended to gravitate into the care of the clinician whose major interest it was.

And with numbers in any one field came exceptional expertness. Dr. Plummer's facility in diagnosing exophthalmic goiter was uncanny, and Dr. Graham had become one of the world's best at the difficult task of differential diagnosis among diseases of the upper abdomen. He was so generally right that Dr. Will used to say he thought Kit Graham could *smell* a diseased gallbladder. When he asked him how he knew the trouble was gallstones, Dr. Graham could not tell; he had just developed the sixth sense that comes with accumulated experience.

In other disorders frequent repetition had made the signs so clear that an experienced nurse could guess the diagnosis. This was notably true in the case of duodenal ulcer, which the Rochester men were diagnosing readily before many in the medical world had come to appreciate the commonness of the malady, let alone recognize its symptoms.

A member of the Surgeons Club told the story of a South American dignitary who arrived in town accompanied by a large retinue of subordinates. He had sought the aid of several European specialists without benefit and on the recommendation of a German surgeon had come to try the Mayos. While Dr. Graham's assistant was taking the case history a nurse standing by remarked, "Why, it sounds like duodenal ulcer," and the young doctor agreed. Whereupon the mogul stalked from the office in a rage, saying he had not come halfway around the world to have his case diagnosed by a nurse when it had baffled the foremost surgeons of Europe. Members of his retinue managed to pacify him, however, and his personal physician was able to see for himself at operation that the nurse's guess was correct.

3

As the number of operations mounted the surgeons too needed more help, especially Dr. Charlie, who sometimes feared he would have time for nothing but removing goiters. Dr. Justus Matthews was brought down from the Minneapolis City Hospital and hired to do the ear, nose, and throat work, first under Dr. Charlie's supervision and later as an independent specialist, with Dr. Gordon B. New from the Hamilton City Hospital in Ontario to assist him. And Dr. Carl Fisher, a trained ophthalmologist, was employed to take over the diagnosis and, after a period of training under Dr. Charlie, the surgery in diseases of the eye, while Dr. Booker Granger (Dr. Booker had married George Granger in 1900) continued in charge of refractions of the eye until she became Dr. Charlie's deputy health officer in 1914.

Foreseeing that they would soon need more help in general surgery than Dr. Judd could give them, the Mayos sought another man they could train in their methods, and they found Dr. Emil H. Beckman. The officials of Minneapolis must have been startled when their able city physician and the chief internist of their city hospital resigned both positions to become an assistant to the Mayo brothers in Rochester.

Dressing the wounds of the convalescent patients who were crowding the smaller hotels and boardinghouses of Rochester was now enough to occupy the full time of one man, and Dr. Beckman was given that job for a few months. Then after a period of apprenticeship with the Mayos he became a full-fledged associate, first sharing Judd's operating room and later in a room of his own. The Surgeons Club then elected two more daily reporters to cover the work of the new men, both of whom rapidly gained nationwide reputations for judgment and skill but little short of the Mayos' own. A celebrated Scottish surgeon said of Dr. Beckman's technique, "It is as perfect as a professional's golf."

When Beckman moved into the operating room the work of postoperative dressings was taken over by Dr. Melvin S. Henderson, a graduate of the University of Toronto who was just concluding his internship at the City and County Hospital in St. Paul. "Beckman met me at the train," Dr. Henderson recalled, "and I thought he would fall on my neck, he was so glad to have someone take over the dressings." Dr. Henderson soon learned why; some days he dressed the wounds of from one hundred to one hundred and fifty patients. Unable to afford a horse and buggy, he made his rounds on a bicycle, lighting his way with an electric torch after the Rochester street lights were turned off. As he said, "The going was hard sometimes," and he was glad to transfer to an assistantship in surgery.

# The Mayo Brothers

The Mayos were naturally choosing their new men from among the graduates of medical schools whose faculties and standards they knew: principally the University of Minnesota, the Johns Hopkins Medical School, and the University of Toronto, with whose staff Dr. Will became acquainted when he went there to receive the honorary degree they bestowed on him. A second man came from the Canadian school in 1907, Dr. Donald C. Balfour, a classmate of Dr. Henderson's. After a year as an assistant pathologist Dr. Balfour was transferred to a clinical assistantship in the offices downtown, to take charge of the postoperative dressings of ambulatory patients. Like Dr. Henderson he had only an annual appointment and expected to leave at the end of the year, not in the least aware that his work was carefully watched and discussed by the Mayos. But one day Dr. Will walked into his little office.

"We'd like to have you stay with us, Balfour. We think you're the kind of man we want here. We've noticed that patients like you; they come back to say good-bye to you when they're ready to leave." Dr. Balfour was quite willing to stay and soon joined Dr. Henderson as an assistant in surgery.

They performed some of the simpler operations, tonsillectomies and an occasional appendectomy perhaps, but for the most part they served as first assistants to the attending surgeons, including Dr. Will with increasing frequency as Sister Joseph began gradually to retire from her operating-room post. Then one summer, about 1911, while Drs. C. H. Mayo and Judd were out of town Dr. Beckman suddenly fell ill, and Dr. Will had to have independent help immediately. Knowing his man, he unhesitatingly called Dr. Balfour into the breach, and in the words of one of Balfour's associates "He turned out to be a wonder. He performed a series of more than two hundred operations without a single death." The following year he was made an attending surgeon.

The Mayos had never been satisfied with the work they were doing in orthopedic surgery, though it was on a par with that elsewhere in the country. Dr. Will used to say orthopedists were not surgeons at all, just "saddlers and harness-makers" who covered up with contrivances of leather and steel the deformities they could not correct. So he was warmly enthusiastic about the work of Robert Jones of Liverpool when he saw it on his trip to England in 1907. Jones was applying real surgical principles to the treatment of deformities, and doing it so successfully that the number of his patients forced him to specialize in orthopedics. Dr. Will thought him "one of the greatest surgeons it has been my good fortune to meet," and talked so much about his work during the rest of the trip that some of the English surgeons went to visit Liverpool themselves and returned home to improve their own work in orthopedics.

Of course Dr. Will was anxious that Jones's ideas should be applied in Rochester, but at the moment there was no one with sufficient leisure to develop the specialty, which is slow and time-consuming work. Dr. Mayo may have suggested it as a possibility to Dr. Henderson—it was his way to drop suggestions of that sort—or Henderson may have retained an interest in the field from the time of his apprenticeship under Dr. Arthur J. Gillette, the St. Paul orthopedist whose influence made Minnesota the first state in the Union to treat crippled children at public expense.

At any rate, when Dr. Henderson declared his desire to specialize in orthopedics the Mayos were delighted. They assigned him to work for a year with Dr. Judd, who was doing most of the orthopedic surgery at the time, and then sent him to England for six months' study under Robert Jones, Harold Stiles of Edinburgh, and Arbuthnot Lane of London. When he returned all the work in orthopedics was turned over to him, and he began the development of a new surgical specialty in Rochester.

Once these men, and those who came after them, had been given equal standing with the Mayos as attending surgeons, their cases became entirely their own. Neither of the brothers ever interfered to dictate the operative procedure or aftercare, though they were willing to give advice when it was asked for. And of course their associates asked for their advice all the more willingly on that account.

### 4

The chance to observe at close hand over an extended period the work that experienced surgeons found it worth time and travel to watch for a few days made the surgical assistantships at Rochester worth much more in experience than the hundred dollars a month they paid, and the Mayo brothers never lacked applications from able, well-trained young men. Some of them have testified to the "priceless and inspiring experience" that was theirs during their service with the Mayos. Apart from the daily clinical lectures the brothers did little instructing by precept; they chose to let association do its own teaching. They might give a word of advice or mild criticism sometimes, but never a reprimand or scolding about mistakes. Dr. Will believed that any man worth his salt would recognize his own errors and learn from them, and if he could not it was of little use to point them out to him.

Neither brother had the prima donna temperament. "No surgeon should allow himself to be irritated," said Dr. Will. "When I feel irritated I always tell a funny story, anything that will take my mind from the irritating incident." So in the Mayos' operating rooms there was none of the profanity and tantrums that were the rule with many operators. In pleasant contrast to the German surgeon notorious for his habit of throwing knives at his assistants when they displeased him is this picture of Dr. Charlie given by one of his assistants:

I can vividly remember my first nervous clumsiness as his assistant when he suddenly interrupted the curious mixture of half-scientific and half-popular medical lore with which he delighted his crowded theater to whisper in my ear: "You're doing fine; so long as you don't drop the bits on the floor I don't mind."

And of Dr. Will another assistant wrote:

To me he is the greatest personality I have ever known or ever expect to know. I have felt that it was worthwhile studying medicine merely for the sake of having the opportunity of standing across an operating table from him as his assistant. Even as I write . . . I can see his grave, yet kindly face, and those keen blue eyes as he used to look quizzically into mine from time to time while we were struggling with some difficult problem of surgical technique. . . . He was the soul of kindness always. He never spoke an unkind word to me in the operating room, yet the provocation was on occasion surely great.

The assistants profited almost as much from the hospital rounds they made with Dr. Will and Dr. Charlie as from the operating-room experience, for the two brothers, each in his own way, had become consummate masters of the art of handling patients. One or the other of them visited every patient at least once a day during his stay in the hospital, and oftener if necessary. The great and the wealthy took this attention for granted, but it was not reserved for them, and to lowlier ones the daily visit from "my doctor" with his word of cheer, little joke, or just his attentive, sympathetic ear became a vivid memory to be talked of or written about many years later.

Sometimes on Sunday mornings Dr. Charlie took two or three of his children along with him on his rounds. He was always more informal, more chatty, in his visits than Dr. Will, and his assistants never knew what amusing incident the morning's calls would bring forth. This is a memory one of them treasured:

Years ago when we were making rounds in St. Mary's we called in the room of a large and fat dowager who seemed to be dissatisfied with nearly everything in spite of every effort to please her. She was endowed with unusually immense and pendulous mammary glands one of which Dr. Charlie had removed because of carcinoma. She was all set for him when he entered the room and began a tirade of vituperation because of the "fearful disfigurement," the "intolerable mutilation," etc., etc., stating she wished she had never come to Rochester. In any event, she wanted to know what could be done to re-establish her former rather ample figure.

After cogitating a few minutes and with perfect seriousness, Dr. Charlie said, "Well, you might stuff in a little hay." Then patting her on the shoulder and with that infectious smile, so expressive of his sincere friendliness, he immediately won her over.

## 5

As more clinicians saw more patients they requested more analyses of the urine, blood, and sputum, and the number of young women at work as technicians in the clinical laboratory, which was still under Dr. Plummer's supervision, rose from one to five—in spite of the fact that ordering laboratory tests was by no means a routine procedure and that only a few of the tests commonly used today were known. Commensurate with the increase in patients as a factor in the expansion of laboratories in Rochester were the new procedures made available by the continuous progress of medical science and the education of clinicians in the use of them.

For example, the diagnostic uses of the x-ray were increasing rapidly. Through techniques for rendering the soft parts and cavities of the body opaque to the ray, it was becoming possible to detect organic abnormalities as well as the presence of foreign bodies or fractures.

# The Mayo Brothers

The first x-ray diagnosis of cancer of the stomach in Rochester was made about 1909 by Dr. Vernon J. Willey, the roentgenologist employed to carry on the x-ray work under Dr. Plummer's direction. Dr. Eusterman, who as Plummer's clinical assistant administered the bismuth meal and with Dr. Willey watched its progress through the digestive tract, recalls his excitement when he was easily able to recognize the presence and location of a gross tumor. "I always had faith in the x-ray thereafter."

Led to hope that improvement of this technique might make possible the ready diagnosis of gastric cancer in its operable stages, Dr. Will gave special encouragement to the use of the x-ray, and development was rapid, especially after Dr. Russell D. Carman, a St. Louis physician who had published several contributions to roentgenology, was engaged to take full charge of the laboratory. Carman was original and thorough. In order to check his readings of the x-ray pictures with the actual physical conditions, he followed the patients to the operating table and the specimens to the surgical pathology laboratory. His work quickly became one of the attractions for visiting surgeons, who thought they saw the reason for his excellent results in the number of mugs that had to be filled with the bismuth stuff for one day's work. Soon Carman was kept so busy with the x-ray diagnosis of gastro-intestinal diseases that he had to have two associates to take over the rest of his work.

For several years Drs. Wilson and MacCarty performed all the varied duties of general pathologists, doing the surgical pathology and the autopsies and whatever else they could manage in the time left over. In spite of their best efforts and intentions they could not keep up with the possibilities in the rapidly maturing fields of bacteriology and biochemistry. They hopefully bought a new bacteria incubator, for instance, but they could find no time to use it, except as a convenient storage space for record blanks. "We couldn't do everything and pick the chickens too," quoted Dr. Wilson to describe the situation.

By this time Paul Ehrlich, applying the principle of the benzene ring to the chemistry of living cells, had announced his side-chain theory of immunity, and one of its first offspring was a reliable diagnostic test for syphilis devised by August von Wassermann. Since in its original form the Wassermann test was a long, involved procedure that took considerable learning, the Rochester men had to turn once more to the laboratories of the state board of health for help. Obviously another pathologist, preferably one trained in bacteriology, was needed.

Dr. Thomas the urologist sent word of the opening to his friend, Dr. Arthur H. Sanford, who was teaching physiology at Marquette University. Having the desired training in bacteriology and being interested in the possibilities of laboratory diagnosis as a specialty in medicine, Dr. Sanford went to Rochester for an interview with Dr. Wilson, who found his qualifications eminently satisfactory, especially when he learned that Sanford knew how to perform the Wassermann test. Two extra rooms were rented above a storeroom near the Masonic Temple offices, and there in August 1911 Dr. Sanford opened a second clinical laboratory, for work in bacteriology and its budding branches, serology and parasitology.

At about the same time gastric analysis was rescued from its stepchild state. Although the pathologists had taken over the work of making the chemical analyses, the urologists were still doing the tubing, for no logical reason but simply because they had inherited the task from Dr. Millet. Now a separate gastric analysis laboratory was opened in the basement of St. Mary's Hospital, and Dr. Frank Smithies, the demonstrator of clinical medicine at the Universiy of Michigan, was engaged to manage it.

When another experienced pathologist had been employed to take charge of the necropsies, Dr. MacCarty was free to specialize as he wished in surgical pathology and Dr. Wilson to give more time to his administrative duties and general research problems. The varied functions had been distributed, and a group of specialists had replaced the general pathologists.

6

Those various laboratories were set up for the sole purpose of aiding in diagnosis. Each urinalysis, x-ray picture, or fresh-tissue examination was made as a purely clinical performance. Yet, given men with scientific curiosity and professional vision, research was an inevitable byproduct because of the volume of data accumulated in the clinical processes. Findings from thousands of blood counts or thyroid specimens invite, indeed demand, analysis and induction. And to research of that sort the Mayos gave wholehearted encouragement from the beginning, because it was merely an extension of the review of cases the brothers had always tried to practice themselves.

The development of independent research based on experimentation came more slowly because it was less urgent, and because Dr. Will was of two minds about it. Incidental investigations immediately related to some specific clinical or surgical problem he considered legitimate, but he could not decide how far beyond that the Rochester group ought to go. After all, they were engaged in the private practice of medicine; they were not an endowed or a state institution.

The principal trouble was a conflict between Dr. Will's intellect and his emotions. His mind forced him to recognize the truth of Dr. Plummer's and Dr. Wilson's contentions that a research program was necessary to the vitality of the group, that it would broaden the horizon of every member of it and keep alive in him as much scientific curiosity as he was capable of feeling, and that it would go far toward keeping the practice from sinking to routine on the dead level of present knowledge. But, like many practicing physicians, in his heart Dr. Will resented the collective arrogance of the "pure research" men in assuming that the pursuit of knowledge which may bear fruit in some distant future is necessarily more commendable than efforts to relieve pain and disability in the present. He admitted the value of what he called abstract research, but he preferred "investigative research that will benefit the patient, even if no more aristocratic than the improvement of methods of handling fistula in ano."

Nevertheless, he came step by step to support an extensive development of experimental laboratories staffed by full-time research men.

Dr. Wilson began work in experimental pathology and surgery shortly after going to Rochester, keeping his animals in the basement of St. Mary's Hospital. But he could never be sure of the state of his subjects, for the kindhearted sisters would slip them extra bits of food and sometimes even let them out of their cages. While he was making plans to build a new barn at his farm home in 1908 it occurred to him that he might include space there for the animals, and he offered to do so if the Mayos would contribute five hundred dollars to the cost of the structure. They did, and Dr. Wilson fitted up accommodations for the monkeys, rabbits, rats, and guinea pigs on the second floor of the barn, including also an operating room and a small laboratory. The Wilsons' big barn became a landmark in the community, viewed more than a little askance by some who had more feeling than knowledge about vivisection.

When the experimental work threatened to become one of the chickens Dr. Wilson couldn't pick, Dr. Charlie proposed that they ask John W. D. Maury, director of the laboratory of experimental surgery at Columbia University, to take it on. And Maury accepted the offer. But two years later when he changed his name to John W. Draper and went back to occupy an endowed chair of experimental surgery at Columbia the animal experimentation became once more incidental to the necropsy service.

Then one day Dr. Wilson received a letter from the professor of pathology at Indiana University. Was there an assistantship in pathology available for an exceptionally able Indiana graduate? There was, replied Dr. Wilson; tell the young man to come right on. It took no more than two months to convince Dr. Wilson that keeping Frank C. Mann on an assistantship was a waste of time and talent, so despite his youth Dr. Mann was put in charge of the work at Wilson's barn, and experimental medicine in Rochester was really on its way.

7

Almost in the same mail Dr. Wilson received another letter, from Edward C. Kendall of New York City, a young research chemist looking for a new position. After taking his Ph.D. in chemistry at Columbia in 1910 he had gone to work for a pharmaceutical manufacturing concern, where he was set the task of isolating the active constituent or hormone of the thyroid gland. Irked by the conditions of employment in a business firm, he left at the end of a year to take a minor post in a New York hospital, which, though it paid little, at least allowed him to order the materials he wanted. He had made considerable progress on his thyroid problem, and it had been suggested to him that the Mayos might have a place for him. Did they?

Isolation of the active product of the thyroid gland was what the Rochester men interested in exophthalmic goiter were waiting for. Two fellowship men had tackled the problem and were making some progress with it, but it was exceedingly difficult. Only one of the ductless glands had yet been made to yield the secret of its hormone to the chemists. Two Johns Hopkins pharmacologists had isolated adrenalin in 1901, but once done that was seen to be a relatively simple matter, for adrenalin lies loose in the adrenal glands, just waiting to be taken out. The hormones of the other endocrine glands, including the thyroid, are so tightly bound into the glandular secretions that isolating them seemed almost a hopeless task. If Kendall had made the progress he thought he had, it would be a good idea to give him a chance to go on with his work at Rochester. So Dr. Wilson wrote him to come out for an interview.

He arrived carrying in his pocket a test tube full of a whitish substance that he had obtained by treating thyroid glands with sodium hydroxide. This residue exhibited all the physiological properties of thyroid extract, and he felt sure that with further refinement it would yield the essential constituent.

Dr. Plummer was all for putting him to work at once, but Dr. Will demurred. He was not sure they were ready to undertake a program of biochemical research in Rochester at that very moment; they had better give the matter some further consideration. Then Dr. Charlie added his voice to Plummer's: Kendall had a big job half done and he would like to see him get on with it without delay—in Rochester. In the end Dr. Will capitulated and Dr. Kendall was hired.

That was in February 1914. Within a very short time Dr. Kendall discovered that barium hydroxide was the proper agent for purifying his material and raising the iodine content of the residue, and by December he had obtained a compound containing forty-seven per cent of iodine. But each treatment with barium hydroxide reduced the amount of his material, and there was now such a small fraction left that another treatment would dissipate it entirely. So he decided to try to crystallize something from the fraction he had.

Being a true member of that "queer breed of cats," the research men, Dr. Kendall could think of no pleasanter occupation for Christmas Eve than this experiment. He dissolved his pinch of material in alcohol and put it in a crystallizing dish over a steam bath. Then while waiting for the liquid to diminish to a small volume he fell asleep. When he woke up he went into action in a hurry, for the alcohol had entirely evaporated. He added more at once, but a marked change had occurred; a crust of white material had formed that would not dissolve in alcohol. Before throwing it away Dr. Kendall analyzed it—and found it contained sixty per cent of iodine!

Christmas Day or not, the next morning found him in his laboratory early. He dissolved the precious little crust in a mixture of alcohol, acetic acid, and sodium hydroxide, and the crystalline substance that resulted proved to be the active hormone of the thyroid gland. He later named it thyroxin.

Excitement rose high in Rochester then. It was decided to repeat the experiment on a larger scale in order to secure enough thyroxin to test its properties thoroughly; Dr. Kendall was moved into a larger room, and the necessary vats and supplies of glandular material were secured. But try as he would he could not repeat his experiment successfully. For more than a year he worked at it, so entirely in vain that he sometimes wondered whether he had dreamed that Christmastime success. Then he discovered, again by accident, that carbon dioxide was the agent needed to cut the bond fastening thyroxin into the protein molecule.

Well and good, that problem was solved. But where had the necessary carbon dioxide come from in his first success? The question nagged at Dr. Kendall until he finally remembered there was an automatic microtome in the room he had been working in. Unbeknown to him the freezing chamber of that instrument had provided the dash of carbon dioxide needed to release the thyroxin.

Dr. Kendall admits that though he is not superstitious he has often in the years since 1914 dropped into his laboratory on Christmas and other holidays, "just to see whether anything might turn up."

The isolation of thyroxin was of tremendous importance, quite apart from the therapeutic possibilities of the compound. In Rochester it provided the basis for the next big step in the treatment of exophthalmic goiter, it contributed immeasurably to the reputation of the Rochester clinic for achievement in medical science, and it won the support of all concerned for the development of research activities as an integral phase of the clinic's program. In the world of medical science generally it served as an impetus to the development of endocrinology, for it demonstrated the possibility that the ductless glands could be made to yield the secret of their functions.

# The Mayo Brothers

8

Along with the expansion of the professional group went the steady development of accessory services. While Dr. W. W. Keen of Philadelphia was convalescing from his abdominal operation, Dr. Will asked him one day, "Now that you've seen what we're doing here, what improvements would you suggest for us?"

"You ought to write more, make more reports to the profession, all of you," was Keen's recommendation.

Write more! Dr. Will had long preached that preparing a paper was of immeasurable value to the writer, but he and Dr. Charlie well knew how laborious a task it was to assemble the data and get them into words. Although each member of the staff had a half day or a day a week off for reading and study, it was all he could manage in that time to keep up with the outpouring of medical literature.

Soon after joining the staff Dr. Giffin suggested that it would help if the men shared their reading through reports at a weekly meeting. The Mayos immediately approved the idea, asked Dr. Giffin to take charge of the programs, and opened their homes turnabout for the gatherings, since none of the office rooms was large enough. At each meeting several members of the group summarized for discussion the current periodical articles they had been asked or had volunteered to read, and their abstracts were filed for future reference. Members of the Surgeons Club privileged to attend one of these weekly sessions thought they saw in them the explanation for the extraordinary knowledge of medical literature that impressed them in the Mayos and their associates.

But the sessions also revealed the ineptness of some members of the group in extracting the essence of an article and reporting it without distortion. If they were to write more, and of a kind it would not be a disservice to the group to publish, they must have assistance and supervision of an expert sort. The question was where to find it. Dr. Will took the problem to his friend Ochsner, who immediately recommended Mrs. Maud H. Mellish. She was just concluding a year's work for him, cataloging the Augustana Hospital library and helping him prepare a book for publication. Quick to recognize her intelligence and ability, Dr. Mayo invited Mrs. Mellish to take on the job at Rochester at his first meeting with her.

# The Clinic Takes Shape

The offer came at a psychological moment in her life. As a child, the youngest of seven in a Swedish family living near Faribault, Minnesota, Annie Maud Headline displayed such marked strength of mind and character that her intelligent parents allowed her unusual independence in ordering her own life, and came to rely much upon her advice in directing their own. She decided early that she wanted to study medicine. Lacking money enough for that and discouraged from it by doctor friends who did not think it a proper vocation for a woman, she chose the nearest thing to it, nursing.

She decided to take her training at the Presbyterian Hospital in Chicago, "because the hospital opened into Rush Medical College," and throughout her course she attended all the medical school lectures she could gain admission to. Many of the Rush professors, including the great Moses Gunn and Charles T. Parkes, impressed by her persistence and her unusual abilities, became her warm personal friends.

After a year's work as superintendent of a children's hospital in Chicago, she married Dr. Ernest J. Mellish, whom she had met as a student at Rush. For sixteen years she put her training to use in assisting him, and Dr. Mellish once recorded in his diary, "Maud is of inestimable aid to me in revising my papers. I am sure they are much more readable for the revision. There are no superfluous words left in them."

When Dr. Mellish died in 1905 his wife was forty-three. She did not want to return to nursing, and she felt it was too late to take a formal course in medicine. Accepting temporary employment with Dr. Ochsner, she resolved to take the first real offer that came to her in any line connected with medicine. That offer was the one from the Mayos.

Mrs. Mellish did not want to go to Rochester, but she was determined to abide by her resolve, and besides she was attracted by the extraordinary form of Dr. Mayo's offer. After outlining his problem he said to her, "Come up, look us over, and see what you can do that you think we most need to have done."

She arrived in Rochester on March 1, 1907. Her introductory tour of the offices included the "library," which contained an easy chair, a table, a few straight chairs, and one revolving bookrack on which were arranged a miscellany of medical books and magazines. Was that the extent of the book collection? she asked. Why yes, it was. Of course each member of the staff had his own library, and there were some reprints and back numbers of periodicals around somewhere. Mrs. Mellish's quick imagination saw the room *lined* with books and in use as a real library workroom for the staff, and she suggested that her first task be to assemble and centralize a collection of essential reference materials. The Mayos agreed enthusiastically, promised her a free hand, and offered their personal libraries as a nucleus.

The next morning Mrs. Mellish set out to find the old reprints and journal numbers. The care of those, along with the filing of the correspondence, had been entrusted to old Jay Neville. Asked where they were, Jay led Mrs. Mellish to the coalbin in the cellar.

Maud Mellish was a tall, handsome woman, regal in appearance and in manner, but she never hesitated to do anything that had to be done. She went right to work in the coalbin. With Jay's grumbling help, she separated the papers from the coal, stacked them, and carried them to the room upstairs. There she cleaned, sorted, and classified them, arranging them in convenient files. She ordered missing numbers to complete the periodical sets and had them bound in annual volumes; she bought book shelves, books to fill them, and more tables and chairs; she arranged to borrow reference materials from other libraries.

Then she was ready to give the group editorial assistance in their writing and publishing. Her view of this task did not stop with checking grammar and punctuation. Medical writing at the time was uniformly bad, and medical editing was usually only incidental to some doctor's practice or some publisher's business interests. Consequently medical literature was almost entirely lacking in distinction of style and often in coherence and accuracy. With a few exceptions, the Rochester group showed these defects of their profession, and Mrs. Mellish set herself the task of seeing to it that they said what they meant to say, that they were accurate in their facts and their references to the works of others, and as far as possible that they were straight in their thinking.

She was a severe critic, never minced words in expressing her opinion, and was inclined to be highhanded in correcting and revising. Like most authors, the Rochester men did not welcome such interference. But the Drs. Mayo, quick to recognize the improvement she worked in their own papers, backed her loyally, and the others came gradually to appreciate her assistance. In time it became an accepted policy to refer all papers to Mrs. Mellish for revision before submitting them for pub-

# The Clinic Takes Shape

lication, and then the editors and readers of medical journals began to remark upon the uniform technical excellence, the clarity and readability of papers emanating from the staff of St. Mary's Hospital.

In 1909 Mrs. Mellish undertook to issue a volume of collected papers, comprising the publications of the group from 1905 to 1909 and including some of the reprints she had rescued from oblivion in the coalbin. The problem of a title was discussed at length. Should it be *The Collected Papers of Drs. Mayo, Graham, Plummer, and Judd?* Hardly. Instead it was decided to adopt the name given the group by members of the Surgeons Club and to call the book *Collected Papers by the Staff of St. Mary's Hospital Mayo Clinic*. It was the first of a series of annual volumes that still continues.

## 9

Another step in the evolution of the group's name took place about 1912. Although the Mayos and their partners inaugurated their various assistantships solely as a means of securing additional help, they gradually became conscious that they had an obligation to the young men who held the positions. They came to realize that the effective training of these assistants was part of the professional and social responsibility that Henry Plummer insisted the development at Rochester entailed.

Dr. Will evidently had the problem on his mind during one of his trips east, because the morning after his return he wandered into the pathology laboratory to talk it over with Dr. Wilson and Dr. Beckman. He said he had been impressed anew with the undesirable status of interns, residents, and house physicians in most eastern hospitals. They seemed to spend their days in subservient yessir-ing, in being flunkies for the permanent staff. He did not want any such attitude to prevail at Rochester, and he thought it might help if they called the men something other than interns or assistants.

Dr. Beckman suggested the term in use at Oxford University, *fellow* from the Middle English *felawe* meaning comrade or companion. That appealed to Dr. Will. But fellows of what? Certainly not of Drs. Mayo, Graham, Plummer, and Judd. And "fellows of St. Mary's Hospital Mayo Clinic" was not much better. Well, why not just "fellows of the Mayo Clinic"? So that is what they became.

A committee was formed to supervise their training, with Dr. Beckman as chairman and Drs. Plummer, Wilson, and Sanford as members. They were to select the new men, assign them to services, and schedule lectures and conferences to supplement the practical experience of the fellowship. They worked out a three-year rotation by which each fellow would spend one year in pathology, one in diagnosis, and one in surgery, but the plan was left flexible enough to be adapted to each man's special interests. Enough fellows were to be appointed so that each of them could spend one third of his time in the laboratories. As was their custom, the Mayos sent Dr. Wilson on a tour of the United States and then of Europe to study the methods and standards of such postgraduate training elsewhere.

## 10

Almost simultaneously with Mrs. Mellish's coming a new system of keeping records was installed. The old ledger system had served well enough when the staff numbered three or four and the patients a thousand or two a year, but as the numbers grew it proved intolerably cumbersome. When a patient returned for a second examination, if his memory did not supply the exact date of his former visit the doctor had to leaf through several volumes to find the earlier records. And then there was little room for additional data. The findings of return visits had to be scribbled in like a marginal wreath around the original case history.

Worse still, the records were not complete in one place; the clinical history was set down in Dr. Graham's book perhaps, the laboratory findings and x-ray readings in several others, the surgical record out at St. Mary's. To make a study of case records on any given subject required a time-consuming and irritating search in many places. Perhaps the findings had not been recorded at all, or so sketchily as to be of no use beyond the immediate moment and immediate clinician. The possibilities of the records as a resource for the study of disease and treatment were not being realized.

The great volume of the practice and the brothers' tremendous reputation were making St. Mary's Hospital a kind of national proving ground for hospital and surgical procedures. Other practitioners seeking to determine the worth of some technique or instrument would write to ask or go to see how it had worked out in Rochester. That being so, the Mayos owed it to the profession and to society as well as to themselves to make their records as complete, accurate, and readily accessible as possible.

Henry Plummer was painfully aware of that social responsibility and of the fact that the methods in use did not meet it. Moreover, there was taking shape in his mind the conception of the group as a unit, and a logical corollary of that conception was the revolutionary idea that the doctor's records did not belong to him alone but to the group, and ought therefore to be immediately available to any member of it.

It was not hard to make the Drs. Mayo see the need for something better in the way of record-keeping, and with their approval Dr. Plummer set out to devise a new system. For more than a year he studied the problem, went traveling to see what others were doing and, getting no help from medical men, turned to business and industry for ideas.

The dossier system he subsequently evolved has become a model for medical records. Each patient is registered upon arrival and assigned a serial number. An envelope bearing that number is set up in a central file, and in that envelope is placed all information about that patient: the diagnostician's clinical history, the surgical and hospital records, and the findings of all laboratory examinations, each set down on standardized record forms that Dr. Plummer drew up in conference with his colleagues. All subsequent correspondence with the patient is filed in the same envelope, and if he returns for a second, third, or fourth visit, he is always given the same number and the records are put into the same envelope. Thus is accumulated in one place a full and accurate history of each patient's physical condition as far as it is known to the Rochester doctors.

The history is immediately available to any member of the group upon request, but whenever an envelope is removed from the file a charge card bearing the exact date, hour, and destination is put in its place, so that the whereabouts of any history not in the file can be known at a glance.

When the patient has been discharged and before his history goes into the permanent file, the records are cross-indexed according to disease, surgical technique, surgical results, and pathologic findings. Thus whenever one of the group wishes to study a series of cases of any one kind, he has only to get the list of case numbers from the index and ask the file clerk to pull out the envelopes bearing those numbers.

Patient number one was registered under the new system on July 19, 1907. It was not easy for all the doctors to make the change. To some of them the new way seemed more cumbersome than the old, just a lot of unnecessary red tape. It seemed much simpler to jot down a few notes in a ledger lying open on the desk than to fill in all the blanks on a form sheet, much easier to pull out one's own volume and look up what old record was there than to call for an envelope and wait till it was brought from the file. At first some of the men just forgot about the record blanks and used their ledgers when they were very busy, but in time they all saw the worth of the new system, and it became a routine followed without question and with tremendous benefit.

## 11

When the needs of the business office outgrew the help that Jay Neville and a few girl clerks could give, Dr. Will asked the president of the bank to recommend a good man to assist Mr. Graham and improve the business system. The banker recommended one of his tellers, a tall, handsome young man of twenty-one years, a native of Minnesota and a graduate of the Winona high school. His name was Harry J. Harwick.

When he began his work for the Mayos in 1908 he was able to keep their payroll without crowding on the back page of a single-leaf checkbook. The bookkeeping was still done in the old-style ledgers, but he was soon able to persuade Mr. Graham that a card and loose-leaf system would be more convenient. The doctors were still making their own collections and coming in at the end of the day to empty their pockets onto "Daddy" Graham's desk, and that Mr. Harwick could not immediately change, but in 1910 he took over the duties of purchasing agent for the group. Until then all and sundry had a finger in the buying, each man ordering whatever he needed with little regard for cost or duplication. Jay Neville, as the self-appointed guardian of general office supplies, was the only one who took time to bother about economy. If he thought the clerks or even the doctors were using too many towels, for instance, he reminded them sharply that it cost money to have towels laundered.

# The Clinic Takes Shape

Jay was growing more eccentric with age, and his antics often relieved the tedium for the patients in the hallway. He could not endure seeing the benches out of order, so whenever he heard the screech of wood on wood that meant one had been moved he darted out to set it straight again. Sometimes the hackmen waiting outside for fares would peer in through the doorway to see whether anyone was getting ready to leave, and, outraged by such open eagerness for customers, Jay periodically dashed through the hallway and out the door to send them scurrying back to their hacks.

One Saturday in July 1914 the Mayos' *Oronoco* remained at the dock in Winona. Informed that the scheduled trip had been postponed because somebody was sick, a Winona reporter called Rochester to find out who it was. Jay Neville, the caretaker of the offices, had been stricken with apoplexy and was near death, Dr. W. J. Mayo told him. When he implied his surprise that this should interfere with the Mayos' plans, Dr. Will answered shortly. "We wouldn't think of leaving. Jay has been like one of our family. He worked for my father for twenty years and he has lived in my home for twenty-four. He was an exceptional employee."

Jay was buried from Dr. Will's home. To the "boys," Will and Charlie, he bequeathed his most prized possession, the automobile they had given him.

## 12

Because additions to the group were always a step or two behind the growth in the number of patients, everybody was working very hard. Newcomers were often surprised, sometimes dismayed, to learn just how hard. When Dr. Logan arrived in Rochester on December 31, 1909, he thought he would have the next day to help his wife get settled. But Dr. Mayo's wire had said to report on January 1, so he thought he had better put in an appearance at the office. He worked from the time he got there until six o'clock in the evening.

When he asked about his working hours Dr. Will told him they all began about eight o'clock in the morning and worked until they got through, and Dr. Logan soon learned that he had practically a twenty-four-hour job. Being the latest cub on the scene, he was given most of the house calls in Rochester and the immediate countryside. His first year he was called out almost every night either to give some special attention to a surgical case or to look after a medical case of his own. The street lights were poor and sometimes failed altogether, and with the town in darkness and many a board unexpectedly missing from the sidewalks, he found it a trying business to make his way about the unfamiliar town.

Some who joined the group found the hours too long and the work too hard, and they soon left. When those who stayed are asked why they did so, their answers are astonishingly similar, in general tenor this:

The variety and volume of the work was fascinating and the opportunities for professional growth unequaled. The Mayos worked just as hard as we did, and they made us feel important to their success. They never bossed us; we didn't have to call at the office each morning to get an outline of our duties for the day. They allowed us plenty of time off for vacations and for the kind of study trips they took themselves. They even paid our way and often added enough money for us to take our wives along. We each had a day every week free for reading and writing in the library. Those were luxuries a doctor practicing alone could not afford. When he took a vacation his income stopped, and if he was away too long his patients went to other doctors. But when one of us stopped to catch his breath, the group went on. We all worked a little harder when one man was gone because we knew our turn to go would come.

## 13

The Mayo brothers had by this time arranged their schedule so they operated on alternate days, Dr. Will on Tuesday, Thursday, and Saturday and Dr. Charlie on the other three. To fill up his Friday schedule Dr. Charlie had to use a little blarney, telling his patients that far from being an unlucky day Friday was his very luckiest.

The final decision whether or not to advise operation in a doubtful case was theirs, though they were often guided by the opinion of the clinician. They still depended on each other primarily, however. If Dr. Will could not be sure about a patient he would tell the clinician to have Charlie examine him, and then the two brothers would reach a conclusion together.

The afternoons in the office were often hectic, especially for Dr. Charlie. An extra measure of the consultation fell to his lot, partly because Dr. Will needed time for the duties of management and partly because Dr. Charlie had trained most of the younger surgeons. When Dr. Judd or Beckman or Henderson wanted advice it was likely to be in a field he had learned from Dr. Charlie. The eye, ear, nose, and throat men often wanted his opinion on some obscure case too, and the younger clinicians usually turned to him when they were in difficulty. They found it easier to confess their perplexity to him than to Dr. Will, and they knew he would always find a graceful way out of an awkward situation involving a patient.

As a consequence of the many demands upon his time Dr. Charlie was often so worn out by late afternoon that he slipped quietly away and went home. But this usually complicated matters in the office, so the staff took to hiding his hat and coat. The strategy worked sometimes, but if Dr. Charlie was very tired he just went home without them.

There was fun as well as work, though. The number of young men in the group made for high spirits and gay times. On warm summer evenings Dr. Will and Dr. Charlie would send their drivers to pick up any of the staff who wanted to go for a ride, and there were many picnics, hay rides, and sleigh rides on which romances budded and bloomed. Dr. Will's elder daughter Carrie became Mrs. Donald Balfour, the two Berkman girls, Daisy and Helen, married Henry Plummer and Starr Judd respectively, Nellie Stinchfield was soon Mrs. William Braasch, and Harry Harwick married Margaret Graham, the daughter of his chief in the business office.

These friendships and relationships contributed to congeniality in office hours. "Daddy" Graham lived on a farm, and sometimes when he came back to the office at noon he brought along a big basket of apples and put them on a table in the laboratory. Then during the afternoon the doctors would slip out to eat an apple and talk for a few minutes. On such occasions Dr. Will proved himself a tease, often tossing off some remark that would start a hot political argument. He never took any further part in it; he just "liked to hear them rave."

## 14

The rapidly accelerating growth was making the problem of more space acute. The surgeons took over the operating rooms at both the

Kahler House and the Chute Sanatorium, and new additions were built to both. Then in 1912 Mr. Kahler and his associates ventured to construct a larger and more pretentious hotel, the Zumbro, thus relieving pressure on the Cook House enough so that one of its floors could be turned into quarters for the orthopedic surgeons (Dr. Henry W. Meyerding had come to act as Dr. Henderson's assistant), giving them forty beds and an operating room of their own. In the same year still another addition was built to St. Mary's Hospital, raising its capacity to three hundred beds and six operating rooms.

Expansion at the offices was not so easily managed. Because it occurred only as forced by need and without previous plan, what had resulted was a collection of offices and laboratories sprawled helter-skelter along the block and mixed honeycomb-fashion with shoe stores, drug stores, and restaurants. When the partners needed another room or two they rented them wherever they could find them, boarding up their street fronts and building a passageway at the rear to connect them with the other offices.

After a while there were no more rooms of that sort available, so the partners began to build their own extensions. When they had to find more space for the library, which under Mrs. Mellish's energetic management had grown to several thousand volumes, they built a two-story structure on the lot behind their offices and moved into it the library and the editorial office, the general correspondence office, and the art studio, which now had a staff of four photographers and two medical artists. Needing still more space the next year, they built an annex connecting the library with the offices to house the x-ray department. Then they began to crowd other services into these new buildings. Room was made in the library for the diagnostic work in orthopedics, and the x-ray technicians were squeezed together to make room for the department of postoperative dressings.

The crowding finally became intolerable. Several expedients were tried to relieve it, among them a plan for dividing the staff into two shifts, one working from seven-thirty to three, the other from three to ten. But that merely added to the confusion, which was already quite enough for the patients. Special personnel had to be provided to direct them through the maze, and Kate Fitzgerald, transferred from Dr. Sanford's laboratory to serve as the first "routing clerk," soon found herself in charge of a small corps of desk girls scattered about the various corridors. Because there was no system of definite appointments, the patients had to spend a great many tiresome hours simply waiting their turn to see their doctor or the surgeon or laboratory man he had referred them to. This took more patience than many of them had, and on the general registration card was printed the request, "Please do not ask to be favored out of turn."

More serious still, such conditions made close cooperation difficult. Surgical consultation was taken for granted, and the red and green cardboard signals for Dr. Will and Dr. Charlie had given way to devices like railroad semaphores above each examining-room door. The color of the light indicated which surgeon was wanted in that room. But consultation among the clinicians, highly desirable as special interests developed among them, was only by individual impulse, and it was not encouraged by the lack of quick and easy means of communication. Dr. Plummer had tried to remedy that by installing a cable carrier system like those used in department stores, to circulate correspondence, case histories, and memoranda. But in damp weather the cotton cables would swell and the baskets would get stuck between offices.

At last it seemed clear that the only way out of the difficulty was the one Henry Plummer was urging: the construction of a separate building large enough to meet the needs of the group and adapted to its peculiar purposes. Dr. Will hesitated to take the step; he was afraid it was too ambitious. But finally one Saturday night when the group after a particularly hectic day voted in favor of the move, the Mayos gave their consent. Dr. Plummer was named chairman of the building committee, which included Mr. Harwick to look after the business arrangements and Dr. Wilson to supervise provisions for the laboratories. By ten o'clock the next morning Plummer had called an architect down from St. Paul and was outlining the problem to him. That was Henry Plummer.

The site selected was that of the old Mayo home across from the Central School. Perhaps moved in part by a sentimental wish to locate their clinic building on the spot where one of them had been born and both had spent their childhood, Dr. Will and Dr. Charlie arranged to buy the property from their sister Mrs. Berkman, to whom the Old Doctor had deeded it several years before his death.

# The Mayo Brothers

The cornerstone was laid on October 9, 1912. In the center of the massive block of white Missouri marble was placed a copper box containing the photographs of the Mayo brothers and their partners, a list of the surgical operations performed that morning, and a roll of the members of the Surgeons Club present for the occasion, including doctors from Alaska, South America, Denmark, Norway, and Sweden, as well as from many parts of the United States. While Dr. Charlie wielded the trowel Dr. Will spoke the words of dedication:

The object of this building is to furnish a permanent house wherein scientific investigation can be made into the causes of the diseases which afflict mankind, and wherein every effort shall be made to cure the sick and the suffering. It is the hope of the founders of this building that in its use the high ideals of the medical profession will always be maintained. Within its walls all classes of people, the poor as well as the rich, without regard to color or creed, shall be cared for without discrimination.

It was nearly two years before the building was ready for use. Working without a precedent to guide them, the architects had to rely upon Henry Plummer for their knowledge of the exact purposes to be served and the problems to be met, and Dr. Plummer proved as much of a perfectionist in this as in everything else he undertook. No detail of mechanics or materials was too small to receive his personal scrutiny and decision.

But what principally took the time was Plummer's efforts to formulate a plan of organization that would coordinate and integrate the activities of the group. The Mayos had long since been persuaded to his view that the advantages of specialization in medicine could be achieved and its dangers avoided only if the group of specialists functioned as a unit in relation to the patient. As Dr. Will said repeatedly, a sick man is not like a wagon, to be taken apart and repaired in pieces; he must be examined and treated as a whole. As early as 1910 he told the graduating class of Rush Medical College:

As we men of medicine grow in learning we more justly appreciate our dependence upon each other. The sum total of medical knowledge is now so great and widespreading that it would be futile for any one man . . . to assume that he has even a working knowledge of any large part of the whole. The very necessities of the case are driving practitioners into cooperation. The best interest of the patient is the only interest to be considered, and in order that the sick may have the benefit of advancing knowledge, union of forces is necessary. . . . It has become necessary to develop medicine as a cooperative science; the clinician, the specialist, and the laboratory workers uniting for the good of the patient, each assisting in the elucidation of the problem at hand, and each dependent upon the other for support.

Just now evidence of teamwork is best seen in large hospitals, in the regular employment of laboratories . . . and of still greater importance, the union of the physician and surgeon, not as an occasional event but as a part of the daily routine. . . . The people will demand, the medical profession must supply, adequate means for the proper care of patients, which means that individualism in medicine can no longer exist.

Dr. Will could look far forward into the future and lay out broad policies, but neither he nor Dr. Charlie had much gift for arranging the fine details of organization and method, popular belief to the contrary notwithstanding. It was their way to hire a good man when they needed one, the best they could get, then give him his head to make the most of his opportunities. And Dr. Plummer, himself an intense individualist, wholeheartedly approved of that policy, but he saw nothing incompatible with it in allocating general responsibilities and standardizing routine. That just prevented wasteful duplication of effort and futile frittering away of energies. So with the Mayos' permission he was trying to put this idea into effect in designing the new structure.

## 15

The building was formally opened on March 6, 1914. During that afternoon and evening the rooms were shown and their intended uses described to some sixteen hundred persons. They saw the spacious first-floor lobby, cheerful and restful with soft-colored marbles, semi-direct lighting, wicker furniture, and a fountain banked with palms—so different from the old hallway waiting room! Around it were ranged the business offices, registration desks, and principal examining rooms. From it they climbed an impressive double stairway to the second floor, where they saw more examining rooms, the x-ray cubicles and dark rooms, and some of the clinical laboratories. On the third floor were the handsome library, the assembly hall, and more laboratories, on the fourth the pathologic museum, art studio, and the workshops of the instrument-makers, and on the fifth the experimental laboratories with adjacent roof-top runways for the animals.

All the research and diagnosis had been gathered into the one building and organized into divisions and sections. Each senior clinician was now the head of a section in the division of surgery; each attending surgeon was the head of a section in the division of surgery. With the exception of the sections in ophthalmology, otolaryngology (ear, nose, and throat), and orthopedic surgery, these were all sections in general medicine and surgery, for Dr. Will insisted that specialization should go no farther here than the *addition* of a "major interest" to general practice in each section.

The scattered clinical laboratories were at last brought together in a section of clinical pathology under the direction of Dr. Sanford. Dr. MacCarty was named head of the section of surgical pathology, though he of course remained at St. Mary's Hospital, Dr. Mann of the section of experimental medicine, and Dr. Kendall of the section of experimental biochemistry. Together they made up the division of laboratories, of which Dr. Wilson was the director.

The library, editorial office, and art studio were joined in a division of publications, with Mrs. Mellish its general director as well as the head of the editorial section. A trained librarian had been engaged to relieve her of direct responsibility for the library. Into the division of records and statistics, in charge of Mabel Root under the supervision of Dr. Plummer, were gathered the registration clerks, desk girls, and filing clerks. And finally, to the business office, from which Mr. Graham had retired, leaving it in the highly capable hands of Harry Harwick, was allocated full responsibility for investigating the financial status of the patients, assessing their fees accordingly, and collecting them.

Those were the various members of the body. Its veins and arteries were the ingenious system Dr. Plummer had devised for the prompt circulation of the case histories, and its central nervous system was the means of ready communication by telephone, signal lights, and telegraph ticker. Each floor was connected with the main file desk in the basement by a constantly moving conveyor belt. When a history was wanted on floor three, say, the desk girl there had only to pencil the number on a request card and put it on the carrier. In the file room below the desk girl pulled the history and put it into the proper compartment of the carrier, from which it was automatically tripped off at desk three above—in two or three minutes, with no more trouble for the doctor than a spoken number.

A flat panel with room for many signal lights had taken the place of the ungainly semaphores above each examining-room doorway, and to each doctor had been assigned a specific call on the new ticker. When his tick sounded, no matter where he was in the building he had only to lift the receiver of the nearest telephone to learn from the operator what was wanted of him and where.

When Henry Plummer appeared at the offices of the telephone company asking them to install a system that would enable the doctors to talk to each other directly, to the operator, or to an outside person at will, the officials stared at him. That was impossible, they said. "No, it isn't," replied Plummer calmly. "Call in your engineer and I'll show him how to do it." The engineer came, and Dr. Plummer explained with diagrams. So the first intercommunicating telephone in the country was installed in the new building. As far as mechanical aids could contribute to effective cooperation, Henry Plummer had provided them.

At his suggestion too the custom of making definite appointments for each patient was now adopted, to eliminate many hours of tedium for the patients and to encourage the reference of patients from one doctor to another. But here again Dr. Will stepped in with a warning. The sick person was not to become the patient of the group in the sense that he was to be referred from one man to another with no one in charge of his case. He must remain the private patient of the examining clinician, who should have full responsibility for his case, making use of the special knowledge of his colleagues as he thought best.

## 16

It is not possible to assign a date for the founding of the Mayo Clinic. It came into being too gradually for that. The germ of one phase of it existed in the Old Doctor's clinics at Mrs. Carpenter's; the outpatient aspect appeared when St. Mary's was built and the brothers began trying to persuade their patients to come in to them instead of calling them out to the homes; adding the first partners and adopting a program of laboratory development initiated other phases. But with the reorganization and the new building of 1914 the Mayo Clinic emerged as a distinct institution, "a complete clinic, including laboratories, housed under one roof, and *independent of any hospital.*" It has grown to three times its size then, its building has climbed fourteen stories farther into the sky, its sections have multiplied and its activities expanded, to take in medical treatment and put surgery in something like its proper place in the whole of medicine, but the central idea and the fundamental organization had been achieved by 1914.

That central idea, of cooperative group practice, is considered by some doctors the most important practical achievement in modern medicine. In a discussion of medical practice some years later Dr. Will remarked that he and his brother had been called the fathers of group medicine, but "if we were we did not know it." They had not proceeded according to a blueprint drafted in advance; they had merely tried to solve the problems of their overwhelming practice in the way that seemed at the moment most likely to improve their surgery. As one Minnesota surgeon summarized it, they "found the surgeon working alone with assistants of a kindred spirit in his workshop [and they] succeeded in exciting the interest successively of pathologist, roentgenologist, and internist in surgical problems and brought into the surgical clinic the experience of a group of men whose special knowledge pyramided the usefulness of the surgeon." The result was a new kind of private medical practice.

For to be precise, the Mayos were not the fathers of group practice, but of *private* group practice. Cooperation of a sort among clinicians, surgeons, and laboratory men was taken for granted in municipal, state, and university hospitals; it was something quite new in private practice. And the more centralized control made it possible to develop greater homogeneity and integration than was possible with the loose-knit, constantly shifting, and part-time staffs of public institutions, even the best of them.

Given the state of medicine that demanded specialization and the volume of patients that permitted it, what made the Mayo Clinic possible was the brothers' attitude toward their associates. They did not merely mouth the Old Doctor's dictum, No man is big enough to be independent of others; they really believed it. And so they did not consider their employees hirelings but fellow workers, who must also travel to other centers to learn, have time for research and writing, and be granted independence in opinion and action. Their ability and reputation would not dim the glory of the Mayos; it would enhance it. Feeling so, Dr. Will and Dr. Charlie actually managed to retain, in cooperative form, the individualism Dr. Will said could no longer exist in medicine.

# Clinic and Foundation

# CHAPTER NINETEEN

# To the People, from Whom It Came

Shortly after George E. Vincent became president of the University of Minnesota in 1911, he was surprised to learn that one of the most promising members of the medical school faculty had left a few years before to take charge of the laboratories of two country doctors in Rochester, and apparently had never been sorry. The more he heard about the Mayos the more curious he became, so he went down to see them. Not the least impressive aspect of their work, he found, was the well-rounded, systematic training they were giving to their thirty-six fellows. Facetiously he remarked to Dr. Will that he and his brother were poaching on the preserves of the university, for they were actually conducting a graduate school of medicine.

The fellows of the Mayo Clinic were getting an advanced training at least equal to that available anywhere else in the country. Real graduate education in clinical medicine simply did not exist. In the fundamental medical sciences, yes, but nowhere could a doctor of medicine take an organized, long-term course leading to an advanced degree in surgery, internal medicine, ophthalmology, pediatrics or any other branch of clinical medicine.

Much had been done by the best university medical schools to raise the standards in undergraduate training, and more improvement was in prospect as the result of the stinging, plain-speaking report on medical education prepared by Abraham Flexner in 1910 for the Carnegie Foundation for the Advancement of Teaching. State licensing had also helped to improve the quality of general practitioners and certify competent ones to the public. But medicine itself had advanced to specialization, and on that level the door still stood wide open to quackery and incompetence. Specialists were designated solely by self-proclamation, so that there was nothing to prevent a man fresh out of medical school from setting himself up as a surgeon in Oregon or Maine one month and as an obstetrician in Iowa the next.

Not that many were quite so brazen. Most of them waited at least until they had taken a short course or two at one of the proprietary postgraduate or polyclinic schools that had sprung up all over the country on the pattern of those first two established in New York in 1882. The early ones served a much-needed purpose in repairing the glaring deficiencies of the undergraduate schools, but with multiplication their quality declined, until now with few exceptions they were staffed with second-rate doctors whose sole interest in teaching was the profit and prestige it brought them in their private practice. To call their courses graduate education was a mockery of the term.

The preferred form of advanced training was still a period of study in Europe, but for the few who became true specialists through extended and concentrated work in European clinics and laboratories there were many who blossomed as experts after one summer's junket to the Old World, and there was no way for the public to know which group a man belonged to. Besides, Americans were coming to feel that the superior advantages of Europe were traditional rather than actual. When Dr. Wilson returned from his European tour in 1912 he reported his conclusion that Americans could do just as well at home if the facilities here were organized. "American material is equally good, American apparatus is better, American climatic conditions are less depressing, and American beer is less soporific."

The best training available in this country was a period of service as a resident or house physician in one of the good university hospitals, like those at Johns Hopkins or Harvard, where the resident was not treated as a paid servant of the staff doctors but as a student preparing for special practice or teaching. Such residencies were few, however, and they were not capped by any formal symbol to distinguish those who had held them from the certificate-holders of the postgraduate schools. To this group essentially the fellowships of the Mayo Clinic belonged, both in quality of training and in the absence of any authoritative recognition for it except a certificate of internship from St. Mary's Hospital.

There was a crying need, recognized by medical educators east and west, for training and certifying specialists, for teaching men the methods and spirit of research so they could advance the frontiers of medicine, and for preparing qualified teachers of clinical medicine.

# To the People

Johns Hopkins had recently initiated the experiment of hiring full-time teachers in its clinical courses, awaking a controversy over the merits of the idea that is still echoing in medical halls. Such a practice could spread only if the medical schools turned out a sufficient supply of thoroughly trained men who would forego more remunerative private practice for the life of a teacher, as their brethren in the fundamental sciences had long done. When the coming of the First World War in 1914 put a sudden end to trips abroad, the development of opportunities in the United States became imperative.

## 2

By this time the Mayos' personal savings under Burt Eaton's management had piled up to a seven-figure sum. Believing that "it is a disgrace to die rich," as Dr. Will once said, and that it is unwise of parents to leave their children so well off they feel no compulsion to join in the world's work, Dr. Will and Dr. Charlie were content to establish a moderately substantial trust fund for their families and with the rest, a million and a half dollars, to realize the trusteeship they had declared to themselves in 1898. They had come to think they could best give the money back to the people by using it to endow medical education and research, and they were inclined to do so through the agency of the state university. Some of their doctor friends, especially Dr. Frank Billings the Chicago internist, had been telling them for years that they ought to move their clinic to Minneapolis so its facilities for education and research would be available to the university; in his report in 1912 Dr. Wilson had pointed out how much more the Rochester men could do for those who came there for study if they were working in conjunction with the university; many Clinic staff members and fellows were graduates of the university medical school; and service on the board of regents of the university had convinced Dr. Will that such a state-perpetuated group would be more likely than a group of bankers and businessmen to realize the social purposes of such a public trust as he and Charlie intended to establish.

As the only medical man among the regents, Dr. Will had played an important part in the development of the university medical school and had become deeply interested in its welfare. The school came into being in 1888 when representatives of two Twin City proprietary colleges offered to surrender their charters and tender the temporary use of their buildings to the university if the regents would establish a school of medicine. A few weeks later the homeopathic medical college in Minneapolis volunteered to suspend operations too if the regents would include a department of homeopathy in the new school.

The beginning was not impressive, just a three-year course in surgery, internal medicine, and obstetrics, and when the school was moved to quarters on the campus the "academics" were upset, as though "the invasion . . . by the medics were the alarum of the barbarians at the gates of Rome." But more subjects were added as the space and equipment became financially possible, and the required course was gradually lengthened until during Dr. Mayo's second year as a regent a six-year course was made compulsory and rewarded with both the B.S. and the M.D. In that year too the last private medical college in the state merged with the university school, thus centralizing all medical education in the state institution.

The next year a rift in relations with some of the Twin City hospitals forced the university to begin building its own hospital and the problem of the department of homeopathy was finally solved, in a way suggested by Dr. Mayo. That department had steadily refused the reforms applied to the rest of the school and was no credit to the university, yet to abolish it outright would cause noisy and bitter protest in some quarters. Dr. Will suggested that students in homeopathy simply be required to take the same preclinical science courses required of the other medics. What he thought would happen did; the students decided that if they had to do all that work they might as well be regular doctors, and the number enrolled in homeopathy dwindled to zero. Then an obviously superfluous department was quietly dropped.

Thus when Flexner made his survey in 1910 he was able to report that Minnesota was "perhaps the first state . . . that may fairly be considered to have solved the most perplexing problems connected with medical education and practice."

But the university officials were painfully aware of a problem that Flexner may have missed: The various consolidations had accumulated a preposterously large faculty of part-time teachers; at one time there were at least eight full professors of "mental and nervous diseases." Everyone agreed that the staff ought to be drastically deflated, but each of several personal factions thought the others ought to be the ones to go. Finally the regents decided they must act and Dr. Will helped to formulate their plan. All members of the medical faculty were asked to resign, and then a committee of those whose reappointment no one could question nominated a compact staff which the regents appointed, along with a new dean from outside the state, Elias P. Lyon, a physiologist from St. Louis University. The reorganization was necessary and ultimately of great benefit, but it left behind resentment and rancor to plague the school for many years.

## 3

Early in 1914 the administrative board of the medical school appointed a committee to make plans for instituting graduate work in clinical medicine. Left to themselves the medical faculty would probably have set up another short "refresher" course such as several universities were offering in futile imitation of the proprietary post-graduate schools. But part of President Vincent's plan for a closer integration of the university's various colleges was to centralize the control of all advanced work in one graduate school, and he would not willingly let another shoot of separatism come to bud.

Quite apart from his wholehearted agreement with this idea, Guy Stanton Ford, newly appointed dean of the graduate school, had been conditioned against the evils of the short course. The son of a doctor in Iowa, he well remembered his father's spate of wrath and ridicule whenever he received a prospectus from one of the commercial poly-clinic schools, "in which a group of busy city practitioners gave a hurried six weeks' course to other practitioners who went home with a certificate to frame and a debt to pay by sending patients to the city specialists."

Possessing a firm conviction that it was the university's obligation to train specialists and mark them out so the discriminating public could tell them from brazen imitations, Dean Ford felt that graduate work in medicine ought to be pulled up to the level of graduate work in other branches of learning and art, and that it could best be done in association with established graduate units. Fortunately Dean Lyon of the medical school was also a man with the university idea, unlike many other members of the medical faculty whose every thought was for the glorification of the medical school irrespective of the rest of the university.

So in September 1914 eleven students who had been granted teaching fellowships or graduate scholarships began graduate work with selected members of the medical faculty under the supervision of the graduate school. They were to take a three-year course combining study, practice, and research, pass an oral examination, prepare an acceptable thesis, and receive a "degree with designation," that is, a Ph.D. in Surgery, or an M.S. in Pediatrics, for example. Here was something truly new under the sun.

Almost from the first discussion of the plan the idea of a possible affiliation with the Mayo Clinic had been considered, for among those on the responsible committee were Drs. James E. Moore, Clark Stewart, and Harold Robertson, all of whom knew the work of the Mayos well. But the first formal step was taken in October 1914 when Dean Lyon proposed that the medical administrative board consider the question and they in turn appointed a committee to confer with the medical alumni and the Drs. Mayo.

In the succeeding three months much unrecorded discussion and many recorded conferences were carried on in the Twin Cities, at Rochester, and between the two. Early in January Dean Ford went down to Rochester to investigate the situation from the standpoint of the graduate school, that is, to see what the Rochester setup had to offer in the way of qualified students, qualified instructors, and adequate material and support. As he reported when he returned,

I found a condition that satisfied me upon all three points. . . . I am not speaking of the first floor of the Mayo Building primarily, nor of the operating rooms of St. Mary's Hospital. I found what I was looking for in the laboratories, museums, and library of the upper floors, and in the countless case records in the basement of the Mayo Building. The richness of this material, not seen by the casual visitor, furnishes opportunities for graduate medical work in certain lines such as can be found nowhere else on this continent, nor probably in the world. I found a research and teaching staff available and at work, sufficient to do its full part . . . in a co-operative plan such as that under consideration. Some of these were doing nothing but research. The only difference observed between those who were engaged part time in clinical practice and our own part time staff was that the private practice in Rochester was conducted under the acid test of observers from all over the world.

# To the People

An obstacle to the affiliation appeared early in the negotiations: The Mayo Clinic was not a corporate body with which the university could readily make a contract. President Vincent suggested that to overcome this the Mayos form a corporate foundation to handle the educational and research phases of their work, and Dr. Will immediately recognized the excellence of the idea; it would provide an agency for managing activities essentially outside the scope of the Clinic proper and would also make unnecessary the affiliation of the university with the Clinic. So on February 8, 1915 Drs. Mayo, Graham, Plummer, Judd, and Balfour (Dr. Balfour had been made a participating partner in 1914) executed articles incorporating the Mayo Foundation for Medical Education and Research, and the next day Dr. Will and Dr. Charlie endowed it by transferring to three trustees, Burt W. Eaton, George W. Granger, and Harry J. Harwick, securities amounting to a million and a half dollars.

Meanwhile the conferences and discussion had produced tentative terms of affiliation between the university and the Foundation to be submitted to the regents. The university would conduct a part of its graduate education in medicine at Rochester for an indefinite period of trial, during which the Foundation would make available free of charge all the facilities of the Mayo Clinic and the Rochester hospitals and the Mayos would personally pay all expenses, so the interest on the endowment could be added to the principal until the fund reached a total of two million dollars. The work at Rochester was to be carried on by a board of "scientific directors" and a selected faculty, both appointed by the university regents on nomination by the Foundation and approval by the administrative board of the medical school. All details as to courses of instruction and the requirements for degrees were to be worked out by a joint committee, under the supervision of the dean of the graduate school, in which school all the students would be registered and from which they would receive their degrees. The trial affiliation could be terminated by either party on one year's notice, but if and when the affiliation became permanent the Mayos would transfer the endowment fund from their trustees to the university regents, subject to the condition that the income be used to maintain the graduate work at Rochester.

# Clinic and Foundation

## 4

Barely had the regents received this proposal for consideration when the opposition to the whole idea, which had been evident in the close votes by which the plan was approved by the medical faculty and the advisory committee of the medical alumni association, showed itself to be unexpectedly widespread and intense. The Hennepin and Ramsey county (Minneapolis and St. Paul) medical societies passed resolutions of emphatic protest and supplemented them with petitions requesting the regents to discontinue immediately all consideration of the proposal. The Minneapolis document was signed by two hundred and two doctors. Then as Twin City practitioners spread the word among county and district groups resolutions and petitions in similar vein began coming in from them. Seventeen county societies declared against the affiliation, though four expressed approval. Pamphlets picturing the evils of the plan in lurid light were distributed, one of them entitled "A Phantom Gift and a Trial Marriage," in which the university medical school was described as an unwilling bride. Finally a bill forbidding the regents to effect any such affiliation was introduced into the state legislature, then in session.

The objections on which all this opposition was presumably based were many and long, but the chief ones, those most often repeated and from which most of the others followed were these: Since it would be impossible in practice to separate the activities of the Foundation from those of the Clinic and since the Clinic was legally just a family partnership, Dr. Graham being a brother-in-law, Dr. Balfour a son-in-law, and Drs. Plummer and Judd nephews by marriage of the Drs. Mayo, the university would actually be affiliating itself with a private business firm. Not only that, but because the partners as incorporators of the Foundation were, through their secondary board of scientific directors, to control the appointment of teachers, expenditure of funds, and in practice the granting of degrees, the regents would in effect be delegating their powers derived from the state, granting to a private partnership scholastic rank equal to that of the medical school. If they gave such privileges to one business firm they must give them to any other that asked, and medical education in the state, so lately centralized at great cost, would again be dispersed, more widely and weakly than before.

# To the People

With revealing inconsistency, however, the opponents of affiliation added to that argument a suggestion that the Mayo Foundation be encouraged to conduct an independent graduate school and grant its own degrees.

Furthermore, the objections went on, the entire income of the endowment was to be spent in Rochester; the university was not to have a cent of it for its own medical school. This was a "phantom gift." Indeed, affiliation with the Foundation, with its endowment and clinical facilities all earmarked for graduate instruction, would cause advanced medical education to overshadow undergraduate work so completely that actually the scheme would check the development of the university's own medical school. And then in the future, when the Mayo Clinic deteriorated to mediocrity, as it surely would when the Mayo brothers died, the university would be saddled with the responsibility for maintaining it and would have to divert to that purpose a share of the legislative appropriations intended for the medical school.

Some of those objections were valid criticisms of the plan as it stood, and some of the objectors were unquestionably sincere in raising them. In the group were lifelong friends and admirers of the Drs. Mayo, four of whom made a special trip to Rochester to tell Dr. Will and Dr. Charlie they must oppose the affiliation because they thought it unwise, though they did not at all doubt the nobility of the Mayos' motives. Dr. Will replied as honestly, telling them to go ahead because if there was anything wrong with the idea he and Charlie wanted to find it out before they put their lifetime's savings into it.

Other men used the same arguments but for reasons less worthy. The bitterness left smoldering by the reorganization of the medical school flared into blaze against the affiliation, presumably because it promised advantages to the hated school. Yet the most active agitators were half a dozen or so of the medical faculty who could see *no* advantages for the school that was their life and love. That the Foundation was affiliated with the graduate school instead of with the medical school was fortunate for the ultimate success of the enterprise, but at the time it was called a misfortune by the medical faculty and contributed to the resentment of those who did not care a fig for any unit of the university except their own. If the Drs. Mayo had made an outright gift of a hundred thousand or two to the medical school or

547

had even agreed to finance some additional university fellowships, a substantial share of the opposition would have vanished, but if anyone thought to suggest such a gift to them at the time they did not see fit to make it.

None of those elements in the situation, however, can account for the personal spite and malice, the disgraceful misrepresentation and abuse, that accompanied the respectable arguments. For that there seems but one explanation: Anxiety for the welfare of the medical school and zealous concern over the precious powers of the university regents were a convenient arras through which jealous competitors could thrust their rapiers at the men whose success infuriated them. The bile that had been accumulating for years overflowed in action now that it could be screened, or at least rationalized, by lofty intent.

This episode provides one of the few instances in which the antagonism toward the Mayos found its way into print. It was implicit in charges that the real object of the affiliation was to perpetuate the Mayo Clinic, the name of its founders, and the prosperity of their beloved Rochester, that it was just another effort to increase the Mayos' dominance of Minnesota medicine—they had monopolized medical practice, now they wanted to monopolize medical education too—that contact with the Mayo Clinic would commercialize the standards of medical students, that the Foundation fellowships would provide the Clinic members with good help cheap, and so on.

And it was *ex*plicit in—for it must have been the source of—the articles that appeared in a Minneapolis newssheet of the kind that exists without paid subscribers. After promising its readers to investigate the proposed affiliation, it published a list of questions, which though rhetorical the Mayos were invited to answer. They were many and some of them were columns long, but paraphrases of a few will sufficiently illustrate them.

Isn't it true that the Mayos have made many appearances before state and county medical societies for advertising purposes, making absurd statements about cures, "such as claiming to cure cancer of the stomach with a knife"?

Isn't it true that the Mayos decided not to appear at a meeting of an Iowa medical society because they didn't need to advertise there any more, and didn't they say, "To hell with them, we don't need them any more"?

Didn't the Mayos advertise in an Iowa paper with a long write-up of the Clinic and then say it was done by the Rochester Commercial Club? "You are just as responsible for it as though you had done it yourselves and . . . you were advertisers and . . . you are sneaking under the cloak of ethics of the American Medical Association and have put up a howl with them for medical ethics."

Isn't it true that the Mayos split fees with doctors who bring them patients?

Won't it benefit the Mayos' hotels and banks to have students at Rochester, though it will add to the students' expenses to have to go that far?

Isn't it true that railroads running to Rochester boost the Clinic and that the trainmen approach people on the trains and advise them to go there?

Why did Charles Mayo go East to have his operation? Didn't the Mayo Clinic recognize the cause of his trouble? If so, why didn't they operate at Rochester? Didn't they feel the Clinic surgeons were capable of operating?

Of course the Mayo brothers did not stoop to reply. Dr. Will often remarked that if you fight with a polecat you'll smell like a polecat. So the paper published a series of abusive editorials calling the Mayos "the highest classed team of advertising grafters in the medical profession," and said since they suggested the deal with the university they must be getting something out of it. "Did you ever see a fellow with a million who didn't want more millions?" This deal is a good bet for the Mayos. Through it they will get a lot of advertising, turn the charity patients over to students, and grab off fat fees on private cases that can pay. "Who gets the advertising? The Mayos. Who pays the freight? The People. Who grabs the profits? The Mayos."

## 5

Somewhat to the annoyance of the advocates of the affiliation the Mayos steadfastly refused to make any effort in explanation or defense of their position. They did write out a statement of their case, including the history of the endowment fund and of their motives in applying it to medical education, but for what purpose is uncertain, since they headed it "A Private Statement in Regard to the Mayo Foundation (Not for publication or general distribution)." It did not appear in print and only one copy is known to exist, a typescript carbon in Dr. Will's file of personal papers. In it they said:

# Clinic and Foundation

We have avoided the public print. We have made no attempt to control county medical societies or to get up petitions among physicians, among whom we have at least our share of friends. We have trusted to the good sense of a public unfortunately too well acquainted with the professional jealousies of physicians.

The public justified their trust, for despite all kinds of form letters and postcards, petitions and public hearings, the laymen refused to see the bogeys the medical men were so exercised about. When it was announced that the general alumni association of the university disapproved the plan, a large insurgent group of "academic" alumni met to declare their dissent in angry terms. When the opposition leaders appeared at a meeting of the St. Paul Civic and Commerce Association with prepared resolutions for the group to adopt, the association members instead voted overwhelmingly in favor of the affiliation.

The press of the state was preponderantly in favor of the plan. The *St. Paul Pioneer Press* maintained a strict neutrality at first, saying the laity ought not to meddle in a technical question, but at last it came out with an editorial urging the regents by all means to accept the affiliation and adding that it was impelled to this action "by the line of argument advanced in opposition, which seems to be founded in selfishness, adorned with commercialism, and capped with a touch of envy."

Downstate papers came to the same conclusion. Said one of them:

It will be hard for the doctors of the Twin Cities to convince us that their protests are not inspired by a selfish, self-grasping spirit. . . . They are not thinking of the benefit it might bring to the state, but rather they are afraid that it might bring a little more business to the Mayo Institution. They may not be selfish in their protest, but it certainly appears that way and we certainly hope that the Mayos' offer to the State will be accepted in spite of the opposition of the Twin City doctors.

Another editor set down his version of some of the objections and then "the obvious answers that will occur to most laymen":

The university would confer power, prestige and financial benefit on the "foundation."
Well, why not? The university would receive more than it would give.

It would confer a special privilege and show undue preference and favoritism.

# *To the People*

. . . At present the special privileges and undue preference are shown to St. Paul and Minneapolis alone.

It would help to perpetuate the Mayo clinic, thus becoming a menace and a danger to medical education.

This is—we regret to disturb the solemnity of the moment—one of the funniest things ever put in print.

The commercial spirit will rule, while the "university spirit" will be lost sight of. . . .

The gift of a million and a half . . . does not bear out the fear of "commercialism." The spirit of the Rochester institution may in certain ways ameliorate the dustiness of university alcoves.

The opposition had another effect its members did not intend and probably did not enjoy, for the *Pontiac* (Michigan) *Press* was well within the realm of possibility when it asserted:

The Mayo brothers of Rochester, Minn., are undoubtedly having the most wretched time of their lives. For if there is anything in the world that these famous surgeons hate and fear, it is publicity, and the giving of $2,000,000 to . . . the University of Minnesota has brought them such a flood of fame as they have never faced before in their lives.

Papers from coast to coast told the story of the Foundation and the proposed affiliation, and took the occasion once again to recount the Mayos' story with all its staple anecdotes. In general all of them wondered what could conceivably be the matter with the University of Minnesota that it should hesitate a minute to accept such a magnificent opportunity to contribute to the welfare of mankind the world over, in this generation and those to come. The *Boston Herald* considered the Foundation "a fitting climax to what has been a distinctively American career. The country has few stories to match that of these scientists, who are still so young." And the staid *Commerce and Finance* was moved to exclamation:

Of all the wonder stories of America there is hardly one to surpass that of the Mayo brothers. . . . What an inspiration their lives must be! Two plain American boys who made an obscure village a shrine of hope to suffering humanity; who have been the means of saving thousands of lives and averting untold pain and anguish; and who crowned their careers by giving their all for the benefit of mankind.

The Minnesota papers quoted these items, pointing out the contrast between such reactions and the ignoble, inconsequential considerations that occupied the opponents of the affiliation.

6

The bill forbidding the affiliation—called by one newspaperman "An indescribable bill [that] implies so curious a hostility to the welfare of the people of Minnesota that an explanation of its significance can evoke little save a gasp of incredulity"—passed the state senate by a vote of thirty-six to thirty-one, but not until too late in the session for the lower house to act on it.

Burt Eaton was astonished, then thoroughly angry, when he saw the record of the senate vote. The senator from Olmsted County, who had vowed his hearty approval of the affiliation, had voted for the bill against it. His explanation when Eaton taxed him with his perfidy did not soothe the lawyer's temper. "Oh, I knew it wouldn't get through the house," he said airily, "so I swapped my vote on that one for a couple of votes for the boxing bill I was interested in."

The opposition had lost in the legislature, but there was still a chance to sway the regents. Recognizing the validity of some of the objections, the Mayos offered new terms for the board's consideration: The proposed board of scientific directors should be dropped and the regents should have full control of all appointments and rules of procedure; the trial period should be set definitely at six years with the express understanding that if the affiliation was in effect at that time the original endowment and the accrued interest should pass automatically into the regents' control, the major part of the income to be used for maintaining the work at Rochester but some of it to be spent at the regents' discretion for work inside or outside the state.

When the regents held a public hearing on this new proposal the spokesmen for the opposition appeared with sheaves of arguments, for they considered the new plan no better than the old. But they were no match for one regent, the facile-tongued lawyer, Pierce Butler. His tormenting cross-examination, if the press reports were accurate, twisted them so tightly in the coils of their own words that they finally stopped arguing entirely. That did the cause of the affiliation little good, for the humiliation rankled and merely intensified the hostility of the opponents.

# To the People

The Hennepin County Medical Society promptly called a special meeting and by a vote of two hundred to ten adopted resolutions insisting that the regents must not enter into this business contract with one of their own number.

But when an executive committee charged with analyzing the terms of the proposal recommended its acceptance, the board of regents acted immediately. On June 9, 1915 they voted unanimously to accept the proposed affiliation for a trial period of six years. Then they resolved "That the best interests of the university require that the new plans for developing the Graduate Medical work of the University should not hereafter be opposed by any member of the faculty of the Medical School, but . . . should have the loyal support of all members thereof." The head of the department of medicine and several other members of the medical faculty immediately resigned, raising the cry of gag rule. Even those who stayed on were uneasy until it was officially explained that "no abridgment of proper academic freedom was intended in the Resolution adopted by the Board of Regents and all members of the Medical faculty who are willing to give the plan of graduate work adopted by the Regents a fair trial may continue as members of the faculty with complete self-respect."

The consummation of the affiliation was hailed generally with relief and applause. The American Surgical Association, in session at Rochester at the time, sent resolutions of congratulation to President Vincent and the regents and several individual members gave statements to the Rochester newspaper expressing their conviction that the affiliation promised a great future for the University of Minnesota in the field of medical education.

## 7

To supervise the graduate work under the new arrangement the regents authorized the appointment of a committee of nine, including President Vincent, Dean Ford, Dean Lyon, three from the medical school faculty, and three from the staff at Rochester. Sixty men, twenty-six of them from Rochester, were named to a graduate faculty, and sufficient outline of the proposed work was drawn up to permit the graduate school to announce it. The response of medical educators and students all over the world was immediate. Two hundred and fifty applications for fellowships were received and the sixty-odd chosen to fill up the quota of fellows represented thirty different undergraduate schools in places as widely separated as Italy and India, Louisiana and Canada.

The eyes of the university medical faculty were opened by the arrival of a young East Indian who had chosen Minnesota for his undergraduate training because of the graduate work he could look forward to there. The possibilities of the experiment led one important man from outside the state to accept a position on the faculty and persuaded two of the most able local men to exchange part-time private practice for full-time teaching. So gradually harmony was restored and everybody settled down to work out the very real problems presented by the new experiment, serene in the belief that they had six years in which to solve them.

Then almost as from the blue all the fuss and fury broke out again. When the legislature reconvened in 1917 the old opposition crowd appeared with a bill instructing the regents to dissolve the affiliation with the Foundation at once.

To the familiar charges they had added some new ones, chief among them the ugly suggestion that the whole Foundation idea was a fake, just a huge publicity stunt on the part of the Mayos, who had no intention of making the affiliation permanent or of surrendering the endowment to the regents. As soon as they had squeezed all possible advertising out of the scheme, they would give notice to terminate the affiliation. The medical faculty was said to be torn with dissension and the school to be deteriorating so rapidly that a casual visitor could see it. The ringleaders in the opposition had been carrying such tales throughout the state during the previous fall and winter and downstate men too far away or too busy to go and see for themselves believed them, so that the opposition was able to claim ninety per cent of the state's physicians on their side.

The outrageous untruths brought some of the friendly members on the medical faculty out into the open at last. They had hung aloof two years before, perhaps because they feared to alienate other doctors who were accustomed to refer patients to them. But now they immediately issued a flat denial of the charges, asserting that the medical school had never been in a more flourishing condition, and one of them gave the newspapers a scorching indictment of the disgruntled doctors who were conducting this campaign of deliberate misrepresentation.

On their part the Mayos acted as promptly to scotch the new accusation in the most effective way possible. They agreed to give the regents absolute possession of the endowment immediately, though they would continue to pay the expenses of the Foundation until the sum reached two million dollars, and to relinquish their right to terminate the agreement, leaving it solely up to the regents whether or not the affiliation became permanent. About the only solid leg they left for the opposition to stand on was the stipulation that the major part of the income be spent to maintain the work at Rochester.

The renewal of the attack brought letters of protest from many outstanding medical men of the country. Dr. George Blumer, dean of the medical school at Yale, wrote:

I freely confess that it is difficult for me to regard with patience the attempts that are being made to hamper what seems to me one of the greatest opportunities in graduate instruction offered in this country. The Doctors Mayo have developed and organized at Rochester an enormous Clinic, the efficiency of which is recognized not only in this country but the world over. . . . I wish somebody would give me $100,000 a year for the Yale Medical School on condition that I administer it from Hartford, Connecticut, or from Oshkosh, Wisconsin, or from any other place.

And Dr. W. W. Keen of Philadelphia agreed:

I am amazed at the stupidity of those who oppose the acceptance of [the Mayos'] magnificent gifts. There are no other agencies in this country which have advanced medical knowledge and which have been more beneficent than the Mayo Foundation and the Rockefeller Institute. That anyone, and especially any doctor, should stand in the way of such a successful effort to ameliorate the condition of the human race is to me amazing.

8

When a public committee hearing on the pending bill was announced, some of the university officials considered the situation serious enough that they asked Dr. W. J. Mayo to appear for the Foundation. It was an amazing request to make—to ask a man to defend himself for being magnificently generous! But after a minute's thought Dr. Will replied, "I'm a good soldier. If you gentlemen think it's necessary, I'll do it."

The chamber was crowded the night of the hearing. The backers of the bill presented their arguments at length and with vehemence, President Vincent and Regent Fred B. Snyder replied, and then Dr. Mayo took the floor. The chairman had asked the audience not to applaud the speakers, but now forgetting his own injunction he led the crowd in a resounding tribute to the state's most famous son.

Then the people hushed as Dr. Mayo began to speak. He talked without notes or manuscript, simply, earnestly, colloquially. "Every man has some inspiration for good in his life," he began. "With my brother and I it came from our father. He taught us that any man who has physical strength, intellectual capacity, or unusual opportunity holds such endowments in trust to do with them for others in proportion to his gifts."

He went on to describe the unusual opportunity that had been his and his brother's and what they had sought to do with it. He told how as their income grew with their practice they had come to feel a sense of trusteeship for the money. He explained the ideals they had sought to apply in their practice and the purpose they wished to achieve with this gift of money and service.

As he continued his voice rose. "I can't understand why all this opposition should have been aroused over the affiliation with the university. It seems to be the idea of some persons that no one can want to do anything for anybody without having some sinister or selfish motive back of it. If we wanted money, we have it. That can't be the reason for our offer. We want the money to go back to the people, from whom it came, and we think we can best give it back to them through medical education.

"Now let's call a spade a spade. This money belongs to the people, and I don't care two raps whether the medical profession of the state like the way this money has been offered for use or not. It wasn't their money."

He paused a minute and his voice was quiet again as he resumed. " 'That these dead shall not have died in vain.' That line explains why we want to do this thing. What better could we do than help young men to become proficient in the profession so as to prevent needless deaths?"

Except for those few lines reported by the newspapermen present, no record of Dr. Mayo's talk survives. It is a "lost oration." But twenty-five years later men from varied walks of life who had heard it were still referring to it as the greatest, most eloquent speech they had ever listened to.

Needless to say, the bill died. It was reported out of committee and given a second reading but that was the last heard of it. And once again the opposition subsided to a rumbling growl.

9

That was in March 1917. America declared war against Germany on April 6. Dr. Will and Dr. Charlie had already joined the Medical Reserve Corps and it seemed likely that within a few months or a year at most one or the other of them would be going overseas. So they decided to put their house in order, and one room to be finished off was the affiliation with the university. They suggested to the regents that it be made permanent at once, agreeing to waive most of their one remaining stipulation as to the use of the endowment income. The graduate work should remain at Rochester for twenty-five years, but then the regents could move it elsewhere if they thought best, providing three fourths of them concurred in the decision in two votes at a three-year interval. Ten per cent of the annual income was to be spent outside the state, investigating disease in India or Argentina or wherever, so as to keep the Foundation's work worldwide in scope. Another ten per cent was to be earmarked for meeting emergencies within the state, such as epidemics of infantile paralysis, influenza, and the like.

The regents agreed to the proposal, and articles making the affiliation permanent were signed on September 17, 1917. As Dr. Will emerged from the room after the signing he was met by representatives of the Twin City press, all primed with the questions he had steadfastly refused to answer for them, and he gave in.

What we want to do is to make the medical experience of the past generation available for the coming one and so on indefinitely, so that each new generation shall not have to work out its problems independently, but may begin where its predecessors left off. This foundation, its fund, and all that goes with it are the contribution of the sick of this generation to prevent sickness and suffering in the next and following generations.

The health needs of the community surpass the possibilities of the state. It cannot meet them except under special stress, as in epidemics. We aim to supply the need so far as we may by this contribution of money, of trained men, of equipment and of service.

Why do we choose the university to carry out this purpose? Because we believe the people can be trusted. Anyhow, it is their money. We don't know a private board that could handle the fund better than the board of regents. . . . Certainly such a body as the university . . . will always attract as great an amount of idealism as any other organization.

Why do we do this now? What has led us to the offer of the affiliation in the first place and to a change of terms that modifies materially the relation? My brother and I are at a time of life when we see things as clearly as we may ever be able to see them. As one gets older one's horizon becomes more limited. We are in our fifties, and we don't want to take a chance on what the future may bring.

We are at war. My brother and I expect that next year when the recruits go over one or the other will go too. . . . War is serious business, especially to men of our years. . . . If I should not come back, I shall be satisfied. I have done the thing in life that I wanted to do.

Reporting the terms of the permanent affiliation, one Twin City editor commented drily that now the last objection raised by the opponents had been removed it would be interesting to see whether they could find any other basis for opposition. They could. Among them were some petty minds who when they got an idea clung to it with bulldog tenacity; they would still be fighting the Foundation battle when they died. They now declared that the new arrangement only made the position of the Mayos more secure, because in twenty-five years they would have such complete control of the university that removing the Foundation from Rochester would be impossible. The medical alumni were advised by a special committee from among them that all who were loyal to the best interests of the university must continue their opposition until the new contracts were abrogated or so modified as completely to divorce the private interests of the Mayos from the university.

For at least four years longer the opposition flared up in periodic attacks on the Mayos or the university administration. Once Dr. Will was publicly charged with malfeasance in office and his removal was demanded "for carrying out a corrupt combination of a state institution with his private business." The writer warned the public to expect some new move to the advantage of the Mayos because the brothers had recently taken the university president and regents for a cruise on their yacht. He was invited to appear before the regents and substantiate his charges, but all he had to offer was a lengthy rehash of the old arguments, and he would have suffered the fate of his predecessors at the hands of Pierce Butler if Dr. Mayo had not interfered to ask that he be allowed to state his case without interruption. Dr. Will offered to resign from the board, but his fellow regents would not have it. He insisted on giving up his post as their vice-president, however, ostensibly because of onerous duties elsewhere.

On another occasion it was charged that the "Mayo faction" was disrupting the entire university and that Marion LeRoy Burton, short-term successor to President Vincent, had resigned his position because he was unacceptable to the Mayo faction. From his new post as president of the University of Michigan, Burton sent an emphatic denial of the charge and declared there was no such thing as a Mayo faction in the university. What was more, he said, he had told the medical alumni so at the time of his resignation.

Dr. Will took it all with good grace. When one of the most persistent of the opponents seized the occasion at a gridiron banquet to deliver in Dr. Mayo's presence a vindictive and in the circumstances inexcusable attack on the Foundation, Dr. Will merely said to him when he had finished, "That's the best speech I ever heard you give on that subject, Soren." But those who were close to him say he was deeply hurt by the misrepresentation of his and Dr. Charlie's motives.

Minnesota men might carp and heckle; others took the gift at its face value, and when the affiliation was made permanent another wave of articles about the Mayos rolled over the land. The *New York Post* thought their story "one of the most stirring in the annals of medicine"; the *New York Sun* said, "The world can scarcely ask more from the fund than that it will develop more Mayos"; and the *Kansas City* (Missouri) *Journal* added, "The finest feature of the whole enterprise is the exemplification of the theory of stewardship, which holds that human talents and the financial results they produce are in fact held in trust for the benefit of the community or for the race as a whole. That sets the final seal of enlightened philanthropy upon the gift." But the editor of a Colorado newspaper capped them all. He concluded his account with a burst of uncontrollable feeling, "God, but it's good to live in a generation of such men!"

# The Clinic and the First World War

The 1914 session of the Clinical Congress of Surgeons of North America, at which Dr. Charlie was elected its president, was held in London to the accompaniment of rumbling rumors of war, sharpened for the members by the sudden summoning home of Professors von Eiselsberg of Vienna and Tuffier of France. Peace was still alive on August 1, when Dr. and Mrs. Charlie and Dr. and Mrs. J. B. Murphy sailed from Liverpool for New York on board the *S.S. Mauretania,* but the passengers had good cause to suspect that war had come when the crew suddenly began camouflaging the ship by draping tarpaulins of canvas over the sides, ordered the portholes covered with blankets, and ran in darkness at night. So great was the excitement on board that some imaginative person reported sighting a German cruiser every fifteen minutes.

In the middle of the night before the boat was to dock, most of the passengers were jarred awake as the huge liner suddenly and sharply changed its course, stopped entirely for a few minutes, and then moved forward, with its engines racing so the ship shook with the vibration. Thoroughly frightened, Mrs. Mayo woke her husband, told him what had happened, and said she was going out to see what was the matter. Quietly he said he wouldn't bother if he were she, because there wouldn't be anything she could do whatever was wrong. "This is somebody else's worry. The captain and the sailors are on the job. Just come lie down again; we'll keep very still and you'll go back to sleep." His calm voice soothed Mrs. Mayo to quiet but not to sleep. She lay listening to the engines and thinking of Dr. Charlie's words, "This is somebody else's worry." She understood what he meant as she thought of the times when the worry was his and Will's, like the night Governor Johnson died.

They landed next day, but at Halifax instead of New York, much to the surprise of the Nova Scotians. Then they were told that the sudden change of course had been due to wireless instructions from the British cruiser *Essex,* which had sighted a German raider in the waters.

2

When the Committee of American Physicians for Medical Preparedness was organized in 1916, as a step in the Wilson administration's "preparedness for peace," Dr. Will was named its chairman and Dr. Charlie another of its members. The committee made a classified survey of American hospitals and medical personnel and at the request of the surgeon general of the army began enlisting civilian doctors in a Medical Reserve Corps. When the committee for medical preparedness became the General Medical Board of the Council for National Defense Dr. Will was made a member of its executive committee, with Dr. Charlie as his alternate.

In the fall of 1916 the medical board decided to organize, through the medium of the Red Cross, fifty base-hospital units, according to a plan Dr. George W. Crile had suggested the preceding year because he believed "that mediocrity well organized is more efficient than brilliancy combined with strife and discord." Each unit was to include twenty-seven medical officers, sixty nurses, and one hundred and fifty-three enlisted men—carpenters, plumbers, x-ray technicians, orderlies, stenographers, undertakers—presumably a force sufficient to manage a hospital of five hundred beds, and each was to be recruited from the staff of a large hospital or medical school, which would also be responsible for outfitting the base hospital with necessary medical supplies.

The Mayo Clinic was asked to sponsor such a base hospital from Minnesota, but the affiliation with the University of Minnesota was then on trial and Dr. Will tactfully said he thought the university would be a more proper sponsor. He and Dr. Charlie contributed fifteen thousand dollars toward the expenses of the unit and enlisted approximately a third of its personnel from Rochester. The rest came from the university and the state at large, and Dr. Arthur A. Law, associate professor of surgery in the medical school and a man with previous experience as a medical officer in the Spanish-American War, was chosen to lead the group. Minneapolis citizens subscribed an additional fifteen thousand dollars and later donated an equal sum in supplies of various kinds.

# Clinic and Foundation

By early June 1917 Base Hospital No. 26 was reported ready, but it was not mobilized until December 13. Then after spending two weeks in makeshift quarters on the university campus it was ordered to camp in Atlanta, Georgia, for a period of intensive training, and the following June set sail for Europe on the British ship *Adriatic*—amid great excitement and "with a remarkable escort of scores of submarine chasers, destroyers, a cruiser, five hydroaeroplanes, a dirigible, and a balloon towed by a destroyer," because the day before German submarines had sunk fifteen small vessels in American waters. Sometime during the first night out the convoy turned back, leaving only the cruiser *Leviathan* to escort the *Adriatic* to England.

When the unit, minus its nurses, who had been detached for service elsewhere, reached its station at Allerey, Saône-et-Loire, it found barracks under construction to house ten base hospitals and a convalescent camp for five thousand. For No. 26 itself there were fifty-three buildings, twenty of them receiving wards and the rest kitchens, dispensaries, and laboratories, with a total capacity of just over two thousand men.

The Minnesota unit was the first of the ten on the scene, and all its members pitched in to help finish the plumbing and wiring and dig the sewers. The wounded were coming in from the front long before the supplies arrived from Minneapolis, so the staff contrived a hundred and one ingenious makeshifts—tubs and sinks and laboratory receptacles out of biscuit tins, bathing slabs out of lumber and roofing materials, sterilizers out of empty barrels, and refrigerators from gunny sacking stretched over frames and kept wet by dripping water. The doctors scoured the surrounding villages for whatever drugs, dressings, and suture materials they could find, to serve until their own supplies arrived a month or so later. As the great summer offensive of 1918 continued, Base Hospital No. 26 received hundreds of wounded a day, and when its sister units arrived it became solely a surgical hospital, while they took over other specialties such as contagious, venereal, and nervous diseases. By the time the unit was ordered home, it had treated seven thousand two hundred men.

During this war service some of the younger members from the Clinic had their first personal experience with the antagonism toward the Mayos. In spite of Dr. Will's tactful efforts the popular name for Base Hospital No. 26 was "the Mayo unit," and the men were constantly asked to explain why, or when the Mayos were coming to France, or why there were not more of the Clinic men at the front. One of the young men, disturbed by all the sly digs and innuendoes, wrote Dr. Will about them and asked his advice as to what answer to make.

Ignore it all, was Dr. Will's reply. He said he had been bitten by these small insects for so many years that he no longer paid any attention to them. As to the number of Clinic men in the service, sixty-three of the staff members were already working overseas, said Dr. Will. How many more did they expect the Clinic to furnish?

### 3

In the first summoning of energies that followed America's declaration of war against Germany, the Mayos jumped to the conclusion that of course they would serve with the medical forces at the front in France, but the authorities in Washington saw other uses for their peculiar abilities. At the suggestion of Dr. Welch of Johns Hopkins, Surgeon General William C. Gorgas—far famed for one of the greatest achievements in the annals of preventive medicine, the conquest of yellow fever and malaria in Panama—asked Dr. Will to act as his adviser on surgical questions in general and on the caliber of surgeon members of the Medical Reserve Corps in particular. He told Dr. Will to pick whatever associates he wanted, and Dr. Will immediately arranged a rotating advisory service, choosing ten well-known surgeons —mainly from the South and West, since the East was already amply represented in administrative positions—each of them to act as surgical adviser to the surgeon general two weeks at a time and to be completely independent in the decisions made during his term on duty. Drs. Stuart McGuire, W. D. Haggard, A. J. Ochsner, and J. F. Binnie were to serve during July and August 1917, then Dr. Charlie would take a turn, and Drs. Arthur D. Bevan, Leonard Freeman, Sam Mixter, Emmet Rixford, and Kenneth Mackenzie would finish out the year, with Dr. Will coming up again next.

Distributing the honor and responsibility of the position was a typical Mayo idea, and theoretically it was an excellent way of acquainting a number of men with the problems of the service, but in practice it did not work well. Each man was on duty just long enough to find his way about in the job; then off he went and a new man came on. Few of the surgical advisers proved able to cut through the tangle of petty jealousies among the various offices and agencies in Washington, and they often wrote to ask Dr. Will what they should do about this problem or that obstreperous individual. "Probably," wrote Dr. Binnie, referring to Dr. Charlie, who was to succeed him, "C. H. will . . . in his smooth way help correct the evils."

Dr. Charlie did precisely that. He soothed ruffled feelings and settled difficulties so rapidly that Dr. Franklin Martin, chairman of the medical board, asked Dr. Will whether he and Dr. Charlie couldn't alternate on the job in place of the rotating service. The brothers agreed to do so, each serving three weeks at a time while the other carried on at home. It was a little difficult to explain the change to some members of the rotating advisory board, but most of them were glad to be relieved of the unpleasant responsibility.

The brothers' principal task was "to insure and maintain, as far as possible, the proper standard of character and professional ability in the medical men taken into the medical service [about 40,000 of them], and to plan ways and means for their special training." It was their job too, until a special committee (with Henry Plummer as one of its members) was appointed for the purpose, to judge the worth of the scores of devices and methods recommended by would-be inventors for use in the army medical services.

One of the ticklish matters they had to manage was the insistent requests from chiropractors, osteopaths, and chiropodists for admission to the medical corps. Each of these groups had legislation pending in Congress to give them equal rank with regular physicians and surgeons, and they wanted the sanction of the surgeon general as support in securing passage of their bills. Dr. Will and Dr. Charlie did not scornfully advise peremptory rejection of their claims, because they saw a possible use for all of them in the army service, particularly in the rehabilitation of disabled soldiers, but of course they could not concede them the authority or responsibility of medical officers.

4

The medical officers were themselves much exercised about the question of rank. The highest position accorded them when war came was that of colonel for the regular army doctors and major for members of the Medical Reserve Corps. Some of America's best doctors—men like Harvey Cushing, John Finney, George Crile, Hugh Young, and Hugh Cabot—went overseas with the rank of major and were quite content with it until they discovered that many English and French medical officers were colonels and generals. When the Europeans looked beyond the title and insignia and discovered a man of international reputation, they treated him as an equal. More often, however, they considered an American doctor inferior in status, and the Americans resented the disadvantage and humiliation. But it was a tussle to get Congress to vote the doctors military rank, in part because the War Department and the army chiefs considered doctors a necessary evil and begrudged them equal recognition.

Finally on July 9, 1918 Congress accorded to medical officers the right to all ranks from lieutenant to major general. Dr. Will and Dr. Charlie were immediately moved up from majors to colonels and later became brigadier generals. Although they appreciated the principle for which their medical colleagues were fighting, personally they cared little what they were called or what insignia they were entitled to wear on their shoulders. In fact they scandalized their military fellows by continuing to wear their major's emblems—"in order to save a lot of talk and hard feelings."

When the War Department in June 1918 saw fit to appoint Dr. Will and Dr. Charlie, acting as alternates, to an advisory post on the general staff, their colleagues on the medical board, including Surgeon General Gorgas, were delighted, because the action seemed to promise more of the badly needed cooperation between the army and the medical branches. Apparently the general staff was less pleased, for when Dr. Will reported for duty he was told "his presence would not be required . . . except on occasions when advice was needed." Quickly sensing an intention to make him a mere figurehead, he protested. He would prefer not to take the position if his duties were to be merely perfunctory; he was not looking for an impressive title but for a place to be useful in the business of licking the Germans. So presently new orders transferred him back to his former position, with the title of chief consultant of the surgical services.

The episode was reported in the *Army and Navy Register* as "a refusal to serve on the General Staff . . . a rare and somewhat refreshing instance of a determination not to obey official orders," and was given wider currency through a subtly satirical editorial in the *Military Surgeon*. Soon all Washington was laughing at the joke on the general staff, and Colonel John Hoff, associate editor of the *Military Surgeon,* was forced to resign his position for "permitting this disgrace."

5

In addition to their general advisory work, "Dr. W. J. Mayo *or* Dr. C. H. Mayo" was appointed to several special committees of the medical board, and Dr. Will was named medical aide to the governor of Minnesota to supervise the administration of the selective service law. To him also came many calls for help from men who needed the word of "a man of influence" to get them commissioned or discharged or transferred from one camp or company or regiment to another, or to convince the authorities that they were needed at home to care for the civilians of their community. Nevertheless, the brothers managed to give a good many wartime pep talks before various medical groups, and what Dr. Charlie said about the beneficial effects of sacrifice and discipline on the nation's character and the contributions of war to medicine was widely reported because he was president of the American Medical Association. He was elected and was in his turn tendered a banquet and loving cup by Rochester citizens in 1916, and he took office in 1917.

His presidential address was typical of him, a miscellany of unrelated ideas delivered with animation and humor that brought repeated cheers from the fifteen hundred members assembled in the ballroom of the Waldorf Astoria in New York. The medical profession was under considerable pressure at the time, both from the Allies and from temperance crusaders at home, to endorse national prohibition as a means of food conservation, and after considerable debate the convention adopted a resolution declaring that "alcohol has no drug value . . . and its use as a beverage or as a therapeutic agent is detrimental rather than beneficial to the individual." There were a sizable minority who contended with good sense that the effects of alcohol could not be scientifically determined by a mass vote, even of the nation's doctors.

Press accounts of the matter, under headings like "When Doctors

Disagree," featured Dr. Charlie's stand against the use of alcohol, because as he often did he contributed an idea that was novel and plausible, whether historically accurate or not:

That disease is frequently water-borne is a practical observation that has existed for many centuries. To a large extent among Orientals the danger of such transmission was overcome by the drinking of tea and coffee, the water for which was purified by boiling. In Europe the same results were obtained in the manufacture of weak wines, brews, and liquors, the fermentation and yeast germs of which destroyed the virulent bacteria. Now that we know how and why water was dangerous, the necessity especially of alcoholic drinks has been removed in every community in this great country by an abundance of pure water. No one except the policeman sees more of the results of overindulgence in alcohol, demonstrated in poverty, sickness, immorality, and crime than the physician. Medicine has reached a period when alcohol is rarely employed as a drug, being displaced by better remedies. Alcohol's only place now is in the arts and sciences. National prohibition would be welcomed by the medical profession.

The strain of their war service, added to the extra efforts needed to keep the Clinic going and continued for more than two years without a pause, finally took its toll in the health of both men. Dr. Charlie came down with pneumonia during one of his turns in Washington and Dr. Will was forced home in the fall of 1918 by a severe case of jaundice that kept him off duty for more than two months. Since Dr. Charlie carried on at the capital, this was the first time that the brothers were both absent from the Clinic for any extended period. But Will reported to Charlie that all was well, adding, "It is not very flattering to say that everything is going so well without either of us at work."

## 6

Although Dr. Will thought things were going well, the Clinic staff themselves found the days rushed and upset. As one man after another volunteered or was called, the load doubled and tripled for those who stayed, because a simultaneous increase in registrations carried the annual total from thirty thousand in 1914 to sixty thousand in 1919. The tremendous publicity given to the story of the Mayo Foundation, followed almost immediately by the boomingly prosperous "silk-shirt era" of the war, sent people in droves to Rochester, more of them than the attenuated staff could readily handle.

# Clinic and Foundation

Not only that, there were draftees to examine and the war training school to keep going. Dr. Will and Dr. Charlie had agreed to provide short courses for incoming members of the medical corps, courses of clinics, lectures, and laboratory work designed to bring the doctors quickly abreast of the latest developments in scientific medicine and surgery. Each new class, numbering from twenty to forty, was divided into small sections, and each section was assigned to one of the operating rooms every morning, rotating from room to room day by day. They all spent the afternoons observing diagnosis on the Clinic floor or in one of the laboratories and assembled five evenings a week for lectures by the Clinic staff. Altogether they got about two hundred hours of intensive training in surgical technique, in giving blood transfusions and local anesthesia, administering salvarsan, Paul Ehrlich's famous 606 for syphilis, reading x-rays, and making autopsies.

The Clinic men also gave courses for noncommissioned officers and privates who were to serve in the ambulance corps or as hospital orderlies or laboratory assistants, but St. Mary's Hospital took charge of the nurses who were sent, fifteen or twenty at a time, to brush up on anesthesia and operating-room procedure. All told, there were always between sixty and seventy persons—in addition to the Foundation fellows—in training at Rochester throughout the war years, and the responsibility for supervising their work was heavy on the time and shoulders of Dr. Judd, who directed it all.

Under such conditions patients sometimes had to wait days or even weeks for examination, and the well-known Clinic rule, "First come first served," was changed to "The needy first." St. Mary's nurses long remembered how Dr. Graham, white-haired, weary, overworked, would say to someone clamoring insistently for his attention, "Here on my list are the names of two hundred people whom I must see first because they are poor and cannot stand the expense of waiting for medical help."

To the rush of work were added many petty annoyances that came with the war. American laboratories had been almost wholly dependent on Germany for equipment and materials, and when the German supply was cut off doctors and technicians alike found it hard to adjust their methods to the poorer quality of American-made slides, stains, lenses, and the like. For a while the Clinic's surgical pathologists were

# The Clinic and the World War

at their wits' end trying to find a satisfactory methylene blue dye for their fresh-tissue diagnosis. They were finally reduced to the expedient of washing water through the dregs of their old supply to get enough dye to use, because despite frantic efforts in odd minutes they could not discover the formula for a sufficiently neutral, nonalkaline, preparation.

Then one day Dr. Benjamin E. Terry, an independent research worker who had been granted the privileges of the Clinic laboratories, happened in and was told about the problem. He set to work on it and after six days of concentrated effort produced a stain as good as any they had ever had. This interested Dr. Terry in the fresh-tissue method, and he eventually contributed some valuable modifications to it.

## 7

"And then came the flu epidemic!" So sooner or later says anyone who talks about the war years at the Clinic. They had only *thought* they were busy before, for now the people literally poured into the Clinic from the immediate community. Assigned duties and stations were forgotten, and every doctor, nurse, technician, and secretary worked wherever he was needed most at the moment, often until late at night. Relatives or friends with any time to spare were called into service, Dr. Will's younger daughter Phoebe among them. The doctors worked on the Clinic floor until four or four-thirty and then started out on drives through the countryside, sending the worst cases they found to the isolation unit at St. Mary's.

That new addition to the facilities of the hospital was a small hotel building next door to the hospital which the Sisters of St. Francis had bought to get rid of the growing congestion on their very doorstep. It was remodeled and opened for use in June 1918 and so was ready when the influenza arrived in September. The disease broke out in a mild form in the town first, then suddenly and virulently in the hospital itself. On one day in early October twenty persons, eighteen of them nurses, had to be moved to the isolation house. The next day patients began arriving from all over the community, and within a week the new unit was packed, even to cots in the hallways.

The St. Mary's staff also had been greatly reduced by summons to war service, and with the influenza victims gone too it was woefully inadequate to handle the influx, though everyone worked to the limit of her strength. Sometimes the nurses and even the superintendent went down to help in the kitchens and laundries. The isolation house had its own kitchen, but there was no one to staff it, so food was carried over from the main kitchens. And on top of everything else, the sisters were driven nearly to distraction by the constant phone calls from anxious friends and relatives of the patients.

Part of the jam in the Clinic laboratories and offices came from the demand for Dr. Rosenow's influenza serum. Dr. Edward C. Rosenow was a well-known bacteriologist who had been associated with Dr. Frank Billings of Chicago for many years. The Mayos greatly admired him and his work and asked him to join their diagnostic staff in 1909, but he preferred to stick to his research. Late in April 1915, when the Foundation had been organized and its affiliation with the university seemed likely for a trial period at least, Dr. Will wrote to Dr. Rosenow explaining the purposes and possibilities of the Foundation and asking him to join its staff as an experimental bacteriologist. The offer was characteristic of Dr. Will, and the only kind a man of Dr. Rosenow's stamp would be likely to accept: "We have always had it in our minds that someday you might join us, *on your own terms, to do what you wanted to do in your own way.*"

Dr. Rosenow transferred his laboratory from Chicago to Rochester, and when the influenza appeared he began at once to make bacteriological examinations of sputum samples from the patients. Finding one species of streptococcus invariably present, he decided it was the trouble-maker and prepared a serum with it which he offered to administer free to the citizens of Rochester, since he knew it could do no harm and it might do good. Circumstances made a reliable tabulation of results impossible, and Dr. Rosenow would say no more than that the serum seemed to act as an effective prophylactic against the infection. But that was enough. As word spread through the state and beyond, city officials, health officers, and individual physicians and laymen became insistent in their demand for the serum. The day after the *Journal of the American Medical Association* published Dr. Rosenow's offer to furnish it at the nominal cost of manufacture or to tell any qualified bacteriologist how to make it, the Clinic received four hundred telegrams asking for a supply. The job of filling the orders fell largely to the lot of the secretarial staff of the Foundation, and they worked literally day and night at it.

One of the secretaries mailed a bottle of the stuff to the doctor in her home town and sent word to her father and mother to go to his office and take the shots. When he got the girl's letter of explanation the doctor casually remarked to the postmaster that he was going to have some flu vaccine. The news spread through the town with the wind, and the doctor's office was soon jammed with panic-stricken persons who wanted the treatment. Since the vaccine was supposed to be given in three injections at weekly intervals, the harassed doctor called the Clinic secretary long distance to find out whether she could send him more for the second and third shots if he used up this bottle on first ones. She said yes, but even so he had barely enough left for her parents when they arrived.

That experience with varying details was repeated in many a small Minnesota town that winter of 1918–19, but unfortunately, in the rush and out of reluctance to withhold a possible preventive from anyone who wanted it the doctors forgot about records and control groups, so that the true effect of the shots could not be gauged and the widespread use of the serum was of little value as a scientific experiment.

## 8

When word came that the armistice had indeed been signed Dr. Will at once cabled greetings to his professional friends in Germany and Austria. Within a few hours a member of the secret service appeared at his office asking whether he had tried to "communicate with the enemy." Amazed, Dr. Will said, "I thought the war was over!"

Even when it was, the prejudice it had whipped up did not quickly pass away. For decades American medical men had been sitting reverently at the feet of German and Austrian masters of surgery and medical science, but under the influence of the wartime loss of balance that denied virtue to *anything* German, many of them suddenly discovered the greatness of those masters to be only another effective fiction of German propaganda. The skill of Central European surgeons, they now declared, was merely an indication of their shamelessness in developing and exploiting as their own the ideas they had picked up from more original British and American thinkers.

Dr. Will and Dr. Charlie shared in this revulsion of opinion, but they were less willing than the majority of their fellows to see it translated into action against individuals. When it was proposed at the 1918 meeting of the American Surgical Association that the German and Austrian honorary members be dropped from the list of members, Dr. Will, in uniform, forcefully opposed the action, insisting that political and military hostility ought not to extend into the world of science. The resolution failed to pass at that session but was adopted at the next one, which Dr. Will could not attend.

When the International Society of Surgery resumed its triennial meetings in Paris in 1920 its members voted some modifications of its statutes, including the adoption of English, Spanish, French, and Italian as official languages in place of German. They also ratified a motion offered by their executive committee to the effect that since the members from the Central Powers had so far forgotten scientific detachment as to subscribe to obviously erroneous statements, had forsaken reason to participate in a villainous outrage, and had made not the slightest retraction of false accusations against the Allies, their names should be struck from the society's roll of members.

After the Pact of Locarno was signed a group of distinguished Japanese surgeons initiated a move for reinstating the ousted Germans and Austrians at the society's next session and solicited support for it among United States surgeons. The Mayo brothers wholeheartedly endorsed the proposed resolution, and Dr. Will campaigned for its passage in an extensive correspondence with both American and German surgeons. When his sponsorship of the move was reported in Berlin the Associated Press wrote him for confirmation and published his answer, in which he declared his conviction that "medical science, like all science, has no country and no language. . . . To continue international rancor based on prejudice is unthinkable, justifiable in neither principle nor fact."

The International Society meeting in Rome in 1926 voted "almost unanimously" to readmit the Germans and Austrians who had been members in 1914, providing only that they subscribe to the revised statutes. But unfortunately the Germans were stiff-necked about it and refused to rejoin the society unless it made German the official language as before and retracted without reservation the unjustified and insulting statements it had made about them at Paris in 1920. Whereupon the executive committee of the society voted to drop the matter entirely.

## 9

"Medicine is the only victor in war." The contributions of military experience to civil practice in preventive medicine, surgery, and nursing are commonplaces of history, but less generally recognized is the impetus the First World War gave to the spread of laboratory medicine. When Dr. Louis B. Wilson went overseas early in 1918 as assistant director of the A.E.F. division of laboratories and infectious diseases he found the entire laboratory setup in a feeble state. Laboratories were few, competent personnel fewer, and the equipment so makeshift it would have been thought impossible in civil hospitals.

Worse still, the usefulness of the pathologists, dependent upon recognition by surgeons and clinicians, was limited by the indifference of many medical officers who had not learned to use laboratory doctors as consultants in civil practice. Hospital commanders were known, not infrequently, to assign their laboratory men to "more important" duties in the storeroom or mess hall, and in most base hospitals clinical pathology beyond simple urine and sputum examinations was little more than something to play with when more serious business was slow. In some units the gross examination of materials removed at operation was routine, in others occasional, depending on whether or not the surgeon was used to such review of his work in civil practice. There was very little microscopic examination of such materials anywhere because there was no time for the preparation of sections. And autopsies were done in no more than twenty-five per cent of the hospital deaths.

Yet the physicians and surgeons of the medical corps had been brought suddenly face to face with physical ills new to them and under emergency conditions that gave them no time for study or reflection before they acted. Gross errors in diagnosis and treatment were many, even with the best men, and a thorough autopsy service was needed to catch those errors and point them out so they could be avoided in similar cases to come. This was not a question of research for some far future but of urgently necessary clinical service in the immediate present.

Change in such attitudes is always slow, but aided by the example and arguments of competent pathologists strategically placed Dr. Wilson and his chief, Col. Joseph F. Siler, worked wonders. Through the monthly reports they required from all laboratories they were able to locate the weak spots, hospitals that made little use or the wrong use of their scientific staff, and then strengthen them by letters of criticism and instruction, visits of inspection, and a continuous program of general education. By early fall in 1918 there were nearly three hundred laboratories in use in the A.E.F., still understaffed but much less so than earlier; the percentage of autopsies had risen to ninety-two, and the records sent to the central office indicated they were providing a reasonably adequate review of diagnosis and treatment; the number of leukocyte counts, blood smears, stool examinations, and other clinical procedures was rising steadily to a fair proportion; and best of all, in many units the internists and surgeons were beginning to view the laboratory doctor as a fully worthy member of the medical fraternity.

Thousands of doctors who first experienced the regular use of a diagnostic laboratory in their war service returned home to demand similar facilities in their community hospitals, and clinical pathology came quickly of age during the next decade. A new professional group, the American Society of Clinical Pathologists, came into being in 1922, and four years later the American College of Surgeons recognized the new specialty by including in its list of minimum requirements for accredited hospitals a complete laboratory service "in charge of a graduate of medicine, *especially trained in clinical pathology.*"

## 10

When Dr. A. L. Lockwood, a young Canadian surgeon who spent four years in service at the front in France, received his discharge he was reluctant to return to the private individual practice he had left, because he was convinced that the future of medicine lay in the kind of planned, coordinated effort he had been sharing in. Stopping off in London for a few days on his way home, he found himself next to Sir Berkeley Moynihan at a public dinner one night and discussed the problem with him. Finally Moynihan said to him, "If I were your age, my boy, I would try to attach myself to the Mayo Clinic, because there in my opinion is the most outstanding center for surgical and medical advance in the world today."

Dr. Lockwood took the older man's advice and three months later arrived in Rochester to begin work with the Mayos. "My first reaction was unutterable amazement," he wrote later, "amazement that increased month by month." For he found in Rochester a degree of integration and cooperation the army medical corps had not approached.

War service gave many a doctor his first taste of organized cooperation among specialists—teamwork in practice. Many did not like it, those who must solo to be happy, but others like Lockwood were sufficiently impressed with its advantages to want them in civil practice. As a result so many private group clinics were organized in the four years immediately following the war that doctors began talking about "this marked tendency toward group medicine." Most of the new clinics appeared in the Middle West and Southwest, where greater distances and thinner settlement made the problem of adequate laboratory and hospital facilities more acute.

But a desire to improve the quality of medical care above what the individual doctor could provide was not the only motive at work; new methods were also bringing to the fore the corollary problem of increasing costs. As the medical course lengthened from two years to six and more, as the family doctor's little black bag grew into a battery of expensive equipment, as x-ray pictures and chemical and microscopic examinations were added to physical examination by the diagnostician, in short, as the horse-and-buggy era yielded to modern scientific medicine, the doctor's investment and consequently his bill multiplied many times. Medical fees were fast becoming prohibitive.

Not for the wealthy or the very poor; the former could afford to pay and the latter were not expected to. But the members of the great middle class had either to be content with a good bit less than the best in medicine or to pocket their pride and accept the charity service of free clinics and dispensaries. Recognizing the latter as a humiliation to self-respecting men and an unjust drain upon philanthropy, some of the more progressive eastern hospital managers established "pay clinics," in which the man of moderate means could receive the benefit of the hospital's specialists and laboratories at a price he could afford to pay. The Boston Dispensary under Dr. Michael Davis and New York's Mt. Sinai Hospital under Dr. Sigismund Goldwater led the way, despite the vociferous protests of independent practitioners.

For doctors the increasing costs meant fewer patients, more unpaid bills, and an overhead out of all proportion to returns. In large cities they attempted to solve the problem by renting offices in a "physicians and surgeons" or a "medical arts" building, where they might share the use of common laboratories, but though that expedient also made it more convenient for patients to see the various specialists, it contributed little if anything to coordination in practice.

Doctors beset with such problems were led to consider group organization by the inescapable example of the Mayo Clinic, where they all seemed to have been solved almost before they arose. Imitation of the Mayo methods had produced a score of small group clinics before the war, most of them fathered by members of the Surgeons Club or by former fellowship men, who had seen for themselves how the idea worked in Rochester. And imitation of the Mayos was publicly claimed by several of the largest groups formed immediately after the war—claimed, because of the Mayo reputation with the public.

The story of the Foundation and the tremendous publicity given it finished the process of making the Mayos national celebrities. Everything they said or did was news the public wanted, and newspapers from Ohio to Wyoming published all sorts of items about them and their Clinic: descriptions of how the Clinic worked written by patients as letters to the folks at home, bits of doggerel verse they composed to while away idle hours, dramatic cases they witnessed or heard about.

In a St. Paul hotel reporters came upon an English airman who was on his way to Rochester because the surgeons at home had told him that was the only place he could get effective treatment for his eyes, injured in a plane crash at the front. Down in Tulsa a man was found lying in the street, paralyzed and unconscious, apparently the victim of thieves, and a wealthy benefactress took him to the Mayo Clinic and then, in the hope of locating his relatives, advertised his story, including the miracle of repair worked by Clinic surgeons. Over in Marinette, Wisconsin, the relief committee of the Lloyd Manufacturing Company, investigating the case of a young man and his wife, both ill and without means of support, discovered that they owed the Mayo Clinic two hundred dollars for services in a previous illness. Informing the Clinic of the circumstances, the committee were so impressed when they got an immediate reply canceling the bill that they thought the story ought to be made public.

The national news services picked up such stories and spread them through the country, and reporters, assigned to get material for feature stories, nosed out more anecdotes that became perennials. There was one about the business tycoon who sent the Clinic a check for a thousand dollars to pay for an operation on a member of his family and promptly got a courteous letter returning his check, informing him that the Clinic set its own fees, and inclosing a bill for five thousand dollars. And another—now become such a favorite that in one of its several versions it turns up in most Minnesota conversations on the Mayos—about the pompous millionaire who, seeing Dr. Will cross the lobby, bustled up to ask importantly, "Are you the head doctor here?"

"No," Dr. Will replied soberly. "My brother is the head doctor. I'm the belly doctor."

On top of all that came a succession of famous patients who carried the Mayos with them into the newspapers. Dr. Will and Dr. Charlie were called to St. Paul to perform an emergency operation on Jim Hill, the railroad magnate; Dr. Charlie was summoned to Washington in consultation on Mrs. Harding, wife of the President; ex-President Taft paid public tribute to the skill of the Mayos, apparently after a visit to Rochester; and Franklin K. Lane, secretary of the interior under Woodrow Wilson, was sent to Rochester by his New York doctor, "to see if it is true that my stomach and my gall bladder have become too intimate," he said. "Rochester is the Reno where such divorces are granted."

During the days of examination Lane wrote many letters, scattering through them bits of comment on the Mayos and their Clinic. To one friend he said:

Truly, this is the most scientifically organized organization of scientists that ever was. Henry Ford could not improve upon it. Combine him with M. Pasteur, add a touch of one Edison, and a dose of your friend, Charlie Schwab, and you have the Mayo Clinic, big, systematized, modernized, machinized, doctorial plant, run by a couple of master workmen. . . . Tomorrow I am to be photographed and fluoroscoped—and then will come the verdict. . . . I guess whatever is said will be the last word—the Supreme Court decision. Fine reputation, that, for two young chaps who never went to Harvard, eh, what?

The verdict was a diseased appendix and gallbladder; "the latter was a stone quarry and the former a cesspool," said Lane. But he had angina pectoris too, and Dr. Will advised him against operation, since with care he could live for some time without it. But Lane was tired of his invalidism, and after a few months in California he returned to Rochester determined to run the risk of surgery. Dr. Will performed the operation, using local anesthesia at first because of the bad heart but forced to ether in the end. Lane came through well and was making such a rapid recovery that everyone was jubilant, when an attack of angina carried him off suddenly ten days later.

Then his last letters, colorful accounts of his reflections on life and death and politics, were widely published and made the subject of much editorial and pulpit comment. In the one he dictated the day after his operation, to be sent to his many anxious friends, he described his thoughts during the ordeal and concluded with, "What a great thing, what a pride, to have the two men of greatest constructive imagination and courage in surgery in the world as Americans, Dr. Charles and Will Mayo."

## 11

Thus it was that *Mayo* became a household name in America, so generally familiar that a Michigan newspaper could actually print the following notice: "Goodfellows' Barber Shop Closed for Two Weeks, On Account of Having to Go to Mayo Brothers."

Attempts to cash in on this reputation were many and varied. Scarcely a month passed without some new report that the Mayos intended to establish a branch of their famous clinic here, there, everywhere—in Red Wing, in Winona, in Manitoba, on the Salton Sea! Where the rumors came from was a mystery, and Dr. Will's emphatic denials did not always put a stop to them. The story that the Mayos planned to move to southern California persisted for months, and when it was denied in one town it sprang up in another, one Pasadena real estate agent going so far as to declare that the famous brothers were just about to close the deal for one of his properties.

Finally the story settled on the Ambassador Hotel in Los Angeles;

the Mayos had bought it and would turn it into a sanatorium. Angrily the manager of the hotel denied the story; the Ambassador was having the best season in its history, and no part of it had been sold or was for sale. But his statement was discounted on the grounds that the Mayo brothers wanted to discourage the real estate promotion the rumor had started. At last Dr. Will wrote to his old friend, John Willis Baer, president of Occidental College, asking him to do anything he could to squelch the story. There had never been the slightest foundation for it, he said; he and Charlie did not have and never had had any intention of starting a branch clinic anywhere. Baer gave the letter to the newspapers, and the story died.

Equally numerous and more annoying were the fakers who traveled about the country proclaiming themselves representatives of the Mayo Clinic or exhibiting testimonials from the Mayos for the nostrums they were selling. One scoundrel in Winnipeg actually called himself Dr. Gordon Mayo, opened a luxurious suite of offices, and was the busiest doctor in town until the authorities, suspecting he was performing abortions, uncovered his identity as Russell Dumas, an ex-convict.

The impostors in Canada got so numerous that the Clinic finally, as a warning, threatened to prosecute two doctors who established "a branch of the Mayo Clinic" in a Manitoba town, saying the Mayos' large Canadian clientele had made it necessary to do so. The threat was enough to force a public apology from the doctors and the closing of their clinic.

It was not so easy to deal with those who clung to the edge of truth and artfully implied their connection with the Rochester institution. A practitioner in Brazil, Indiana, managed this by saying that such clinics as his were approved by the Drs. Mayo because they had so many more patients than they could handle and that his surgeons and anesthetists had spent years at the operating table with the Mayo brothers—though only one of those listed had come from Rochester, a former Clinic fellow who resigned from the Indiana group after a few months.

So it is not surprising that members of legitimate groups were also glad to claim as their model the form of practice "originated by the celebrated Mayo brothers" or say their building was planned by the architect who built the Mayo Clinic plant in Rochester, Minnesota. All in all, there is no doubt that the brilliant success of the Mayo Clinic was a primary factor in the spread of group practice.

The idea had its critics even then, but as yet they went little beyond argument by analogy: A clinic was like a department store, convenient because the customer could buy everything in one building, but if you wanted goods of quality you did your buying in a specialty shop. The glib analogy did not hold for the Mayo group. The divisions and sections of the Clinic may have made it look like a department store, but it did not function like one. Thanks to Dr. Plummer's scheme of integration, its sections were not independent units, clustered in one building for convenience; they were integral parts of a working whole. And thanks to Dr. Will's insistence on the personal responsibility of the clinician, the patients did not wander from section to section, "buying" an x-ray or a blood test at will. To make the department store analogy at all valid, the store would have to be one in which the task of outfitting a bride for her wedding is given to one *coutourier,* who draws from the stock of many departments and asks the advice of many expert buyers to achieve a complete and harmonious ensemble.

Unfortunately too many of the Clinic's imitators, like its critics, missed the fundamentals in method and policy and copied only the externals. There were even some who, long suspecting that the Mayos had the most profitable practice in the history of medicine and convinced of it when their gift of a million and a half to the Foundation was announced, joined a group clinic for the primary purpose of increasing their income—disregarding Dr. Will's repeated insistence that the benefits of cooperative practice were not financial.

# CHAPTER TWENTY-ONE

# Toward the Future

When the war fixed American minds on Europe, the American College of Surgeons shelved tentative plans for extending its fellowship, originally limited to the men of Canada and the United States, to "all worthy surgeons of the American continents." After the war Dr. Will Mayo, president of the college from 1918 to 1920, helped materially to revive the idea and translate it into action, for, wearied by all the postwar debate over the proper role of the United States in the affairs of Europe, he thought he saw in Pan-American cooperation a less controversial and more fruitful possibility. Foreseeing a tremendous expansion in commerce and travel between the Americas, he thought it wise for the college to promote intercourse with Latin American surgeons.

With the approval of the board of regents of the college, letters were dispatched to ask the eminent surgeons of several South American countries whether they would be interested in affiliation with the North American body and in an organized exchange of professors and students in medicine. Then to stimulate interest further and to see for themselves what the neighbors' hospitals, medical schools, and surgeons were like, Dr. Will and Dr. Franklin Martin, secretary of the college, decided to visit the southern continent, and with their wives sailed from New York early in January 1920. They left their Minnesota and Illinois homes shivering in zero cold, but three days out from New York they were lolling on deck in summer clothing.

That is, most of them were; Dr. Will as usual had planned an occupation for the interval. For some time professional and lay friends had been urging him and Charlie to publish their own version of how the Clinic and Foundation came to be, and they had finally decided to do so through the Clinic division of publications. So Dr. Will asked Mrs. Mellish to go with him to South America, and he spent much of his time on the way dictating to her an outline of the story she was to write.

When at the proper place in the narrative he paid tribute to Dr. Wilson's work in organizing the laboratories, Mrs. Mellish was moved to interpolate some sentences of her own. "L. Wilson is tremendously brilliant," she wrote. "I have met few men his intellectual equal. In addition to his scientific abilities he has a most pleasing personality." Her admiration for Dr. Wilson was fully reciprocated, and shortly afterward they were married. Together they wrote the *Sketch of the History of the Mayo Clinic and the Mayo Foundation* that was published anonymously in 1925. As they worked on it they discovered they were too close to the story and its dramatis personae to see it in proper perspective, so with Dr. Will's approval they deliberately stripped their sketch to a skeleton of statistics, names, and dates, and left it for someone with more temerity to flesh the facts.

2

Greatly flattered by the coming of the two northern medical leaders, the gracious Latin Americans turned their tour of the major cities of Peru, Chile, Argentina, and Uruguay into a veritable triumphal procession. Wherever their boat docked or their train stopped, a smiling reception committee was waiting, ready to whirl them into a round of luncheons, dinners, and receptions on the lushly beautiful estates of medical men, government officials, and wealthy civilians. In between times they attended clinics, toured hospitals, and addressed many gatherings of medical students and practitioners. In impressively formal ceremonies they were both declared members of the Society of Surgery of Peru, and Dr. Will was awarded an honorary degree by the University of San Marcos in Lima, the oldest university in the western hemisphere. Everywhere they were impressed by the wealth and social influence of their surgeon hosts, and even more by their learning in literature and art, their fine private libraries and art collections. After a dinner in the home of one gentleman whose hobby was collecting the skulls of Inca chiefs, they were overcome when the next morning he sent them each a skull as a memento of the occasion.

The spaciousness of the hospital and medical school buildings and the elaborately landscaped gardens surrounding them amazed the visitors from the United States. Nor could they find any fault with the instruction offered. Throughout South America the medical course was seven years in length and the examinations were so exacting that few North American or European surgeons could pass them, as they must in order to receive a license to practice. In the hospitals the visitors could criticize only the general indifference to screens at the windows and the scarcity of trained nurses. The former fault was being remedied by education; the latter was more difficult to correct because South American social organization included no middle class to provide daughters for such service. What nurses there were had been imported from the United States or Europe.

In Santiago, Chile, Mayo and Martin were taken to see a new dental college that was entirely equipped and staffed by North Americans. When they asked how it happened they were told a story worthy of Dr. Watson, one Dr. Will always enjoyed telling, though his taste in fiction ran more to fast-action westerns than to detective novels.

Some years earlier a fire broke out one night in the German embassy, and amid the debris in the basement afterward was found a charred body that was identified from a ring, watch, and bits of clothing as that of the German consul. A fortune in negotiable securities had been taken from the embassy vault, and the janitor of the building was missing. The authorities promptly issued a warrant charging the missing man with murder, theft, and arson.

Germany displayed great diplomatic indignation about the crime, and the anxious Chilean government tried to make amends with fulsome eulogies of the dead consul and plans for elaborate obsequies. But it did not suspend the law requiring that in all cases of death by violence the corpse must be examined by a member of the jurisprudence faculty of the medical school, and the body in the basement came under the eye of Dr. Germán Valenzuela, who found it furnished with a perfect set of teeth except for one missing molar. This was so unusual for a man of the consul's age that the curious Valenzuela sought an interview with the bereaved widow. Yes indeed, she said, her husband had had a great deal of work done on his teeth, and she gave the good doctor the name of the dentist who had done it. When the dentist's records showed a long list of bridges and fillings that should have graced the consul's mouth, Dr. Valenzuela went to see the wife of the missing janitor. As far as she knew her husband's teeth were quite sound, except for one he had had pulled.

A new warrant was immediately issued, and the German consul, in disguise, was caught at the Argentine border, where his escape had been delayed by a landslide that blocked the Trans-Andean railroad. The stolen securities were found in a money belt he was wearing, and he was tried and forthwith executed for the murder of the janitor. When the grateful Chilean government told Dr. Valenzuela to name his own reward, he asked for money to build and equip a dental college on the American plan. The school Drs. Mayo and Martin were visiting was the result.

After a month of concentrated touring, the Mayo-Martin party, literally worn out by the "persistent but unobtrusive hospitality" of their hosts, boarded ship for the United States. They had left home with more than a suspicion of the North American's condescension toward Latin Americans, quite sure that the requirements for fellowship in the American College of Surgeons and for registration on its list of accredited hospitals would work highly beneficial reforms in Latin American medicine; they returned with a wholesome respect for the southerners' ability to manage their own progress. As Dr. Martin said, they went as Pizarros bent on reconquering Peru but returned more conquered than conquerors.

Both he and Dr. Will published long accounts of their trip, stressing the unexpected excellence of South American hospitals and surgeons, and Dr. Will summarized his impressions by declaring that the men he had watched operate were "the equal of any representative group from any country in the world." When his unbelieving fellows argued that he had seen only the best men, he retorted that he went to see the best in any country, because his purpose was to learn. He urged them to make the trip themselves, assuring them they would find it profitable, if only in an access of humility and modesty, which the United States so sadly needed in its relations with South America.

Others did go, a few at first and then hundreds as the American College of Surgeons began organizing large clinical cruises of the sort Mayo and Martin had made. When the Pan-American Medical Association was organized in 1926 the cruises, or "floating congresses," were continued under its sponsorship, and either Dr. Will or Dr.

Charlie was usually among those enrolled, often as an officer of the group. When they were not they were missed, for their deep personal interest in the movement was greatly appreciated by the Latin Americans. Dr. Herrera Vegas, president of the Academy of Medicine and the Surgical Society of Buenos Aires, once concluded his address to the congress thus:

One request I have to make of you . . . that when you arrive again in your own country you will give my warmest and most affectionate greetings to Doctor William Mayo, one of the pillars of modern North American surgery. To him, and to Doctor Martin . . . do we owe the inspiration of these happy scientific cruises which have done, and will do, so much good service to the cause of closer and warmer relations between our two great democracies.

### 3

In his account of their trip in 1920 Dr. Martin insisted that the enthusiastic welcome they received was not wholly due to their official mission but was in part a personal tribute to Dr. Mayo, whose work, he found, was widely known and admired in South America. It was a proud month for me, said Dr. Martin, "to see our president and chief, Dr. Mayo, honored everywhere and always. No conquering hero has ever been accorded more royal treatment. 'Mayo' has become a household word in four countries where before it was only known by reputation."

Latin America had contributed its share of members to the Rochester Surgeons Club, and Mexico at least was already sending occasional patients to the Clinic, among them relatives of both Obregón and Calles. Then one day early in 1921 Dr. Howard Hartman, one of the younger clinicians, answered his phone to hear Dr. Will ask, "How would you like to go to Mexico City?" Very much, of course, but he doubted he could make the train when Dr. Will told him it left in twenty minutes. Dr. Mayo was sure he could and said that Dr. Lockwood the surgeon was going too. A telegram had just come from President Obregón asking for someone to attend General Benjamín Hill, his trusted companion in the many political rough-and-tumbles that attended his rise to power.

Dr. Hartman made the train, though it had to be held for him, but before he and Lockwood got across Iowa they received a wire telling them to come back to Rochester; word had come from Obregón that Hill was dead.

About two weeks later Dr. Hartman got another call from Dr. Will asking how he would like to go to Mexico City. "Wolf, wolf," laughed Hartman, but Dr. Will said there had been a mistake somewhere two weeks before, because another telegram had come from Obregón calling for Clinic men to take care of Hill. So once again Drs. Lockwood and Hartman started for Mexico City.

It took them more than a week to get there, and the trip was a thriller. First they were stopped at the border because a railroad strike was in progress in Mexico and train travel was uncertain and risky, and when they did get across, in a train that started secretly at night, they were delayed several times by the efforts of the strikers. Once they drained the feed tanks and once they made off with the engine, stranding the train for a day and a night in the middle of the desert, with nothing for the passengers to eat but some unappetizing goatflesh the Mexican peasant women in the boxcar ahead cooked over an open fire. Finally the ragged, unarmed soldiers sent along to guard the train got the engine back, and the doctors eventually arrived in Mexico City.

As they stepped off the train they were mobbed by Mexican newspapermen who had somehow got the idea, and would not be dissuaded from it, that the two doctors were emissaries of President Harding bringing word of official United States recognition for the Obregón government. And when at last the two men got away from the reporters and reached the president's palace they learned that they had come quite in vain. The Clinic translator, a fellowship man of dubious attainments in Spanish, had gone astray; Hill *had* died three weeks before, and Obregón's last wire was merely to ask the amount of his bill for their previous start.

Nonetheless, Obregón kept them in Mexico for ten days and gave them a good time. He supplied them with a car, a guard, and an interpreter, and they saw the sights in royal fashion. They met many government officials and medical men, and though they could attend no clinics because a fiesta was in progress during which little work, even in surgery, was done, they returned to Rochester singing the praises of Mexican scenery and Mexican hospitality.

# Toward the Future

## 4

The next spring Dr. Ochsner invited several of the Clinic staff and their wives to vacation on his ranch-estate in Mexico. Not for the first time; both Dr. Charlie and Dr. Will and their wives had had many good times with the Ochsners on that ranch. This time Dr. Will was in the group along with Drs. Plummer and Balfour, and as always he found time to visit surgeons and hospitals. While the party were in Mexico City they called on Obregón and Calles, head of his cabinet, and were invited to attend a bullfight as the president's guests the next Sunday afternoon.

It was a benefit performance for the widow of a famous Mexican matador lately killed in Spain, and several of his most popular fellows were to appear. The huge crowd in attendance cheered wildly as the first fighter presented himself before the president's box and with a flourish of florid oratory dedicated his bull to the chief guest of the nation, Dr. Mayo. The second man was the youngest of the lot, Luis Freg, the idol of the moment. His bull was Obregón's, and he sought to dazzle the crowd by a display of extra daring, but his luck slipped and the bull gored him. He was carried from the field bleeding badly, and word soon went round that he was dying. Feeling an extra measure of responsibility since Freg's dedication was to him, President Obregón asked Dr. Mayo to see whether he could do anything to save the young man.

The little hospital in the rear of the ring was full of noise and confusion, crowded with the weeping friends and relatives of the injured matador, and the doctors, having no success in their efforts to check the hemorrhage by external pressure, gladly stepped aside for Dr. Mayo. After a quick glance he called for scissors, gloves, and gown. There were no gloves available, but he slipped on an apron and washed up as best he could in a hurry. Then by the simple expedient of splitting the skin above the bleeding artery he was able to catch hold of the vessel and tie it. The ease and speed with which he stopped the hemorrhage made a tremendous impression on the watching group, and word somehow got back to the crowd in the ring, so that when Dr. Will returned to his seat he was given a prolonged ovation.

The effect was as if some visiting Canadian doctor were to save the life of Joe Louis or Babe Ruth when American doctors could not.

Everybody in Mexico heard the story and learned the name and fame of Dr. Mayo.

5

An unforeseen by-product of these incidental activities was a noticeable spurt in the number of Clinic patients from Latin America. Some were so obviously poverty-stricken that the Clinic men wondered how on earth they had managed to scrape together the money for the trip, but of course it was mostly the wealthy and ruling classes who came. In the succession of revolutionary governments in Mexico the officials seemed to consider it essential to their prestige to follow the precedent of Obregón and Calles, and the car of the Mexican secretary of war was virtually an ambulance carrying ministers and generals to and from the Clinic. Indeed, its driver became so familiar to the Rochester residents that they exchanged greetings with him on the street.

One satisfied patient brought half a dozen others, and the numbers coming from south of the border increased steadily to a thousand a year or more, depending on the rate of exchange in effect at the moment. This was the principal factor in the inauguration of a special airline from Minneapolis through Rochester to San Antonio, Texas, where the Latin American passengers fanned out by plane or train to their respective countries.

Among the earliest of the regular patients was the wealthy and highly cultured Larco Herrera of Peru. His lavish generosity to his doctors and nurses was soon a byword in Rochester. On one of his first visits he noticed how little there was for his compatriots, ill at ease in English literature and conversation, to do in their free time, and shortly after he returned to Peru he sent the Clinic several hundred books in Spanish and French for the use of his people. He and others added to the collection from time to time until the Clinic possessed a Spanish library of well over a thousand volumes, shelved in a room set aside for the accommodation of Latin American patients.

After the fiasco over Obregón's telegram the Clinic staff could feel little faith in their Spanish fellow, yet more than ever they needed someone to translate letters and act as interpreter. In 1924 Beatriz Montes, an English-speaking teacher of Spanish literature and history in Havana, came to the Clinic for an operation, and during her convalescence she was so helpful in smoothing the way for other Spanish patients that the Clinic asked her to stay on with them as a full-time Spanish secretary and librarian. There were so many patients and visiting doctors to be entertained and guided from section to section that in time they had to give her an assistant.

It was the reputation of the Mayos that attracted the early patients of course, but since by no means all of them were in need of surgery Dr. Will began referring them to Dr. Hartman.* Quick to realize that these people could not be expected to adapt themselves to American ways in the short time they spent in Rochester, Dr. Hartman began studying them as well as their language, so that he could understand how they thought and felt and could meet them halfway. Consequently they soon learned to trust him and feel at ease with him and to ask for him when they registered. Eventually, according to Miss Montes, they came to think of the Mayo Clinic in terms of Dr. Hartman, and many a letter from South America came addressed to "Dr. Howard Hartman, Director of the Mayo Clinic." Only with difficulty and much explanation could he persuade these patients to see other doctors when consultation was necessary.

The growth of the Clinic's Latin American practice led the residents of Rochester to take an unusual interest in things Spanish. When Dr. and Mrs. Hartman returned from one of the many journeys they made to Central and South America, warm with enthusiasm for the lands and peoples they had seen, they often gave travelogs before various local groups, illustrating them with motion pictures they had made or with bits of native handicraft they had brought back with them, and soon other Rochester folk, inside and outside the Clinic group, were spending their vacations below the border.

Clinic secretaries bought Spanish dictionaries and registered for correspondence courses in the language, Spanish-speaking nurses were imported for the hospitals, and the public demanded that Spanish be

---

*When the Clinic granted the university the privilege of interviewing its staff members, the request was made that members of the staff still active would not be included in the story. Accepting the proscriptions of the medical code, the university agreed to this request, with the reservation, however, that the author's judgment should determine where historical accuracy required the factual introduction of living men. In this chapter and the next that judgment has been exercised. The biography of the Doctors Mayo would be pointless without the story of the Clinic, and the story of the Clinic told solely in the names of its two great founders would be a historical distortion they would not have approved.

taught in the schools. The school board was slow in responding, however, so when WPA came along the citizens persuaded its director to give them a night class in Spanish. The first time the class met the teacher got the surprise of her life, because she was expecting to meet ten or twelve persons and instead faced a crowd of nearly two hundred—barbers, waitresses, and clerks who felt a need for Spanish in their daily duties.

6

Meanwhile far-reaching changes were taking place in the Clinic. On Wednesday night, October 8, 1919, the former interns, assistants, and fellows who were back in Rochester for the annual convention of the Clinic Alumni Association were guests at the weekly staff meeting, and Dr. Will addressed them as usual. But what he had to say was not usual, for he told them that at three o'clock that afternoon he and Dr. Charlie had signed a deed of gift conveying all the assets of the Mayo Clinic to the Mayo Properties Association, to provide for the perpetuation of the Clinic and the ideals it stood for.

The announcement was sudden but the action was not; it was the culmination of several years of thought and planning. One cannot be sure just when Dr. Will and Dr. Charlie first awoke to the fact that their partnership had become an institution with obligations to the public, to the Sisters of St. Francis, and to the younger men on their staff beyond those a personal partnership or the family inheritance of a private practice could fulfill. Perhaps the realization came when the Clinic building went up, or perhaps when the opponents of the Foundation harped so persistently on the uncertain future of the Clinic. Certain it is that the organization of the Foundation made those obligations inescapable, for something less ephemeral than a personal partnership was necessary to guarantee the contract with the University of Minnesota.

At any rate, no sooner was the affiliation with the university made permanent than the Mayos persuaded George Granger, the lawyer who as a boy was cured of his speech defect by the Old Doctor, to exchange his district judgeship for a position as the Mayos' legal adviser, with the specific task of working out a plan of reorganization for the Clinic.

The war postponed action, but through all those months of strain and disorganization, thought for the future of the Clinic was never far from Dr. Will's mind. At one point it became painfully urgent. When Dr. Charlie relieved him in Washington in the fall of 1918 and he returned to Rochester darkly yellow with jaundice, he said to Harry Harwick, "This is either a benign condition that will clear up in sixty days or it is cancer of the liver. I must assume that it is cancer of the liver."

Probably in conference with his brother, he had chosen the young business manager as the one among their associates he considered most capable of carrying the Clinic forward in the event of his own death, and for the greater part of the next two months Harry Harwick virtually lived with him, riding for hours through the countryside, listening to his hopes and fears, his plans, his dreams for the Clinic.

Perhaps no one else, except Dr. Charlie, was ever allowed so intimate a revelation of the heart and mind of William Mayo as Harry Harwick got in those months, and what Dr. Will in his turn saw and heard of Harwick confirmed him in the wisdom of his choice. The jaundice cleared away and Dr. Will returned to the helm himself, but from that time onward, in his mind at least, Harry Harwick was his heir apparent as executive head of the Clinic. Since both were men of strong independence and intellectual integrity, they spoke their minds to each other and often disagreed, but their differences could not destroy their deep mutual respect.

As was their wont, Dr. Will and Dr. Charlie contented themselves with determining the general ends they wished to accomplish and left it to their lawyers and Mr. Harwick to work out the legal forms for achieving those ends. Endowing the Foundation had wiped out their personal savings, but as the "principal partners" they still retained ownership of the properties and capital of the partnership, and they wished now to turn these into a permanent endowment for the Clinic. Yet, well aware that no man can be sure of the future, they did not wish to make the disposition of the properties so specific and inflexible that in years to come the terms of the trust might defeat their purpose. So they decided to define only their general intentions in making the gift and to leave it for able men of future generations to realize those intentions in accordance with changing conditions. One thing above all they wanted to ensure—that the trust would contribute to the advancement of medicine and not to the enrichment of any individual or group.

As the first step toward the realization of those ends, on the advice of their lawyers they incorporated the Mayo Properties Association, a self-perpetuating charitable organization without capital stock, made up of nine trustees, one of whom should always be an experienced lawyer and one a competent businessman accustomed to managing large affairs. All should be residents of Olmsted County except the lawyer, who should reside within the state. The trustees were to serve without compensation and were to be responsible before the law for administering the trust in accord with the purposes outlined in the deed of gift—

to aid and advance the study and investigation of human ailments and injuries, and the causes, prevention, relief and cure thereof, and the study and investigation of problems of hygiene, health and public welfare, and the promotion of medical, surgical, and scientific learning, skill, education and investigation, and to engage in and conduct and to aid and assist in medical, surgical, and scientific research in the broadest sense. . . . No part of the net income of this corporation, or of its property or assets upon dissolution or liquidation shall ever inure to the benefit of any of its members, or of any private individual.

The first trustees were Dr. Will and Dr. Charlie and their partners, Drs. Plummer, Judd, and Balfour, with Lawyers Eaton, Granger, and L. L. Brown of Winona, and Harry Harwick. (When Mr. Brown resigned a year or two later, Dr. Charles W. Mayo, Dr. Charlie's elder son, was chosen to take his place.) To them the Drs. Mayo with the consent of their partners transferred the ownership of all the properties of the Mayo Clinic from the building itself down to the last test tube, case record, and pathologic specimen in it, along with all accumulated cash and securities. By 1925 the properties were valued at five million dollars and the securities amounted to five and a half millions more.

The only stipulations attending the gift, other than the statement of its general purposes, were that the trustees respect the contract with the university making the Clinic facilities available for the uses of the Foundation and that they maintain their principal place of business at Rochester. The ultimate beneficiary of the trust, should the trustees at any time decide that its purposes could best be met by a transfer of ownership (that is, should they ever decide that the Clinic was no longer fulfilling those purposes) was to be some class A medical school in the United States. The Mayos originally intended to designate the University of Minnesota, but in view of the continuing opposition to the Foundation and at the suggestion of their advisers, they finally decided it would be wiser to leave that decision too to the judgment of future trustees.

The income from the association's funds was to be added to the principal at least until it reached the sum of ten million dollars, when the trustees might at their discretion add the income to that from the Mayo Foundation endowment.

Because as a charitable organization the Mayo Properties Association is exempt from the federal income tax—though it pays local real estate taxes—its books are periodically inspected by federal revenue agents to make sure that the trustees have devised no dodge by which the income is diverted into the pockets of individuals. Its tax returns and the agents' reports came to the desk of Andrew Mellon when he was secretary of the treasury, and he paid it the flattery of imitation in the incorporation of his Mellon Institute, because, as he told Dr. Will when the latter attended the dedication of one of the Institute buildings, the Properties Association setup was the most practicable arrangement he had come across for safeguarding the purposes of a public trust.

### 7

The second step toward the brothers' goal was the reorganization of the Clinic itself. For four years it remained a partnership, but in 1923 that legal form was replaced with a "voluntary association," a kind of cross between a group partnership and a corporation. At that time all proprietary and participating interests in the Clinic income ceased, and the former partners, including Dr. Will and Dr. Charlie, joined the rest of the staff on a fixed salary basis.

Then by a formal contract the Properties Association leased its building and all its equipment to the Clinic, the annual rental being the total net income of the Clinic, which was added to the endowment funds of the Association. To prevent the Clinic at some future date from raising the salaries of its staff to eat up the gross income and reduce the rental, thus defeating the purpose of the arrangement, the contract stipulated that all Clinic salaries must be approved by the Properties Association. As Dr. Will explained, he and Charlie wanted to provide their staff members with a reasonable living and a guarantee of security in their old age, but they did not want anyone to receive enough wealth from the Clinic "to keep his children on the beach at Miami when they ought to be working."

The administration of the Clinic was vested in a board of governors made up of the former partners, Mr. Harwick, and two members chosen from the staff. Vacancies were to be filled by a seven-ninths vote of the Properties Association on nomination by a seven-eighths vote of the board itself. The supervision of professional activities was entrusted to an executive committee of five members appointed by the board of governors from a list of fifteen nominated by the staff, and all matters of general policy were to be determined by a council made up of the board of governors, the executive committee, and the president of the staff.

Despite the new degree of representation thus accorded to the staff, Dr. Will was not satisfied. Looking toward the future, when he and Dr. Charlie and their partners would be gone, he felt that a wider distribution of administrative responsibilities was necessary to educate more members of the group to an understanding of its problems and policies. So he proposed entrusting various phases of the administration to standing committees appointed from the staff. Dr. Charlie approved, and in spite of strong opposition from other members of the board of governors the committee system was gradually put into effect throughout 1923 and 1924. There the brothers let the reorganization rest for the moment, to allow time for consolidation and testing before further steps were taken.

Expecting a revolution of some sort when these changes were announced, many members of the Clinic group were disappointed and came to consider the committee system a great joke, because to all intents and purposes Dr. Will remained what they all called him, the Chief. As far as they could see they still had one-man rule exactly as before—"one-man" rule because Dr. Will as the executive carried into effect the decisions the brothers reached together. As a matter of fact, Dr. Will did not believe in revolutions and never had any intention of relinquishing the reins until he was satisfied that the machinery for self-government was adequate and that the group was sufficiently imbued with the traditional policies of the practice to continue them. Those who watched the general development over a period of years instead of judging from one or two isolated incidents saw the board of governors become increasingly responsive to the *crystallized* opinion of the staff, though never to the whim of an individual.

This process of reorganization was marred by one outstanding unpleasantness. Dr. Graham was too wholeheartedly a clinician to be able to appreciate his partners' efforts toward making research and education auxiliary functions of the Clinic. He had disapproved of the Foundation and its affiliation with the university, and when it came to underwriting that affiliation by assigning the assets of the partnership to the Mayo Properties Association he refused to give his consent.

Since Dr. Will would not yield in his determination to carry the plan through, the two were at an impasse for some time. Mr. Harwick tried to work out a compromise settlement, but he could find none that both men would accept, and in the end Dr. Graham resigned from the Clinic, receiving the one year's income allowed him by the agreement he and Dr. Stinchfield had signed some twenty years earlier.

Dr. Will was sincerely sorry to see Graham go, because, as he said, "I would rather have his opinion on the medical aspects of a surgical case than that of any other man I have ever had the privilege of working with." It was undoubtedly Dr. Charlie, however, whose position was least happy. As Graham's brother-in-law, he was caught between two loyalties, but in the test the bond between him and Will did not fail. Gently but unequivocally he backed his brother's decision.

Retiring to his farm, Dr. Graham gave his whole time to the stock-raising that had been his hobby for several years. He had more time to think than his Clinic job had ever left him, and as he watched the growth of the Foundation and its effect on the Clinic he came finally to see that Dr. Will had been right. When he did, he was big enough to go and tell him so, and the day of their reconciliation was a happy one for both of them.

## 8

The phenomenal wartime increase in patients produced a crisis in the history of St. Mary's Hospital. It was once more sadly overcrowded, but the Sisters of St. Francis could not make up their minds to plunge into debt again and the future of the hospital stood at stake. It could carry on as it was for a time on the momentum of its reputation, but further progress depended on expansion. While the sisters wavered, trying to make up their minds, the Clinic registrations and operations were mounting rapidly, and, seeing that something must be done, Dr. Will turned again to John Kahler.

Once started, Kahler had moved steadily ahead in grasping the business opportunities the Clinic practice offered. He and Harry Harwick had built a large modern laundry to serve the hotels and hospitals, and in 1915 they and Dr. Judd financed the building of the Colonial Hotel. Or that's what they intended it to be, but while it was building the need for hospital beds became so acute they changed it into the Colonial Hospital, and the next year added a new wing to it to raise the number of beds to two hundred and forty-four and the number of operating rooms to four.

To provide nurses when the war reduced the ready supply, they opened the Colonial Hospital Training School for Nurses, which, later named the Kahler Hospitals School of Nursing, grew rapidly in size and prestige to become one of the best in the state.

In his look toward the future Dr. Will saw clearly that it was as necessary for these facilities to be secure from dispersion on the owners' death as for the Clinic itself to be so. On his urgent recommendation Mr. Kahler and his friends in 1917 consolidated their holdings, organized the Kahler Corporation, and entered in real earnest into the business of providing hospitals and hotels for the Clinic patients. But they could hardly keep pace with the demand, though they opened three new hospitals in as many years, the Stanley, the Worrall, and the Curie, with a combined capacity of just under three hundred beds and five operating rooms.

When those were still not enough and the addition of a large annex to the Zumbro Hotel did not fill the pressing need in that direction, the Kahler Corporation plunged. They bought the site across the corner from the Clinic and began building a huge new hotel-hospital, a truly remarkable structure to rise almost in the midst of cornfields.

Then came the postwar agricultural depression. Registrations at the Clinic dropped swiftly back from sixty thousand in 1919 to just above forty-nine thousand in 1922, and the proportion of non- or little-paying patients rose sharply. Meeting a high fixed overhead under those conditions left neither the Clinic nor the Properties Association in any condition to help the Corporation out of a serious situation. Individual staff members along with Rochester businessmen put money into the venture to keep it afloat, and for the first time the investment of outside capital was sought; Kahler Corporation stock was put on the open market and sold throughout the country. For a while the prospects were very dark indeed, but by the middle 1920's conditions had greatly improved, registrations were climbing fast again, and the Kahler stock rose to a peak value of two hundred dollars a share in 1929.

The new Kahler provided two hundred and ten hospital beds, one hundred and fifty more for convalescent patients, and two hundred and twenty for hotel purposes. When it was opened on September 27, 1921 the old Kahler House across the street was renamed the Damon in honor of Mrs. W. J. Mayo and turned into a hospital for a few years. Then it was changed back into a hotel, which it still is.

While the Kahler was under construction Henry Plummer, seeing the possibility of a further convenience for Clinic patients, suggested that it be connected with the Clinic by an underground passage. Recognizing a good idea, the Corporation and the Properties Association joined forces to build the first subway tunnel, between the hotel and the Clinic building, in 1921. With the years this grew into an extensive system of subways connecting the Clinic with all the Kahler hospitals and hotels, a convenience that both patients and staff greatly appreciate, especially in wintertime.

The Mayo organizations and the Kahler Corporation were mutually independent in financing and management, though a number of individuals in the Clinic group owned Kahler stock and Harry Harwick was a director of the Corporation as well as an administrative officer of the Clinic. The Properties Association owned Corporation stock only to the amount, relatively small, of the Mayos' investment in the old Kahler House, which the brothers turned over to the Association along with their other securities. However, a formal contract gave the Clinic complete control of medical policies in all Kahler hospitals, stipulated that none but Clinic surgeons should operate in them, and further provided that the Properties Association could buy them on one year's notice should it ever seem expedient.

To that legal connection between the two organizations there was added a strong extra-legal bond because of their mutual dependence, and through this the Clinic has been able to enforce some of its wishes, such as that there should be no bar in any Kahler hotel connected by tunnel with the Clinic and that if the earnings of the hospitals at any time amounted to more than a six per cent return on the investment the charges to patients should be reduced.

9

Dr. Will and Dr. Charlie made no move to transfer their operating from St. Mary's, but as the beds provided by the Kahler hospitals pulled ahead of St. Mary's three hundred, the threat of being superseded in their preferred position was enough to spur the sisters to action. And they decided to have done with halfway measures, with building additions that were full again almost before the carpenters left. This time they would really build for the future. Encouraged by the Right Reverend Patrick Heffron, Bishop of Winona, who said, "We have the best surgeons in the world, the best sisters in the world, and why can't we have the best hospital in the world?" they arranged to borrow two million dollars and signed the contracts for a big new surgical pavilion to double the capacity of the hospital at a single stroke.

The pavilion, opened in the spring of 1922, provided spacious quarters for the surgeons on its fifth floor—ten new operating rooms ranged in a row and grouped in pairs with a small sterilizing room between each two. Everything was the latest in design and equipment, providing a measure of the astounding progress of surgery by its crying contrast to that first St. Mary's operating room.

Amid all this cold, clean, gleaming tile, in this bare, bright world of white, so sterile and stripped, there was no place for the old makeshifts of handrail platforms and slanting mirrors; here members of the Surgeons Club were accommodated on two rows of concrete benches railed off above the table on two sides of each operating room. And across the corridor a comfortable lounge was set aside for them, furnished with an electrically operated bulletin board that in combination with the schedule of operations printed each day told them at a glance what operation was in progress in each room at any moment. After registering at the desk in the corridor and donning a gown and mask, the visitors—only nurses and doctors allowed—were free to go anywhere and see anything on the floor. The Mayos were sticking to their promise that everything they did should be open to inspection by their professional fellows.

## 10

The unexpected and almost unbelievable surge in registrations, only momentarily interrupted by the postwar depression, rapidly made the Clinic building, which had seemed so luxuriously spacious in 1914, totally inadequate for the group's needs. Resort to all kinds of expedients was necessary. The old annex and library buildings and even some of the storerooms previously used were reoccupied; one floor after another of the adjoining Zumbro Annex was rented from the Kahler Corporation, connected with the Clinic by a covered bridge, and filled with the overflow of offices and laboratories; and finally the section on urology and the Foundation offices were transferred bodily to space requisitioned on an upper floor in the Kahler Hotel. The close integration so happily achieved in 1914 was physically shattered by 1925, but the attitudes and habits it had developed in the group survived and intersectional cooperation and consultation were maintained in spite of the difficulties.

The multiplication of diagnostic sections went on as before, though at an even faster pace, through a process of reproduction by cell division. Each section swelled in number of associates and of major interests till the limit of practicability was reached and somebody split off to start a new one. For example, Dr. Plummer's section eventually gave rise to a second section in diseases of the thyroid, to one in diseases of the esophagus and bronchi, and to one in cardiology, or heart disease, as well as to an electrocardiograph laboratory to aid in diagnosing cardiac disorders.

Though Dr. Will encouraged this development and always declared there was a place in the Clinic for anyone with originality, ability, and energy enough to develop a new field of specialization, he was always uneasy lest the process go too far and the patient be viewed as a body part instead of as a complex, intricately meshed whole. And lurking beneath the surface was an unsuspected justification for his fear.

# Clinic and Foundation

It had always been the accepted policy that the patient should choose his own doctor if he had a choice. Anyone asking for a certain member of the group or referred by his doctor to some specific Clinic man was sent to that man by the registration clerk. Of course it often happened that he asked for a surgeon when he did not need surgery or for an eye specialist when his trouble was in the stomach or the kidneys. Then it was up to the doctor he had chosen to explain the situation and transfer him to the care of one of the general clinicians.

But many persons, an increasing proportion of them, came without any choice, and these were assigned to some section by the registration clerk. Before anyone was fully aware of what was happening the clerks had fallen into the habit of making the assignment on the basis of the patient's complaint. Suppose he said he had come to see about a bad heart, what was more natural than for the clerk to send him to the expert in heart disease? But it was almost an even chance that the trouble was not with his heart at all, yet the specialist, humanly prone to find what he was looking for and interested in, might well miss the little signs pointing elsewhere. In effect the diagnosis was being made by the patient himself or by the registration clerk, and as the tendency developed into custom it inevitably led the doctors to specialize exclusively in what was supposed to be only a major interest.

When realization of this situation and its import dawned on the group, they promptly made a decisive change in the method of registration. Personal requests were honored as before and old patients were assigned to their former doctors of course, but the others were allocated to the sections in rotation with only such modification as was necessary to keep the load balanced. That is, if a sudden flurry of personal requests or returning patients filled up some one section today, it was skipped in the rotation tomorrow and the next day until the load was even again.

Thereafter the man who thought he had heart trouble was examined by a clinician who had no blinders directed that way; if he decided the heart actually was at fault and an electrocardiogram confirmed him in the opinion, then he called the heart specialist in consultation, and if they agreed on the diagnosis the patient was transferred to the care of the cardiologist. It was obviously safer for the ailing man to have two doctors go over him, both possessing a thorough knowledge of general medicine, than to see only one whose mind was full of his own specialty.

So what appeared on the surface to be mere change in routine was in purpose and effect fundamental for maintaining a desirable balance between skill in general diagnosis and specialization in one or two phases.

By this time diagnosis had attained its majority as an independent function of the group, and during the decade it matured rapidly to a point near equality with the surgery that had brought it into being. The full equality of which it is worthy it could not attain so long as shortsighted laymen would cheerfully pay a whopping fee for a nice scar to take home but grumbled about the cost of the clinician's efforts to find out what was wrong with them—though a correct diagnosis required at least as much knowledge and skill and was quite as important to their ultimate recovery.

As doctors themselves came to appreciate the possibility of more nearly exact differential diagnosis and its importance, more and more general practitioners acquired the habit of referring their uncertain cases to the Clinic, or some similar institution, just for such a diagnosis, so they could proceed with greater confidence in their own treatment of the case.

Further, some doctors began to see that their proper job was keeping people well instead of getting them well, and the medical profession experienced a long overdue awakening to the need for taking the public into its confidence instead of shrouding its work in ignorance-breeding mystery. The two developments produced a noticeable increase in what may be called preventive examination, a periodic physical checkup designed to catch incipient disorders before they reach a disabling stage, even before they give rise to symptoms of illness. Although this movement is even yet only at its beginning, it has already proved important in the growth of the diagnostic function at the Clinic.

## 11

Such advance in diagnosis was possible largely through the progress of laboratory medicine. Granting that there is danger in letting chemical and microscopic procedures replace the personal study of the patient by the clinician—a point stressed almost as much by Dr. Will and Dr. Charlie as by the stubbornest opponent of laboratory procedures as quite unnecessary foolishness—the fact remains that the best of clinicians cannot by observation alone diagnose pregnancy as surely as a simple laboratory test does, or detect syphilis as often as the Wasserman and Kahn tests reveal it, or recognize tuberculosis as early as a chest x-ray shows it up. In its proper place, as a supplement to direct physical examination, laboratory science is fundamental in modern medicine.

Its development at the Clinic during the postwar decades was a matter of continuing differentiation or division of function, owing to the volume of work, which in turn was due to the application of more and more valid procedures to more and more patients. The one clinical laboratory of early days became a whole cluster, one each for serology (serum tests and therapy), hematology (blood counts and smears), bacteriology, parasitology, urinalysis, and gastric analysis. These constituted the division of clinical pathology under the joint directorship of Dr. Sanford and Dr. Thomas B. Magath, who joined the group in 1919. Under their supervision too were laboratories for the simpler analyses maintained for convenience in the hospitals.

The development of clinical chemistry was so rapid and so extensive that it became a separate section entirely. Begun in its modern phase under Dr. Magath it was soon transferred to Dr. Kendall's section, and then when it threatened to interfere with his research activities, or vice versa, it was given separate quarters and status under Dr. Arnold Osterberg, Kendall's associate. In addition to the tremendous job of making all chemical analyses of blood, urine, and spinal fluid, the section was charged with the manufacture of all new solutions and compounds required in treatment, those not yet standardized or widely enough used to be put on the market by a commercial company.

Dr. MacCarty's work in surgical pathology grew with St. Mary's Hospital until in the new pavilion his laboratory across the hall from the operating rooms was considerably larger than the whole of the surgical floor in the first building. A similar laboratory was established in each downtown hospital as it was opened, and these were placed in charge of Dr. Albert C. Broders, who as assistant and then associate had been trained by Dr. MacCarty.

The postmortem pathology, or pathologic anatomy, laboratory cannot be called directly clinical since the patient is past help when his case reaches it, but its work is fundamental in the clinical process just the same, by virtue of the constant check it maintains on medical and surgical procedures. Among the requirements of the American College of Surgeons for accredited hospitals is that autopsies be performed on at least fifteen per cent of the deaths in the institution and also that a regular clinico-pathological conference be held at which the post-mortem findings are reported to the internists and surgeons. In spirit this requirement is often met in the breach, for it is not easy to assemble the scattered staff, most of whom are busy elsewhere a good share of the time. In such cases the interns and residents profit most from the postmortems, the active attending staff little at all.

At Rochester the percentage of postmortems had long been many times that requirement, and such a conference had been customary long enough to have settled into a sterile routine. Those of the staff who remembered to attend met around a table in the library and engaged in a desultory discussion of the pathologist's report, presented to them on a mimeographed sheet.

Then the pathologist went off to war, and when he did not return Dr. Harold E. Robertson of the state medical school was invited to take his place during the summer vacation at the university. Realizing to the full the importance of his function, utterly fearless and impersonal, regarding his findings as scientific truth to be told no matter whom they concerned, Dr. Robertson put meaning into those weekly conferences. He gave his crisp, concise reports in person with the aid of microscopic slides and short protocols flashed on the screen. No error, whosoever it was, was omitted or glossed over, and when the report was finished the clinician or surgeon on the case was called on to contribute his comment or explanation. Robertson even criticized the methods of the business office, because he found they were not taking sufficient care to adjust the Clinic's bill when the death of the patient changed the financial status of the family.

At first the staff members resented the seemingly merciless public exposure of their mistakes, but as one after another had his turn, even Dr. Will on one occasion, they came to take it with good grace. By the end of the summer everyone on the staff was attending the meetings, "to see whose head would get knocked off this time."

Considerably to Dr. Robertson's surprise, Dr. Will encouraged him, telling him to go to it, because what he was doing was the most salutary thing that had happened to them in a long time. Only once did he criticize, and that was when Robertson's report was aimed at one of the newcomers on the staff. Dr. Will suggested that it would be better to point out a younger man's mistakes to him privately, so as not to discourage him by public censure.

When the summer ended Dr. Will asked Robertson to take the job permanently, and though he was under contract to the university for the following year, in 1921 he did join the Clinic as head of the section on pathologic anatomy. The sensational novelty of the weekly conferences had passed, but attendance did not slacken, because Dr. Robertson kept them short and interesting and the men had come to recognize their superlative value for keeping everyone on his toes. Many of the clinicians soon learned to follow up their diagnoses by attending any postmortems as well as operations on their patients.

## 12

Another aid to improved diagnosis was the rapid development of endoscopy, direct examination of the body cavities through instruments devised for the purpose. To the early ophthalmoscope and cystoscope were added the proctoscope, esophagoscope, and bronchoscope, all for peering down a straight opening, such as along the urethra to the bladder or the esophagus to the stomach, and the gastroscope, which by an ingenious arrangement of tiny mirrors and electric lights permits the doctor to see lesions in parts of the stomach, even though that organ lies to one side of the passage from the mouth.

But the x-ray remained the biggest single aid to diagnosis, and together with x-ray and radium therapy it constitutes the recognized medical specialty of radiology. At the Clinic x-ray diagnosis and therapy were originally combined in the section on roentgenology, then the x-ray treatment was put into a separate section and transferred to the Curie Hospital, along with the newer radium therapy, which had previously been in charge of Dr. Stacy in Dr. Graham's section. Finally the radium treatment work was split off into a new section and transferred to the Worrall Hospital.

The section on x-ray diagnosis expanded steadily for many years under the leadership of Dr. Russell Carman. Then one afternoon in 1925 he looked at an x-ray plate of his own abdomen and told his assistant it showed an incurable cancer. Yet calmly he drove to St. Paul that same night and addressed a gathering of six hundred physicians on the x-ray diagnosis of cancer. An exploratory incision a few days later confirmed his opinion that the cancer was inoperable, and he died the following June. He had made a place for himself and his section at the very heart of the Clinic, by virtue of his personal qualities and his professional ability. He had been president of the Radiological Society of North America and was president of the American Roentgen Ray Society when he died. His place at the Clinic was taken by Dr. Byrl R. Kirklin.

Major among the many improvements that have made modern x-ray the wonderful tool it is was the further discovery of agents and techniques for making one organ after another opaque to the ray. To this development the Clinic men have contributed, especially in the vascular and genito-urinary systems and the gallbladder, though the fact that theirs were private patients on whom they could not experiment prevented them from doing much before new methods were proved safe. Then they were able to contribute greatly to the solution of such problems as whether administration of the agent by mouth is better than intravenous injection or the other way around.

The sheer volume of the work passing through the section forced the staff to make technical improvements. For instance, they simply could not handle a thousand and more films a day in the usual way, immersing each film in the developing bath for a few minutes, drawing it out to see whether it was ready, then putting it back for a minute longer. With the help of experts from the film company they worked out an exact timetable: exposure so long and immersion so long for perfect results. Then they could develop the films in units of eight or ten at a time. They also devised apparatus for controlling the heat and humidity in the drying room, so they could finish the drying of a film in twenty minutes instead of the usual hour. As a result of such improvements they could make their report to the clinician the same day he called for the x-ray, providing the call and the patient arrived in the section before three-thirty in the afternoon.

To interpret the abnormal bulge in outline here, the too deep shadow there, by which the x-ray tells its diagnostic story requires an expertness that comes only with extensive experience, and to consider any M.D. capable of reading an x-ray properly is as absurd as to consider any M.D. capable of performing major surgery. Yet patients sometimes wonder why the Clinic doctors will not accept the x-ray interpretations of their home-town doctors. The same is true of the diagnostic process in general. Experience taught the Rochester men early that it was wiser to ignore any previous diagnosis and start from scratch themselves. Sometimes the patient, fresh from an examination at home, is impatient at having to go through the bother a second time, and if the final verdict is the kidney or stomach ailment he claimed to have when he registered he is resentful of all the trouble he had only "to be told what I knew to start with." He does not know how often the final diagnosis is far different from what the patient "knew" he had.

Despite an apparently widespread impression to the contrary, there is no diagnostic "routine" at the Clinic. Except for the basic urinalysis, the laboratory tests are not given as a matter of course but only as called for by the clinician in accord with what he considers the necessities of the individual case. True, most patients are sent sooner or later to the x-ray division or to the hematology laboratory to give up a specimen of blood, but by no means all for the same purpose. There are dozens of tests, chemical and microscopic, that require the blood specimen and nearly as many body parts that may be x-rayed. Some clinicians call for more tests than others, but the administration tries constantly to discourage *unnecessary* use of laboratory procedures, if for no other reason than, as Dr. Will used to say, "We must consider the patient's pocketbook too."

## 13

The addition, at long last, of internal medicine and medical specialties to the Clinic practice was the most sweeping development of the postwar period. Medical treatment had never been entirely lacking, but it was so incidental and so little in proportion to the rest that to all intents and purposes it did not exist. Henry Plummer of course had always insisted that the group was only half effective without it, and some outsiders thought so too. When Dr. Frank Billings of Chicago saw the Mayo setup about 1910, he told Dr. Will that fine as it was it would never round the circle of its potential greatness until it could offer medical as well as surgical treatment to its patients.

It was neither perverse stubbornness nor lack of appreciation of the benefits of medicine that kept the Mayos from taking the step. Surgery, being their own specialty, had developed so rapidly that hospital expansion could hardly keep up with *it,* let alone provide room for the hospitalization of medical patients too. And in the world of medicine generally, surgery was an overgrown tail that exuberantly wagged the whole dog. For two decades the best energies of the profession were concentrated on surgery, and what effort did go into medicine was given to advancing diagnosis rather than therapy. As a result, surgery offered more real hope of healing than did medical treatment.

Recognition of this indisputable fact led to the organization, early in the century, of the Rockefeller Institute for Medical Research. For the first few years the institute directors contented themselves with granting fellowships to make qualified men independent of practice so they could concentrate on study and research in internal medicine. Then from 1907 to 1911 plans materialized for building a hospital and laboratories devoted to clinical investigation—that is, to the study "of human disease in its clinical aspects, under conditions as near as possible to laboratory standards of exactness and efficiency." Perhaps from this stimulus, the search for new and effective methods of medical treatment became widespread and by 1915 was producing sufficient results to promise an unprecedented expansion in internal medicine.

Beginning in 1912 the Mayos made several attempts to incorporate medicine in their practice. When the 1912 addition to St. Mary's was built its fourth floor was set aside for medical patients, and the Colonial Hospital was intended to be largely a medical unit. But each time before the internists could gather sufficient momentum to fill their beds with patients, the busy surgeons, needing more room than they had, took over the empty medical beds and literally crowded the incipient development off the scene.

The predicament of the Rochester schools of nursing showed up the defect clearly. In order to secure the listing as accredited schools that would give their graduates the right to be licensed as registered nurses they had to arrange to send their students to St. Paul hospitals for the experience in medical wards the Clinic practice did not provide.

# Clinic and Foundation

But it was the organization of the Foundation that finally made action imperative. No matter how fine the Clinic provisions for training young doctors in diagnosis and surgery, it could not pretend to true graduate school status without facilities and staff for teaching internal medicine. As soon as the affiliation with the University of Minnesota became permanent, Dr. Will and Dr. Charlie ordered a section of beds in the Stanley Hospital set aside and kept free for the use of the clinicians who wanted to add medical treatment to their work in diagnosis. But that was only a beginning and promised too slow a growth; they needed new men who were experienced in clinical investigation and could direct students in it.

Here too the war interrupted the development, but it performed a compensatory service. There were not yet many qualified internists with the investigative turn of mind, but in the course of their war duty the Mayos and Dr. Wilson made the acquaintance of some good ones, who, left foot-loose when the war ended, were persuaded to join the Mayo Clinic and set going a new medical unit.

The Kahler Corporation provided temporary quarters for them in an old hotel, which was renamed the Olmsted Hospital, the Clinic furnished them with laboratories and assistants, and they began treatment and research in pediatrics and certain diseases of metabolism. They found the opportunities for clinical investigation incomparable, and their medical unit grew rapidly. Eighteen months later, when the surgeons moved into the new St. Mary's pavilion, the medical men took over the beds of the old building and set up their laboratories in the old operating rooms.

Because of the importance of diet in the management of diabetes, one of the diseases in which the medical unit was especially interested, a department of nutrition was established in the Olmsted Hospital, with Mary A. Foley of Boston, a trained dietitian, in charge. Always much interested in the possibilities of corrective diet, Dr. Will persuaded the department staff to extend its services to other Clinic patients who needed special diets and instruction in proper eating habits. When the medical hospital unit was moved to St. Mary's and a diet service was provided for the hospital patients there, the Kahler Corporation opened the Diet Kitchen in a room downtown to accommodate ambulatory patients for whom the doctors prescribed a special diet. This new service was a pet of Dr. Will's. The week after it opened he took some visitors to see it, and though only three of the room's forty seats were occupied at the time, he predicted confidently that the Diet Kitchen would become one of the distinctive features of the Clinic and would shortly require larger quarters.

His prediction was verified when the Kitchen had to double its capacity six years later, for by that time it had become a resource used by most of the Clinic sections instead of the two or three for which it was started. Doctors were writing prescriptions for corrective diets as for medicine and were referring more than five thousand patients a year to the Diet Kitchen for instruction. So important had diet therapy become in the Clinic practice that a special committee on diet was appointed—and so divergent were the doctors' views on the subject that the lay secretary of the committee recorded many a furious argument at its meetings.

In most cases it was necessary for the patient to take his meals at the Kitchen for three or four days, long enough to get started on his diet and be taught the principles of it he could apply at home. The dietitians soon learned that often half their task was to rid the patient of some wild idea he had picked up about foods. One woman had been told that proteins caused headaches, and so she must avoid eating milk, meat, fish, eggs, and cheese and must rely upon one English walnut a day to supply her with the necessary protein. It took just plain arithmetic to show her that she would need more than a hundred walnuts a day to get her ration of protein. Another protested vigorously against being served proteins and carbohydrates at the same meal—until the dietitian told him that the two were mixed in the milk he had been living on for some time past.

The development of the medical practice was pleasingly rapid, eventually passing surgery in the volume of patients handled. Besides the growth of the original medical group, one diagnostic section after another came to have its own group of hospital beds for the accommodation of patients in its special field of interest. For it was thought best to let specialization have full sway in the hospital services.

The day when the internist and laboratory members of the group served solely to pyramid the usefulness of the surgeons was gone. The Mayo Clinic was no longer just a surgical clinic, for surgery was beginning to assume its proper role as one useful tool of the clinician, and far across the sea, from his post as professor of medicine at Oxford University, William Osler noted the change and hailed it with joy: "The surgeons have had their day—and they know it! The American St. Cosmas and St. Damian—the Mayo brothers—have made their Clinic today as important in medicine as it ever was in surgery. Wise men! They saw how the pendulum was swinging."

## 14

All that is not in the least to imply that surgery, either at the Clinic or in the general world of medical practice, slackened in its progress or declined in its usefulness for the patient. True, in their advance the internists took back the treatment of some maladies they had surrendered to the surgeon, such as duodenal ulcer, but in more instances they made discoveries and originated methods of pre- and postoperative treatment that brought within reach of the scalpel a host of cases which earlier would have been unlikely subjects for operation.

The medical and laboratory men have found ways of combating the effects of anemia, jaundice, diabetes, obesity, heart deficiency, and other such departures from normal, which in the past were frequently prohibitive surgical hazards. They have also learned how to prevent or lessen the effects of postoperative complications like shock, hemorrhage, pneumonia, hiccup, and even to some extent embolism, the plugging of an artery or vein by a clot in the blood stream. Peritonitis, that bugbear of early abdominal surgery, has been so completely conquered that the able surgeon of today considers its appearance a disgraceful reflection on his technique, except of course where he has a septic condition to begin with, as in the case of a ruptured appendix. Even there much progress has been made in the development of serums and vaccines to be given before operation to prevent the spread of the infection.

The postwar development at the Clinic was a matter of multiplying and expanding the sections in general surgery and marking out new surgical specialties alongside orthopedics, urology, ophthalmology, and otolaryngology. Operations on the brain and nervous system had gravitated almost entirely into Dr. Beckman's section, and by 1916 his work in that field, particularly in the extremely delicate technique for removing tumors of the spinal cord, was one of the most promising phases of Clinic surgery. It was a severe loss to the group when he contracted an infection during an operation on a septic case and died from it. One American surgeon, commenting on the misfortune, remarked that Dr. Beckman was the gentlest, safest operator he had ever seen at work and that it would take many a year for the Clinic to train another to fill his place.

After Beckman's death the neurologic cases were assigned to Dr. Alfred W. Adson, a young man of thirty who had been Dr. Beckman's associate. Adson was not proud of his first efforts, and he determined to "beat this thing." So he went to Boston to study a while with Harvey Cushing, one of the world's great neurosurgeons, and returned to carry on Beckman's work with greater success.

One morning shortly after he got back from Boston he was preparing to operate on a case he had diagnosed as a tumor of the spinal cord when in walked Dr. Will, Dr. Charlie, and a guest, none other than the great Moynihan of Leeds. Exact diagnosis of spinal cord tumor was a difficult matter, and young Adson standing beside his patient under the eyes of those three felt he was on the spot. His hands began to perspire, and he felt other symptoms of the jitters. Sensing his predicament, Dr. Charlie considerately suggested that they might move on since it was nearly time for lunch.

"No," said Moynihan, "I want to see this." And he pulled a chair close to the table and sat down. He was their guest, so there was nothing the Mayos could do but stand by, and Dr. Adson had to proceed.

"Well, the tumor showed up where I had believed it to be," he said in telling the story, "and after that I relaxed again because the operation itself was not difficult."

When Moynihan returned home and was asked what he had seen at Rochester on this trip, he replied, "A high school boy operating for spine tumor!" But the "high school boy" did so well that three years later a special section on neurologic surgery was established with him in charge, and it rapidly developed into one of the distinctions of the Clinic.

The section on thoracic surgery had a rather checkered career until it finally came into the hands of Dr. Stuart Harrington. The Mayos were pleased when they persuaded Dr. Samuel Robinson to come out from the Massachusetts General Hospital in 1915 to establish it, but when he resigned to enter military service two years later the chest work was distributed once more among the general surgeons. Then during the war, as Dr. Will once observed, "a great many chests were opened very suddenly," and thoracic surgery came to the fore. It was revived at the Clinic in 1919 by Dr. Carl Hedblom, but after a few years of it he decided he would rather do general surgery, and the section was placed in charge of the Canadian, Dr. Lockwood. When Lockwood left to establish his own clinic in Toronto, Hedblom resumed the chairmanship, but then suddenly resigned to become professor of surgery at the University of Wisconsin—and the Clinic was caught for the moment without a qualified chest surgeon. This taught Dr. Will a lesson, and thereafter it was the Clinic rule to have on the staff at least two competent surgeons in each field and each surgeon skilled in two fields.

The Clinic's thoracic surgeons have made a specialty of repairing diaphragmatic hernia, which is the rupture of some abdominal organ, usually the stomach, through the diaphragm into the chest cavity, and they have also made considerable progress in the surgical treatment of tuberculosis and in removing chest tumors previously inaccessible to the knife.

15

Plastic surgery was another specialty given a strong push forward by the needs of wartime casualties, but at the Clinic the general surgeons continued to do all plastic surgery except that on the face and neck, which became a specialty by virtue of volume. Through the removal of a malignant lesion many of the patients in the section on otolaryngology and rhinology (ear, nose, and throat) lost their nose or an ear or some part of the mouth or throat. Their postoperative state was often sad indeed, and agreeing with Dr. Will that "every human being has a divine right to look human," Dr. Gordon B. New, an associate in the section, concentrated on the problem of restoring these patients to something like a normal appearance.

As his work grew to include the correction of deformities like harelip and cleft palate and the repair of facial injuries received in automobile accidents, it proved necessary in 1917 to establish a separate section on "laryngology, oral and plastic" with him in charge. Within two decades the section had grown to a staff of four full-time surgeons, using three operating rooms in the Kahler and performing over two thousand operations a year. Although only a minor part of the section's work was of the kind the layman thinks of as plastic surgery—face-lifting and the like, more specifically called "cosmetic surgery"—Dr. New and his associates learned to exercise special care in selecting only those patients who could benefit psychologically as well as physically from operation. They had to weed out those who came with a dream of sudden transformation from ugly ducklings into glamorous swans, for though the results achieved by plastic surgery are often amazing enough, such persons were likely to be disappointed in their exaggerated expectations and so their end, psychologically, would be worse than their beginning.

Originally Dr. New's specialty included the work in orthodontia (straightening crooked teeth) and other such cases of major dental surgery as came to the Clinic, but presently this grew into another separate section, on dental surgery, under Dr. Boyd S. Gardiner, and with the years it too has come to require the full time of several surgeons.

The section on urology also flourished mightily after the war. A method of injecting an opaque oil into the urinary tract to make it visible by x-ray was a tremendous aid to diagnosis, and techniques for transurethral surgery—that is, operation through the urethra without an incision—made treatment easy and relatively safe in scores of cases. For example, a tumor of the bladder could now be removed, bit by bit, by manipulating a slender instrument through the urethra instead of opening the abdomen, and the obstruction caused by enlarged prostate glands could be relieved by literally punching a hole through it, also transurethrally. The punch operation, originated by Hugh Young of Johns Hopkins and extensively developed at the Clinic, has reduced the mortality in this common and troublesome affliction of elderly men to almost nothing and incapacitates the patient for only two or three days.

For many years diagnosis by use of the proctoscope, an instrument that permits the doctor to make a direct examination of the rectum, was one of the incidental duties of the urologists. Then one day Dr. Will remarked casually to Dr. Louis A. Buie, one of the younger associates in the section, that there was a big opportunity waiting for someone enterprising enough to concentrate on proctology. Because no one seemed to like the idea of spending his days examining and treating rectums, a great many persons were suffering from uncorrected deformities or diseases of that body part, and though they were not very ill, perhaps—because the serious cases were treated— they were decidedly uncomfortable and would seek relief if it were available.

The seed fell on good soil, and by 1919 Dr. Buie was doing so much work in his new field that a separate section on proctology was formed with him as its head. Today that section is one of the busiest at the Clinic—another demonstration of Dr. Will's genius for seeing opportunities.

At Rochester anesthesia was not much different in 1919 than it had been under Alice Magaw in 1905. Her successors had refined their art to such a degree that the surgeons felt little need for change. But Dr. Charlie always kept an eye out for new developments in the field, and on a trip to Europe in 1920 he was so pleased with what he saw of Gaston Labat's work in regional anesthesia that he persuaded the Frenchman to come back to Rochester with him and introduce his methods at the Clinic. Dr. Labat stayed for some ten months, and trained Dr. William Meeker to take his place when he left. But after two years Dr. Meeker decided he did not want to specialize in anesthesia but in surgery, so he passed the work on temporarily to the fellowship men, who rotated in the service. This was obviously unsatisfactory; there could be no progress in the field under such circumstances. But good men who were willing to specialize in anesthesia were still scarce in the profession.

Then at a banquet in Seattle in 1923 Dr. Will met a young man who was not only willing but anxious to specialize in anesthesia if he could find the opportunity, because the field was not overcrowded and he believed it had big possibilities of development. On the spot Dr. Will told him he could have his opportunity at the Clinic, and Dr. John S. Lundy moved to Rochester and organized the section on anesthesia.

Inhalation anesthesia, primarily with ether, given by nurse anesthetists continued to be the mainstay of the section's work, but by standardizing techniques and improving apparatus Dr. Lundy and the several doctor associates he soon had to have were able to demonstrate the greater worth of local and regional anesthesia in certain kinds of cases. Then these were gradually superseded in many operations of brief duration by their development of agents for intravenous anesthesia, the injection of the anesthetic directly into the blood stream. By accumulating a great many effective agents and methods they made it possible to select an anesthetic suited to the needs of the individual case instead of selecting the patient according to the limitations of one or two kinds of anesthetic.

In the days before the general use of intravenous therapy produced medical graduates trained in its procedures, the Foundation fellows, who as surgical assistants were responsible for giving blood transfusions, were none of them adept at hitting the vein if it was hard to find. The results were not disastrous, but they were sometimes unpleasant to see. The relatives of one patient complained about it to Dr. Charlie, and he appeared at the next meeting of the surgical staff to demand that someone take on the blood transfusions who could make a competent job of it. All eyes turned to the anesthetists, because their work in intravenous anesthesia had given them the necessary finesse. So blood transfusion and later intravenous therapy were added to the work of the section on anesthesia.

Thus through more accurate diagnosis, better anesthesia, and greatly improved pre- and postoperative treatment, added to its own steady progress in technique, surgery has reached a point far in advance of its state in the days when the Mayo brothers won their phenomenal reputation. In all these developments the Clinic of course shared in the progress of medicine and surgery generally. It pioneered in its share of instances, but in most it continued the peculiar contribution of the Mayo brothers themselves by adopting the best discoveries of others and through intelligent use of them in its huge practice refining them and extending their scope.

# CHAPTER TWENTY-TWO

# On the Frontiers of Medicine

When the members of the Association of Military Surgeons, meeting for an annual convention, learned from their programs one night that they were to be addressed by Dr. Royal N. Chapman, director of the Pineapple Producers' Cooperative Association of Hawaii, on "Research in the Pineapple Industry" they thought they must have got into the wrong hall. What had that subject to do with military surgery or any other kind? But Dr. Chapman by his vivid description of the part played by the research scientist in industry made a telling case for his importance in the practice of medicine.

Every major industrial concern today sets aside a sizable budget for scientific investigation to find new needs, new products, and better techniques, and in agriculture, business, even in government, progress depends on the research division. It is certainly proper then for a humanitarian institution devoted to the care of the sick to support a program of investigation aimed at pushing forward the frontiers of effective treatment, pushing back the boundaries of the wilderness of the unknown and incurable.

The research program at Rochester, greatly expanded and extended after the organization of the Foundation, has been responsible for attracting and holding some of the ablest men on the staff, men who would chafe at the limitations of a purely clinical position. As with one voice, they and the administrative officers insist that the additions to knowledge that have come from the laboratories, important as some of those have been, are not the sole or even the primary benefit the research program confers on the group. Of much more significance, they maintain, is the gift of a disciplined, constructive imagination it brings to the practice.

As Thomas Huxley said, "He who does not go beyond the facts will seldom get as far as the facts," and the practitioner who is content with wrapping up a swollen ankle or cutting out a peptic ulcer will soon be falling short in even those processes. But the influence of the questing spirit of a research laboratory near by is likely to set him asking why the ankle swelled or the ulcer developed, and that attitude gives vitality to medical practice and lifts the doctor's horizon beyond the immediate case to possibilities for the future. A vision of the ideal always brings a man a little closer to realizing it.

Having given their blessing to research by making it one of the functions of the Foundation, Dr. Will and Dr. Charlie for the most part kept hands off. If Dr. Will was still occasionally disturbed because the clinical application of some of the projects was not immediately apparent, he took his worry out in general talking and did not interfere to dictate the choice of problems or the expenditure of money. Having put the work into the hands of men he believed were competent, he left it to them to set its course and was content with lending his moral support. On his part Dr. Charlie did not bother about purposes or justification; new theories or facts in any field of science fascinated him, and he delighted in the whole research program.

The major part of that program is the work of four divisions in the Mayo Foundation, one each for animal experimentation, experimental bacteriology, biochemistry, and biophysics. Their research laboratories are quite distinct from the clinical laboratories already described, but they function as component parts of the Clinic, from which they receive most of their financial support, because the income of the Foundation is not enough to meet more than a fraction of even their salary budgets.

2

Dr. Frank C. Mann did not like the quarters provided for his animal experimentation laboratory on the roof of the Clinic building. Perhaps roof-top runways could be made to do in the heart of a city where there was no other way of housing animals within working distance of the laboratories, but with the space and isolation of the countryside so near at hand Dr. Mann did not see the reason for keeping the animals in the Clinic building, where they would be a constant incentive to opposition from sentimentalists.

So the animals were never moved into their intended quarters. Instead Dr. Charlie offered space for them on his farm and told Dr. Mann to pick his own site. He chose forty acres in a lovely little valley, built spacious new kennels, and added a veterinarian to his staff to look after the animals. Later Dr. Charlie bought an adjoining forty acres to give the farm ample space to grow in.

For a time the farm was used only for housing the animals, the experimental work being done in the laboratory in town, but Dr. Mann was eager to move that to the country too, because space was limited in the Clinic building and he wanted room for expansion away from snooping cranks. Although Dr. Will, entirely converted to the value of a close correlation of all the services, preferred keeping the laboratory in the building, he finally yielded to Mann's arguments, and in 1922 the building of laboratory quarters on the farm was begun.

When the structure was nearly completed, at a cost of eighty thousand dollars, a fire burned it to the ground. Some people said the blaze had been set by opponents of animal experimentation, but that was never proved and was probably only rumor. At any rate, the fire raised the question of rebuilding, and a special meeting of the executive committee was called to consider it.

Dr. Will came in, took his place at the head of the table, then asked each man in turn his opinion. "We all knew what he wanted us to say, and we said it," recalled one of them. All but Dr. Mann, who said he had already given his reasons for wanting to move out of town and could not see that the fire had changed them. But the others all voted against rebuilding, and Dr. Will was heard to mutter as he left the room, "That was a great fire."

Just another instance of what a joke this committee system is, said the staff. Yet within a few months the laboratories on the farm were being rebuilt, and early in 1924 the work in animal experimentation was moved to its new quarters. Dr. Mann and Dr. Plummer had changed Dr. Will's mind—as the committee members might have done had they spoken their true opinions instead of supinely answering yes. A few years later, when hotels and hospitals had risen high around the Clinic building, everyone, Dr. Will included, admitted that it had been wise to get the animal work out from under the eyes of visitors looking down from the hotel windows upon the roof of the Clinic. The fine country location for the experimental laboratories is much envied today by visitors from New York and other cities, where providing suitable quarters for animal subjects is a vexing problem.

The Institute of Experimental Medicine, as it was thereafter called, grew steadily to a staff of nine and a crew of more than twenty expert technicians, with a budget of a hundred thousand dollars a year. It provided excellent facilities for experimental surgery, pathology, biochemistry, biophysics, bacteriology, and physiology, as well as first-class accommodations for some fifteen kinds of animals.

The Institute serves the Clinic group like any other laboratory, except that it works with problems instead of with patients. Any clinician can use its facilities for his research, or if he does not have time to do the experiments himself, some member of the Institute staff will do them for him. As part of its routine the Institute group does much testing of drugs and therapeutic agents, determining their exact effects and the proper dosage, but apart from that the members spend little time on so-called practical problems of technique. They concentrate on fundamental problems, though always on some question directly related to the field of medicine.

With growth a measure of specialization developed among the men, one concentrating on physiology, another on biochemistry, and so on. But Dr. Mann kept them working in teams nonetheless, instead of splitting off each into a little pigeonhole of his own—and wisely, because a team can undertake problems of greater magnitude than any one individual alone would have either the time or the technical knowledge to tackle. Institute teams have made especially outstanding contributions to knowledge of the cause and processes of surgical shock and the pathology and physiology of the liver.

3

Both Dr. Kendall the biochemist and Dr. Rosenow the bacteriologist make frequent use of the Institute's facilities whenever their work requires animal experimentation, but their own laboratories are in the Clinic building, and both men are research workers of the lone-wolf type. Dr. Kendall has contributed to the solution of many problems, some of them directly clinical, but his major effort and most of his time has been spent on one project in endocrinology. Although he has not worked directly with the thyroid gland for many years, he has never really left that problem; he has only gone on to hunt other knowledge essential to its final solution.

Finding himself at a dead end with the thyroid itself, once thyroxin had been isolated and synthesized, he turned to approach it from the angle of its relation to the other endocrine glands. Concentrating on the cortex, or capsule covering, of the adrenal glands, he took the first steps toward isolating its hormone, one essential to life, and several times has had reason to think he stood within sight of the sesame he seeks, the key to the intricate gearing of the endocrine system.

The possibilities, should he find it, stagger the imagination, and Dr. Kendall is one of those who willingly stake the efforts of a lifetime on the chance of cracking such a tremendous problem. The project is a costly one—Dr. Kendall holds some kind of record for the purchase of adrenal glands, for he has used tons of them in his experiments— and it is one of the most heartening facts in the story of the Clinic that the Mayos and their successors have been willing to support the gamble financially. They and Dr. Kendall both may lose, for others have taken up the same problem, and someone else may uncover the secret first and at one stroke nullify Kendall's years of work. But without the courage and vision to support his effort, the group would be poorer in spirit if not in pocket.

Dr. Rosenow's work has been a bone of contention in the world of medical science and has occasioned much criticism. His theories are disputed by other bacteriologists, partly because they violate the rules laid down by the great Koch in the early days of bacteriology, rules that are still the decalogue for bacteriologists. But Dr. Rosenow refuses to grant their immutability.

Many of his colleagues at the Clinic call his theories cockeyed; others think he is a genius, far ahead of his time. The Mayo brothers always gave him their full support, though without taking sides in a matter they knew themselves incapable of judging. One night at the weekly staff meeting one of the other laboratory scientists took decided issue with Dr. Rosenow, saying that though he was probably right in his ideas his evidence simply did not add up to what he claimed it did. Dr. Will was present and afterward asked the critic to see him the next morning. He did not ask him for an opinion on the validity of Rosenow's conclusions but only whether he thought he was honest.

"Oh, absolutely," the man answered; "he is the soul of honesty. He would never pour a tubeful of stuff down the sink because it didn't support his ideas, or make up a tubeful that did."

That was all Dr. Will cared to know. The dispute between Dr. Rosenow and his fellow bacteriologists was not settled, he said, and as long as Rosenow was sincere and honest, the verdict on his work could be left to the future. Besides, he added, whether Rosenow was right or wrong, his work was of inestimable value because of the impetus it had given to research.

4

The fourth of the research laboratories to be established was that in biophysics, the application of physics to biology. When physicists make a discovery the biophysicists adopt and develop the part of it that can be applied to animate beings. It was the x-ray and radium that first introduced the physicist into medical practice, and it was the need for a radium plant to permit radium therapy that led to the establishment of a physics laboratory at the Clinic. When such radium plants were still new the Mayos sent to Harvard for a man to install one for them and to Dartmouth for an engineer to operate it, but nothing more was attempted for several years.

Then during the winter of 1922–23 Dr. Charles Sheard, formerly professor of physics at Ohio State University, was invited to Rochester to lecture to the ophthalmologists on applied optics, and two years later he became the head of a Foundation division of physics and biophysical research.

The work of his laboratory has been varied and valuable, and he and his associates have contributed to most of the group's major research problems by devising the necessary apparatus and techniques for accurate physical measurement of body functions. They have also helped in solving some of the practical problems of the clinical laboratories. For instance, when the hematology laboratory was swamped by its job of performing two or three hundred hemoglobin tests a day, Dr. Sanford called on Dr. Sheard to help him devise a mechanical way of doing the work. The result was the Sanford-Sheard photolometer that performs some fifty kinds of chemical tests mechanically and quite without the human propensity to occasional error.

Since the research men seldom come into direct contact with patients and therefore seldom witness the effect of their work on human well-being, they find it peculiarly satisfying when they do. Dr. Sheard had the experience when Dr. New, the plastic surgeon, asked him to try his hand at contriving a device for restoring the power of speech to a man who lost his voice through removal of the pharynx. Dr. Sheard fashioned a "voice box" that did the trick. As he described his subsequent experience, "You can't explain electric potentials to the man in the street, but John Jones doesn't have any trouble understanding a little tube and box that make him able to talk. There is a real thrill in seeing a man hopeless, discouraged, unable to speak, turned into a whole human being again by a simple contraption that lets him speak as well as we can, from Alaska, Arizona, or anywhere as clear as a bell." The voice boxes have to be custom tailored to fit the individual, and Dr. Sheard has made and fitted more than three hundred of them.

5

In addition to the work of the full-time research men most of the Clinic internists and surgeons are continually engaged in some piece of investigation, reviewing their own experience and studying case records and pathologic specimens as the Mayo brothers and their pioneer associates had always done. All this mounts to an impressive total in the course of a year. Few problems arise for which the vast accumulation of Clinic records and specimens cannot provide a series of cases that yield valuable statistical information.

Little research is done in the clinical laboratories. The division of clinical chemistry does a great deal of work in testing the value of all new therapeutic agents announced in medical literature, but in the other laboratories the volume of purely clinical work leaves the staff no time for research, and they indignantly deny that any of their specimens are taken or their tests made for research purposes. But their findings are filed with the case histories and so contribute to the investigation that is an important by-product of all the clinical work.

The surgical pathology laboratories provide a case in point, as a continuation of a story already partly told. In examining slide after slide from cancer specimens Dr. Broders, the surgical pathologist in the Kahler hospitals, noticed how greatly the cell patterns varied, and it occurred to him that the microscopic difference might indicate a clinical difference. Perhaps all cancers were not of the same degree of malignancy. So he turned back to the collection of slides from former cases and grouped them according to the postoperative course of each case as shown in the history. Then he compared those cases in which the patient had lived only a little while after the operation with those in which he was alive ten or fifteen years afterward. When he got so he could tell from the slide alone what had happened to the patient after operation, he knew he had found a valid principle of differentiation and a clinically useful classification of cancers.

One of the overwhelming mysteries of life is the process of cell differentiation by which the fertilized ovum gradually develops into a cluster of cells, each with its characteristic place and function in the body. The cells that make up the skin of the hand differ in form and function from those of the fingernails, and both from the hair cells or those of the underlying tissues. But when degeneration into cancer takes place the cells lose their characteristic function and retain only the power of growth and reproduction. Therein lies the malignancy of cancer. Consequently, the more nearly the cell approaches normal —that is, the more of its typical function it retains—the less is its degree of malignancy. Thus, according to Dr. Broders, the blacker a pigmented growth the less its malignancy, because the cells that produce pigment are performing their natural function and are therefore not wholly abnormal.

On the basis of that principle Dr. Broders worked out an artificial grading that permits him to tell the surgeon not merely that the growth is cancer, but that it is cancer grade one, two, three, or four, and from this the surgeon knows how drastic his operation should be. Roughly, if the diagnosis is grade one or two he need not remove so much of the surrounding tissue; if it is grade three he had better take everything within reach; if it is grade four he might as well not remove anything, for the patient will not long survive the operation in any case.

So at least the men at the Clinic believe. Other pathologists accept the grading of cancers as a useful refinement in surgical diagnosis but believe it is enough to report whether the malignancy is *high* or *low* in degree.

# Clinic and Foundation

For all medicine's rapid progress there are still many diseases for which no effective treatment is known, and in some of these the Clinic sees as many as a thousand patients a year. The entire research program is aimed more or less directly at cutting the number of unconquered ills, but most specifically charged with the task is the phase of the work called clinical investigation—clinical because it studies the disease in the patient himself.

Aside from what clinical research Henry Plummer found time for, little of it was done at the Clinic until the addition of the medical unit after the war. To secure more of it was one of the reasons for adding that unit, and its members developed medical treatment and clinical research side by side.

They promptly set up their own laboratories at St. Mary's for urine, blood, and gastric analysis and then one by one acquired special laboratories for their investigative work, until each man had his own, complete with equipment and technicians. Stimulated by the incomparable opportunities the Clinic practice provided, they were soon producing results that won favorable notice from the medical world.

Older internists on the Clinic staff, some of whom had long wanted hospital services themselves, were irked by the attention and seeming preference given the newcomers and grumbled about the space and money spent on them and the time off allowed them for trips to medical conventions, where they were in great demand as speakers. The others might have retorted that the extra favors were justified by their accomplishments and the good they were doing for the reputation of the Clinic as well as for their patients. But the tide of resentment rose and spread through the group, till it threatened to reach disruptive intensity.

Because the men in the medical unit were getting results, the administration would probably have found a way of restoring harmony without changing the setup, had they not been disturbed themselves by certain characteristics of the unit. Primary among these was its lack of integration with the rest of the Clinic. It was rapidly developing into a little medical clinic within the Clinic, with its own staff, its own laboratories and technical crew, drawing its financial support and its patients from the Clinic but otherwise quite independent. That gave excellent opportunities to a few men, but it shut out the rest and fell considerably short of its potential service to the Clinic as a whole.

Besides, the duplication of laboratories was a big expense and if allowed to continue as the unit grew would soon become an intolerable financial drain, as well as a fertile source of strife if one man thought he got less allowance for his laboratory than another. And in such individual workshops there was no way of checking up on the soundness of a man's science, no way of being sure, without repeating his experiments in another laboratory, that his whole reasoning did not rest on some faulty laboratory technique. Why could not the medical men use the existing clinical and research laboratories, each under the supervision of a trained expert who could ensure the soundness of experimental procedures?

Furthermore, two or three of the men were showing a distressing tendency to let their younger associates do the work while they went off on one trip after another and then to claim the credit when the results were published. This discouraged the younger men, and that above all else Dr. Will Mayo would not stand for. He knew it to be a threat to the very life of the Clinic, to the spirit that had made it and upon which its continued success would in large measure depend.

When the medical unit sought to establish its own laboratories for animal experimentation, it was clearly time to call a halt to the growing separatism. So the board of governors voted to disperse the medical unit and distribute its staff and laboratories among the Clinic sections.

Some of the members resigned, but most of them accepted new posts as consultants in the medical sections. The unit's general laboratories were made a part of the divisions of clinical pathology and clinical chemistry, and its research laboratories were completely dismantled and their rooms returned to general hospital purposes. The hospital beds were distributed so each medical section had a hospital service in which to develop medical treatment in the field of its special interest. Thereafter, it was announced, any clinician could do clinical research to the extent of his interest and ability, and whatever facilities and assistance he needed would be provided for him in the proper clinical or research laboratory.

These drastic measures were clearly a further and highly important step in the integration of the Clinic, one forced by a painful experience. Yet the medical unit had not been a failure, nor was the investment in it unwise, for its spirit and the work it began left an impress on the Clinic that still endures. After a brief period of readjustment its former members went on with their research projects, but now within the body of the Clinic instead of in a separate unit.

In time the special service for clinical investigation came slowly to life again, as an unofficial outgrowth of the work of Dr. George E. Brown, one of the members of the former medical unit. He was a man of tact and had an undeniable flair for clinical research, so that soon some of the other clinicians were of their own volition referring obscure cases to his hospital service for the detailed study they themselves had not the time to make.

Finally the board of governors recognized this development by giving it official status as a clinical investigation laboratory with Dr. Brown in charge. But the lesson of the previous experience had been well learned. It was clearly understood that the new laboratory belonged to no one man, but was open to all. The clinicians referred their patients to it for special study just as they sent them to a clinical laboratory for a blood test, and within the limits of the available space any clinician could use its facilities and equipment to work out his own problem, just as he used the other research laboratories. As it turned out, only a few men felt the urge to do so, once they knew they could.

Although it is called the clinical investigation *laboratory*, the layman would not recognize it as such, for it is not a place of benches, sinks, and Bunsen burners. It consists of a section of hospital beds, a group of rooms equipped with the special apparatus needed for whatever study is under way at the moment, and quarters for a sizable outpatient department. Perhaps clinical investigation *service* better describes the setup.

7

The patients referred to the clinical investigators are of two types. For the first: Suppose a clinician at work on the Clinic floor gets stuck with a case which for some reason he cannot diagnose. He can't spend half a day or more studying that case; he simply hasn't the time. But the patient is not to be turned away on that account; instead he is referred to the clinical investigation service. Sometimes its staff can

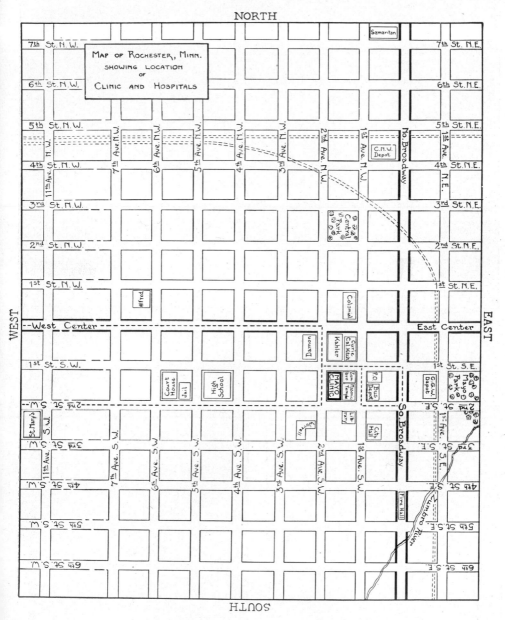

A sketch map of modern Rochester

George E. Vincent                    Guy Stanton Ford

*To the People, from Whom It Came—The Mayo Foundation*

Dr. Judd and Dr. Wilson

Dr. Charlie and Dr. Will

Sister Joseph, an exceptional woman, highly intelligent,
spirited and positive in personality

*Modern St. Mary's*

The nurses' clinic

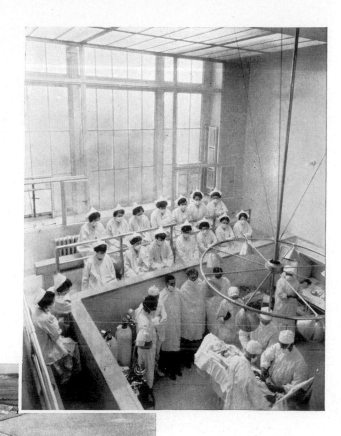

The sun deck

The pathology
laboratory

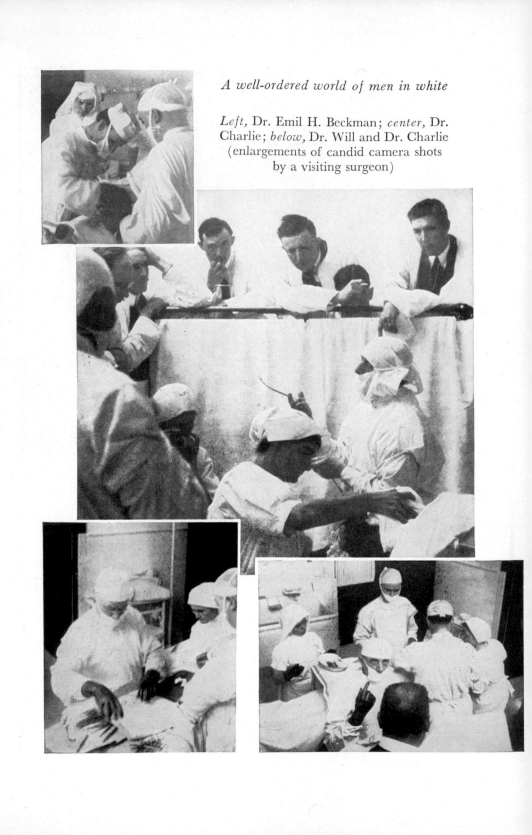

*A well-ordered world of men in white*

*Left,* Dr. Emil H. Beckman; *center,* Dr. Charlie; *below,* Dr. Will and Dr. Charlie (enlargements of candid camera shots by a visiting surgeon)

The Institute of Experimental Medicine

For the education of the public—an exhibit of an appendectomy,
Mayo Foundation Museum of Hygiene and Medicine

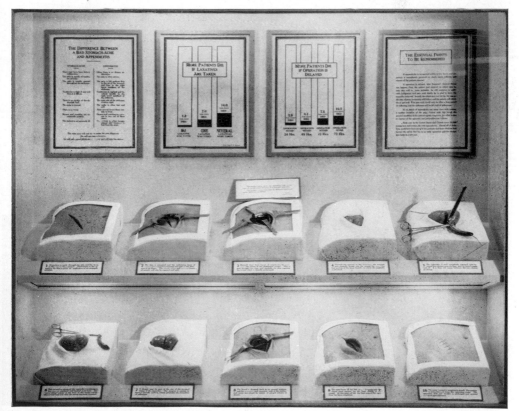

The Honorary Professor S. Alexander, *center*, conferred the degree of doctor of law (honoris causa) on the Drs. Mayo at the University of Manchester, July 24, 1929.

Dr. Charles speaking before the students of the London Hospital Medical College and Dental School

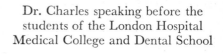

*Below,* Dr. Ochsner's party in Mexico. Calles stands at Dr. Will's left.

Mrs. Will

A week-end cruise with a party of professional friends refreshed Dr. Will as nothing else could.

The *North Star*

*Dr. and Mrs. Will and*
*Dr. and Mrs. Charlie*

Dr. and Mrs. W. J. Mayo's golden wedding anniversary; Mrs. Berkman (Gertrude Mayo) is in the center.

*The Mayo Clinic
1928*

It was William and Charles Mayo who
turned a pin point on the charts of
commerce into a great starred capital
on the map of medicine.

Three great humanitarians. President Roosevelt joined the American Legion in honoring Rochester's famous brothers in 1934.

Burt W. Eaton
financial adviser to the Mayos

Harry J. Harwick
executive officer of the Mayo Clinic

Henry S. Plummer
"the best brain the Clinic ever had"

Dr. Plummer's dream realized.
In over a million case histories
the accumulated experience of
the group is available for education and research.

Diploma-lined walls of the board of governors room and the library of the Mayo Clinic

St. Mary's Hospital, including the new surgical and medical units

The Foundation House and the painting presented by the Alumni Association
of the Mayo Foundation in 1940

*The Paradox of Rochester*
In the saucerlike valley of the Zumbro lies modern Rochester, its
metropolitan skyline rising to dramatic climax in one tall tower.

solve his problem and sometimes they cannot, but at least they have given him the benefit of special study.

An interesting illustration is the case of a woman who came to the Clinic complaining of spells of sudden collapse. She was so ill at ease, so upset that the clinician could not get enough information to warrant a diagnosis. He suspected that her trouble might be caused by an abnormal sensitivity to cold, but he could not be sure from the few facts he was able to coax from her in an hour or so of questioning. So he called on the investigation service for help.

The patient was made comfortable in bed for a few days while one of its staff, a friendly, personable young woman, worked to put her at ease and win her confidence. Then by conversational questioning she was able to get the facts, all of which bore out the clinician's guess that the woman was hypersensitive to cold—all of them, that is, but one: Her worst spell had occurred in the midst of a heat wave the preceding July, and she could recall no circumstance of unusual cold attending it.

As the doctor tried to think what to do next, she turned through the pages of a magazine on the table and, passing an advertisement for electric refrigerators, aimlessly commented on their usefulness.

"Yes," agreed the patient, "they're wonderful. My husband bought me one last summer, and for the first time in my life I had all the frozen desserts and iced drinks I wanted. I just about lived on them the first few days after we got it."

Immediately alert, the doctor asked casually whether she had got it early in the summer.

"Yes, in July. Why, it was just a few days before I had that bad spell!"

The problem was solved, the diagnosis made, and treatment instituted. Never in the world could the clinician in his office have elicited from the patient the fact of that simple domestic experience.

Good luck plays a part too in solving the problem of the other kind of patient referred to the service, the one for whose ailment no successful treatment is known. "Parasites of diagnostic obscurity" Dr. Will used to call the vague abdominal miseries that were lumped together under the term *dyspepsia,* and in the same category are the unclassified headaches similarly grouped in the modern catchall, migraine. The clinical investigators learned to distinguish one of these headaches and were apparently having gratifying success in treating it with histamine. So the clinicians referred to them all patients with headaches of obscure cause, and if the person's headache was of this particular kind treatment was given.

One day a patient was sent to them who had not only this kind of headache but also a bad case of Ménière's disease, a fairly common malady named for the Frenchman who first described its symptoms in 1861. Neither its cause nor any treatment for it was known. But to everyone's immense surprise, when the patient was given the histamine treatment for the headache the Ménière's disease vanished too.

The doctors could hardly believe it. Could it be that histamine was a remedy for that malady too? They sent word of the possibility to the clinicians, who now instead of sending the victims of Ménière's disease home without hope began telling them of the possibility of relief, carefully explaining that they did not know whether the treatment would benefit them or not, but it would do them no harm, and they could try it if they wished. There was scarcely one who did not jump at the chance to try it, and within a month the clinical investigators had treated fifteen cases of Ménière's disease with histamine. The number was too few and the time too short for them to make a positive statement about the results, but the immediate success was so striking that they felt it warranted the publication of a preliminary report announcing to the profession the possibility that histamine would cure the supposedly incurable Ménière's disease.

Some patients, quite unfamiliar with the ways of modern scientific medicine, complain about the various laboratory procedures used for diagnosis at the Clinic, because they think they are done for research purposes. Doubtless from that has come the charge occasionally heard that at the Clinic the patient is a guinea pig. He is probably less so there than in most medical institutions, for the Clinic is engaged in the private practice of medicine and cannot make any patient the subject of investigative study without his full knowledge and consent.

When a study is under way on some disease for which no treatment is known, the doctors put their cards on the table, telling the patient that they know what is wrong with him and cannot do anything to help him at present, but that they would like to make a special study of his case, that it will not harm him and will cost him nothing except a few days' time, that it may help him if his should be the case in which the lucky break comes and will certainly help others who come after him. Given such a frank explanation, few refuse to cooperate.

But in the majority of cases, even on the clinical investigation service, the patient is treated as an individual and not as a subject in research, for the study of his case is aimed at helping *him*. Of course, the doctor learns something from every such instance, and by putting together what he learns in half a hundred cases he may publish the results as research, but that is very different from using the patient as a subject for experiment.

Undoubtedly some of the men step over the line sometimes in their enthusiasm, but not very often or very far, for the administrative officers and the section heads are alert to nip short anything of the kind. They well know that the Clinic, being a wealthy institution, is fair game for any patient who thinks he has a grievance or for any lawyer who thinks he can make a malpractice charge stick.

This situation has imposed a limitation on the research program at many points, for the Clinic men must wait till new methods of undetermined effect have been proved safe elsewhere before they can adopt them, but they accept the restriction with good grace, knowing they can make their contribution in standardizing and refining the methods through observation in large-scale use.

8

The foregoing is not to say that the Rochester group is unique in its research program; animal experimentation, clinical investigation, and all the rest of it are common features in all university medical schools and hospitals and in the research institutes that have been established in various phases of medical science. Where the Mayo Clinic is unique is in making a comprehensive research program auxiliary to a *practice* of medicine, and more especially in the degree of cooperation among the various units of the organization. Teamwork is a characteristic that has been forced upon modern science by the expansion of knowledge beyond the power of any one man to be expert in all its phases, but close collaboration is naturally more difficult to attain in the loosely cohesive groups attached to university schools and institutes than in an organization in which cooperation in everything is the cornerstone of executive policy.

As one of the Clinic men enthusiastically expressed it, "Here we have a gang working together in grand fashion. There is a problem relating to the body to be solved; it takes the knowledge of the physicist, the chemist, and the doctor. Here we have them all, and they all work together to solve the problem, each contributing his part and each criticizing the work of the others as far as he is able."

The very differences between the experimental research men and the clinical investigators is salutary in its effect on both. The former are hypercritical of the work of the latter, for much the same reason that laboratory scientists in general are dubious about the attempts of social scientists: The rigidly controlled conditions that are fundamental for good work in laboratory experiments simply are not possible in dealing with variable human beings. And the clinical investigators keep reminding their laboratory fellows of that fact. As Dr. Plummer once told Dr. Sheard, "Don't try to reduce everything here to the laws of physics; there's a factor in men that just isn't reducible to physical terms." And the most critical of the Clinic's laboratory men never had any fault to find with the scientific soundness of Henry Plummer's reasoning or results.

## 9

With the years Henry Plummer had developed into a real eccentric —tall, thin, stooped, with a long, lean face, and the eyes and mouth of an eager dreamer. Mention him to anyone who knew him and you'll start a stream of stories, most of them illustrating a degree of abstraction that makes the absent-minded professor a practical man of affairs by comparison.

He always ate his lunch at the same restaurant and always ordered the same meal, so that sometimes when he sat talking overlong his waitress would clear away the table and a second girl coming by would bring him his order all over again. And he usually ate it, forgetting he had had one lunch. His table companions never knew whether their conversation would end up on a Cook's tour or on the fine points of Italian marbles. But they could be fairly sure they would have to pay the check, for Plummer never remembered it. There are half a dozen versions of the story that once when he was host to a visiting doctor at lunch he took so little notice of the check that the guest finally paid it himself. But when the waiter brought the change Henry Plummer picked it up, with a vacant thank-you.

One day he sold his car to one of his young assistants and the next morning listened with great interest to the young man's excited tale of its disappearance the night before. Suddenly Dr. Plummer started for the door with a queer look on his face and in half an hour came back to explain sheepishly that the car was in his garage. He had driven home in it, forgetting that he'd sold it.

A favorite tale one hears again and again from his former associates is that one morning Mrs. Plummer arrived at the Clinic breathless and carrying a pair of her husband's trousers over her arm. When she saw that Henry was fully clothed she sighed with relief, and at his reproachful glance, said, "Well, dear, the coat to these was gone and you know you might . . ."

Mrs. Plummer says that story is not true, but that it easily could have been. She does corroborate the story that once when Dr. Plummer could not remember where he had left his fur overcoat, one of the Clinic janitors found it at the end of the day in the women's toilet!

Often he would wander into the office of one of the administrative officers to discuss something he had on his mind, then suddenly break off in the midst of a sentence, stand lost in thought for a few minutes, turn and walk out. In half an hour or an hour perhaps, he would come back and take up his sentence exactly where he had left off, apparently quite unaware that in the meantime the other man had started a conference with someone else.

Sometimes he would disappear from his office on the Clinic floor and was nowhere to be found when he was needed. Finally one of the assistants would be sent to hunt him up, in the Clinic or out of it. And many times the young man found him in the basement, sitting on an old wooden chair, its back tilted against the furnace—just sitting there thinking and smoking, the ash long on the end of his cigar and the part that had fallen scattered over the front of his vest.

But one man who worked closely with Plummer for many years as his student, assistant, and associate insists that what most people considered his absent-mindedness was really a superb power of detachment that he developed as a defense. Someone was always hunting Henry Plummer to ask him about this or that or to have him see a patient or something else, and if he was to have the time to think that was so important to him he had to protect himself somehow. So he learned to hear, see, and remember what he wanted to and ignored the rest.

No matter which was the case, all but a few who disliked Plummer intensely are agreed that he was a great thinker and a superb clinician, "the best brain the Clinic ever had," in Dr. Will's opinion, and "the only genius on the Clinic staff," according to Dr. Mann. If genius is, as someone has defined it, "the ability to deduce correctly from observation without the benefit of previous experience," Dr. Plummer undeniably possessed it. His ability to reason straight, forward and backward, from a few data was phenomenal.

Among his many medical interests the thyroid gland remained his most enduring preoccupation, and his power to diagnose disease of the thyroid from the patient's appearance was at once the wonder and the despair of his associates. One of them tells about a patient he had whose symptoms were confusing, some of them pointing to one trouble and some to another. He concentrated on the case, determined to have the solution before he called Dr. Plummer in consultation. But before he was quite ready, Plummer walked through the waiting room one morning while the woman was sitting there. He gave her no more than a glance, but when he got back to the examining rooms he asked whose patient she was and said he wanted to see her. Then he described her exactly and outlined her case more completely than the younger man was able to after many hours of examination and thought.

Plummer undoubtedly knew at least as much about the thyroid gland as any other living man. Once a week all the men especially interested in the goiter problem, the clinicians, surgeons, chemists, and pathologists, met at the Kahler Hotel for a "goiter lunch," at which they discussed the problems in the field and the progress of their current cases. Plummer led those discussions, and some of the younger men now admit that often they understood about ten per cent of what he said; the rest was over their heads. Plummer thought so fast and looked down so many alleys in order to pick the right one that other men were likely to get lost and left behind.

## 10

Once thyroxin had been isolated, the next step in the problem was to measure the effects of it, and Dr. Kendall suggested that the Clinic get Dr. Walter Boothby to do that. He had heard Boothby speak at a medical meeting and was impressed with the work he was doing. Boothby, then with Dr. Harvey Cushing at Harvard, was concentrating on the problem of determining the normal rate of metabolism, the rate at which the human motor burns its gasoline. Physiologists knew how to find the rate in each individual, and they had a set of standard rates based on a series of studies of a small number of cases each, but a single study of a vast number was necessary to answer with reliable exactness the question, What is the normal rate of metabolism and at what point does pathologic variation begin? The Mayo Clinic offered a peerless opportunity for such a study, so Boothby accepted the invitation to join its staff.

Over a period of years he and his associates in the new metabolism laboratory measured the rates of thousands of persons—patients, doctors, nurses, Rochester citizens, everyone they could persuade to submit to the simple procedure that is now a common diagnostic practice. On the basis of their findings in that vast series they set up new standards, which were generally adopted because everyone admitted that nowhere else in the world had so many metabolism tests been made. Dr. Boothby explained the process for laymen in these terms:

The ten-minute test is a collection of flue gases to see how much oxygen you are taking out of the air and how much carbon dioxide you are putting in. The air you expire is analyzed in terms of heat and compared to a normal standard. We have made the most extensive tests recorded anywhere to determine this normal standard.

By measuring the expired air you find out whether, let us say, one, two, or three Bunsen burners are working in your body. If it is one, you are myxedematic or hypothyroid; if two, say, you are normal; and if three, you are hyperthyroid and may have goiter. Thyroid hormone causes food to burn rapidly; you have too hot a fire and you burn out your boiler. Hypothyroid cases are treated with thyroid extract, but if you are hyperthyroid you are probably a surgical case.

In other words, the Boothby standards made the rate of metabolism a reliable aid to diagnosis, serving the same purpose in diseases of metabolism that the clinical thermometer does in fevers. It advanced the differential diagnosis of thyroid disorders, but not the *treatment* of exophthalmic goiter.

## 11

That remained virtually at a standstill from 1913 to 1922. There was no effective treatment for a patient in an acute crisis, and from one to two per cent of the Clinic patients died in such a crisis before they could be prepared for surgery. Nor was there any sure way of determining the need for the multiple-stage operation, which was used in nearly two thirds of the cases, or any way of eliminating the postoperative crisis that caused most of the mortality. Consequently most surgeons were still afraid to operate for exophthalmic goiter and referred their patients to other surgeons, often to Dr. Charlie and his associates in thyroid surgery, who stood preeminent in the field. That was the situation in 1922.

Dr. Plummer meanwhile had been elaborating his theories about the mechanism that produced the disease. When thyroxin proved to be sixty-five per cent iodine, he posed the possibility that the X, that extra toxic substance which he postulated as the cause of the crises in exophthalmic goiter, was a non-iodized molecule of thyroxin. He reasoned this way: Some stimulus causes the thyroid gland to work too fast, and if there is not enough iodine readily available in the blood, the gland turns out a half-finished product, a molecule of thyroxin with the essential iodine left out. On the basis of that working hypothesis—Plummer was too good a scientist to consider it anything more—it would be logical to give the patient iodine to increase the amount of raw material for the gland's production process.

The importance of iodine in the prevention of *simple* goiter was already well established, and it had also been used occasionally in cases of exophthalmic goiter. Yet no one had given it a real trial in the latter because everyone was sure it was dangerous. The great Kocher of Switzerland had found that it aggravated the disease in some cases, and "In all his papers he so emphasized the dangers of the 'improper' use of iodine that the members of the medical profession were led to believe that it was malpractice to give a patient with Basedow's disease [exophthalmic goiter] iodine in any form, in spite of the reports of almost miraculous benefit which occasionally appeared in the medical literature and the cases which Kocher himself had observed."

After the composition of thyroxin was discovered, those who held this opinion even formulated a theory to account for the bad effects of iodine in exophthalmic goiter. An overstimulated thyroid saturated the body tissues with iodine, they reasoned, so to give more just made matters worse.

Apparently Dr. Plummer succumbed to that general idea, because for some years he made no attempt to follow his own reasoning into practice. Then early in 1922 he settled to the task of writing an account of thyroid disease for a new edition of *Oxford Medicine*. That in itself was unusual, for Dr. Plummer's major defect, in the opinion of his Clinic colleagues, was that he seldom carried any of his work to the conclusion of publication. He was too much a perfectionist to write anything up until he was satisfied that he had rounded it off in at least its current phase. And since he seldom considered anything so rounded off, he wrote and published little.

When he was persuaded to undertake a piece of writing he spent months on it and turned out a gem of a job. It was so with this article; he did not write it from what he knew but insisted on reviewing all the literature first. And as he mulled over the reports on the use of iodine, he suddenly saw why Kocher might have gone wrong— by not distinguishing between simple goiter accompanied by hyper-thyroidism and true exophthalmic goiter. It was that fundamental conviction of Plummer's—that the two symptom complexes were distinct disease entities—which was at the bottom of his whole accomplishment in the field.

Reviewing his reasoning again and trying to visualize the probable effects of iodine if his hypothesis was correct, he decided that iodine should have a thorough trial on his goiter service at St. Mary's. The results were spectacular. Patients in the coma of a crisis were rational within a few hours after the first dose of iodine solution, and some who had been in crisis for days or weeks were able to take food the next day without vomiting. One normally athletic traveling salesman who was tossing about in bed, a nervous wreck with all sorts of things wrong with his heart, was in the best of health ten days later, exercising on the horizontal bars in his gymnasium. Most patients, no matter how bad they were when they arrived, could be made ready for a complete thyroidectomy in from ten days to three weeks, and the multiple-stage operation was no longer necessary. The dreaded postoperative crisis was gone too, and mortality dropped to less than one per cent, about one fourth what it had been, in spite of the fact that many of the previously hopeless cases had entered the operable class.

After testing the iodine treatment thoroughly for a year Plummer announced to the profession at a meeting of the Association of American Physicians in May 1923 that the administration of iodine would prevent the crises that caused death in exophthalmic goiter. The experience of others quickly confirmed the fact, and the method was adopted throughout the world, completely changing the surgeons' attitude toward the disease and inaugurating a new era in thyroid surgery. For Plummer's iodine treatment turned the most treacherous operation known to surgery into one of the safest, in the hands of any competent surgeon. It was hailed as one of medicine's greatest gifts to surgery, and the Germans coined a fitting word for it: *Plummerung*.

## 12

Meanwhile Dr. Boothby had got Plummer interested in the possibilities of oxygen therapy. Haldane of Oxford, the leading English authority on respiratory disorders, had initiated the modern phase of that form of treatment when he used it for victims of poison gas in the First World War, and it developed rapidly in civil practice afterward when clinical investigators in eastern hospitals proved its worth in treating pneumonia and other lung disorders. As the use of it spread, special oxygen chambers were set up in most hospitals, and Boothby and Plummer built two such chambers in the hospital quarters of the Kahler Hotel.

Dr. Will did not think much of them. They might be nice to play with, he said, but they were of little use in practical medicine because it cost twenty-five dollars a day to use them. When the portable oxygen tent came along in 1925 he liked that better; it used less oxygen and cut the cost in half. It was still inefficient and wasteful, however, but since the tent and the tanks of gas could be moved around the hospital easily no great need was felt for improvement, and for years none was made.

Then came the rapid development of aviation. Planes were built that could fly at altitudes of twenty thousand feet and more, but their human pilots could not ride with safety at more than ten thousand. The lack of oxygen in the higher air lessened the pilot's efficiency and increased the danger of accident. Obviously the pilot could not operate his plane from within an oxygen tent, and there was no room for the big supply of oxygen he would need. So the realization of mechanical possibilities in aviation waited upon the invention of a simple and efficient apparatus for administering oxygen.

Northwest Airlines officials explained this difficulty to some of the Clinic men at a social gathering one day, and Dr. Boothby was soon at work on the problem with the active aid of Dr. William R. Lovelace, one of the Foundation fellows in surgery who was especially interested in it. They revived an idea that Haldane had put into effect during the war with fair success, the use of a facial mask.

Boothby and Lovelace worked out the mechanical details, how to get the oxygen to the mask and mix it with any desired amount of air, but when it came to designing the mask itself they were stumped. That was a task for an artist. So they took their problem across the street to Arthur H. Bulbulian, the director of the Foundation museum, who was used to modeling facial features in wax for the museum exhibits.

The two doctors outlined their requirements: The mask must be small and light, it must not interfere with vision, and it must fit snugly over the nose so as not to allow the escape of the gas, yet loosely enough to permit easy, comfortable breathing. Dr. Bulbulian was equal to the task, and the result was the "B.L.B. inhalation apparatus," a small nasal mask that opens at the lower corners into two hollow tubes rounding the mouth and meeting again just above the chin. From that point a single tube leads to the small breathing bag in which the oxygen from the tank is mixed with air let in by small portholes in the metal fitting on the tube. In laboratory tests and under actual flying conditions the mask proved one hundred per cent efficient, and that aviation problem was solved.

Not only that, the mask was a simple, efficient, comfortable means of administering oxygen to sick folk, and one that could be used as easily by the country doctor in his patient's home as in a hospital. Further, with the mask the use of oxygen was inexpensive, costing only five dollars a day under home conditions and only half that much on a large scale in hospitals. That alone was enough to win Dr. Will's hearty approval for the mask and its inventors.

Even more, it greatly extended the scope of oxygen therapy. In the old chambers and tents the possible concentration of oxygen ranged from forty to sixty per cent, but with the new mask any concentration up to pure oxygen could be given. And the doctors soon learned that the higher concentrations were effective in a number of diseases that responded little if any to lower concentrations. Early results suggested possibilities of great benefit in speeding up wound healing, relieving heart attacks, treating asthma, preventing certain postoperative complications, and even killing some kinds of bacteria. Medical practice was to benefit from the needs of aviation.

Drs. Boothby and Lovelace went on from that to other physiological problems of flying. For instance, airplanes were available that could climb at a rate of a mile a minute, but their human pilots could not. If a deep-sea diver rises from the depths too fast, faster than his body can give off the nitrogen it has accumulated under water, the gas expands and forms little bubbles in his blood and he gets the painful and often highly serious cricks and cramps known as the bends. Precisely the same thing happens when a flyer ascends from the earth to the upper atmosphere too quickly.

Since oxygen removes accumulated nitrogen from body tissues and cavities, Boothby and Lovelace suggested that by breathing oxygen for an hour before taking his plane up, the flyer could climb as fast as he wanted to. But that was no practical solution at all, for the time he gained by making a swift ascent he lost in sitting around on the ground breathing oxygen. So the doctors began hunting for a speedier way of decompressing the body.

One thing led to another, and soon the Clinic section on metabolic investigation included a full-fledged and completely equipped laboratory of aviation medicine. Although its work had sprung from the needs of commercial aviation it was equally important to military aviation—when the invader planes come over, the faster the defenders can get into the air the better. So the new laboratory at Rochester has been made a highly important cog in the vast machinery of preparation for national defense.

### 13

The Clinic story provides many such instances of extensive developments from chance occurrences, made possible by the size of the group and the tradition of ready collaboration among its members and sections. One other will illustrate how a single idea may grow into a vast program of investigation.

Dr. Will and Dr. Charlie never relaxed their custom of bringing back some specific contribution from every trip they took, and Dr. Will's journey to Australia in 1924 yielded a peculiarly fruitful one. He and Mrs. Mayo traveled again with Dr. and Mrs. Martin and a party of good friends, including John Kahler and his wife and Dr. Richard Harte of Philadelphia. It was a vacation trip and the party enjoyed it to the full, experiencing again the ready hospitality they had encountered in South America. In New Zealand Dr. Will was made a chief in a tribe of Maoris and in an ancient ceremony of "rubbing noses" with the belle of the tribe was presented with the "robe" and club of the office. Thereafter when anyone asked him which of his many honors pleased him most he would say, "The grass skirt of the Maoris and my wand of office as the Chief."

But as usual Mayo and Martin did much professional visiting and observing too. They found the Australians deeply interested in the form and program of the American College of Surgeons and addressed several medical meetings called to hear them describe the work of the college.

In Sydney they found the whole medical community talking about the work of two young men at the University of Sydney, Dr. John Hunter the anatomist and Dr. N. D. Royle the orthopedic surgeon. Hunter was making a study of the effects of the sympathetic nervous system on muscle tone, and on the basis of his findings Dr. Royle had achieved extraordinary results in treating spastic paralysis by severing certain branches of the nervous system. The two Americans spent an entire afternoon with the young men, looking over their case records, watching a demonstration of Royle's operation on a goat, and examining some of the patients he had operated on. Greatly impressed, they spread the fame of the two Australians throughout the United States, and the American College of Surgeons brought them over later in the year to address its annual clinical congress.

In the meantime Dr. Will had given a detailed description of Royle's operation to Dr. Adson, the Clinic neurosurgeon, who promptly used it in his next case of spastic paralysis. Watching the patient's postoperative course carefully, he observed a curious fact: The temperature of the skin on the man's feet was much higher than it had been before the operation. This suggested to him that severing the proper nerves in the sympathetic system might prove an effective treatment for diseases of the peripheral vascular system, the veins and arteries of the hands and feet. That was another field in which relatively little was known. Its various diseases had not been differentiated, and there was no treatment for them except amputation when they were so advanced that circulation failed entirely and gangrene developed.

Dr. Adson promptly reported his observation to Dr. Brown, the clinical investigator, who began to study the patients on whom Adson performed sympathectomy for spastic paralysis. In every case the skin temperature of the feet increased on an average of four hundred per cent.

The significance of this rests on a curious fact in physiology. The human body has a hot-water heating system, in which the blood is the circulating medium, the heart is the pump, the stomach the boiler, and food the fuel. Somewhere there is also a thermostat that keeps the mouth temperature always the same in a normal body. Extra heat, like that produced by eating a meal, is carried to the hands and feet by the blood and there eliminated. But if something goes wrong with the circulatory system at those exit points they fail to perform this function. It seemed logical therefore to deduce from the increased temperature of the feet that Dr. Adson's operation improved the peripheral circulation. Consequently he tried sympathectomy in a case of peripheral vascular disease in March 1925, and cured it.

Then the clinical investigators and the neurosurgeons concentrated on vascular diseases. Dr. Brown examined, compared, correlated, and classified till he was finally able to differentiate the various diseases and describe ways of making a differential diagnosis among them. He and his associates studied the effect of every promising treatment from drugs to postural exercises, including baths, rest, diet, and massage, in order both to learn more about the mechanism of the vascular system and to find some effective treatment less radical than surgery. Often their methods were successful in milder cases, but for the severer types the neurosurgeons had to provide the treatment. Sometimes, however, their operations did not work, so some means had to be found for telling *before* operation whether or not surgery would help in that particular case. Dr. Brown finally found a way. He gave the patient typhoid vaccine to induce fever, and if the rise in the skin temperature of the foot was proportionately much greater than the rise in mouth temperature, the patient would benefit from the operation.

Fundamental in all this work was the measurement of variations in skin temperature, and finding early that the devices available were not adequate, the clinical investigators sought assistance from Dr. Sheard the biophysicist. He contrived an electrothermometer to do the job. As the patient lies on the bed with thermocouples on his hands and feet, a pencil of light from an electric eye automatically registers the temperature on a numerical scale across the top of the room, and as the temperature changes the light shifts along the scale.

Thereafter Dr. Sheard participated actively in the study, contributing techniques and apparatus for many of the mechanical treatment methods that were tried. When it became apparent that more rigidly controlled room conditions were needed to make sure that the changes in skin temperature were produced by the patient's own heating plant and not by that of St. Mary's Hospital, Dr. Sheard devised and installed equipment for keeping the room temperature and humidity absolutely constant.

As the investigators dug deeper into the physiologic aspects of their problem, they undertook a study of the rate and volume of the blood flow and the factors that speed it up or slow it down, and for parts of that experiments on animals were necessary. So the services of the Institute of Experimental Medicine were requested. There the work was done by a team that included a physiologist to direct and interpret the whole, since the problem was one of physiologic function, a biophysicist to arrange and supervise the intricate physical technique the experiment required, and a surgeon to handle the animals.

# Clinic and Foundation

Thus did Dr. Will's trip to Australia and Dr. Adson's close observation of his patient's condition grow into an investigative study that is still continuing and that in fifteen years produced nearly eight hundred published reports of progress, some of them containing findings of great general significance. Such an accomplishment, involving many special skills and fields of science, would be quite beyond the power of an individual, even if he gave a lifetime to it.

# CHAPTER TWENTY-THREE

# Training Young Doctors

After 1917 the work of the Mayo Foundation was a vital factor in every phase of activity at Rochester, for the alliance with the university imposed new obligations and set new standards that took some striving to meet. The experiment in graduate medical education was administered by a committee of five from the Minneapolis faculty headed by Dean Lyon of the medical school and a committee of five from the Rochester faculty with Dr. Louis B. Wilson, who was named director of the Foundation, as chairman. Each group was in full charge on its own campus, but in deciding matters of general policy they acted as a joint committee under the chairmanship of Dean Ford of the graduate school, who, in his own words, felt "like a land lubber presiding over the navy department."

It was something new, this putting a layman, and a historian at that, in charge of a project in medical education, but it proved wise, because there was no precedent to guide the leaders of this pioneering venture save as the experience and example of established disciplines could be applied. Dean Ford was a man of deep wisdom and broad social and educational vision, alive to the need for raising professional education of all kinds above the mere teaching of techniques, the mere learning of a trade. But could it be done? Could clinicians with a training and tradition wholly practical be turned into scientists imbued with the spirit of inquiry and the methods of scholarship? Men in the basic medical sciences, long since become a true graduate discipline, doubted it, and Dean Ford himself sometimes wondered:

Could surgery, obstetrics, ophthalmology, urology, internal medicine, pediatrics, and orthopedics be allied, associated, or developed in connection with a kind of training and in a kind of institution that talked in terms of science and research and discovery and additions to a body of knowledge that could be reduced to generalization? That was a poser for anybody but a real optimist. It was true that the words *research* and

643

*scientific method* rolled off the tongue of the surgeon quite as easily as they did off the tongue of the anatomist, but identity of vocabulary is no proof of common ideals or purposes even in a political program. All one could do was to hope that results would justify an attempt to make surgeons better than technical operators and ophthalmologists more than refractionists. Toward that end one had open a free field for experimentation in educational procedure.

Graduate work in other fields suggested the apparatus necessary for the experiment: high standards of admission, qualified teachers, adequate laboratory and library facilities, rigid examinations, and preparation of theses to demonstrate the power of the student to do productive research. But the clinical men had no idea what a thesis or an examination at the graduate level meant. The first theses their candidates presented were nothing more than ordinary case reports, and when those were rejected they turned to the Clinic files, pulled out a stack of histories, and came up with a statistical study of how many red-haired women had developed cancer of the left breast, or something equally futile. Finally terms of description were found that meant something to them: The subject should be important enough and the work sound and original enough to warrant publication in the best professional journal in the candidate's specialty.

The theses gradually improved in quality, and finally the graduate committee decided to publish a few annual volumes of them, not because they were world-shaking in their contributions to knowledge—how many theses in any branch of learning are?—but because they provided objective evidence to the medical world of what it took to get this new advanced degree in clinical medicine at Minnesota. And men of medicine competent to judge found them worthy.

Then the oral examinations! For a time the results there were so discouraging that the administration considered the advisability of bringing in outside examiners. The clinicians made the examination a little classroom quiz or turned it into a clinical conference among friends and spent the time arguing a point among themselves while the candidate sat quietly by doing nothing. It was also hard to persuade them to give an adverse vote on each other's candidates. They insisted on applying the principle of professional courtesy, and when one of them presented a student, saying in effect, This is my man and I know he's good, he expected the others to take his word for it. That was his diagnosis, and to have it publicly challenged and discredited was a personal affront to him.

For a while Dean Ford loaded the examining committees with faculty members in the basic sciences, because they had gone through the academic mill themselves and were used to putting others through it, and he frequently dropped in on an examination himself to put questions of his own to the candidate. Gradually the idea of academic detachment took hold, so that a professor of the clinical branches "no longer roared, he only grumbled subterraneously" when his candidate went down before the questioning of his colleagues. And conditions were further improved when younger men who had gone through the process were added to the faculties and began appearing on the committees.

It was not only the Rochester men who experienced those difficulties; clinicians on both campuses faced them, for they were the result of the newness of the experiment, not of personal inadequacy. It was easier for the Minneapolis men to overcome them, however, for they worked in the university atmosphere and were somewhat less submerged in a tide of practical preoccupations. Without Dr. Wilson to administer the program in Rochester the transformation of attitude there would have taken much longer, but he understood the purposes of the university procedure and was fully in sympathy with them, so he stood ready always to pull the Rochester faculty up to the mark.

With understanding came pride that the Clinic group was functioning as a part of the state university, and this was attended with a conscientious concern about meeting its standards. For fear the mortality of Rochester fellows in the final examinations would disgrace the Foundation faculty, its members began giving their candidates a stiff preliminary examination at home before they let them appear before the joint examining committee at Minneapolis. That the Rochester faculty members feel a deep obligation to hold the university's banner high is apparent to anyone who talks with them about their Foundation activities.

Not all the benefit of the affiliation flowed in one direction, however. The constant "Why must we do it this way?" from the Rochester group forced a salutary review of the reasons for established academic routines in the graduate school.

In this game too Dr. Will and Dr. Charlie, after starting the ball rolling, were content to cheer the team on from the sidelines. Dr. Charlie was made a professor of surgery on the Foundation faculty, he sometimes gave a course of lectures on the Minneapolis campus, and for a brief period he served as nominal head of the department of surgery in the undergraduate medical school, but Dr. Will, because of his position on the board of regents, was not even a member of the faculty.

His willingness to keep hands off, on which all accounts agree, was the more remarkable because he had very positive convictions about medical education. He thought the educators were lengthening the undergraduate course beyond all reason, were overemphasizing the preclinical sciences, and were giving the students too little contact with patients. Sometimes his university friends twitted him about his ideas, telling him they were only trying to do for *all* the clinical branches what he himself had done for surgery—marry them to the full panoply of medical sciences. But they did not convert him; he insisted that the job of the undergraduate school was to turn out general practitioners and that it would do better to make sure its graduates had a good fund of general knowledge and knew how to apply it than to try to cram them so full of facts in special fields that they were burned out mentally by the time they graduated. The fact that his ideas had no apparent effect on the development of the undergraduate course at the university medical school is good evidence that he was not the untrammeled dictator of its affairs he was sometimes called.

2

From the beginning the requirements for a fellowship either at the university or in the Foundation were put on the high level of a bachelor's degree plus the medical degree and one year's internship. During the first years, when the war was providing a counterattraction for able young medics, it was hard to hold to these requirements, for there were scarcely enough qualified applicants to fill the vacancies. After the war applications continued to come in considerable numbers from tired, dissatisfied, middle-aged practitioners who wanted to become surgeons in six months. But as time went on the idea sank in that the Minnesota plan was not postgraduate work, not an easy short cut to

646

specialization, but a real graduate course, requiring three years or more of hard plugging for the guerdon it promised.

With increasing appreciation of that kind of training the number and quality of the applicants rose, until the eighty-odd annual vacancies in the Foundation were being filled from some two thousand applications, permitting the appointment of about one in twenty who applied. With so high a degree of selection the stated requirements faded to an almost forgotten minimum; a goodly number of those chosen had a master's degree, some had teaching experience, and the majority had served more than one year's internship, though applicants were not given preference on that basis alone and a fair proportion were always appointed direct from the internship.

The applications came from all over the world. By 1940 the fellows of the Foundation represented seventy-three medical schools in the United States and Canada and sixty universities in twenty-six foreign countries. As a result of one or two unfortunate early experiences, the Foundation now refuses to accept a foreign applicant without a letter stating that he has a position waiting for him when he has finished his three years' work, so that if he decides to stay in the United States afterward the Foundation cannot be accused of bringing foreigners into the country to compete with American doctors.

### 3

In the traditional manner of graduate students the Foundation fellows choose major and minor subjects for their graduate work. The major subject may be internal medicine or general surgery or any one of the recognized medical and surgical specialties, and the minor must be in some basic science related to the major field. Two years of the fellowship are to be spent in various aspects of the major, six months in the minor, and six months in either or neither, as the fellow may elect. Within those broad general limits the arrangement of the specific program is determined by the fellow in consultation with his major adviser.

The Foundation office announces typical programs, such as: for a major in general surgery, one year in two or more diagnostic sections, a year in two or more general surgical sections, six months in surgical pathology or experimental surgery, and six months in a surgical specialty; or, for a major in internal medicine, a year in two or more diagnostic sections, a year on two or more hospital medical services, six months in clinical pathology, and six months in some medical specialty. But no man is asked or expected to follow even such general suggestions exactly. In effect the Foundation says to him, Here is a sample program, but you may vary it to suit your own needs and interests. And they are proud to report that to date no two Foundation fellows have followed identical courses of study. Such flexibility and latitude of election is possible only because of the number and variety of the Clinic sections.

Each fellow states his intended major and minor in his application, and if he is appointed the Foundation secretary assigns him to a section in his major subject for the first quarter, to give him time to learn the institution and its faculty. Thereafter he chooses his own sections and usually gets the ones he asks for, though perhaps not quite in the order he names them. The secretary must do a good bit of juggling to make the selections fit the vacancies, and where choices conflict or pile up for one or two sections—as for Dr. Will's and Dr. Charlie's sections in surgery during their lifetime—the preference is given to the fellows with the best records, thus providing an unofficial spur to excellence. And allowing the fellows to choose the sections they want to work in provides an excellent check on the faculty.

Sometimes entirely unsuspected interests come to light as a result of the first arbitrary appointment. In one case the fellow was late arriving for his first quarter, and the harassed Foundation secretary had to fill the place in internal medicine she had allotted him. So when he arrived she explained offhand that she had assigned him to dermatology, since he would probably want a quarter's work in that specialty for his major in internal medicine. He confessed later that he did not want it and was quite disgruntled but didn't say anything because he thought he had better not begin with a complaint. Once he got started in dermatology, however, the poor secretary could hardly tear him away to do anything else. He took his degree in that specialty and has become a nationally known dermatologist.

During the first five years sixty-six per cent of the Foundation fellows elected general surgery for their major, but the proportion has decreased to thirty-one per cent in the last five years (1935–40), whereas the proportion choosing internal medicine has risen from nine per cent to twenty-eight per cent in the same period, much to the satisfaction of the Foundation officers. They interpret the better balance as an indication of rising standards for specialists in medicine. Undoubtedly other factors have contributed to the change, among them certainly the Clinic's own rapid development in medicine.

The duties of the surgical fellows vary from section to section and individual to individual, but in general they are said to be these: The fellows live in the hospital during their term of service in the surgical sections and are responsible for the pre- and postoperative care of the patients in the surgical wards, under the supervision of the surgeon whose assistants they are. In the mornings all are on duty in the operating rooms. There a first-year fellow performs general duties or merely watches. During his second year he acts as a second assistant in a surgical team—each surgeon has two teams of assistants, one for each of his operating rooms—and if he shows the necessary ability he may stay on as a first assistant for a third year.

The first assistant makes the incision and closes the wound, but the remainder of each operation is performed by the surgeon himself, because all Clinic patients, whether paying or nonpaying, are private patients and none of them can be turned over to the assistants. The fact that the surgical fellows perform no complete operations on their own responsibility has occasioned considerable criticism of the Foundation's fellowships in surgery, and the opportunities for practical experience in operating are said to be better in university fellowships or hospital residencies where the private-patient restriction is not in effect. On the other hand, the Foundation men maintain that by mastering the routine motions till they are second nature and watching an experienced operator meet the problems of many major cases, the fellow becomes a more competent surgeon than he would by performing a limited number of less important operations himself.

4

In internal medicine and the medical specialties the duties of the fellows vary even more widely, according to the inclination of the individual clinician and the ability of the fellow. In general, however, during his service on the Clinic floor the young doctor takes the case history, makes the preliminary examination, arranges for the simpler diagnostic tests required, and prepares a résumé of the case stating his opinion as to the diagnosis and the treatment indicated. Then the staff internist takes over, and as the case progresses both he and the fellow can see where the latter was right, where wrong, and why. In his résumé the fellow may suggest a cystoscopic examination or a special kind of x-ray, but only the staff consultants may order any diagnostic procedure that involves considerable expenditure or is hard on the patient.

In the Foundation the Clinic sections on x-ray diagnosis, x-ray treatment, and radium therapy are combined in one division of radiology. There are usually eight or nine fellows majoring in it at a time, with two or three graduating each year. It is one division that does not accept fellows majoring in other specialties, except as observers for brief periods, because its staff do not want any fellow to go out with the smattering of knowledge he can gain in three or six months and proclaim himself a radiologist trained at the Mayo Clinic. Occasionally, however, the division will accept as a special fellow on a year's service some qualified student who is carrying on a three-year course of study in some other university.

In the section on pediatrics, where the program is rather less flexible than in most, two extra services are added to the customary ones on the Clinic floor and in the hospital wards. One is a six-months' service in the local practice in and around Rochester, which the head of the section considers necessary to give his fellows experience in handling common colds, stomach upsets, and other such ordinary ills as make up an important part of the practicing pediatrician's work. The other is a six-months' service in preventive pediatrics, during which the fellow participates in the periodic examinations of the local school children and helps to conduct the baby clinics and infant welfare conferences that the Clinic staff provides for Rochester and Olmsted County residents.

When the Foundation's work began, the university graduate school recognized only nine legitimate major fields, but as the Clinic developed more specialty sections they were also accepted for degrees, and by 1940 the number was twenty-one. The faculty in these newer fields, self-conscious about their youth and determined to prove them worthy of recognition, select their fellows with special care. In this class are anesthesia, now called anesthesiology, to which fellowships were allowed in 1929, and physical medicine and plastic surgery, both accepted into the family in 1937.

Physical medicine is the application of physical and mechanical agents, such as light, heat, water, and electricity, to the treatment of diseases. It was recognized as a legitimate branch of medical practice in Europe before the turn of the century, but in the United States it was left to the mercies of the quacks until recently, and the Clinic was slow to encourage it because of the Mayos' distrust of it. They never got over the attitude that made them replace the spark-throwing connections with wooden plugs on their first x-ray machine—a suspicion of anything that seemed likely to impress more than help the patient. When Dr. Will returned from his trip to Australia in 1922 he discovered that some enterprising soul had established a mud bath in the basement of the Zumbro Hotel, and in high scorn he gave orders that no Clinic doctor was to refer a patient to that place unless he was absolutely sure its treatment was what the case demanded. The mud bath did not long survive.

But Dr. Will was finally convinced that physical therapy could be very helpful in the management of many ailments and in 1935 he was persuaded to sanction the establishment of a Clinic section on physical medicine, in charge of a qualified specialist about whose professional bona fides there could be no doubt. Well aware that his specialty can be easily discredited because the gadgets and apparatus it must use invite exploitation by charlatans, Dr. Krusen goes over the applicants for fellowships with a fine-tooth comb. He wants to be sure of their integrity, so that he will not turn out any specialist in physical medicine who will betray it for the sake of quick commercial success.

In line with its express purpose of lifting medicine and its sister professions above the level of mere craftsmanship, the Foundation also tried its hand at giving advanced training in dentistry, but it has discovered that there will be few positions available for men so well trained until the dental profession itself reaches the point of demanding them and paying for their services.

The Foundation offers only a limited number of fellowships in the basic sciences, twenty-five in 1937 as compared with eighty in internal medicine and one hundred and five in general surgery. It has facilities for a more extensive development in that direction, but its setup offers no such peculiar advantages there as it does in the clinical subjects, so the major development on that side of the Minnesota program has been left to the university, where the laboratory fields are well developed in connection with the undergraduate medical school.

More than half of the science fellowships at Rochester are given in pathology, with major emphasis on surgical pathology, clinical pathology, or pathologic anatomy, according to the fellow's preference. In any case a year on the postmortem service is recommended.

Many fellows in medicine or surgery also choose to spend six months or a year in that service, because it is fundamental to so many phases of practice. A postmortem does not tell the doctor merely what caused the patient's death; the coroner's autopsy stops there, but a real postmortem does not. The patient's state of health throughout his lifetime is recorded in the lesions of his body, and from the organs of a man who has died of pneumonia the pathologist may learn a great deal about the workings of an operation for gastric ulcer twenty years before or about the effects on the liver of removing the gallbladder ten years ago. An ample experience on the postmortem service is likely to teach a young surgeon, in the words of the section head, "How important is the protection of the Lord in any operation, even a supposedly harmless one."

There is always one fellow in this section on twenty-four hour duty. Whenever a death occurs in any of the hospitals, boardinghouses, or hotels of Rochester the manager or superintendent immediately notifies the Clinic telephone operator, who relays the message to the pathology fellow on call. He goes at once to interview the relatives and secure permission for an autopsy, then notifies the consultant and the patient's doctors if they were not present. When the autopsy has been completed he and the consultant hold another conference with the relatives to report the findings and to offer all possible assistance in making arrangements for shipping the body, filling out insurance blanks, and the like. This is a courtesy service given without charge. The fellow is

also charged with the responsibility for notifying the business office of
the death and of any changes it may have caused in the family's
financial condition, so that proper allowances may be made in com-
puting the Clinic's bill.

Then begins the cataloging and preservation of the autopsy specimens, the making of microscopic slides, and writing of reports. The
case is discussed among the fellows and consultants in the section, then
with the clinician and surgeon in the case, and finally at the weekly
clinico-pathological conference. By the time that program has been
completed the postmortem has yielded its full quota of instruction to a
wide circle, of which the fellows are the inner ring.

Fine as the facilities in that section are, they have their limitations.
Fellows in pediatrics, for instance, take their minor in pathology on the
Minneapolis campus because the excellent postmortem service there,
drawing from the entire state as it does, provides more autopsies on
babies and children than does the Clinic section.

Those who wish to minor in anatomy also go up to the university
for the six months' work because, except for some incidental dissecting
supervised by the section on anesthesia, the Clinic provides no work
in anatomy. The attempts of the Foundation to develop a division in
that field have been discouraged by the university members of the
medical graduate committee, who think it best that the Foundation
should not become too independent of its university affiliations. The
exchange of students between the two campuses has not proved practicable to the extent hoped for in the beginning. The medical graduate
committee has not been able to devise any plan of rotation that will
work with a hundred fellows on one side and three hundred and fifty
on the other—especially when the university operates on a fixed budget
that fits each fellow to a specific job, whereas the number of Foundation fellows is flexible enough to permit one or two to take six months'
work on the Minneapolis campus without leaving a vacancy at
Rochester.

6

Although there are seldom more than two or three majoring in any
one of the other sciences at Rochester, the laboratories are full of fellows most of the time, because of the required minor in a basic science
and because much of the research for the theses is done in the various

laboratories. There are always from fifteen to twenty-five fellowship men at work at the Institute of Experimental Medicine.

Some educators object to requiring all medical graduate students to attempt research, because they think nothing worthy of the name can be done in six months. Besides, they say, it is absurd to think a man cannot be a good surgeon or internist without the ability to do original research. But others, including most of the Minnesota faculty on both campuses, believe that if a subject of proper scope is selected the fellow can accomplish enough to give him an introduction to research techniques and problems, enough to make him wary of accepting as gospel everything he reads in his medical journals. In the process some men discover an unsuspected interest in scientific investigation. In the laboratory experiments of their undergraduate days they worked only for the correct answer printed in their laboratory manuals; in graduate research the problem is theirs to solve, the unknown answer theirs to find.

With research of all degrees and kinds as pervasive as it has become in Rochester, the fellows take in its spirit with the air they breathe. If a man has any capability whatever for that phase of medicine, he can hardly fail to be caught up in one of the many projects under way, and frequently he contributes appreciably to it. At least he is likely somewhere along the way to assist his adviser or some other staff member in working up the materials in files and museums for a paper or two.

There, as well as in the work on his own thesis, the fellow makes the acquaintance of the wonderfully rich resources that have resulted from the decisions taken and the policies instituted in years past. There is first the library, grown with the years to nearly forty thousand volumes, rich in the periodical sets that are essential tools of research in any field. When the financial strain of the postwar period forced the sale of many European libraries, Mrs. Mellish called Dr. Will's attention to this rare opportunity for filling out the Clinic collection of important reference books, and with his approval agents in European centers secured many valuable volumes for the Rochester library.

But in so dynamic a subject as medicine the present is as important as the past, and the bound periodical volumes are supplemented by subscriptions to more than six hundred journals, about one third of them American and the rest representing all the major countries of the world from Africa to Norway and Japan to Ireland. If a basic requirement for graduate education in any subject is access to the literature of that subject, the Foundation qualifies, through the Mayo Clinic library.

In finding their way through this material both Clinic staff and Foundation fellows have the full assistance of a corps of trained medical librarians, whose task the Clinic administration conceives in rather more comprehensive terms than is usually the case. Here as elsewhere in the organization everything practicable is done to help the staff members accomplish as much as possible in the time at their command by relieving them of work as easily done by others. The librarians, and secretaries too, are expected to give an unusual amount of assistance in the preliminary task of finding references and preparing bibliographies. Without such help the Clinic members could never do all the writing and publishing they do.

Within limits the same service is available to the fellows, though they are expected to learn enough about the indexes and guides to medical literature that they will not be helpless if they find themselves working where expert service is not provided for them.

## 7

As the library opens to them the heritage of their profession, the division of records and statistics makes available to them the accumulated experience of the Clinic. Here certainly is an undeniable advantage of the group over the individual; the group can shoulder the social responsibility of preserving beyond the lifetime of the individual the written record of his experience. Now at the command of the Foundation fellows as well as of Clinic staff members are the complete health histories of over a million patients, thoroughly indexed and immediately accessible.

Their value depends of course upon the proper and significant use of them. In the middle 1920's the Clinic men suddenly awoke to the fact that their collection of records and the uses they made of them had outgrown the simple clerical system that had served so well in earlier years. Not having kept pace with developments in the science of biometry, the Clinic was being criticized for publishing unreliable statistics. Plummer urged that a trained statistician be employed to correct the difficulty forthwith, and a former Foundation fellow who had become a professor of biometry at Johns Hopkins was called back to put the section of statistics on a professional, scientific basis. He did so, among other things replacing the laborious manual cross-indexing with the swifter and more efficient mechanical punch-card system.

He and his successors were charged with supervising the collection of statistics for all Clinic publications, and also, as professors of biometry and medical statistics in the Foundation, with the task of teaching Foundation fellows how to do statistical research, how to collect numerical data and interpret them.

For graduate students to assist their teachers in research is customary the world over, but in the Foundation the fellow who does the leg work on the literature or the experiment is listed as one of the authors in the published paper. It has been known to happen that his name came first in the list, though usually it is the senior clinician who heads the author team, and that is to the fellow's benefit, for it is the older man's reputation that secures the paper a hearing. It is understood, however, that the name of no man shall appear who has not contributed actively to the project. As one of the administrators expresses the Clinic idea, "We do not believe you can do research from a swivel chair. You can suggest it or supervise it from your desk, perhaps, but then the men who do the work must have the credit for it."

Since the quality of the work published is of great importance to the reputation of the Clinic, it is surprising to find so little official censorship of results. There is a committee on medical education and research to which all topics for papers, including the fellows' theses, must be submitted, but its chairman insists that its job is merely that of registration, to guard against duplication of effort. Anyone can initiate a piece of research that needs nothing more than his time and the use of the laboratories and technicians. If it is something that requires a special grant of money, however, the approval of the board of governors is necessary, for obvious reasons that have nothing to do with regimentation.

The results of all research are reported to the entire group at the weekly staff meetings before they are published or announced outside, and anything decidedly off color is quite likely to be discovered within the group. If a piece of work gets by that barrier it next passes through the committee on medical education and research, and care is taken to see that the personnel of that committee is well mixed, including surgeons, clinicians, and laboratory men, so that some one of them will be able to judge the validity of most papers that come before it. And finally there is the hurdle of a competent medical editor in the division of publications, trained to watch out for logic and accuracy as well as to "check the grammar." Only a defect far down in the structure is likely to escape detection at one of these three stages, and when something wrong is found it is usually enough to point it out to the author. The fact that results and theories have been published by Clinic staff members which the majority of the group did not approve supports the committee's statement that their function is to advise and suggest, not to prohibit.

8

The Foundation fellowship program is clearly one of practical apprenticeship, very like the preceptorship of earlier days, except that the student has many preceptors instead of one. The course of study includes no formal classroom work or lecture courses, and in that respect it is more truly of graduate stature than many academic programs. Yet the practical service of the fellows is supplemented at many points by conferences, lectures, and seminars. There is a succession of outside speakers throughout the year, all of the highest standing in their respective fields, and there is a group meeting of some sort almost every night in the week.

The most important of these, with the possible exception of the clinico-pathological conference, to which second- and third-year fellows are admitted, is the weekly staff meeting on Wednesday night, held in beautiful Plummer Hall in the new Clinic building. This is a continuation of the weekly conference initiated years ago by Dr. Giffin for a review of periodical literature but now given to reports of clinical and research experience. Tacitly limited to an hour each, its programs are an index to the range of Clinic activities, for the topics at one week's session may range from an internist's report on a study of vitamin deficiency in the diet to a statistician's report of population trends since Malthus. It not only serves to keep all staff members informed of new developments in every section but it constitutes the finest kind of seminar for the Foundation fellows. The meetings are open to visitors, and outsiders find them extremely impressive. Nor has habit dulled the staff's own appreciation of their value.

Their interest and scope is greatly increased by full use of modern methods of rapid and vivid presentation. Statistical charts and tables, before-and-after shots of illustrative cases, microscopic slides, and x-ray plates, all are flashed on the screen, and surgical techniques are demonstrated by colored motion pictures made in the operating rooms. The Clinic's large and excellently equipped photographic studio, the outgrowth of that lone photographer Dr. Wilson persuaded Dr. Will to hire years ago, has pioneered in the use of the motion picture for medical instruction. Its collection of more than seven hundred films on all kinds of medical matters serves the Clinic's staff and patients well, and items from it are borrowed by medical colleges, schools of nursing, and professional societies in the United States, Canada, and South America.

Dr. Will's last gift to the Foundation was his own home, which as Mayo Foundation House has become a center for the fellows' activities both social and professional. There every Tuesday night some two hundred young doctors meet with their teachers to discuss medical problems. Not all the fellows are there, because some are on duty and a few sections hold their meetings elsewhere at another time. There are ten groups—first-year medical fellows, second-year medical fellows, junior surgical fellows, senior surgical fellows, and so on—each meeting in a room equipped with blackboards, stereopticon, tables, and chairs.

Suppose it is the senior surgical seminar and the topic is "Surgical Risk in Renal Disease." The evening starts off with a formal paper by one of the fellows who has been making a special study of the topic. Then a staff member from the section on cardiology talks about the things a bad heart can do to wreck a kidney operation, and the head of the division of medicine, whose specialty is the study of diabetes, cites some examples of the surgical trouble that disease can cause and adds some figures the statistician has gathered for him that show the surgical mortality of diabetic patients is rising. He is worried about the reason for the rise, and lists some of the possible explanations he has considered. Perhaps the trouble is a slackened rate of circulation, he suggests, whereupon someone reminds the group of recent findings in the study of blood flow and somebody else adds that if the circulation proves to be at fault, the new treatment with high concentrations of oxygen may solve the difficulty.

After a while the head of the postmortem service reports cases that have come to his division because some risk was overlooked in a seemingly simple operation. The surgeon may be operating for nothing more than an ingrowing toenail, he says, but if he has failed to take into account a leaky heart and the patient dies during operation, the death is charged to the ingrowing toenail, because that's the only way to keep the mortality figures straight. Finally one of the staff surgeons brings the seminar to a close with a brief review of his own experience in deciding whether or not to operate for kidney disease.

Except for the first paper it has all been informal and free, with questions and comments and additions from all sides. The discussion goes on here and there as the group breaks up and moves into the dining room next door to join the members of the other seminars for doughnuts and cider and perhaps to join in a hot argument left over from another meeting.

These Tuesday night seminars are said to be unique in the world of medicine, and that is not hard to believe, because even the academic world offers few such striking examples of consistent cooperation among specialists in teaching and in learning with their students.

9

Three years of such training, in some cases four or five, and the fellow becomes a candidate for the degree. Because so much of the work is of a practical nature it seemed unfair to take no notice of the fact in the requirements for a degree. A man might show impressive learning in an examination and yet be most inept at applying his knowledge to the patient, or to a lesser extent the other way around. So, since competence in practice is one of the primary purposes of the program, to the requirements for the degree was finally added the "certificate of proficiency," a statement by the fellow's adviser that in his opinion the candidate is competent to begin the practice of his specialty in a scientific way without supervision.

Armed with that, his thesis accepted, and a successful oral examination by representatives of both faculties behind him, the fellow receives from the University of Minnesota the advanced degree he has earned, a degree that through long usage the public has come to understand is a sign of the trained specialist. The master's degree is granted to those who give evidence of scientific proficiency in practice; the doctor's degree is reserved for those who show marked ability to advance medical science by original investigation.

By no means all the fellows receive a degree. Some drop out before they have completed the three years, others go through the term in residence but do not fulfill the other requirements, still others try and fail. Undoubtedly some enter upon the fellowship for the clinical experience and without any intention of taking the degree, though that attitude has decreased and the proportion seeking the final stamp of approval from the university has risen with appreciation of the Minnesota degree. Only eleven out of forty-three who began their fellowships in 1915 took degrees; fifty-three of eighty-six who began their work in 1935 have done so. Because the fellowship is granted on the assumption that the appointee intends to take the degree, the Foundation gives no token of any kind to those who do not run the full course.

## 10

These fellowships are not salaried positions but subsidized opportunities for graduate education; the fellow is considered a graduate student, not an employee on salary. Those who have criticized the fellowship stipends as too low forget that fact. In other branches of learning and of recent years in medicine at other universities the student pays a tuition fee for such work. But knowing what a long period of training the young doctor has already passed through and wanting to select their fellows according to ability, not the size of their fathers' bank accounts, the Foundation and the university both prefer to pay a stipend—without, however, making the position so desirable financially that it would attract men for that reason alone.

At the Foundation the stipends began with six hundred dollars for the first year, nine hundred for the second, and twelve hundred for the third. Then, lest the staff members be tempted to impose more work with each increase in stipend, it was changed to a straight nine hundred dollars a year. If the fellow becomes a first assistant he is paid fifteen hundred dollars if single and eighteen hundred dollars if married.

# Training Young Doctors

The medical graduate committee sets the amount of the stipends, and university members have insisted on keeping the Foundation payments somewhere near those at the university, so as not to weight the scales of preference too heavily in the Foundation's favor. The Rochester men have raised the question often and vigorously, pointing out that living conditions in Rochester are not geared to student life as they are on the Minneapolis campus and that the town simply does not offer suitable living quarters at rentals the fellows can afford to pay. Yet they have sportingly played the game and kept their stipends within reach of those the university budget can support.

Sensitive to the charge, made when the affiliation of the Foundation with the university was under fire, that the Mayos' purpose was to provide the Clinic with good help at the tax-free Foundation's expense, the Clinic has from the beginning paid the stipends of all fellows in the clinical branches, that is, all those whose work could be considered "help" for the Clinic. At first it paid them directly; later it deposited with the university in advance the sum of twenty-seven hundred dollars for each clinical fellow appointed. If he stays longer than three years, either as a fellow or as a first assistant, the Clinic pays his salary.

Until the Foundation endowment reached the sum of two million dollars the Mayos through the Properties Association paid all its expenses, and in 1934 they added another half million to the endowment. But the yearly income from the entire sum is not more than a hundred and twenty-five thousand dollars, whereas the annual budget of the Foundation is about five hundred thousand. The Mayo Properties Association pays the difference.

11

At the end of its first twenty-five years the Foundation has reason to be proud of its accomplishments. Its influence, on the Clinic, on the university, and on progress in medical education, has been incalculable. Its chief benefit for the Clinic comes from the stimulus to improved practice provided by its university obligations. Most practitioners agree that there is no incentive like the challenge of able, alert young minds to keep a man abreast of his field and on his professional toes. And under the Foundation program this advantage is not offset by the drain of classes to meet, lectures to prepare, and examinations to grade.

Then too, the fellowship program has allowed both the Clinic and the university to draw additions to their staffs from the cream of the country's medical graduates. Many of the younger staff members and department heads in the university medical school are university or Foundation alumni, and one hundred and five members of the Clinic staff are former Foundation fellows.

Other alumni, numbering more than two thousand now, are scattered all over the world, literally from Kalamazoo to Timbuktu. Many of them, enthusiastic about Rochester methods and spirit, have tried to achieve a measure of them in their own practice, and small group clinics on the model of the Mayo Clinic have been established in many cities of the United States and Canada. There is even a good-sized one in Brussels, Belgium. And in far-off India a former fellow is the director of the University Medical College of Mysore, from which he has sent a succession of able men to take advanced training at Rochester and at the University of Minnesota and then return to practice and teach in India.

Two hundred and forty-two of the Foundation alumni hold responsible teaching positions in the United States and abroad, to the deep gratification of the Foundation's early leaders. When they began their experiment, the clinical faculties of medical colleges were not recruited from a pool of trained teachers regardless of geography, as are academic faculties and those in the basic sciences. The professor of economics might come from Kansas, the associate professor of English from Vermont, but all the teachers of clinical medicine were sure to be from the local bailiwick, chosen solely because of propinquity and home-town influence. Progress in medical education depends on correcting that situation, and it is a major achievement of the Foundation that it has made the University of Minnesota a recognized source for trained teachers in the clinical branches.

The example of the Foundation has inspired other universities to offer graduate training in clinical medicine, and most of them have taken the Foundation as their model in whole or in part, though unhappily few if any of them have been able to secure the degree of control over the standards of affiliated faculties and hospitals that the university exercises at Rochester. And there are still too few such schools to provide either enough teachers or enough certified practicing specialists.

Consequently the medical profession has moved to establish its own agencies of certification. In 1916 the eye specialists united to form the American Board of Ophthalmologists, with power to establish standards, give examinations, and issue certificates to qualified ophthalmologists. Eight years later the ear, nose, and throat men took the same step, and six years after that the obstetricians and gynecologists set up their certifying board. From then on the naming of specialty boards was rapid, and in 1940 they numbered fourteen. In 1934 the existing boards and the American Medical Association joined in establishing the Advisory Board for the Medical Specialties to secure uniformity in requirements and methods of certification.

By 1942, according to the advisory board's announcement, three years of advanced training beyond the internship will be required of all candidates for certification as specialists. To provide this training, in the absence of sufficient university graduate courses, three-year hospital residencies have been multiplied, but, whatever the advisory board may say to the contrary, these cannot be called graduate education in any generally accepted meaning of that term unless adequate safeguards are provided to make sure they give the resident something more than an extended internship or a three-year postgraduate course in clinical techniques.

Nonetheless, though the movement is still young, it has gone far toward putting the self-proclaimed specialist out of business. But its purpose will be greatly furthered when the doctors make some effort to acquaint the public with the work of the qualifying boards, for the certificates they issue can hardly help the layman to distinguish between a competent specialist and a brazen imitation if he knows nothing about them.

In this development the Mayo Foundation has exercised a strong influence. Dr. Louis B. Wilson, its director, was the first president of the advisory board, serving until his retirement in 1937, and in that year no fewer than ten of its section heads were members of their respective qualifying boards. Its requirements have served as models for the boards and its experience has guided them through many problems.

On the whole, thanks to the professional vision and personal generosity of the Mayo brothers, the University of Minnesota, through the work of the Foundation on the campus at Rochester, is today the largest and most influential center of graduate medical education in the world.

## 12

To such extent as the prohibitions of the medical code will allow, the Foundation has added the medical education of the public to its functions. That was always a pet idea of both Mayo brothers. As Dr. Will once observed, "The quacks 'educate' the public. Why shouldn't we?" In the Diet Kitchen, in the section on physical medicine, on the diabetic wards in the hospitals, teaching the patient to manage his own treatment at home is an important phase of the clinical program. Charts, lectures, motion pictures, anything is used that will impress on the patient's mind the necessity for following the doctor's orders and show him how to do so. Because many patients with arthritis come from rural homes without electricity, the section on physical medicine has prepared mimeographed instruction sheets showing them how to use ordinary jelly-jar paraffin for heat treatments and how to make other cheap and simple substitutes for the expensive apparatus beyond their reach.

More general are the purposes of the Mayo Foundation Museum of Hygiene and Medicine housed in the old Central School building across the street from the Clinic. When the city put the building up for sale, the trustees of the Properties Association thought they ought to buy it, but they could not persuade Dr. Will; he thought the price was too high and he could not at the moment see what use the Clinic could make of the building. That was his answer after an afternoon's arguing, and the men left his office shrugging good-bye to the idea: Well, that's that. But the next morning he called them back and told them they could buy the school. Overnight he had planned practical uses for every room of the building.

A feature of the Foundation's exhibit at the Chicago Century of Progress Exposition was a "transparent man," a life-size figure of transparent material through which the internal structures of the body can be seen as the lighted form revolves on its platform. Another very popular one, probably because about a fourth of the adult population have lost their appendixes, was a series of life-size, colored wax models showing the various steps in the technique of appendectomy. When the exposition closed, these exhibits became the nucleus for a museum of hygiene and medicine in Rochester. Dr. Arthur H. Bulbulian, formerly with the natural history museum at the University of Minnesota, was named its director and he and his associates have done much pioneering in methods of designing and displaying exhibits for the instruction of both profession and public.

The technical exhibits are sent to medical conventions all over the country, carrying graphic information on many medical matters to thousands of doctors. So enthusiastic has been their reception that now each year one section of the Clinic is assigned to develop a detailed exhibit for the annual meeting of the American Medical Association.

Requests from visitors have served as a guide in selecting topics for popular museum treatment; among recent ones are cancer of the breast, the development of the human embryo, and gallbladder disease. From charts, photographs, and lifelike wax models the patient with idle hours on his hands—or perhaps more often his friends and relatives—can see what this operation or that is like, why it is necessary, what it does, and in some cases how the need for it may be avoided.

The local community, however, makes up about half the annual attendance of nearly one hundred thousand. On a fine Sunday afternoon the crowded rooms look as though the whole countryside had driven in to pore over the exhibit cases, study the captions, and listen to the hourly lecture illustrated by the transparent man. Idle curiosity doubtless brings many of them, but some deeper drive to pierce the mysteries of health and disease is apparent in the earnestness of others. And even the most thoughtless can scarcely fail to take away some new idea or have a mistaken one corrected.

# CHAPTER TWENTY-FOUR

# My Brother and I

For many a Foundation graduate his diploma from the University of Minnesota had only half its meaning until he had had it counter-signed by Dr. Will and Dr. Charlie. Not alone because of the prestige of their names, but because of the deep respect and admiration they inspired as men and as surgeons. Few of the fellows who won the coveted assignments to their sections did not come out with an abiding affection for Dr. Charlie and something close to reverence for Dr. Will.

The fellows in other sections knew the brothers from their regular attendance and frequent talks at one or another of the group con-ferences. They seldom missed the weekly staff meetings if they were in town, for they appreciated their value and knew the younger men would argue that if the meetings were worth Dr. Will's and Dr. Char-lie's time they certainly were worth theirs.

Often after the meeting one of the section heads would get a tele-phone call from Dr. Will. "That was an excellent piece of work your fellow reported tonight. He's a good man, isn't he? I thought he must be. Well, see that he has everything he wants to work with. He's the kind we want to encourage."

He gave direct encouragement too. As one young doctor told it, "You'd read a paper at staff meeting and afterwards he'd see you in the elevator or the hall, would shake hands, or put his hand on your shoulder with a quiet 'Good work' and a straight, warm look that made you think he meant it. Or perhaps a day or two later you'd get a note from him, just a short one, saying something like 'Dear——, I learned more about —— from that paper of yours the other night than I ever knew before. It was a good job.' Believe me, a fellow prized those notes. I have two or three and I wouldn't take anything for them."

Dr. Will sent such notes of personal appreciation to the permanent staff members as well, when they published an exceptionally worthwhile article, received some professional recognition, or when the fifth, tenth, or twenty-fifth anniversary of their joining the Clinic came around. "An ounce of taffy is worth a pound of epitaphy," he used to say. He kept track of good work going on throughout the country and often sent notes of congratulation. The surprised recipient in acknowledging the note sometimes commented on how rare it was for a man established in the profession to take notice of a newcomer's work or to express appreciation of it when he did.

Dr. Will also on occasion, though less frequently, called some man's attention to an error in his ways. Once when a young man on the staff got into a fracas with his older colleagues he went to Dr. Will's house in the evening to talk it over with him. He was upset about the incident, but Dr. Will told him, "This business won't do you any harm, son. A man needs a knock every once in a while. One knock to every two pats is about the right ratio." And one knock to every two pats was about what he gave.

2

As long as they were serving as active surgeons, the brothers' pace never slackened and they carried their full share of the duties in the operating rooms. They still alternated, each operating in the mornings and acting as surgical consultant on the floor in the afternoons three days a week. Their days on duty began at seven-thirty in the morning with a round of visits to those patients on whom they were to operate that day. Then came the morning's schedule of operations, lunch at home with a brief nap afterward—for both of them now, because to Mrs. Mayo's great satisfaction Dr. Will had got a secretary who was able to handle the correspondence without his dictating letters at lunch—and a busy afternoon on the floor.

Neither of them nor any of their surgical colleagues ever operated on a patient he had not personally examined beforehand; the division of labor between diagnosticians and surgeons was not allowed to go so far that the patient became just one body in a series passing across the operating table, though some descriptions of Clinic methods would lead the reader to suppose that was the way of it.

To the end of their lives Dr. Will and Dr. Charlie struggled to keep the sheer size of the organization from making it an impersonal ma-

667

chine, and this attitude permeates the staff from the doormen up. Though there are over six hundred numbers on the Clinic telephone exchange the operators know every one of them, and the names and voices of all the staff members and half their wives to boot. Pick up the receiver and ask for any man in the group and they'll have him on the line for you in no time, or tell you where he is if he is not in the building. Give them your name half a dozen times and thereafter their pleasant voices will be calling you by name too.

For the brothers to look after all the Clinic staff—in round numbers two hundred professional members, a thousand non-professional, and three hundred Foundation fellows—personally and individually as they once did became impossible. So they inaugurated elaborate insurance and pension plans, and provided for generous vacations and sick leaves. In addition, every staff member was expected, not just permitted, to go off for a month of study each year. He had only to present an outline of where he wanted to go and why. If the trip was approved, as it usually was, unless too many were asking at the same time, the Clinic paid his expenses. Where conflicts occurred the preference, contrary to custom, was given to the younger men, to encourage their professional growth.

Knowing, however, that no formal plan can meet all needs, since some men must recharge their batteries more often than others, Dr. Will continued to finance privately many an unofficial trip for rest or study. If a valued man was wearing noticeably thin or his wife was acting bored he would receive a check from Dr. Will and a note telling him to go off to Florida or to Europe and take Mary along to make the trip more pleasant. After a while Dr. Will had to stop that because oversights were causing trouble, so he set up a small trust fund to pay for just such extra trips, which could not properly be financed by the Clinic itself.

In much the same fashion provision for needy patients was formalized through the section on social service. With Dr. Will's special permission this section was organized early in the 1920's to help patients whose personal problems interfered with the plan of treatment proposed by the physician, and as the medical social workers demonstrated the value of their service, more and more of the Clinic doctors came to appreciate it and to refer patients to them.

# My Brother and I

Perhaps a man from some distant state is found to have tuberculosis. He needs to enter a sanatorium, and the members of his family ought to be examined to make sure that they have not contracted the disease. The doctors cannot possibly know the names of the proper public agencies to look after the matter in the patient's state, so he is referred to the section on social service, where one of the trained workers locates the information, notifies the agency, and keeps track of the patient until the proper arrangements for his care and the examination of his family have been made. A patient in the orthopedics section has lost an arm or a leg; he needs help in rehabilitating his life, perhaps even to the extent of learning a new occupation and finding a new job. A diabetic child is brought in in a coma; obviously she is not following the prescribed diet, and her parents show a strange indifference to helping her readjust her life to the demands of the disease. Somehow the reason for their apathy must be discovered and corrected if the girl is to live. In all such cases the section on social service takes over the job and tries to overcome the obstacle that is hampering the doctor's program for the patient.

But for the majority of patients referred to the section the problem is wholly or chiefly financial. Some patients arrive without money for hospitalization or for maintenance, others are stranded without transportation home when they have to stay longer than they planned, still others need supervision to make the amount they have cover the costs of their residence. By acting as a clearing house for a multiplicity of social agencies and generous individuals throughout the country, the section performs its peculiar service to all such patients and to the Clinic.

Yet Dr. Will could never bring himself to leave financial aid entirely to the section. He usually asked his secretary to get him some cash from the business office before he started his rounds for the day, and she knew the chances were better than even that he would return from them without a cent in his pocket. Nor did he hesitate to make his own arrangements about payment if it seemed best. He was called in consultation one afternoon on the case of a boy just out of high school. When he decided the lad needed an operation, the boy exclaimed, "But I haven't any money to pay for an operation." Dr. Will looked at him soberly. "Do you think you could earn some after

669

you get well?" The boy was sure he could. "All right, you see if you can send me ten dollars a month till you've paid a hundred dollars."

Two five-dollar bills came to his desk regularly each month, and when the tenth pair arrived he sent the boy a check for a hundred dollars plus generous interest, with a note, "You've shown yourself and me you could do it. Now you can put this in the bank and make it grow."

For the most part, however, setting and collecting the fees was left entirely to the business office. The Clinic operates on strictly business principles, but the policies adopted by the brothers in their early years as partners still obtain, with such modifications as the size and nation-wide scope of the practice have made necessary. No note is taken, no mortgage allowed, for the payment of a Clinic bill, and no lawsuit is ever instituted to collect one. The bills are set in accordance with the size of the patient's income, and for many years the percentage of paying patients has varied little. Twenty-five per cent pay nothing for the Clinic's services, thirty per cent pay the bare costs of their treatment, and the other forty-five per cent defray the expenses of the institution and its program. Consequently some fees are high, and Dr. Will was sometimes disturbed to learn just how high. A Seattle doctor tells the story of a multimillionaire friend of his who was charged ten thousand dollars for a major operation on his wife and paid the bill willingly. But in looking over the accounts Dr. Mayo happened to see the amount of this fee on the books and immediately ordered four thousand of it returned, with the comment that the patient had been overcharged. Indignantly the millionaire returned the refund, saying his wife's life was well worth ten thousand dollars.

Many stories are told of bills reduced and canceled for patients who, because of the loss of a job or the death of a husband or parents, found themselves unable to meet them. When asked if these stories are true the Clinic men say, Yes, but don't give us undue credit on that account. Every doctor in the country does the same thing. And it's only good business practice. If a person's financial condition makes it unlikely that you will be paid anyway, you might as well cancel the bill, save the expense of carrying the account, and gain good will at least.

The Clinic allows generous terms for payment, and as long as the patient pays something regularly on his account he is not disturbed. But some people need to have their memories jogged occasionally, and for that purpose the Clinic maintains a corps of collectors, or adjusters, as Dr. Will preferred to call them. One works in Milwaukee and Chicago, another in the Twin Cities and Duluth, another in the Rochester vicinity, and the fourth travels from place to place. He goes into a town, takes a hotel room, and notifies delinquent accounts in that area that he is there and would like to see them. The Clinic figures that those who really intend to pay their bills will comply with his request and so they get the cream of the outstanding accounts. The chances are the others would not pay in any case, and to try to collect from them would cost more than it would return.

3

No phrase was so often on Dr. Will's lips as "my brother and I." Every honor that came to him he accepted "on behalf of my brother and myself," so consistently that one of his friends remarked, "I believe if Dr. Will were elected President of the United States he would accept the office in the name of his brother and himself."

In so many phases of the story, however, Dr. Will is the dominant figure, the man who acts and speaks, the Chief, that one must wonder whether "my brother and I" was a legend he deliberately fostered for the good of the Clinic. The success of the institution had come to mean so much to him, to occupy so much of his thought and effort, that he was perfectly capable of doing precisely that, but the overwhelming testimony of his friends and associates is to the contrary.

It is certainly true that Dr. Charlie alone could never have built the Clinic, but then neither could Dr. Will. He would have gone far on some road but not on that one. It took the two of them to do that job, each complementing the other. But the task of administration fell mainly to Dr. Will's lot. He had the decisiveness and single-mindedness of the successful executive; Dr. Charlie did not. He lived in the present, savoring it to the full; Dr. Will lived in the future, not planning for tomorrow or next week but for ten or fifteen years ahead. After one address by Dr. Will in which he spoke of how well he and Dr. Charlie had always got along, Dr. Charlie added, "Yes, we did get along. Will liked to handle the organization and I was glad to

671

have him do it. We had about two hundred and sixty-five pounds between us—two hundred and sixty pounds Will and about five pounds me."

But those who worked closely with the brothers insist that though as the executive head of the Clinic Dr. Will gave the decisions and enunciated the policies, he reached them in conference with Dr. Charlie, who contributed his share of the good ideas Dr. Will put into effect. When Dr. Will or anyone else in the organization got to sailing his dreams too far above the clouds—and for all his ability to keep his feet on the earth while his head was in the clouds, Dr. Will sometimes soared—Dr. Charlie was quick to prick the balloon, often with a mere sentence tipped with dry sarcasm.

The two brothers did not always agree by any means, and when they did not they scrapped it out. In the early years Dr. Plummer and Mr. Harwick sometimes tried to referee their disagreements, but they soon learned that it was best to keep out, for as soon as anyone took sides with one of the two the other would immediately round on him. They might disagree themselves, but they instantly joined forces against an outsider.

Dr. Will usually got his way at such times, but it was because he had convinced Dr. Charlie. If he could not the plan was laid aside or modified until Charlie did approve. Dr. Will never rode roughshod over him. "When Charlie says no, it means no for me," he declared.

All accounts agree that Dr. Charlie never felt the least resentment about the greater glory that was Dr. Will's. He might be hurt sometimes when credit was given to Will for some pet idea of his own, but the feeling was never directed against his brother, for the fair reason that Dr. Will never claimed the credit. Families, friends, and employees might split into camps and be jealous for the due honor of their favorite, but they could never drive a chisel between the brothers. They might start one, but as soon as the two men realized what was happening, they stopped it short and for a few days overwhelmed each other with special kindnesses.

There can be no doubt that the affection between them was real and strong; no sham could have withstood the strains put upon it. And it was cause for frequent remark among their many professional friends. "Such brotherly love and loyalty as yours was one of the finest things on earth for your friends to see and we have had it for an example, lo, these many years," wrote Dr. Lund of Massachusetts. And Dr. Haggard of Nashville, a close friend and frequent guest of both: "Your great success was not as surgeons. It was as brothers. There has never been anything like it."

## 4

The two men were utterly unlike. Dr. Charlie's supreme gift was for human contacts. He had a way about him that won the liking of everyone he met, grumpy patient or hard-boiled doctor, and to the end of his active service the men on the Clinic floor called on him to pull their chestnuts out of the fire when they were in trouble with an obstreperous patient. He was at his best in allaying the groundless fears that in many cases needlessly complicate physical disorders, and his Clinic colleagues still give thanks for the lessons he taught them in the art of medicine. The simple expedients he suggested—like eating half a bag of popcorn every night to correct an imagined stomach ailment—might not be justified in physiology or pharmacology, but they were good psychology and invariably turned the trick of settling the patient's worried mind.

His daily visits to his patients were like those of a wise, gay-spirited friend. If the patient was discouraged, perhaps at the prospect of a life handicapped by ill health or the loss of a limb, Dr. Charlie would sit down on the edge of the bed—he knew when the best of rules should be broken—and talk for ten minutes or half an hour if necessary, till he had made the future seem less dreary. "Even his smile would make you want to get better, just to show the world you could," wrote one patient in after years. "Because he always made me feel so much better I asked for him often," wrote another. "And he always came."

Dr. Will's visits were likely to be rather impressive ceremonies, conducted in the presence of a group of assistants. He was as kindly as his brother and even wiser, but his cheer was studied, his jokes deliberate. Unlike Dr. Charlie's they did not flow spontaneously. He had to take thought to be friendly.

One day as he was leaving St. Mary's a patient who was also leaving spoke to him, to say good-bye. Dr. Will had his hat in one hand, his coat in the other, so he just bade the man a cordial good-bye and wished him health. But later that afternoon he told his secretary about it, saying he had failed in that case, that he should have dropped his coat on the floor or something, anything to shake hands with that man. He spoke of it several times in the next day or two, wishing he had shaken hands with that patient.

Dr. Charlie always had "a tickle at the end of his tongue for a pleasantry." Many of those who knew him have likened him to his friend Will Rogers, both in the slow nasal drawl with which he spoke and in his ability to put a common-sense truth in homely, salty phrases that gave it added punch. He was quick to deflate pretentiousness. When some member of the family was boasting about a connection with the Mayos who had come over to Virginia in colonial days, he remarked, with something less than historical accuracy, "Yes, that was when Virginia was a penal colony."

Dr. Will was more austere always. Some of his staff and associates, even some of the younger members of the family, were more than a little awed by him. One of the younger sisters at St. Mary's who worked closely with both men expressed the reaction to them this way: "We all loved Dr. Charlie; he was so easy and approachable, so democratic. Whereas we were all scared to death of Dr. Will; he was so dignified and reserved."

Part of that reserve was the schooled aloofness of every executive, set apart by the mere fact of his authority and condemned to impartiality regardless of his personal feelings. But in the main Dr. Will's reserve was a trait he could not help. Although intellectually he sympathized with and understood the reactions of the common man, he was an aristocrat in disposition.

Sitting on the lawn at Mayowood one afternoon, Dr. Will looked after Dr. Charlie, who was just walking away with a trio of friends, and in a rare moment of self-revelation remarked to Mrs. Charlie, "Everybody likes Charlie, don't they? They aren't afraid of him. No one ever claps me on the back the way they all do him." And then after a minute, "But I guess I wouldn't like it if they did."

When that story was repeated to one of the Clinic executives he exclaimed, "That's it. That was the difference between them. Many a time when Dr. Charlie came in to talk to me I helped him on with his overcoat and then with my arm around his shoulders walked out into the hall with him. But I would never have thought of touching Dr. Will in any way." And another of the staff members put it succinctly: "You could visit for hours with Dr. Charlie, but when Dr. Will came in you got right to the point." The very names by which they were known reflect this difference; the affectionate diminutive did not survive early childhood for the elder brother.

## 5

Even in appearance the two men were opposites—Dr. Will blond, Dr. Charlie dark in skin and hair; Dr. Will's eyes keen and direct of glance, Dr. Charlie's deep-set and somewhat sad; Dr. Will erect, compact, commanding, "he couldn't slouch"; Dr. Charlie more homey and comfortable looking, never so precise or neat. Once when Dr. Charlie was to give an address in Chicago a former classmate asked him to stay overnight with him. When the day arrived the Chicago doctor donned a well-worn suit. His wife was horrified. Was he going to meet the famous Dr. Mayo in that old suit? Of course, said her husband. Wait till you see his; it will look worse. And it did. But the Chicago couple had never had a more considerate or entertaining guest.

With Dr. Will professional dignity, even in appearance, was almost a religion. If he saw one of the fellows in soiled linen, or unshaved, without his shoes shined, or acting flippant on the Clinic floor, he would call him in and talk to him, tell him he must look and act like a doctor as well as be one. Feeling so, he found Charlie's indifference to appearance something of a trial. When they went to have pictures taken, he could snap into position in an instant, but he always had to fuss with Dr. Charlie to get him primped and posed properly for an official photograph. One of the staff found him in his office one day poring over proofs, trying to select the one of Dr. Charlie to be finished. "That is the best, isn't it?" he asked. But the other man thought this one looked more like Dr. Charlie. "No, that makes Charlie look like a groceryman," objected Dr. Will.

To illustrate the different attitudes of the two men in this regard a member of the board of governors tells this story: "I remember once when we were to have our annual New Year's Day reception for the staff at the house that is now Foundation House. The board of governors and their wives always stood in line to greet the staff. Henry Plummer was not a drinking man, but this one New Year's Day he had fallen among the Philistines in the morning and when he arrived for the reception he was still in high good spirits and the whisky was easy to smell. Dr. Will didn't like that a bit. But Dr. Charlie edged up to Henry and said, 'I want to stand by you, Henry.' Henry looked up at him in some surprise and said, 'Why?' and Dr. Charlie answered, 'Oh, because you're so stimulating.' Well, they stood together through the whole afternoon, Dr. Charlie keeping up a constant kidding of Plummer and Plummer himself feeling fine, still high. But Dr. Will was more than a little embarrassed by all the horseplay."

Not that Dr. Will had no sense of humor, but it was his own brand. He once went with the board of regents to inspect one of the university agricultural experiment stations. A long research project was under way there, trying to find means of making muskeg-land good for farming. The project had been costly, and the results were not very promising, but the men in charge were asking for a further appropriation and they explained at rambling length what they wanted to do and hoped to accomplish. With a twinkle Dr. Will proposed they make sure of a good crop by covering the muskeg with a concrete floor and topping it with several layers of good soil.

His emphasis on dignity was all for the sake of the Clinic and its reputation; personally he was no more pompous or snobbish than Dr. Charlie. Visiting doctors were often amazed by the way the Rochester townsfolk referred to the Mayos. If one of them went into a local shop to buy some suture thread, the storekeeper, if he was an older man, was quite likely to ask whether he wanted Charlie's favorite brand or the kind Will used. After such an experience one Australian doctor remarked, "No higher tribute to the greatness of these men could be given than the fact that they have survived the affectionate familiarities of their townsfolk."

Men from the world of finance and industry having business with one of the brothers were surprised by the ease with which they could reach the inner sanctum and fairly gasped when desk girls, secretaries, even old-timers among the patients, referred habitually to "Dr. Will" and "Dr. Charlie" and only a little less generally to "Mrs. Will" and "Mrs. Charlie."

Their simplicity and kindliness were unfailing. When the American Medical Library Association held its annual convention in Rochester, Dr. Will gave the welcoming address. He spoke seriously and soberly about books and the part they had played in his and his brother's lives. Then at the luncheon meeting Dr. Charlie was called on to talk. He had noticed that it was always so, he said; if an intellectual impression was wanted Will was the family representative called on, but if people wanted to laugh while they ate they asked him to talk. When he learned that the group were going out to visit the Institute of Experimental Medicine that afternoon he said they might as well stop at Mayowood on their way, and without further ado called Mrs. Mayo to say they were coming and she should see they didn't miss anything.

Mrs. Charlie met the invasion with perfect composure and showed the hundred-odd librarians around the estate. Then they returned to the Clinic library for a late afternoon tea, and Dr. Charlie and Dr. Will both joined them. "It never occurred to us that they wouldn't," said the Clinic librarian. "They always came to our little parties when they were in town." But the visitors were amazed. They seized the opportunity to ask the brothers to autograph Clinic bookplates for them, and went home completely won, as visitors always were, by the unpretentiousness of the famous Drs. Mayo.

6

Dr. Will was almost too successful in impressing his idea of dignity for the Clinic's sake on the rest of the staff. It has been hammered into them for years on end that they must not talk for publication and must be careful what they tell to friends and acquaintances outside the group, lest it find its way into print and reflect upon the Clinic and the Mayo name it bears. As a result most of the writing about the institution has been done by outsiders after a brief visit, and it has almost invariably stressed externals like size and system, so that many laymen have come to think of the Mayo Clinic as a huge, efficient machine, utterly impersonal, staffed by a race of cold-blooded supermen.

# Clinic and Foundation

The efficiency is there, and the systematic precision by which hundreds of patients a day are moved easily and quickly from section to section through the diagnostic process. And of course it is hard to introduce much friendliness into the mechanical process of a venapuncture or an x-ray. But within the examining rooms the degree of human warmth and personal interest in the patient varies with the individual doctor precisely as it does elsewhere.

The Clinic doctors themselves enjoy hugely the joke on their "machine" when occasionally it slips a cog. Even Dr. Will liked to tell this story: The doctors use their examining rooms in rotation, seeing one patient while another is getting undressed, and carefully trained desk girls are responsible for getting the patients into the rooms and ready for examination. Then they snap on the doctor's light above the door to tell him as he passes that a patient is waiting for him in that room.

Answering such a light one day, the doctor found a man sitting on the table, partially undressed, with the usual cape over his shoulders to cover the nakedness beneath, and on a chair in the corner a woman, presumably his wife. After exchanging the time of day with them, the doctor read through the case history, laid out for him on the desk, and then looked sharply at the patient. "You've lost weight, haven't you?" he asked.

"Why no, I don't think so," said the man. The doctor walked over, took off the cape, and felt of his arms and shoulders. "You must have lost some weight." Then turning to the woman in the corner, "Haven't you noticed it? Isn't he thinner than he was?"

Wide-eyed, the woman answered, "Why, doctor, I don't know. I never saw him before." The doctor got the woman into another room in a hurry, with profuse apologies.

Many encounters with the vagaries of minds upset and confused by illness have given even the men in the administration a sympathetic understanding of the ways of sick folks. Once half the staff engaged in a hunt for a patient's overcoat and hat. Nobody could find them anywhere, and finally one of the executives told the desk girl to call the man's hotel and see whether he had left them there. "But he *couldn't* have come over without them today," she remonstrated. "It's freezing cold and snowing hard."

"You call and see just the same," he told her. "That man is half out of his mind with worry about this operation he's got to have and it's hard telling what he might have done." She called and the bellhop found the missing coat and hat lying on the man's bed.

Such cases as that have taught the Clinic men to phrase their directions and give their explanations in the simple abc's that irk some persons who do not need their instructions blueprinted and diagramed.

7

"Will Mayo was the most imperious of autocrats," a few outsiders will tell you, and some within the Clinic found him ruthless in enforcing his decisions. When the opinion of his close associates is asked, they say yes, that he could be an autocrat, as every executive must be at times, but that he was always amenable to argument if one's ideas were good and his reasons sound. And, they add, though many on the staff did not realize the fact, Dr. Will never wanted a man to say what he thought the Chief would like to hear; he wanted an honest opinion when he asked for it. Nor was he often fooled as to which the answer was.

He himself once told Burt Eaton, "I may be wrong, but I decide things around here. Somebody has to, you know." Sometimes he lost patience with the attitude of the group and acted arbitrarily on that account. When the question arose of what to do with the pathologic specimens that were overflowing the space allotted to them, he proposed that some of them be arranged in cases around the walls of the main library reading room. Everybody protested loudly, especially the librarians, who, with the layman's repugnance for such things, did not want their lovely room spoiled by a lot of ugly old gallbladders and appendixes. Dr. Will waited for countersuggestions, and when none was forthcoming he gave orders for the specimens to be placed in the library. "Let them howl," he told his secretary. "I don't give a cuss. They haven't any constructive ideas; they just don't like this one."

He did care, however, and when it became possible to move the specimens to the museum across the street, he mollified everyone by a gift of new furniture for a browsing room in the library.

He was capable of complete detachment in his decisions, and for men who are not that is difficult to understand or forgive. No matter who was involved or how much he liked him personally, if the man was disrupting the Clinic he had to go. Ordinary frictions did not bother him; a good scrap once in a while hurt nobody. It was when a man wanted to run things all his own way and began to form a faction within the group that the danger point was reached, and Dr. Will firmly arranged for him and the Clinic to part. "We part on a friendly basis, *but we part*." Let a man deliver an ultimatum, "Either the Clinic does so and so or I will leave," and he left forthwith. Willingness to abide by the considered opinion of the majority was as necessary a qualification for a successful member of the Clinic as ability in practice. Dr. Will granted every man the right to persuade the group to his point of view, but to no man the right to dictate a policy to which the majority was not persuaded. "No man can be God here" he often said.

He was as ready to conform to rules and regulations as anyone, and much less demanding of special favors than some. One Sunday morning he called the Clinic library to ask whether they had a copy of the current issue of *Fortune*. They did, and he drove down to get it. Would she rather he used it in the library? he asked the assistant on duty at the desk, or could he take it home for the day? The librarians have never got over that.

Another incident showing the same lack of self-importance occurred one time when he was scheduled to speak at a medical gathering in Nashville. Just before he went on the platform he learned that a young Chicago surgeon who had brought an unusual case of uterine tumor to present to the convention had been refused a spot on the program because of lack of time. Dr. Will said his say in a few sentences and turned the remainder of his time over to the young surgeon. "I have never forgotten it," wrote the doctor years later. "It was a great boost for a young man."

When Dr. Will's impatient decisiveness, growing with the years, offended some of his professional colleagues, Dr. Charlie would come along at the next meeting and jolly them into complete good humor again. "He was genial and conciliatory where I wasn't," said Dr. Will. "If I got my eye on the ball I went after it regardless of who or what was in the way. He smoothed out things I roughed up." Not that Dr. Charlie could not be positive enough himself when he felt strongly on a matter, but his droll humor took the sharpness out of what he said. Again according to Dr. Will, "Charlie was truly a gentle man, salt and pepper, but never mustard."

Certainly there was little conceit apparent in Dr. Will. Looking back on the years when he was president of the University of Minnesota, George E. Vincent remarked on the objectivity with which Dr. Mayo always spoke of the Clinic, as though he were a spectator looking on at the work of his colleagues, proud of it and giving them generous praise for all they did. While everybody was showering plaudits upon him and Dr. Charlie for the miracle they had wrought in building a world center of medicine on the Minnesota prairies, Dr. Will alone kept insisting, in private as well as in public, that their accomplishment was due "to the transformation in medical conditions rather than to personal attributes."

8

Though they were in their sixties now and at the top of their profession Dr. Will and Dr. Charlie did not consider themselves beyond the need of further learning. By the end of the decade Dr. Will could say he had studied surgery in every town in America and Canada of one hundred thousand population or more, and had crossed the Atlantic thirty times—not to mention the side trips to Alaska, Cuba, the Antipodes, and South America. And Dr. Charlie was not much less traveled. No wonder their friend Dr. Haggard dubbed them "the surgical travelers of the world."

It was probably their wide acquaintance with doctors and clinics throughout the world that made them such leaders in the Inter-State Post-Graduate Association of North America. This was an outgrowth of the Tri-State District Medical Association, organized by the physicians and surgeons of Iowa, Illinois, and Wisconsin in 1916 but soon extended to include almost all the Middle Western states and the adjoining provinces of Canada. It was a purely educational society without political or legislative duties, its annual assemblies being given to postgraduate study in the form of diagnostic clinics and symposiums.

For most of the 1920's either Dr. Will or Dr. Charlie served as president of these assemblies, with the duties of planning and leading the clinical programs. Perhaps at their instigation, the society's annual tour of American and Canadian cities was soon supplemented with an international assembly that went to study in the centers of Europe, and Dr. Charlie was in charge of the first European session, in the late spring of 1925.

Through one hectic month he conducted the group of more than a hundred doctors from city to city in the British Isles, across to Paris and Vienna, and back to England. He had not only to preside at every clinic and discussion meeting but also to act as spokesman at all the social functions, and they were many. He conferred honorary membership on the Duke of York, a number of prominent English surgeons, and Madame Curie, and was received in the name of the assembly by King George of England, with whom "he remained in conversation for some time." On his own account he received honorary LL.D.'s at the University of Edinburgh and at Queen's University in Belfast. He had to speak for his degree at Edinburgh, and the occasion was an ordeal for Mrs. Mayo and their daughter Louise, who were with him, because the speakers preceding him were booed and hissed continually by the students assembled in the gallery of the hall. By the time Dr. Charlie's turn came, Mrs. Mayo had twisted her handkerchief to shreds and was nervously worrying the rubber band on her spectacles case. But Dr. Charlie talked directly to the students and held their attention to the end, a rare thing in those halls, it was said.

The tour was an experience for young Louise, just nineteen years old. She had spent her allowance before the trip was well started, and Dr. Charlie said she would have to earn the extra money she wanted by acting as his secretary. She took on the job blithely, but found it a good deal more than she had bargained for, because her father was deluged with fan mail and letters from cranks who wrote to beg or sell or plead a cause. As Louise remembered it, most of the crank letters came from anti-vivisectionists: How can you look a little dog in the eyes and then slit its throat? One man wanted to sell him a pickled Siamese monkey for the Foundation museum.

The heavy duties of the tour exhausted Dr. Charlie even more than he realized at the time, and in Dr. Will's opinion they were partly responsible for the breakdown that came a few years later. At any rate, he dared not try the task again the next year, and, Dr. Will being unable to get away to take his turn, Dr. Wilson took on the job of guide in a tour of Central and Southern Europe.

## 9

The brothers continued their activity in other medical groups as well, rounding out their service till they had held the presidencies of all the major ones in turn. They did an amount of speaking and writing that is almost incredible, even when the help of their secretaries, the Clinic librarians, and other staff members is taken into consideration. Their own bibliographies mounted toward six hundred items each—with less repetition than one might expect. Among technical subjects Dr. Will's favorites were still surgery of the spleen and the problem of cancer, and in the latter he continued to rank first, so that on one occasion the doctor who was asked to discuss his paper began with the question, "What is he to say that cometh after the king?"

But their technical papers were outnumbered now by those on more general topics—most often medical education and the general progress of medicine for Dr. Will and public health and preventive examination for Dr. Charlie. Both talked increasingly often about the relationship of science to medicine, Dr. Will's favorite topic there being the possibilities of biochemistry, and Dr. Charlie's comparative anatomy and embryology. For papers on these subjects they drew heavily upon the work and the staffs of the Clinic laboratories for ideas, and when they sent their papers to the research men for reading before publication, as they often did, the results were good. Otherwise their facts were likely to be wrong and their conclusions unwarranted, to the embarrassment of their Clinic colleagues. Some men criticized them for this, asking why they didn't stick to surgery, on which they were qualified to speak. But others were glad to overlook some errors in fact for the sake of the good the brothers did in furthering the cause of science in medicine, particularly among laymen. The Mayos were not scientists in any sense of the term, but their support of science was judged sufficient contribution to the cause to win them election to Sigma Xi.

# Clinic and Foundation

While Dr. Will was forever in demand as a speaker at college commencements and dedicatory exercises for medical schools, hospitals, and clinic buildings, Dr. Charlie got his calls from Rotary and Kiwanis clubs, chambers of commerce, businessmen's conventions, and innumerable banquets and dinners. His speeches were still the despair of the medical editors, who had to cut them apart and paste them together again sentence by sentence to secure anything approaching coherence. But they were the delight of audiences who heard them with the tickling overtones of Dr. Charlie's personality.

Mr. Harwick recalls an occasion when he was with Dr. and Mrs. Charlie on a trip to Florida. In St. Petersburg the local medical society, learning that Dr. Charlie was in town, asked him to address them and he, amiable as always, agreed to do so. But he wondered what he should wear. He had a dress suit with him but had forgotten to bring the vest along. In a hilarious half hour before they left the hotel he and Mr. Harwick agreed that if Dr. Charlie started to open his coat while he spoke, as was his habit, Mr. Harwick would pull on his coattails to remind him that the vest was missing.

But before the speech was far along Mr. Harwick forgot all about the coat. He and the audience both sat "with open mouths" as Dr. Charlie talked to them extemporaneously for an hour and a half about the analogy of plant to animal life. He spun the analogy to such lengths that Mr. Harwick, fascinated, wondered how he would ever get back to the proposition he started with. But for once in his life Dr. Charlie managed to round his circle and tuck in the ends before he finished, to the great applause of the crowd.

On another occasion he was less successful in that respect. Through the work of the Foundation he had made the acquaintance of Alfred Owre, dean of the University of Minnesota school of dentistry and a great reformer in dental education. Owre was tremendously impressed by the cooperative practice and scholarship in effect at the Clinic and often asked one of the Mayos to tell this or that group of dentists about it. He became a good friend of both brothers, especially Dr. Charlie, who, wholly converted to the theory of focal infection, was greatly interested in the subject of the teeth. When Owre left Minnesota to take a position at Columbia, Dr. Charlie was asked to represent the Foundation at the farewell dinner given in his honor.

# My Brother and I

He began his speech well enough, with an appreciation of Dean Owre's work in raising the level of dental education at Minnesota, but then he started telling jokes, and the rest of his address was simply a string of funny stories that, though quite without pertinence to the occasion, kept the crowd in an uproar. As he resumed his seat, he half turned to Dean Ford of the graduate school, who was seated next to him, and drawled in disgust, "I guess I've made a damned fool of myself again." But Dean Ford and the audience did not think so. Dr. Charlie had brought life into a dull affair.

To all his other duties Dr. Will added the chairmanship of the editorial board of *Surgery, Gynecology and Obstetrics*, organ of the American College of Surgeons. Though the position was merely advisory, Dr. Martin of Chicago being the active editor, Dr. Will would not let it be only nominal. He initiated two departments of the magazine, the editorial section and a feature called "Master Surgeons of America," biographical sketches of the outstanding leaders in American surgery. For many years he assumed full responsibility for these sections and wrote many of the items appearing in them.

It has been said that the recognition of merit accorded the Mayo brothers has never been equaled in extent anywhere in modern times, and if the length of entries in *Who's Who* is a valid criterion that is true. The walls of the board of governors room at the Clinic were fast filling with diplomas, medals, and plaques of all kinds bestowed upon Dr. Will and Dr. Charlie in recognition of their services to surgery, to science, and to society. They came from a wide variety of sources and agencies—medical associations, learned societies, great universities, and governments, at home and abroad. Both brothers were decorated by the king of Italy and Dr. Will by the king of Sweden. Dr. Will received the second and Dr. Charlie the third honorary degree to be granted by the University of Cuba in its four hundred years of existence.

One unusual honor that came to Dr. Will was his appointment to the custodianship of the Rush-Jenner-Pasteur-Lister-Curie Mementos in the possession of the College of Physicians of Philadelphia. The specific mementos are not impressive—a shoe buckle worn by Benjamin Rush, Edward Jenner's inkstand and a lock of his hair, a small case of Lister's surgical instruments, and so on—but the nominal custodianship of the cabinet containing them has, through the distinction of the men who have held it, become the gold-headed cane of American medicine. This, like everything else, Dr. Will accepted as a tribute to "my brother and I."

## 10

But all was not acclaim. Some in the profession could not forgive the brothers their popularity among laymen. That was so extensive that on at least two occasions the politicians tried to cash in on it. While Dr. Will was in South America in 1920 Frank Day of Fairmont, the Minnesota politician and editor who had started John A. Johnson on his gubernatorial career, ran an editorial suggesting that William J. Mayo be named the Democratic candidate for governor. Dr. Mayo was at the zenith of his career, said Day. He stood at the very top of his profession and could win no more laurels as a doctor. But with his splendid business and executive ability he would make a great governor, certainly the most famous in America.

Other Democratic papers took up the idea at once, asking only, Will he run? A few editors, mostly Republican, questioned the wisdom of diverting him from his great professional service into the dirty business of dispensing political patronage; others answered that men of Dr. Mayo's caliber were precisely what politics needed. Day's suggestion had become a good-sized movement by the time Dr. Will returned from his trip, but he put an end to the "balloon ascension" immediately by a public statement, in part thus:

My opportunity for greatest service lies in another direction. Thus far I have devoted my attention unreservedly to the science of medicine and surgery. I have no other interest. . . . My life's work has been wrapped up in the building of the Mayo clinic, the foundation, and associated endeavors. . . . There is still much to be done, and the next ten or fifteen years of my life should provide the opportunity for doing it. It is a life contract I have set out to fulfill, and I believe the people of this state will bear with me in the belief that I can perform the greatest service to them by holding steady to my purpose rather than by launching into an unknown and uncertain path.

I sincerely hope my friends will not consider me ungrateful. They have been most kind, and I have been both pleased and flattered, but I cannot accept their invitation. Of that I am so sure that there is not the slightest chance for reconsideration.

That was too unequivocal to be doubted, and the Democrats reported it with disappointment, the Republicans with relief, admitting that if Dr. Mayo had said yes, their opponents would have had a sure-fire winner.

Four years later Minnesota politicians started a movement to make Dr. Charlie the Democratic candidate for the presidency. It never became widespread or passed beyond the stage of talk, but the idea persisted for weeks and brought him many letters from fellow doctors, old patients, and even governors of other states, urging him to run and predicting that he would be elected by a landslide. Even Republicans would abandon their party to vote for "my doctor," they promised. Dr. Charlie said no too, but "he is not so vehement as one would like him to be," remarked the *New York Times,* calling for an end to these attempts to seduce one of the famous Mayos into politics.

Everywhere Dr. Will and Dr. Charlie traveled they were met by newspapermen. They tried refusing to talk to them, but the reporters had been told to get a story, and when the Drs. Mayo refused to give them one they went back to the files, pulled out the old tales, and refurbished them to suit themselves, sometimes with fantastic results. Or worse, they hunted up some medical paper one of the brothers had given and put its words into his mouth in the form of an interview, not infrequently making him express ideas and quote figures that were already years outmoded. And of course the effect on the hostile medics was precisely the same as if Dr. Will and Dr. Charlie had given the interview.

So the brothers decided to talk to reporters if they must but agreed that they would say nothing about themselves or their work, and nothing about the Clinic or Rochester; they would talk about the problems and progress of medicine in general. For the most part they kept to that resolve remarkably well, Dr. Will somewhat more religiously than the impulsive, amiable Dr. Charlie.

But it helped very little. Newspapermen admitted to medical gatherings did strange things to the brothers' remarks. When Dr. Will addressed the Wisconsin Society of Chicago in behalf of the Ochsner Foundation for Clinical Research, he talked about the growing specialization in surgery. Whereas the best surgeons of the old school were able to perform successfully all the operations then known, he said, no one man could do so now. Saying Dr. Ochsner was of the old school, he continued, "I can count on the fingers of one hand the men I would trust to operate on myself or members of my family for any sort of surgical condition," adding that he himself was not one of them, because there were many operations he would not attempt except in a dire emergency.

The newspapers reported his words accurately enough, but they ran the story under such headlines as "Dr. Mayo Limits Capable Surgeons in America to Five," and apparently doctors as well as laymen read only the headlines. Medical skies clouded and it was thundery for a time. While from laymen came letters like this:

Dear Doctor Mayo,
I read . . . where you said . . . there was about five good surgeons in America. . . .
I have doctored for gall-bladder trouble and find after fighting to keep from the knife I will have to have it out and would appreciate your kindness if you would tell me if one of the five is in Chicago and how close I could go to one. I am so scared of the knife and want the *Best*.

That is a good expression, not greatly exaggerated, of the feeling of fear and helplessness that made the laymen turn, in the absence of other guidance, to well-known figures like the Mayos, especially when they read about this or that movie star, or sports idol, or government official heading for Rochester when he needed an operation. And doctors themselves admit that the Mayos could not be blamed for news items like those.

## 11

Another source of irritation was the Mayos' unorthodox views on many matters of professional policy, which they did not hesitate to express. Dr. Charlie was once dragged into a controversy over the work of Dr. Adolph Lorentz, an orthopedic surgeon from the University of Vienna, who had developed a bloodless operation for treating certain bone deformities, especially of the hip joint. His work had attracted a good deal of attention and, for the most part, approval from American surgeons in the early years of the century, and it was widely publicized when he came to open a clinic for crippled children in New York in the early 1920's. Whatever actually happened, it was charged that the aged Lorentz had fallen into the hands of some unscrupulous New York doctors who were exploiting him for their own financial ends, and the New York medical societies were savage in their denunciation of Lorentz as well as his sponsors. The old man was said to be heartbroken by the weight of professional disapproval and the charges of unethical conduct.

In the midst of the fuss Dr. Charlie went to North Carolina to attend a meeting of the Southern Surgical Association, and while there was asked his opinion of the charges against Lorentz. He answered:

Personally, I am not greatly interested in that phase of the question, but every medical man in the country must realize . . . that the publicity attendant on Dr. Lorentz' work in New York . . . is bound to bring into the light thousands of cases of crippled children whose infirmities have been hitherto hidden from the doctors and hospitals of their communities. Dr. Lorentz should be helped and encouraged by every surgeon, physician, and hospital authority in the country.

The doctors did not like that, but the public did. As one editor said, "Laymen are not interested in the professional storm that has broken over Dr. Lorentz' head." Even if the charges could be substantiated, they "do not impress the lay mind as especially important." They seem petty and the treatment accorded Dr. Lorentz brutal, but "the fact that a world-renowned surgeon like Dr. Mayo has . . . come to the rescue of the Austrian surgeon will go far towards taking the edge off this national humiliation. It will put new heart and new soul into the discouraged old man. It will cause Minnesota to feel another surge of pride in the fact that the Mayos are her sons."

About the same time the *Pictorial Review* decided to publish some articles about the shortage of nurses, and the editor sent a writer to Rochester to ask Dr. Charlie what he thought about it. It happened to be a matter on which he and Will had strong convictions, and he stated them. He said the training course for nurses had been made too long, with the result that nursing fees were so high the man of moderate means could not afford proper nursing care. As a remedy he proposed a two-year course for "sub-nurses," with an optional third year for those who wished to specialize in dietetics or some phase of laboratory technique. He was quite sure that he had never asked anything from a nurse she couldn't learn in two years, providing she didn't have to spend her time in making beds, bathing patients, and other duties a hospital maid could learn to do in six months or less. That statement awoke reverberations that echoed for weeks throughout the country.

A few years later when Dr. Will was asked to talk on "Nursing and Hospital Costs for Individuals in Moderate Circumstances" at a symposium on medical and surgical economics sponsored by the American College of Surgeons, he touched briefly on the same problem, though with rather more appreciation of the nurses' dilemma, adding *in part of one sentence* that the hospital "often shows too much salesmanship and too little humanity." And of course that was the phrase that was chosen for quoting, to the great displeasure of hospital managers, one of whom, in Maine, dismissed it with the statement that Dr. Mayo had merely been talking "to get on the front page."

That was bad tactics. Reporters and magazine writers were continually grumbling in print about the Mayos' reluctance to talk for publication and refusal to discuss their own work, calling them "publicity-shy" and "about as garrulous as sphinxes," and now a number of editors challenged the statement of the Maine medico. The controversy over hospital management was not for laymen to decide, they said, but, to quote one of them,

> The first page charge is another thing.
> It is a matter in which Dr. Mayo is without recourse. Most people who get on first pages have nothing to say about it. . . .
> The first page, in the sense it is here considered under the point raised, is reserved for men who do things. That is the reason Dr. Mayo's name is found there so often. He was never a publicity seeker. None know this better than Minnesota newspaper men called upon to report his varied activities.
> If you would get on the front page do something worth while. Then try and keep off it if you can. It has never been done, even by such uncanny wizards in their profession as Dr. W. J. Mayo.

They might have spared their ink, for many doctors did not, and do not, believe that. They were convinced that all the publicity the Mayos got was deliberate advertising, and every new article brought to Dr. Will's desk a bagful of letters ranging in tone from mild expostulation to vituperation. He answered them all patiently and courteously, denying responsibility for the offending item and assuring the writer that for every such piece that appeared in print he managed to head off three or four. Occasionally, though, a hint of his real feeling crept into the letter. "I am sorry indeed that this matter has caused you any disturbance and hope that you will always come to me directly whenever you feel that my professional ethics need a little polishing," he told one critic.

He knew that all his denials were futile, however, and he no longer made any attempt to publish general disclaimers, having come to believe that the least said the soonest forgotten. But on the several occasions when individuals or local societies, insisting that no man or men were so important as to escape accountability under the medical code, demanded that the Mayos be disciplined for unethical conduct, he and the Clinic officers themselves laid the case before the judicial councils of the Minnesota State Medical Society and the American Medical Association. They were always exonerated.

### 12

Members of the profession themselves have called those who caused the Mayos all this trouble over publicity "a jealous and ignorant minority," and certainly Dr. Will and Dr. Charlie could record on the other side of the ledger many pleasant relations with members of the profession. With the addition of internal medicine to the Clinic practice the Surgeons Club became in name and in fact the Physicians and Surgeons Club, larger and more active than ever, and its members continued to publish accounts of their experiences in Rochester in the professional journals. Many doctors were numbered among Clinic patients, and Dr. Will was always proud of the fact that he and Charlie together had operated on almost fifty fellows of the American Surgical Association or members of their families. Referred cases always constituted a big element in the practice, and the Mayos never relaxed their emphasis on the importance of courtesy and consideration for the referring doctor. Through their instruction on this matter to their Clinic colleagues and the Foundation fellows the Old Doctor's "I did it for the profession" echoed down the years and into the ears of a new generation.

There is no evidence that the brothers ever lost the esteem of the men of standing in the profession. Years of association made some of them close personal friends—Dr. William Haggard of Nashville, Dr. Stuart McGuire of Richmond, Dr. Richard Harte of Philadelphia,

Dr. Carl Beck and Dr. Franklin Martin of Chicago, and Dr. George Crile of Cleveland, to name a few. Dr. Ochsner's ranch in Mexico was a favorite rendezvous for these medical friends. There were some incorrigible practical jokers among them, and though Dr. Will was not one of them he could take the joke when he was the object of the fun.

One time as they were leaving the ranch, Dr. Beck and Dr. Ochsner emptied Dr. Will's trunk of all his clothing and personal effects and filled it instead with coffee beans, on which there was a high duty. At the border inspection was demanded and Dr. Will, with some annoyance, complied with the request to open his trunk. To his, and the inspector's, astonishment the dutiable coffee was revealed. Laughing heartily at the joke, Dr. Will paid the cost and took the beans on home with him.

Dr. Charlie did not escape the jokers. At one surgical convention he talked about a pathological condition which he, taking a figure from his farm experience, called a strawberry gallbladder. When he finished, one after another of the big men present, all his friends, rose to declare soberly that the condition he had described must be a figment of his imagination, that they had never seen it and did not believe it existed. When they had the audience goggle-eyed and Dr. Charlie thoroughly flustered, they all rose again, one by one, and confessed the discussion was a hoax, got up to relieve the monotony of the program. Amid great general laughter, a motion was made and passed to strike the "discussion" from the record.

Dr. Charlie took the joke good-naturedly, and a few weeks later the mail brought Dr. J. M. T. Finney of Johns Hopkins, the ringleader in the affair, a package from Rochester. In it was a jar of alcohol containing a strawberry plant with a gallbladder about the size of a ripe berry hanging realistically among its leaves.

## 13

One or more of these men with their wives were often the Mayos' guests on boat trips, for river cruising was still the brothers' chief relaxation, especially Dr. Will's. The *Oronoco* gave way to the *Minnesota* and that in turn to a trim little yacht, the *North Star*, which Dr. Will had built to his order. Many a summer weekend he spent with Mrs. Mayo on the river, and in spring and fall vacations they cruised slowly down to the Gulf or up the Ohio to Cincinnati.

But not even on the boat could Dr. Will forget his responsibilities. His itinerary was always carefully planned beforehand, and rigidly adhered to, so that at any time the men left in charge at the Clinic could telephone him for advice or to ask him to return immediately if he was needed. Sometimes his chauffeur followed the boat's course along the shore, so that the car would be at hand if it became necessary for Dr. Will to return to Rochester in a hurry. Happily, the need for such precautions lessened with the years.

When Dr. Charlie took the boat, he lived to the full the carefree life he loved. After the boat was tied up for the night he would wander off for a walk, and one of the party usually had to be sent to find him when supper was ready. There he would be, somewhere downstream, sitting on the riverbank, discussing the state of the crops or swapping yarns with some old fisherman he had come across. "Or walk with Kings—nor lose the common touch" was surely true of Dr. Charlie.

Dr. and Mrs. Will were generosity itself with the *North Star*. They always took with them a large group of guests, including anyone, friend, employee, or even patient, who Dr. Will thought needed a respite or an outing to recuperate. And when they were not using the craft themselves they lent it to clubs and groups of all sorts—medical societies, schoolteachers, nurses, commercial clubs—not only of Rochester but of other towns in southern Minnesota as well.

When the depression came Dr. Will's pleasure in the boat was spoiled by the signs of poverty and distress he saw along the waterfront. After 1931 he made no more long trips and only occasionally went for a week-end's rest on the *North Star*. On such a trip in May of 1938 the boat docked at St. Paul during some kind of demonstration that had assembled a large crowd of ragged and shabby men on the dock. The contrast between their obvious poverty and the luxury of his yacht was more than Dr. Will could stand, and when he returned to Rochester he ordered the boat sold and the money received for it added to the funds of the Clinic section on social service.

Next to the boat he got his greatest pleasure from motoring, because it too kept him in motion. "I can rest if what I'm sitting in is moving," he once said. When he left the Clinic in the late afternoon

Mrs. Mayo and the chauffeur were usually waiting, and they went for a ride through the countryside before dinner. In the summertime they picked up others of the family and friends and made a picnic dinner of it somewhere along the road. Some of the pleasantest recollections his family have of him are those hours of relative freedom from Clinic duties.

With Dr. Charlie the pleasures of Mayowood still held first place. In his interest a pair of Japanese deer had succeeded to the place of the Chinese pheasants that laid an "Easter egg." Someone told him that when the first doe was born he could be sure the deer were happy in their new home, so with great anxiety he waited for the event and greeted it with chuckling satisfaction. Knowing his fondness for birds and animals, his friends sent him all kinds as gifts—bears, peacocks, alligators, crocodiles—so many that he was soon able to start a small zoo in Mayo Park.

He turned from animals to flowers finally and began raising chrysanthemums, on such a scale and with such success that the annual chrysanthemum show at Mayowood, with its more than sixty thousand blossoms, came to rank among the largest and finest in the country.

As the children—eight of them in all, two adopted in place of two who died—grew up and went off to college, Mayowood became the favorite visiting place of their many young friends, and often there were as many as fifteen guests in the house at one time, much to Dr. and Mrs. Charlie's satisfaction. When the children married one by one, most of them returned to live in the houses at Mayowood, and Dr. Charlie delighted in showing them how to remodel and rebuild the old farmhouses to the best advantage.

Both brothers liked to read and, without neglecting their medical journals, had become addicts of the thrillers, Dr. Will of western stories and Dr. Charlie of detective novels. These they read to pass their many hours of journeying on trains or in bed at night. Methodical as always, Dr. Will carefully graded each story, giving away those he marked C or D and keeping the A and B ones to read again.

Both men liked music and had electric organs installed in their homes, though neither could play or sing and neither knew much about music. Dr. Charlie had positive convictions on one phase of the art, however; he did not approve of jazz. He thought the popularity of its feverish, nervous rhythms a sign of an unhealthy state of mind in America. "Trying to be happy by means of jazz is as bad as trying to make a meal out of pickles and peppers," he said.

## 14

For eight years, from 1915 to 1923, Dr. Charlie was a member of the school board in Rochester, and, like his father many years before, he sparked the board to ambitious projects. Within five years a building program that cost nearly a million dollars transformed the schools from the wooden buildings of a country village into urban structures of brick and stone. Dr. Will and Dr. Charlie personally donated the instruments and paid the salary of a teacher so the high school could have a band and an orchestra. They gave the school its first motion picture machine too, and Dr. Charlie urged forward the program of visual education. Also on his motion the school system was extended to include a junior college, which was soon offering something unique in the United States—a special course for medical secretaries, most of whose graduates were absorbed in the Clinic offices.

The public health program in the schools was greatly extended too, and quite naturally, for Dr. Charlie was still Rochester's health officer. He tried to resign the post when he had completed his major program and had got the work well started, but the women of the town persuaded him to stay on the job. As he once said, his deputy did most of the field work, but it kept him busy fixing things up with the public and the city council so the deputy could do his job without interference.

Until about the middle twenties the two brothers financed most of the health program; then they convinced the municipality that it ought to shoulder the responsibility, though the Clinic continued to give all the necessary laboratory service free of charge and its staff provided much of the professional service for the program—such as the prenatal clinics conducted by the section on obstetrics and the baby clinics and examination of school children given by the section on pediatrics.

One accomplishment of which Dr. Charlie was especially proud was the establishment of weekly public health lectures in the city. He persuaded the Olmsted County Medical Society to sponsor them, and popular response was soon sufficient to warrant transferring them from the church in which they were first held to the Clinic lobby, where each Thursday night such of Rochester's residents and transients as are so minded, and a goodly number of them are, may gather to see a motion picture on some phase of preventive medicine and hear a Clinic doctor talk in lay terms about his specialty.

Through the years the brothers' policy of contributing to the improvement of the city financed in whole or in part more parks, a baseball diamond, a large outdoor swimming pool, a new public library, and a civic auditorium that includes an art gallery, a handsome little theater, and an "arena" that can be adapted to any kind of show from a symphony concert to a prize fight.

Astute as he was, Dr. Will did not miss the importance of adequate transportation facilities for the success of the Clinic. No sooner did automobile travel become general than he saw its possibilities for widening the radius of the practice in the local district, and he entered actively into the movement for good roads throughout Olmsted County, serving as the president of the first road improvement society in Rochester. In later years he withdrew from active participation, but he was always ready with suggestions and encouragement for the efforts of the local businessmen to secure state and federal routes through Rochester. On his rides through the countryside he kept his eyes open for ways of improvement, not only in graveling and paving, but in rerouting. The network of roads converging on Rochester is not an accident.

Similarly he worked with the railroad companies and the bus lines to extend their service and lower their rates to Rochester. Not even he could secure good train connections to the north or persuade the railroad companies to build a union station, but through the years his suggestions did effect a succession of improvements in service out of Chicago, especially in accommodations for handling the sick, all the way from the first couch placed at the end of the train to the modern Joseph Lister coach that opens wide at the side to give easy entrance and exit for stretchers and wheel chairs.

The Mayo Properties Association carried this policy on from where the brothers left off and by providing Rochester with one of the largest and finest airports in the state put the capstone on a development that began in the Old Doctor's day and was vital in the Clinic's growth.

# CHAPTER TWENTY-FIVE

# A Living Memorial

It was in 1928 that the new Clinic building was dedicated and occupied. Complete with all its equipment it cost the Mayo Properties Association three million dollars and was more than two years under construction. Fifteen stories tall it is, crowned with a bell tower of four more and covering nearly an entire city block. Built of warm, rich-toned Siena stone, its outline and mass please the eye and, though its detail may be too ornate for some modern tastes, its total effect in its setting is extremely impressive. It dominates the surrounding city and countryside, and though men have been known to stop in front of it and ask the way to the Mayo Clinic, most people have no trouble in finding it. Many who come to its massive bronze doors, fresh from farms on the Dakota prairies or cabins in the Canadian wilds, gape at its size and splendor and move in wonder through its marble halls. Throughout its interior the appointments are lavish and often very beautiful.

In the tower that tops the building hangs a carillon of twenty-three bells, cast in the famous bell foundry of Croydon, England. For years Dr. Will had wanted for Rochester a set of singing bells such as he had heard in other cities on his travels, and, Dr. Charlie approving, they discussed the possibility of building a bell tower on the hill in St. Mary's Park. But when the new Clinic building was planned, its height and architectural style lent themselves so well to the purpose that the carillon was placed there. Day in and day out its bells ring the hours, and for half an hour three times a week Rochester seems to hush while the carilloneur sends hymns and folk songs singing through the sky into the farthest hotel and hospital room in town.

This Clinic building, like the first, was the work of Henry Plummer, who was in charge of its design and construction, and the well-nigh perfect fitting of its plan to its purpose is a monument to his genius. Once again as he planned the building he reviewed the entire Clinic

697

organization and system—refining, extending, and integrating it till he had shaped the whole to his conception of needs to come. In this he had the assistance of Dr. Thomas B. Magath of the division of clinical pathology, and Dr. Magath's patience was sorely tried at times by Plummer's exacting and eccentric habits. When Plummer got an idea he would send for Dr. Magath and goad him into picking it to pieces; then in the light of the arguments against it he would accept or reject it as seemed best. But he was more than likely to get his idea about midnight and the argument to last till nearly dawn.

Part of their task was to revise the methods and blank forms for transferring patients and recording and keeping track of case histories. When Dr. Plummer and Dr. Magath had these worked out to their satisfaction and took them to the printer, that worthy gentleman threw up his hands in despair. The forms were so intricate and the doctors' notations so cryptic he was completely baffled. So Dr. Magath, who had worked his way through medical college as a printer, rolled up his sleeves, donned the printer's apron, and set the forms in type himself.

At first sight of the bewildering array of cards, envelopes, and record sheets, each a different color and each fitted to a specific purpose, one is inclined to sympathize with the printer; but a little study arouses admiration for the mind that could order such disparate and manifold details into an effective and essentially simple system, the purpose of which is to reduce to routine motions as much of the work as possible so that it may be transferred from the staff doctors to secretaries and desk attendants.

2

When the new building was opened Dr. Will was sixty-seven years old, alert and active as ever. But on several occasions during the preceding winter he had spoken of retiring from the operating room. His friends would not hear of it; he had many good years left, they said. But on July 1, 1928, he went to the Clinic from St. Mary's in a mood of deep depression. When his secretary asked him what was the matter he replied, "I've just done my last operation."

"But you don't have to quit yet," she protested.

"Yes, I want to stop while I'm still good," he answered. "I don't want to go on like some others I've seen, past my prime, doing the surgery that younger, surer men ought to be doing."

# A Living Memorial

He never spoke of the matter, and never operated, again—so little outward fuss did he make over a decision that must have been a bitter one for him. What brought him to it he described a few years later:

As the years pass, accumulating experiences, some of them unfortunate, leave scars on the mind and spirit, with a loss of resiliency, whereas the young are given courage and enthusiasm by the successes. . . . For a year before I retired from the operating-room routine, I found as I followed through, carefully observing, that the younger men really possessed in the enthusiasm of youth the ability to grasp and orient new knowledge, even though it might conflict with former experiences—an ability that I no longer had in so marked a degree. I had the wisdom of experience, but I carried also the weight of past responsibilities.

When this became clear to me, I was happy to turn, in the interest of the profession that I love so well and of the patients who had been my first thought, from an active surgical career to that of surgical adviser, that I might give to the younger surgeons such of value as I had, and to the patient the benefit of my experience.

Dr. Charlie's retirement came a year and a half later, suddenly and unexpectedly, as the result of a retinal hemorrhage that came one morning while he was operating—and while his elder son was getting ready in the next room for his first operation as his father's assistant. Dr. Charlie was up and about after a few weeks' rest, but he was never really well again. A series of strokes, some so severe that death seemed likely, sapped his physical strength and to some degree his mental powers.

Men still argue about which of the Mayo brothers was the greater surgeon. Some in Europe as well as in the United States considered William Mayo the greatest surgeon of his time; others, some of them closely associated with both brothers, insist that Dr. Charlie was the abler, more versatile, and more ingenious operator. Dr. Will and Dr. Charlie themselves were most likely to say, when asked, that Dr. Judd was greater than either of them. It does not matter; they were both, or all three, masters of their craft, and by reason of their differences the complementary parts of a great team.

But not for their surgery itself will they be remembered in medical history. Their contribution in disseminating and popularizing the new surgery was not of the nailable, datable kind that historians readily record, and even their original techniques have been superseded by the refinements that enable many to do today what the brothers were unique in doing in their time. As Dr. Will once observed, "What a man may do with his own hands is small compared with that he may do to implant ideals and scientific spirit in many men who in endless chains will carry on the same endeavor." The length and strength of the chain the Mayos started by building a clinic upon their surgical partnership will determine the niche finally accorded them in medical history.

3

The brothers' release from active surgical duties carried its own pleasant consolation. For many years they had gone nowhere together; one always remained on duty while the other was away. Now they could travel together. They made their first joint trip to Europe in 1929, for the purpose of dedicating a stained-glass window they had ordered placed to their father's memory in the parish church in Eccles, his birthplace. Their many English friends made much of their presence, and the University of Manchester took the occasion to confer upon them its highest degree, the first they had received together.

The severe cold of Minnesota winters was hard on Dr. Charlie now, and for his sake the two families built adjoining houses in Tucson, Arizona, where he seemed to feel best. There they spent the winter months in pleasant relaxation from the hectic, hurried life they had lived so long.

But Dr. Will did not overnight drop the habits of a lifetime. Early one morning he struck across lots to visit the Tucson hospital. It was a Janus-faced building and, not being able to tell the front from the back, Dr. Will entered the first door he came to, which led him into the kitchen. A woman in uniform asked him sharply what he wanted and he replied mildly, "I am Dr. W. J. Mayo of Rochester, Minnesota, and I'd like to visit your hospital." The superintendent—for the woman was she—nearly collapsed. The great Dr. Mayo coming unannounced and by way of the kitchen! But Dr. Will soon put her at ease. When she led him into the dining room where a shift of nurses were at breakfast and introduced him with a flustered reference to his coming through the kitchen, he spoke whimsically of the many times he and his father in their pioneer practice had eaten breakfast in the kitchen after a night on duty.

# A Living Memorial

While he talked, the word ran from office to ward that Dr. Mayo was coming, and everything was ready for his inspection when he came. Seeing the humor of the incident in retrospect the hospital staff told the story on themselves, and it won the heart of Tucson when it appeared in the newspaper under the heading "Mayo of Rochester Entertained in the Kitchen."

4

While the brothers were in Tucson they received periodic reports on the state of affairs at the Clinic, and when the first one arrived Dr. Charlie read it over, then looked up at his brother with a grin, "Well, well, this is quite a comedown for us, Will. They're doing better now we're away than they did when we were there."

It is not easy for any man to accept the fact that he is not indispensable, especially in an institution he has built, but in nothing was William Mayo greater than in the grace with which he accepted age and yielded place to others. In 1931 when he attended the convention of the American Surgical Association in San Francisco, his friends, learning that the day was a milestone for him, made it the occasion for a public tribute, and he responded:

"Your greetings on this seventieth birthday of mine repay me for living long enough to have it. . . . The years have come upon me so easily and so rapidly that I can look back on each and every one of them without regret, and I feel no older now than I did when I came into this Association. As I have watched older men come down the ladder, as down they must come, with younger men passing them, as they must pass to go up, it so often has been an unhappy time for both. The older man is not always able to see the necessity or perhaps the justice of his descent and resents his slipping from the position that he has held, instead of gently and peacefully helping this passing by assisting the younger man. What pleasure and comfort I have had from my hours with younger men! They still have their imagination, their vision; the future is bright before them. Each day as I go through the hospitals surrounded by younger men, they give me of their dreams and I give them of my experience, and I get the better of the exchange. . . .

"There are many recompenses in a seventieth birthday. I look through a half-opened door into the future, full of interest, intriguing beyond my power to describe, but with a full understanding that it is for each generation to solve its own problems and that no man has the wisdom to guide or control the next generation. It is a comfortable feeling, to be interested in what is to happen, but in bringing it about to be in no way responsible."

Again and again he rang the changes on the idea that it was both the duty and the privilege of the passing generation to hand on the torch for younger men to carry it in the time of their greatest physical and intellectual strength. When he and Mrs. Mayo gave their house and gardens with a sufficient endowment for their maintenance to the Mayo Foundation, Dr. Will made the presentation with these words:

We have no desire in any way to dictate or control the manner in which this adventure in education shall be carried out. It is for the younger people to meet the conditions of their generation in the way that appears to them to be wise and best. We only hope that Mayo Foundation House will be a meeting place where men of medicine may exchange ideas for the good of mankind.

Nor did he stop with preaching. One night in November 1932, he rose to talk at staff meeting. He began with reminiscence and history, tracing briefly the steps in the development of the Clinic, beginning with his father's work in laying the foundation. That was the first period in the story, he said. The second had begun with the building of St. Mary's in 1889; and now a third was at the door. On December 31 he and Dr. Charlie and Dr. Plummer would withdraw from the board of governors in favor of three younger men from the staff. They would form an advisory committee and as long as they lived the benefit of their experience would be at the command of the Clinic, but they were resigning the control and the responsibility to others.

5

They had decided to take that step because the apparatus of self-government instituted a decade earlier was working well enough to convince Dr. Will that it was adequate to its purpose. More and more of the administration had been transferred to the standing committees, and those who had opposed the system when Dr. Will instituted it were now among its most enthusiastic supporters. For it had turned out as Dr. Will expected; committee service was an excellent way of educating the staff members in Clinic problems.

When any member got so full of his own and his specialty's importance that he could not see the rights of the other sections in the organization, the board of governors had only to appoint him to some important committee. Dealing there with the problems of the whole group, he soon had a better understanding of the relationship of his own block to the whole structure and was ever afterward more amenable. Rotating the staff members through the various committees proved to be a superlative means of getting them each to consider the other fellow's point of view.

Moreover, all decisions of major importance were referred to the board of governors for approval, and when they did not conform to established policies the board returned them to the committee with an explanation of why approval was withheld. That was an effective way of making concrete to the committee members what might otherwise remain only platitudes to which they paid lip service.

Yet as long as the Mayo brothers sat on the board of governors and held positions of authority the degree of self-government would be incomplete and the full strength or weakness of the machinery undisclosed. To put the Clinic on its own while the Mayos were still alive to advise in moments of doubt was supremely wise.

There was another factor in the situation. As long as Dr. Will and Dr. Charlie retained their authority there would linger within the institution, outside it, and within their families the idea that the Clinic belonged to the Mayos. Legally they had been out of control since the reorganization effected in the 1920's. It had been hard for Dr. Will to give up the idea of perpetuating the institution through the family; but once he was convinced that its future, which had become his chief concern, would be jeopardized by saddling it with all future Mayos whether they could carry their own weight in it or not, he acted with his customary impersonality and moved to sever the family control actually as well as legally.

It is true that Dr. Charlie's elder son and Dr. Will's two sons-in-law hold life memberships in the Properties Association and on the Clinic board of governors, but in neither case is three a controlling vote, and the Clinic is under neither legal nor moral obligation to place the Mayos of future generations on its staff or its governing body unless they are worthy of the place in their own right.

The brothers were as good as their word. After 1932 neither of them ever attended a meeting of the board of governors or cast a vote in its decisions. Dr. Will's influence was still considerable, but it was exercised solely through the power of his prestige and the value of his advice, and he was proud that it was so.

He sought thereafter to further the transfer of public confidence from the Mayo brothers to the Mayo Clinic—as the Old Doctor had once transferred it to his sons. The process had already begun, and for years people had been going to the Mayo Clinic instead of to the Drs. Mayo. Indeed, sometimes patients were thrown into great distress because Dr. Will or Dr. Charlie called on them as a courtesy to the doctor who referred them; they were sure that if Dr. Mayo came to see them it meant they were going to die. But it was still Dr. Will and Dr. Charlie who held the public eye and the public affection, and to change that as much as he could, Dr. Will deliberately began to withdraw from public activity. He refused more and more of the calls that came to him to speak or to serve on professional committees, saying he thought it best that such opportunities go to the younger men who could make the best use of them.

Ever since the war the Mayos had worked closely with the American Legion in the treatment of disabled veterans, giving theirs and the Clinic's services free of charge to those for whom the Legion hospital association arranged residence and hospitalization in Rochester. In 1934 the Legion recognized this service by a citation read in an impressive ceremony attended by many of the country's medical and civilian great, including no less a personage than President Franklin D. Roosevelt. That the President of the United States should come to Rochester to join in honoring the beloved brothers seemed to many the culminating triumph of their career.

Later in the year, when the medical advisory committee to the Committee on Economic Security was being organized in Washington, President Roosevelt, perhaps as a result of what he had seen in Rochester, had only one suggestion to make as to its personnel: Dr. W. J. Mayo should be its chairman. When the invitation to act in that capacity was transmitted to Dr. Will by Secretary of Labor Perkins, he declined the honor on the grounds that he was too busy at Rochester.

His refusal caused consternation among the medical men who had been "moving heaven and earth"—their own phrase—to make sure the proper men were placed on the committee. No man could be as indispensable anywhere as they made Dr. Will appear in their letters urging him to reconsider. He was the only man capable of heading the committee successfully, they said. But Dr. Will would not be coaxed. He did, however, in answer to a second letter from Miss Perkins, give his real reason for declining to serve.

I cannot join in this movement, not alone because of demands upon my time, but because I think each generation must settle its own problems, and that men along in years who try to project such wisdom as they may have or think they have onto the problems of the future are more likely to do harm than good. I think that such a committee, to do the most good, should be made up of medical men in the active part of their lives, should contain few men over 60, and that at least half of the members should be men of 50. I have passed 70.

6

Dr. Will took almost no part publicly in the debate that churned in medical circles when socialized medicine became an issue after the depression. He did not approve of the idea, however, because he feared that government control would reduce medical practice to "a civil service level of mediocrity." Nor did he approve of the prepayment feature in group medicine, a kind of health insurance plan by which the patient pays the clinic a stated sum each year and in return receives whatever medical treatment he may need in the interval.

One of the outstanding leaders in the minority group of doctors who advocated both those measures was Dr. Hugh Cabot, a distinguished urologist then on the Clinic staff, to which he had come after an extensive experience in private practice and as a teacher on the medical faculty of the University of Michigan. Dr. Cabot was very active in writing and speaking about "the doctor's bill" and "the patient's dilemma," and in reporting his activities the newspapers invariably referred to him as a Mayo Clinic physician.

This upset Cabot's opponents, who feared the lay public would think he spoke for the Clinic and the Mayos. Accordingly some of them wrote to Dr. Will, strongly hinting, though never saying outright, that he ought to muzzle Cabot. To them his answer was unequivocal:

We have always stood for freedom of speech and thought by the members of the staff of the Clinic, and never in any way have interfered with their religious, political, or social opinions. . . . It must be distinctly understood that Dr. Cabot is entirely within his rights in expressing his opinion on a social question, even though that opinion is exactly opposite to that held by the general staff of the Clinic.

The debate over group medicine was another matter, and *debate* was precisely what it had become, as a result of the general review of medical practice induced by New Deal charges of inadequate medical care for large sections of the population. In the debate the Mayo Clinic became a matter for dispute. The advocates of group practice cited the Clinic as the great example and based their arguments on its methods and achievements. The opponents insisted that the Mayo Clinic was unique and therefore not a fair example of group practice, when the majority of group clinics consisted of half a dozen or so members.

To Dr. Will's way of thinking, entirely too much of the argument turned on the financial aspects of the matter—whether or not group practice reduces the costs of medical care to the patient and raises the return to the practitioner, whether or not a fixed salary destroys the initiative of the doctor, and so on. In one of many utterances on the subject he said:

Properly considered, group medicine is not a financial arrangement, except for minor details, but *a scientific cooperation for the welfare of the sick*. Medicine's place is fixed by its service to mankind; if we doctors fail to measure up to our opportunity it means state medicine, political control, mediocrity, and loss of professional ideals. The members of the medical fraternity must cooperate in this work. . . . The internist, the surgeon, and the specialist must join with the physiologist, the pathologist, and the laboratory workers to form the clinical group, which must also include men learned in the abstract sciences, since physics and biochemistry are leading medicine to greater heights. Union of all these forces will lengthen by many years the span of human life, and as a by-product will do much to improve professional ethics by overcoming some of the evils of competitive medicine.

He pointed out that physicians were practicing group medicine whenever they called other men in consultation on their patients or made use of state or university laboratories; so why should they not get together and make their cooperation more effective?

According to Clinic staff members, who have given advice to many men who came to Rochester to find out how to go about organizing a group, a clinic started for the purpose of improving the quality of care given the patient has a good chance for success; one begun with the wholly commercial purpose of making a better living for its members will surely die.

Some of them are frankly dubious, though, about the chances of any group, however well intentioned, that is formed among men long established in general practice. As soon as a doctor in individual practice admits that Dr. Jones across the street knows more about anything in medicine than he does, his patients lose confidence in him, and a doctor who has in consequence developed a pose of infallibility and omniscience just is not capable of sending a patient down the hall to a colleague—the habit that is the lifeblood and reason for being of cooperative group practice.

7

"The most amazing thing of all about the Mayo Clinic [is] the fact that five hundred members of the most highly individualistic profession in the world could be induced to live and work together in a small town on the edge of nowhere, and like it!" So says an English surgeon who spent several years in Rochester as a Foundation fellow. And one is inclined to agree with him. More usual is the reaction of the doctor who said to one Clinic member, "I wouldn't work at the Clinic for any amount of money. I'd be just a cog in a machine there."

But if Clinic men are cogs, they certainly do not know it. Ask the research men why they stay on and they will tell you it is because they have everything they want to work with, and complete independence to follow where their interest and their results lead them. Ask the clinicians why they stay on and you will hear a rhapsody about the opportunity and facilities to practice medicine in the best way they know how without any financial restrictions. The salary question is settled and the business office takes care of the fees; all they have to think about is getting the patient well. They all agree that the size of their salaries is not what keeps them, and the administration says there is not a research man in the group who has not been offered more money elsewhere and not a single clinician who could not make more money as a specialist in individual practice. As for regimentation, the sole complaint seems to be that there isn't enough of it.

"The trouble with the system here is that you can't get a decision out of anybody," says one section head. "The board of governors have the authority supposedly, but they won't use it. They'll send you to this committee or that to talk it over, and they in turn send you to talk it over with somebody else. So you have to see half a dozen persons for a decision one could make. Of course," he admits ruefully, "by the time you're through, you know the majority approve your plan and you can go ahead with it with full support, or else you've been talked out of it yourself." Which, no doubt, is precisely the purpose of the system.

Another section head once asked one of the officers whether he had the authority to discipline an employee. "Yes, you have the authority," was the answer. "But if I were you I wouldn't use it."

There are doctors, good ones, who do not fit into such an organization, just as there are instruments that do not fit into a symphony orchestra, instruments like the saxophone that can carry the solo but cannot blend into the ensemble. There are doctors who are irked by the delay such a system imposes, just as there are men who prefer the efficiency of a dictatorship to the slower processes of political democracy. Patently, cooperative group practice is not for them.

That is not to say disagreement is not permitted. "Yes, we have a lot of friction here," says one of the Clinic laboratory men. "But ninety-five per cent of us can argue about the *thing* without getting sore at the *man*. So we scrap out our differences. The other five per cent leave sooner or later. There's a kind of natural selective process going on here all the time."

Such is the flower the Mayos brought to bloom. How fragile it is no one knew better than Dr. Will, and he spent much of his time those last years describing the conditions necessary for its continued blossoming. Three things he considered of vital importance: an active ideal of service instead of personal profit, a primary and sincere concern for the care of the sick, that is, for the individual patient, and an unselfish interest of every member of the group in the professional progress of every other member. If the Clinic failed, he said over and over again, it would do so because of dissension and jealousies within, not attacks from without. He urged the Clinic men to remember that a boost for a colleague was a boost for the group and so for every member in it, and that taking a dig at a colleague was just cutting a nick out of one's own nose. That point at least he put across, to judge from the unanimity with which Clinic men repeat it.

Whether attitudes and qualities so rare in mankind as those can be perpetuated in an organization beyond the generation of the founders is a social question of the first magnitude. As an experiment in cooperative individualism the Mayo Clinic deserves watching—and not by doctors alone.

## 8

The thirties brought the passing, one by one, of the early members of the group. Mrs. Mellish Wilson was the first to leave, in 1933. A pioneer in the field of medical editing, she made "of the Mayo Clinic" on a medical paper synonymous with good form and clear, readable English. The authors might grumble at her drastic slashing of their sentences and complain that she destroyed their individuality and made them all sound alike, but without her services their annual volume of *Collected Papers* would not have become the "surgeons' Bible" it is called, and the weekly *Proceedings of the Staff Meetings of the Mayo Clinic* would not hold the honored place it does on medical library shelves. Dr. Will always ranked her second to Dr. Charlie and himself in influence on the development of the Clinic.

First after them, of course, was Henry Plummer. Without him the Mayo Clinic would not exist in the form it does today nor in the house it inhabits. That much the story must have made clear. He put rather too much of himself into the second Clinic building, and the spark never burned so brightly thereafter. When he was stricken with bulbar paralysis in 1936, he knew it for what it was, sent for his family and his colleagues, and as long as consciousness remained traced the progress of the disease in his own body—the clinical investigator to the last.

Dr. Judd was the master surgeon first, last, and always. In his own realm he did a prodigious amount of work, but he took little active part in the affairs of the Clinic outside the operating room, in spite of the fact that he was one of the pioneer partners and later a member of the board of governors. He became head of the surgical staff upon the retirement of the Mayos, and in 1931 he was president of the American Medical Association. Four years later he was suddenly stricken with pneumonia while in Chicago attending a football game, and he died there a few days later.

Not a member of the Clinic but important in its story was Sister Joseph. Though she had long since retired from her operating-room post as Dr. Will's assistant, she continued as the superintendent of St. Mary's until her death on March 29, 1939. Had her work been done outside the cloister it would have won her national distinction. Within her lifetime she saw the rise of a great sisterhood, a great hospital, and a great profession. When she began her work, the Sisters of St. Francis considered nursing a kind of glorified maid service, and curious pupils in their day school in Rochester, asking why Sister So-and-So was not sent to the hospital, were told in accents of horror, "Why, she is educated!" But before Sister Joseph died, members of the sisterhood with advanced degrees from Columbia or Minnesota in dietetics, hospital administration, and nursing education had taken back from lay women the management of the hospital and the school of nursing and were recognized as national leaders in their profession.

Dr. Will and Dr. Charlie, Drs. Graham, Judd, and Plummer, and Sister Joseph, all born and reared within a few miles of Rochester! How, some have asked, can one explain this incidence of exceptional abilities in medicine? In view of the circumstances that led each of those six to medicine it seems less likely that the air of southern Minnesota produced unusual medical skill than that the presence of a flourishing medical practice attracted an unusual number of those with talent into medicine instead of something else.

9

Dr. Will returned early from Tucson in the spring of 1939. He was not feeling well and decided to return to the Clinic for a checkup.

# A Living Memorial

The physical examination revealed nothing, but the x-ray showed—irony of ironies—cancer of the stomach.

He was operated on at once and rallied nicely. He was soon so much better that Dr. Charlie, who had come on from Tucson to be with him, decided to make a trip to Chicago for a fitting of some suits he had ordered months before. While there he was taken ill with pneumonia, and on May 26 the newspapers and radio flashed the words across the country, "Dr. Charlie is dead."

The first thought of thousands was for the loving and beloved brother. Would this great loss prove too much for him in his own feeble health? But for Dr. Will the shock was lessened, the grief tempered, by the greater sorrow he had suffered several years earlier when illness took away the real Charlie with whom he had worked and whose strength had supported his own.

Slowly Dr. Will recovered sufficiently to spend an hour or two a day in his office in the Clinic, but the recovery was only temporary, and soon after his seventy-eighth birthday he retired to his bed, where he slept quietly away on July 28, 1939. It seemed fitting somehow that the famous brothers who had worked so closely and wrought so mightily together should die within a few months of each other.

Their deaths produced tributes and eulogies in every major medical journal of America and many across the seas. "Like Lincoln the Mayo brothers now belong to the ages," said one. "Two more names are enrolled among the immortals," said another. And another, "With their passing the curtain falls on an era in American medicine." Many of the articles were written by old friends and former Foundation fellows who had known Dr. Will and Dr. Charlie well and who contributed personal anecdotes and appraisals that taken together make a vivid picture of the two at work. There is in almost all of them a personal note that one who has read many such sketches about the medical men of the brothers' generation recognizes as exceptional, an indirect expression of how many lives they touched personally and deeply.

More impressive still is the flood—no other word is adequate—of letters and telegrams that came to their families and the Clinic during their illnesses and after their deaths. They fill many thick, thick folders in the files, and reading through them one wonders whether any other two men in history have ever evoked such a tribute either in volume or in range. Few countries of the world are unrepresented, and messages of condolence from the wealthy and the well-born lie there side by side with almost illiterate scrawls full of personal grief in the loss of "my doctor." There are notes from both President and Mrs. Roosevelt and literally next is a penciled letter, the handwriting cramped, the words misspelled, from an old woman in Texas who had sent a potted flower and wanted to tell Mrs. Mayo how much Dr. Charlie's kindness twenty years before had meant to her.

Then a little farther on lies the most moving of them all, a copy of the resolutions adopted by the surgical society of the Clinic:

> Those who in years to come peruse these minutes may justly question what manner of men were we, who experiencing bereavement such as ours in recent months, yet inadequately expressed it. Let them remember, then, that those whose greatness they strive to recreate from graven names and printed pages were living men with whom we walked and talked and laughed; our preceptors, our colleagues, and our friends. We are too close to this grief to describe it: "True sorrow makes a silence in the heart."
>
> . . . There is left for us their precedent—that immortal part of them— to cherish and hand on.
>
> Portions of that precedent seem particularly left in trust to us, the surgeons of the institution which our great preceptors founded. They worked for something even greater than themselves, which lies in the future and which must be effected by their successors. Very gradually at first, then more definitely, as old age approached, they withdrew from the affairs of this society and of the clinic, encouraging their successors to plant their feet firmly in the way. They kept to themselves no knowledge or skill which they could impart to younger men. Always available for consultation and advice, yet they did not assume authority in another surgeon's case. They insisted that each surgeon have a full hand on his own service and that he shoulder the responsibility thereof. Guidance without pampering; help without meddling; these are the principles by which we were trained. Let us then train others thereby and as we close ranks for the months and years ahead as our great mentors would have had us do, let it be said of us: "They helped everyone his neighbor."

They may raise shafts of stone and piles of brick to the memory of William James and Charles Horace Mayo, but so long as that spirit lasts in the Clinic they created they will have a monument more fitting, a living memorial in their own image.

*Acknowledgments, Notes, and Index*

# Acknowledgments

The roll of those who have helped me prepare this volume is long, and where the information or assistance given was specific to some chapter or section I have given my thanks at the proper place in the notes that follow. To these others I make grateful acknowledgment here:

Guy Stanton Ford, president of the University of Minnesota and chairman of its committee on the Press, for giving me the opportunity, for advice and encouragement throughout the task, and for a critical reading of the manuscript.

Margaret S. Harding, director of the Press, for invaluable suggestions and direct editorial aid at every step from the first outline to the final page proof, as well as for all-important moral support when my will to sustained effort weakened.

The Mayo family, the staff of the Mayo Clinic, and Sister Domitilla, superintendent of St. Mary's Hospital, for generous cooperation in giving me information and assembling illustrations, and even more, for their rare restraint in permitting me unhampered to make what use of the material I would. I feel a special obligation to Nora H. Guthrey and to Virginia Krause, formerly secretaries to Drs. W. J. and C. H. Mayo respectively, to Isabel Farr, secretary in the office of the Mayo Foundation, to Ann Cooper, secretary to Harry J. Harwick, and to Geraldine Thomas, secretary to Dr. Donald C. Balfour, director of the Foundation, for many courtesies and much practical assistance.

The several staffs of the Minnesota Historical Society, the Olmsted County Historical Society, the medical library of the University of Minnesota, the Ramsey County Medical Society library, and the Mayo Clinic library for their gracious and unfailingly helpful response to my demands upon them and the rich resources they command.

715

# The Doctors Mayo

In addition I want to acknowledge my deep obligation to Dr. Richard O. Beard and Thomas E. Steward, whose work over a period of years in assembling materials and recording interviews enabled me to start with a body of valuable data already accumulated.

My hearty thank-you too to Donald S. Fairchild of New York City for blue-penciling many a symptom of academic hangover; Sarah Davidson for expert research and technical services throughout the last months of the task, and Ida Kramer and Doris Taylor for research assistance in the medical literature and the Rochester newspapers respectively; Jane McCarthy for selecting the illustrations and fitting them with captions, as well as for designing the format of the book; and Mrs. Arthur Katz for preparing the index. And to all my colleagues at the Press I am grateful for their patience and a multiplicity of services, the value of which I well know how to appreciate.

The manuscript has been checked in proof by competent readers from the university medical school, but I am solely responsible for whatever errors remain.

HELEN CLAPESATTLE

University of Minnesota
October, 1941

# Bibliographical Notes

Although the Mayo story has been written for the laymen, who do not often ask for authorities, these notes are added for the sake of any doctors or historians who may want to assure themselves that the author's imagination has not been working overtime. In the hope of satisfying the latter without prejudicing the former, the usual superior footnote numbers in the text are here replaced with page numbers.

In gathering material for this volume over a period of five years a substantial file of papers has been accumulated in the offices of the University of Minnesota Press. It includes correspondence, newspaper clippings, reprints of published papers, manuscript papers, transcripts of interviews, and the like. It is referred to as the Press file.*

Interviews with men and women who played a part in the story, or knew those who did, have been a major source of information, and of these there are three groups. During the years from 1932 to 1934 Dr. Richard O. Beard interviewed the following:

MRS. D. M. BERKMAN, born Gertrude Mayo, daughter of Dr. W. W. Mayo; DR. WILLIAM F. BRAASCH, head of the section on urology, Mayo Clinic; BURT W. EATON, financial adviser to the Mayos; ISABEL FARR, Mayo Foundation secretary; JUDGE GEORGE W. GRANGER, legal adviser to the Mayos; NORA H. GUTHREY, formerly secretary to Dr. W. J. Mayo; HARRY J. HARWICK, executive officer of the Mayo Clinic; MARY HINES, an anesthetist at St. Mary's Hospital since 1905; SISTER JOSEPH, formerly superintendent of St. Mary's Hospital and for many years Dr. W. J. Mayo's first assistant in the operating room; DR. WILLIAM C. MAC-CARTY, head of a section on surgical pathology, Mayo Clinic; DR. CHARLES H. MAYO; DR. WILLIAM J. MAYO.

MRS. H. N. NOWELL, born Helen Cross, the daughter of Dr. E. W. Cross and a childhood playmate of the Mayo brothers and their two sisters; DR. HENRY S. PLUMMER, formerly chief of the division of medicine, Mayo Clinic; MRS. ISABEL PLUMMER, mother of Dr. H. S. Plummer; ANN POWDERLY, anesthetist at St. Mary's Hospital since 1909; MARION L. SLOAN, pioneer resident of Rochester and cousin to Mrs. W. J. Mayo; DR. LEDA J. STACY, formerly head of a section in medicine, Mayo Clinic; MRS. A. W. STINCHFIELD, wife of the Mayos' first partner; DR. LOUIS B. WILSON, formerly head of the division of laboratories, Mayo Clinic, and

---

* As the book appears, the Press file is being distributed, some of the materials being returned to the Mayo Clinic, from which they came, the rest remaining in the possession of the author. The latter will eventually form a collection of Mayo Papers in the Minnesota Historical Society.

director, Mayo Foundation; MAUD MELLISH WILSON, formerly director of the division of publications, Mayo Clinic; MRS. H. H. WITHERSTINE, wife of a Rochester doctor.

Frances Hanger, Dr. Beard's secretary, was present to record many of these interviews, and her transcripts of them are in the Press file.

The information gained in interviews from 1936 to 1938 by Thomas E. Steward, head of the University of Minnesota news service, was incorporated by him in a manuscript narrative, preserved in the Press file. All material drawn from it is listed as from the Steward manuscript.

My own interviews, transcripts of which are also in the Press file, were with the following persons during the years 1938 to 1940:

DR. EDGAR V. ALLEN, head of a section in medicine, Mayo Clinic; DR. DONALD C. BALFOUR, director, Mayo Foundation; DR. JOSEPH BERKSON, chief of the division of biometry and medical statistics, Mayo Clinic; DR. WALTER M. BOOTHBY, head of the section on metabolism, Mayo Clinic; DR. ALBERT C. BRODERS, head of a section on surgical pathology, Mayo Clinic; DR. ARTHUR H. BULBULIAN, director of the Mayo Foundation Museum of Hygiene and Medicine; ELIZABETH COLE, in charge of general correspondence, Mayo Clinic; HELEN COOK, chief technician, serology laboratory, Mayo Clinic; SISTER DOMITILLA, superintendent, St. Mary's Hospital; ISABEL FARR, Mayo Foundation secretary; GUY S. FORD, president and former graduate school dean, University of Minnesota.

DR. FRED W. GAARDE, head of a section in medicine, Mayo Clinic; DR. HERBERT Z. GIFFIN, head of a section in medicine, Mayo Clinic; DR. CHRISTOPHER GRAHAM, formerly head of the division of medicine, Mayo Clinic; NORA H. GUTHREY, formerly secretary to Dr. W. J. Mayo; DR. HOWARD R. HARTMAN, associate in medicine, Mayo Clinic; HARRY J. HARWICK, executive officer, Mayo Clinic; DR. HENRY F. HELMHOLZ, head of the section on pediatrics, Mayo Clinic; DR. PHILIP S. HENCH, head of a section in medicine, Mayo Clinic; DR. MELVIN S. HENDERSON, head of the section on orthopedic surgery, Mayo Clinic; DR. RICHARD M. HEWITT, head of the division of publications, Mayo Clinic; DR. BAYARD T. HORTON, associate in medicine, Mayo Clinic; HERMAN A. JOHNSON, administrative officer, Mayo Clinic; LEONARD A. JULIN, head of photographic department, Mayo Clinic.

PRISCILLA KEELEY, head of the section on social service, Mayo Clinic; DR. NORMAN M. KEITH, head of a section in medicine, Mayo Foundation; DR. EDWARD C. KENDALL, head of the division of biochemistry, Mayo Foundation; THOMAS E. KEYS, assistant librarian, Mayo Clinic; DR. BYRL R. KIRKLIN, head of the section on roentgenology, Mayo Clinic; VIRGINIA KRAUSE, formerly secretary to Dr. C. H. Mayo; DR. FRANK H. KRUSEN, head of the section on physical therapy, Mayo Clinic; ALBERT J. LOBB, administrative officer, Mayo Clinic; DR. ARCH H. LOGAN, head of a section in medicine, Mayo Clinic; DR. JOHN S. LUNDY, head of the section on anesthesia, Mayo Clinic; DR. WILLIAM C. MAC-CARTY, head of a section on surgical pathology, Mayo Clinic; DR. THOMAS B. MAGATH, head of the section on parasitology, Mayo Clinic;

# Bibliographical Notes

DR. FRANK C. MANN, director of the Institute of Experimental Medicine, Mayo Foundation; MRS. CHARLES H. MAYO; DR. CHARLES W. MAYO; DR. WILLIAM J. MAYO.

BEATRIZ MONTES, Spanish secretary, Mayo Clinic; DR. ROBERT D. MUSSEY, head of the section on obstetrics and gynecology, Mayo Clinic; DR. GORDON B. NEW, head of the section on laryngology, oral and plastic surgery, Mayo Clinic; CORA OLSON, first registration clerk, Mayo Clinic; DR. ARNOLD E. OSTERBERG, head of the section on clinical biochemistry, Mayo Foundation; FRIEDA PLIEFKE, librarian, Mayo Clinic; DR. WILLIAM A. PLUMMER, head of a section in medicine, Mayo Clinic; DR. HAROLD E. ROBERTSON, head of the section on pathologic anatomy, Mayo Clinic; MABEL E. ROOT, in charge of old records, Mayo Clinic; DR. EDWARD C. ROSENOW, head of the division of experimental bacteriology, Mayo Foundation; DR. GRACE M. ROTH, clinical physiologist, Mayo Clinic.

DR. ARTHUR H. SANFORD, head of the division of clinical pathology, Mayo Clinic; ERNEST H. SCHLITGUS, administrative officer, Mayo Clinic; DR. CHARLES SHEARD, head of the division of physics and biophysical research, Mayo Foundation; DR. ALBERT M. SNELL, head of a section in medicine, Mayo Clinic; LOUISE MAYO TRENHOLME, daughter of Dr. Charles H. Mayo; DR. OWEN WANGENSTEEN, chief of the department of surgery, University of Minnesota Medical School; DR. RUSSELL M. WILDER, head of a section in medicine, Mayo Clinic; DR. FREDERICK A. WILLIUS, head of a section on cardiology, Mayo Clinic; DR. LOUIS B. WILSON, formerly head of the division of laboratories, Mayo Clinic, and director, Mayo Foundation; DR. FRANKLIN R. WRIGHT, Minneapolis physician.

When it was decided in the early 1920's that the division of publications of the Clinic should publish a history of the institution, Maud H. Mellish, director of the division, accompanied Dr. W. J. Mayo on a journey to South America, and on board ship he dictated to her the story of his father, his brother, and himself, and of the growth of the Clinic as he remembered it. This story as Mrs. Mellish took it down, and typescript copies of it, are at present in the Press file. It is cited as WJM, Story to Mrs. Mellish, with page numbers from the typescript copy.

An analogous source, though much briefer, is the story told by Dr. C. H. Mayo in a paper he read before the Medical History Club of the Mayo Foundation in 1929. There is a typescript copy in the Press file. It is cited as CHM, "Early Days of the Mayo Clinic."

Officials of the Mayo Clinic very kindly made available to me some of the materials in the very extensive files accumulated in the offices of Drs. W. J. and C. H. Mayo. These include correspondence, memoranda, reprints of papers, and the like. I am indebted to the kind assistance of Nora H. Guthrey, formerly secretary to Dr. W. J. Mayo, and Virginia Krause, formerly secretary to Dr. C. H. Mayo, in the use of these files. They are cited as WJM, or CHM, files. Also in the brothers' offices at the Clinic are bound volumes of reprints of their papers, and where these have been used the citation reads CIIM, or WJM, Reprints.

Among the publications of the Mayo Clinic which have been of great value are:

*Sketch of the History of the Mayo Clinic and the Mayo Foundation* (Philadelphia, 1926). This was based in part upon W. J. Mayo's story to Mrs. Mellish and was written by Mrs. Mellish and Dr. Louis B. Wilson, whose wife she became in 1924. As a matter of policy the authors omitted many of the personal details and interpretations given in the dictated story and included many facts and statistics which Dr. Mayo's memory did not provide. It is cited in the notes as *Sketch of the Mayo Clinic.*

*Physicians of the Mayo Clinic and the Mayo Foundation* (University of Minnesota Press, 1937), a directory with brief biographical sketches and full bibliographies of all persons who have served on the professional staff of the Clinic or the Foundation for one year or more. It will be cited as *Physicians of the Mayo Clinic.*

William J. Mayo and Charles H. Mayo, *A Collection of Papers Published Previous to 1909* (2 vols., Philadelphia, 1912), for which the reference form is *Collection of Papers Previous to 1909.*

*Collected Papers by the Staff of St. Mary's Hospital Mayo Clinic,* 1905–9–14, and *Collected Papers of the Mayo Clinic and Mayo Foundation,* issued annually since 1915. For these volumes the short title is *Collected Papers.*

*Proceedings of the Staff Meetings of the Mayo Clinic and Mayo Foundation,* issued weekly since 1926. It contains in full or in abstract the papers and discussions at the weekly meetings of the Clinic staff. It is cited as *Proceedings of the Mayo Clinic.*

For the general history of medicine and surgery I have relied principally upon the following works, cited by author and shortened title: Fielding H. Garrison, *An Introduction to the History of Medicine* (4th ed., Philadelphia, 1929); Richard H. Shryock, *The Development of Modern Medicine* (University of Pennsylvania Press, 1936); Harvey Graham, *The Story of Surgery* (New York, 1939); Francis R. Packard, *History of Medicine in the United States* (2 vols., New York, 1931); Henry E. Sigerist, *American Medicine* (trans. by Hildegarde Nagel, New York, 1934); Abraham Flexner, *Medical Education in the United States and Canada* (New York, 1910); Howard A. Kelly and Walter L. Burrage, *American Medical Biographies* (Baltimore, 1920). Histories and memoirs on more specific subjects are cited where they become pertinent.

In addition to using specific references in medical journals and society publications, I have made a systematic survey of the following, which are cited by abbreviated titles: *Transactions of the Indiana State Medical Society,* 1849–57; *Transactions of the Minnesota State Medical Society,* 1869–1902, and *Transactions of the Minnesota State Medical Association,* 1902–4; "Proceedings of the American Medical Association," 1890–1910, as published in the *Journal of the American Medical Association; Transactions of the Section on Surgery and Anatomy of the American Medical Association,* 1901–10; *Transactions of the American Surgical Association,* 1899–1915; *Transactions of the Western Surgical and Gynecological As-*

*sociation*, 1899–1910; *Transactions of the Southern Surgical and Gynecological Association*, 1902–10.

Invaluable to every historian who works in American history are the local newspapers. Of these I have made full use, for the most part from the newspaper collection of the Minnesota Historical Society. They are listed in the body of the notes. But special mention should be made of the gold mine available to me for the years from 1915 on, the collections of newspaper clippings in the offices of Drs. W. J. and C. H. Mayo and of H. J. Harwick at the Mayo Clinic. These are cited as CHM, or HJH, or WJM, collection. In a few cases, where I have used Dr. Beard's notes from these collections instead of rereading them myself, the citation is ROB notes from WJM collection.

For the sake of convenience a few names frequently used in these notes are abbreviated as follows: CHM for Charles H. Mayo; HC for Helen Clapesattle; HJH for Harry J. Harwick; ROB for Richard O. Beard; WJM for William J. Mayo; and WWM for William W. Mayo.

### THE PARADOX OF ROCHESTER

PAGE 4. The quotation about the Mayo brothers is from A. H. McIndoe, "Charles Horace Mayo," *British Medical Journal*, no. 4092:1207–8 (June 10, 1939).

PAGE 5. Dr. Mayo is quoted in Frank Smith, "The Mayo Clinic: Saga of Two Country Boys in 'Big' Medicine," *Daily Times* (Chicago), July 19, 1937.

### CHAPTER I. THE WAY WESTWARD

Among the published biographical sketches of Dr. William Worrall Mayo, four are of primary importance. The brief account in William B. Atkinson, *A Biographical Dictionary of Contemporary American Physicians and Surgeons* (2d ed., Philadelphia, 1880), p. 602, was based on material that Dr. W. W. Mayo himself must have furnished and is therefore valuable despite several demonstrable inaccuracies in date. The same is true of the longer and more circumstantial sketch in *History of Winona and Olmsted Counties* (Chicago, 1883), pp. 1037–39, and to some degree of that in Joseph A. Leonard, *History of Olmsted County, Minnesota* (Chicago, 1910), pp. 302–4. Leonard was a doctor, lawyer, and editor in Rochester and a personal friend of Dr. Mayo's, though at times his bitter political foe. Among later sketches, by all odds the best is Louis B. Wilson, "William Worrell Mayo, A Pioneer Surgeon of the Northwest," *Surgery, Gynecology and Obstetrics*, 44:710–16 (May 1927).

From those and from statements in the papers of Drs. W. J. and C. II. Mayo most other accounts, including those that have appeared on many occasions in various newspapers, have been drawn. A notable exception is Frank Smith, "The Mayo Clinic: Saga of Two Country Boys in 'Big' Medicine," *Daily Times* (Chicago), July 19–Aug. 8, 1937, in which several inaccuracies in the traditional accounts were first pointed out and much new anecdotal material was added.

In checking tradition and human memory against documentary sources for the years Dr. Mayo spent in Indiana I have used the newspaper, manuscript, and book collections of the Indiana history division of the Indiana State Library in Indianapolis, and for the expert assistance of the staff there I here give my thanks.

I am indebted also to the cooperation of Miss Edith Backus, secretary of the LaPorte County (Indiana) Historical Society, who generously made available to me the large file of documents she has assembled concerning the Indiana Medical College of LaPorte. These will be cited in the notes as the Backus Papers.

I owe much too to the interest and energy of Dr. William R. Reser of Lafayette, Indiana. He located and copied for me the records in the case of William W. Mayo v. Daniel L. Hart in the court of common pleas, Tippecanoe County (Indiana), July term, 1851. The copy is in the Press file. The bill of particulars filed by the defendant includes an itemized statement of W. W. Mayo's account at D. L. Hart's drug store, which provides evidence on a number of points in Dr. Mayo's story at this time. It is cited as WWM, account with Hart.

PAGES 9–10, SECTION 1. There is disagreement as to the exact place of W. W. Mayo's birth. C. H. Mayo ("Early Days of the Mayo Clinic") said his father was born in Eccles, and the brothers placed the memorial to their father in the parish church there. Atkinson, *Biographical Dictionary*, p. 602, states that the Mayo family had lived for generations at "New Barns," but for William's birthplace gives only "near Manchester." Mrs. Berkman, who copied the birth record from the flyleaf of the prayer book given her by a cousin when she was visiting in Eccles in 1929, wrote (letter to ROB, July 1, 1935, Press file) that James Mayo lived at Old Barnes but that William Worrall was born on Old Field's Road, Salford.

In the prayer book she found also a slip of paper bearing the words: "Feb. 6th 1785. Baptized Ann, daughter of John and Tenneson Bonselle. H. C. Smith, curate of Monyark." I have accepted these names and spellings in preference to those usually given, such as John Tenneison Bonsell or Anne Bousal Mayo, which might easily be mistakes of memory or misreadings of phonetic spellings in longhand.

W. J. Mayo (to ROB) is the authority for the Worrall connection. Somehow for several years, during which the *Sketch of the Mayo Clinic* was written, this name came to be spelled with an *e*, but the form with *a* is correct (Mrs. Berkman to ROB, showing him the spelling in the W. W. Mayo family Bible).

For the Mayo genealogy I have followed a long manuscript account of "The Mayos in England" written by Dr. Beard (Press file), who gave many months to the study. He was unable to find any evidence of the connection between James Mayo and the family whose history may be read in Charles Herbert Mayo, *A Genealogical Account of the Mayo and Elton Families* (London, 1882) and *The Mayo and Elton Families* (London, 1908). Dr. W. J. Mayo (to ROB) admitted the lack of documentary evidence but insisted that he had got the story of the connection, complete with dates, from his father.

Mrs. Berkman (to ROB) said she thought that James Mayo had been a farmer, but according to WJM, Story to Mrs. Mellish, he followed the sea as a ship's captain. See also Leonard, *Olmsted County*, p. 302.

PAGES 10–11, SECTION 2. For the Manchester of this period, see Richard Proctor, *Memorials of Bygone Manchester* (Manchester, 1880), pp. 94–110; Archibald Prentice, *Historical Sketches and Personal Recollections of Manchester, Intended to Illustrate the Progress of Public Opinion from 1792 to 1832* (Manchester, 1841).

PAGES 11–14, SECTIONS 3–4. The account of W. W. Mayo's education is based on WJM, Story to Mrs. Mellish; CHM to ROB; WJM, "The Advancement of Learning in Medicine through Biochemistry," *Collected Papers*, 20:968 (1928); Alfred A. Mumford, *The Manchester Grammar School, 1515–1915* (London, 1919); William Charles Henry, *Memoirs of the Life and Scientific Researches of John Dalton* (London, 1854); Robert Angus Smith, *Memoir of John Dalton* (London, 1856); Sir Henry E. Roscoe, *Dalton and the Rise of Modern Chemistry* (New York, 1895).

The problem of identifying the college W. W. Mayo attended is complicated by the persistent tradition that it was there he studied with John Dalton. The earliest available sketch of the Old Doctor's life states that he "got his preliminary education at Manchester coll., England," (Atkinson, *Biographical Dictionary*, p. 602). A later account made it the University of Manchester (Leonard, *Olmsted County*, p. 302) and still later ones called it Owens College, from which the University of Manchester developed (*Sketch of the Mayo Clinic*, p. 1); Wilson, "William Worrell Mayo," *Surg., Gynec. and Obst.*, 44:710 (May 1927). However, Owens College was not founded until 1851, seven years after Dalton's death and six years after William Mayo had left England.

When this fact was pointed out to Dr. W. J. Mayo, he suggested that his father studied at Owens College when he went back to England in the early 1850's (Frank Smith in the *Chicago Daily Times*). But there is no evidence to show that W. W. Mayo returned to England at that time and a good bit that makes it unlikely. An unsigned manuscript, "The Mayo Family," dated Aug. 1929 (Press file), which seems to have emanated from the Mayo Clinic and which bears corrections and additions in Dr. W. J. Mayo's characteristic hand, contains the statement that W. W. Mayo went to England in 1849 and 1850 to study with the chemist Frankland "at the foundation school which became Owens College." Mayo may have gone to England in 1849; he did go in 1850, but not to study chemistry. Letters from the bursar of the University of Manchester (to Mrs. Mellish, Sept. 24, 1920, and to ROB, Feb. 25, 1935, Press file) state that there was never any "foundation school" for Owens College, that Dr. E. Frankland was professor of chemistry in the college from 1851 to 1857, and that W. W. Mayo was not in attendance at the college at any time from 1851 to 1871.

The vague memory of the name of Frankland and of a foundation school, upon which the manuscript's statement was undoubtedly based, lends credence to the contention that it was the Nonconformist Manchester New College which W. W. Mayo attended, because an academy established by one Richard Frankland was the "foundation school" for New College (Manchester College, Oxford, *Prospectus*, 1938, p. 6). Moreover, this school was often called simply Manchester College, and John Dalton taught there from 1793 to 1799. In the latter year the school was moved to York. W. W. Mayo could have studied at New College after its return to Manchester from York in 1840, but not with Dalton, for by 1840 Dalton, having suffered several paralytic strokes, was too ill to do more than putter a little in his own laboratory. In 1889 New College became Manchester College at Oxford. A letter from its principal (R. Nicol Cross to HC, Dec. 29, 1938, Press file) states that there is no record in the college files of W. W. Mayo's having been a student at New College at any time.

There is another possibility. Among the several academies established in and around Manchester in those years was a popular and flourishing private school conducted by a succession of Dissenter clergymen. John Dalton was at one time a tutor in mathematics and natural philosophy in this school, which then or later was called Lancashire Independent College. In the one brief sketch of this school available to me, the dates given are too few to show whether or not W. W. Mayo could have studied with Dalton there (Mumford, *Manchester Grammar School*, pp. 245–56).

PAGE 13. For the Pine Street Medical School: Mumford, *Manchester Grammar School*, pp. 93, 166, 186, 190–91, 213, 249–50; Shryock, *Development of Modern Medicine*, pp. 42, 53–54. The authorities for W. W. Mayo's studying in London and Glasgow are CHM, "Early Days of the Mayo Clinic"; statements by W. W. Mayo in "Transactions of the Minnesota State Medical Society," *Northwestern Medical and Surgical Journal*, 1:51 (July 1870), and the *Rochester Post and Record*, June 3, 1904.

Stillé was in Europe for two or three years sometime after 1836 and before 1848. See Packard, *Medicine in the United States*, 2:1224–25; Charles W. Burr, "A Sketch of Dr. Alfred Stillé," *University* (of Pennsylvania) *Medical Magazine*, 13:759–65 (Jan. 1901); William Osler, "Alfred Stillé," *University of Pennsylvania Medical Bulletin*, 15:126–32 (June 1902).

PAGES 14–15, SECTION 5. This description of Bellevue is taken from Packard, *Medicine in the United States*, 1:253–61; Robert J. Carlisle, ed., *An Account of Bellevue Hospital with a Catalogue of the Medical and Surgical Staff from 1736 to 1894* (New York, 1893).

PAGE 15. It has usually been stated that W. W. Mayo settled in Indiana in 1847, but his residence in Buffalo (*Winona and Olmsted Counties*, p. 1037; Leonard, *Olmsted County*, p. 160) has not often been taken into account. He is first mentioned in the Lafayette newspapers in the *Lafayette Weekly Courier* for July 28, 1848, and his account with Hart contains an item for room rent beginning July 17, 1848.

PAGES 15–16. References to the tailoring establishment may be found in the *Lafayette Weekly Courier*, July 28, Oct. 6, Dec. 8, 1848, and the *Wabash Atlas* (Lafayette), Nov. 28, 1848, April 3, 1849. Although the notice of dissolution of the partnership first appeared in the *Wabash Atlas* for April 3 it was dated March 1, showing that W. W. Mayo had at least decided upon his retirement from tailoring by the earlier date. The Hall of Fashion was still flourishing under Schonfeldt's management as late as the spring of 1851 (*Lafayette Journal*, April 10, 1851).

PAGE 16. Accounts of Dr. Deming are John S. Bobbs, M.D., "Biographical Sketch of the Late Dr. Deming," *Trans. Ind. Med. Soc.*, 1857, pp. 53–56; G. W. H. Kemper, *A Medical History of the State of Indiana* (American Medical Association Press, 1911), p. 261; William R. Reser, M.D., "Medical Reminiscences," a paper presented before the Tippecanoe County (Indiana) Historical Society meeting in Lafayette on Dec. 8, 1937 (typescript copy in the Backus Papers). See also the *Lafayette Journal*, Sept. 18, 1851, citing the *St. Joseph* (Indiana) *Register*.

PAGES 16–18, SECTION 7. This description of pioneer medical education and practice in Indiana is drawn from Kemper, *Medical History of Indiana*, pp. 166–67; Logan Esarey, *A History of Indiana* (vol. I, Fort Wayne, Indiana, 1924, and vol. II, Bloomington, Indiana, 1935), 1:490–92; George W. Kimball, Harvey H. Martin, and Edith J. Backus, "History of the Medical Profession, LaPorte, Indiana," *LaPorte, Indiana: History of Its First Hundred Years, 1832–1932* (typescript in 4 vols., Indiana State Library), 3:1051–52; *Trans. Ind. Med. Soc.*, 1852, pp. 6–7, 21–31.

See also Otto Juettner, *Daniel Drake and His Followers* (Cincinnati, 1909), and George H. Weaver, *Beginnings of Medical Education In and Near Chicago* (reprinted by the American Medical Association Press from the *Proceedings of the Institute of Medicine of Chicago*, 1925). An interesting account of some of the earliest frontier medical schools is Harvey Cushing, "The Pioneer Medical Schools of Central New York," *The Medical Career and Other Papers* (Boston, 1940), pp. 123–52.

PAGES 18–19, SECTION 8. *Lafayette Weekly Courier*, Jan. 15, 1847, Jan. 14, Nov. 10, 17, 24, Dec. 1, 22, 1848; *Lafayette Journal*, Oct. 27, 1848; *Wabash Atlas*, April 24, May 15 (citing the *Cincinnati Gazette*), June 5, July 10, 24, Aug. 7, Sept. 11, 1849; George Sutton, M.D., "A Report . . . on Asiatic Cholera as it Prevailed in This State in 1849–50–51–52," *Trans. Ind. Med. Soc.*, 1853, pp. 109–74, especially the report from Dr. McFarland of Lafayette on p. 140.

PAGE 19. The Lafayette newspaperman was Harry H. Young, who later moved to Le Sueur, Minnesota. His letter to Governor Alexander Ramsey, Sept. 20, 1861, is preserved in the Governors' Archives, Minnesota Historical Society. I have accepted his statement because the cholera epidemic of 1849 was not a thing to be forgotten and also because it helps to explain a statement that William Worrall Mayo practiced medicine before he graduated (Leonard, *Olmsted County*, p. 303). There is another possibility, however. Dr. W. J. Mayo (to ROB) said that his father went back to England in 1849 to study chemistry and physics, and there is a gap from May 7 to Sept. 8, 1849, in WWM, account with Hart. That seems scarcely long enough for much study in England, so perhaps Dr. W. J. Mayo was thinking of the trip his father made to England in 1850. It is worth noting that Mrs. Berkman (to ROB) said her father had gone back to England *once* before he was married, "went over and came back immediately."

PAGE 20. Sources for the history of the Indiana Medical College are the Backus Papers; Harvey H. Martin, "The LaPorte University School of Medicine and the Indiana Medical College," *Surg., Gynec. and Obst.*, 55:673–75 (Nov. 1932); Backus, "Indiana Medical College," *LaPorte, Indiana . . . 1832–1932*, 2:985A–85H; Weaver, *Medical Education In and Near Chicago*, pp. 9–12 *et passim*; *Catalogue . . . of the Indiana Medical College*, 1847–48 and 1848–49. There are copies of the two catalogs in the Indiana State Library. None was published for 1849–50, because the school suspended activity at the end of the session in 1850.

For many years the fact of W. W. Mayo's attendance at, and graduation from, the Indiana Medical College was lost, except for an undocumented statement to that effect in William Niles Wishard, Sr., M.D., *The Pioneer Doctor—Some of His Handicaps* (reprinted from the *Year Book of the Society of Indiana Pioneers*, 1928), p. 4. Dr. Wishard (to HC, Oct. 22, 1938) said that his father, who was a student at the LaPorte school in 1848–49, was his authority for the statement. From at least 1890 on Dr. W. W. Mayo was said to have received his degree from the University of Missouri. The fact that the Missouri M.D. was *ad eundem*, and so contingent upon an earlier degree, was overlooked.

Now evidence of the Indiana college degree has been found. In a letter to Governor Ramsey of Minnesota on Sept. 22, 1861, Governors' Archives, Dr. W. W. Mayo himself stated, "I am a graduate of the Indiana Medical College." His attendance and graduation must have been in 1849–50, for he is not listed among the students in 1847–48 or in 1848–49, and the school was discontinued in 1850. Moreover, WWM, account with Hart shows Mayo to have been absent from Lafayette from Nov. 1849 to March 1850 and at no other time sufficiently long for attendance at the school.

PAGE 21. In the Backus Papers are typescript copies of items from the *LaPorte County Whig* describing the "cliniques" of Drs. Meeker and Shipman. Some of the Lafayette doctors did not take kindly to the newspapers' reporting the operations, and one of them told the editor of the *Courier* that the publication of such reports was a violation of the code of ethics adopted by the American Medical Association. After carefully explaining the matter to his readers, the editor of the *Courier* refrained from further mention of the operations, but the *Wabash Atlas*, less scrupulous, continued occasionally to print an item on Dr. Meeker's work (*Lafayette Daily Courier*, April 23, 24, 1850; *Wabash Atlas*, May 25, June 15, 1850).

For the use of the microscope see the "Annual Announcement for 1849–50," *Catalogue of the Indiana Medical College*, 1848–49, pp. 10–15; Florence R. Sabin, *Franklin Paine Mall* (Johns Hopkins Press, 1934), p. 161; Victor Vaughan, *A Doctor's Memories* (Indianapolis, 1926), pp. 108–9; Garrison, *History of Medicine*, p. 778.

PAGES 22–23. The reaction of the laity to the first news of anesthesia is interesting indeed. They called ether by such names as "somnific gas," "letheon vapor," and "apatheon fluid." They concluded that "inhaling insensibility" was preferable to mesmerism and remarked with wonder that the new discovery could be used to keep horses quiet while they were being shod and bees stupefied while their honey was being taken. But they were led to fear anesthesia by the alarming reports of bad effects: convulsions with frothing at the mouth, raising of blood from the lungs, delirium of several days' duration, and so on. It might prove fatal, the editors told them, bring on epilepsy, or turn a man of talent and energy into a driveling idiot (*Lafayette Weekly Courier,* Jan. 8, Feb. 12, June 4, July 30, Aug. 13, 1847). The doctors, cautious and dubious at first, came gradually to express their delight with the usefulness of chloroform (which had quickly superseded ether in general use) not only in operations but to relax the patient for such procedures as reducing a hernia or setting a broken bone. They found chloroform so much better for the purpose than a warm bath, venesection, or a dose of tobacco infusion, they said. A good picture of this and other aspects of surgical practice at the time is afforded by the reports of the committees on surgery in the *Trans. Ind. Med. Soc.,* 1851–53.

PAGE 24. See the note to page 20. The oath is quoted in William Niles, "The Indiana Medical College," a manuscript in the Backus Papers. "Annual Announcement for 1849–50," *Catalogue of the Indiana Medical College,* 1848–49, pp. 10–15, lists the fees: full course of lectures, seventy dollars; matriculation fee, five dollars; dissecting-room ticket, five dollars; graduation fee, twenty dollars; "Good board with room, fuel, and lights, from $1.00 to $2.75 per week."

PAGES 24–25. For Dr. Mayo's employment with Hart see the records in the case of William W. Mayo v. Daniel L. Hart; *Wabash Atlas,* Aug. 7, Nov. 9, 1848, March 5, 1850.

PAGES 25–26. In the Press file is a copy of an entry in the register book of the parish of Eccles certifying that "Anne, widow of James Mayo" was buried in the Eccles churchyard on May 22, 1850. WWM, account with Hart shows that Dr. Mayo was still in Lafayette on May 25, 1850, and had returned by Sept. 25, 1850. Mrs. Berkman (to ROB) tells of Dr. Mayo's trip to England and, as does WJM to ROB, recounts the arrival of James Mayo and W. W. Mayo's marriage. For the latter see also the *Lafayette Journal,* Feb. 13, 1851; Mrs. William Brown Meloney, "Mrs. Mayo, Wilderness Mother," *The Delineator,* Sept. 1914, p. 9, reporting an interview with Mrs. Mayo.

PAGE 26. For the lawsuit: records in the case of William W. Mayo v. Daniel L. Hart; *Lafayette Journal,* Oct. 16, 1851. Only scattered issues of the Lafayette papers for the period in question are extant, and the one item was all that could be found.

PAGES 26–27. *Trans. Ind. Med. Soc.,* 1853, pp. 3–4, 9, 10; WWM, "Report on the Pathological Indications of the Urine," *Trans. Ind. Med. Soc.,* 1854, pp. 68–77; Graham, *Story of Surgery,* pp. 33–34, 93, 259–60.

PAGES 27–29, SECTION 13. References: the section on "Sickness and Physicians" in William F. Vogel, "Home Life in Early Indiana," *Indiana Magazine of History,* 10:284–88 (Sept. 1914); Ada E. Schweitzer, M.D., "Malaria in Indiana," *Journal of the Indiana State Medical Association,* 4:70–73 (Feb. 1911); William H. Wishard, M.D., "Medical Retrospect of Fifty Years," *Trans. Ind. Med. Soc.,* 1889, pp. 5–19; Wishard, *The Pioneer Doctor,* pp. 5–9, 15–17; G. W. H. Kemper, "My Childhood and Youth in the Early Days of Indiana," *Indiana Magazine of History,* 19:317–18; Joel Pennington, M.D., "Early History of Eastern Indiana," *Trans. Ind. Med. Soc.,* 1873, as quoted in Kemper, *Medical History of Indiana,* pp. 33–41; George Sutton, M.D., "A Review of the Epidemics that Have Occurred in Southeastern Indiana During the Last Fifty Years . . ." *Trans. Ind. Med. Soc.,* 1885, pp. 104–13; M. H. Harding, M.D., "Observations on the Topography, Climate, and Diseases of Eastern Indiana," *ibid.,* 1853, pp. 30–32, 44. Although these articles do not relate specifically to the Wabash Valley, there is little in them for which illustrative footnotes could not be found in the Lafayette newspapers from 1847 to 1853.

For a general discussion of the relations between the profession and the laity at this time, see "Public Confidence Lost," chapter 13 in Shryock, *Development of Modern Medicine*, pp. 241–64. An interesting expression of the layman's attitude is to be found in the many jokes about doctors that were then current. The Lafayette newspapers were full of jibes at the medical men, some of them of home vintage and some copied from exchanges.

PAGE 30. See the note to page 20. The proprietors were serious in their intention to move the college to Lafayette (*Wabash Atlas*, Dec. 18, 1849, Feb. 5, 1850; *Lafayette Daily Courier*, Feb. 8, March 4, 5, June 22, 1850).

The traditional story of the reopening of Indiana Medical College was familiar to all the Mayos. Dr. W. J. Mayo included it in his story to Mrs. Mellish, and it has been told in almost everything written about the Old Doctor since. In answer to a question about it Dr. C. H. Mayo said (to ROB) that his mother had told it to him. By some versions it was Drs. Mayo and Byford who engaged in the enterprise, by others Dr. Deming was included.

The chief difficulty in accepting the story lies in the assumption that the school was reopened in the Indiana Medical College building, which is known to have burned down in Jan. 1856, more than a year after Dr. W. W. Mayo left Indiana. However, that assumption is not valid. It is not known who owned the college building, but Dr. Deming almost certainly did not own more than a fifth or sixth share in it, and perhaps none at all. It was built in the summer of 1847, and he did not join the faculty until the fall of that year. Moreover, the building was much larger than the three men could expect to need for their first session. It is therefore quite possible that they were conducting their classes in smaller, rented quarters, expecting to move to the college building when growth should warrant it.

In that case the problem becomes one of dating the incident. Dr. Mayo left for the West in the summer of 1854. If he was in St. Louis during the winter of 1853–54, then the LaPorte episode must have occurred in 1852–53 at the latest, and that date fits nicely into the schedule of Dr. Deming's activities. But Dr. Byford is said to have been teaching at the Evansville Medical College from 1850 to 1856 and to have shifted from the chair of anatomy to that of the theory and practice of medicine in 1852 (Kemper, *Medical History of Indiana*, pp. 248–49; Kelly, *American Medical Biographies*).

It should be noted too that a thorough canvass of the LaPorte newspapers and other local sources by Drs. Kimball and Martin and Miss Backus of LaPorte, all of them much interested in the question, failed to turn up any evidence of the venture.

PAGE 31. The *Portfolio* (Lafayette), Nov. 23, 1853, carries an advertisement for the medicine. The editor of the *Portfolio* was one Charles Deming, who may have been Dr. Deming's son. Dr. Reser has been able to determine with considerable exactitude the location of the warehouse, the office shared by Drs. Deming and Mayo, and the house, or one of the houses, in which the Mayos lived (Herbert Heimlich, "Founder of Famed Clinic Got Start Here as Surgeon Ninety Years Ago," *Lafayette Journal and Courier*, July 8, 1939).

In a letter to Dr. W. J. Mayo (Feb. 8, 1939, WJM files) Dr. Reser reported finding in the records of an early Lafayette teacher a reference to the private school conducted by a Miss Farnsworth in Dr. Mayo's house. The story of the millinery is told by advertisements in the *Lafayette Daily Courier*, May 26, June 10, Sept. 30, 1853.

PAGES 31–32, SECTION 15. A. B. Barbee, M.D., "History of the Missouri Medical College, from 1840 to 1861," (a clipping of several pages from an unidentified magazine, dated July 1914, Mayo Clinic library). Mrs. Berkman, in answer to a question (from ROB) about her father's work at Missouri, said she thought he had got his degree from "work and study, not from going to school." But Dr. W. J. Mayo (to ROB) was sure that his father had not done "correspondence work," because of the things he had told about the men he worked with, particularly Dr. Hodgen. Hodgen was elected president of the American Medical Association in 1880, and that may have been the circumstance that called forth Dr. Mayo's reminiscences about him.

To Frank Smith of the *Chicago Daily Times* goes the credit for locating the record of Dr. Mayo's degree from the University of Missouri in the files of the School of Medicine of Washington University. A letter from W. B. Parker, registrar of the latter school (to HC, Dec. 19, 1938, Press file), states that Dr. Deming was elected to the faculty on April 9, 1853 and delivered his first lecture on Nov. 1 of that year; that Dr. John T. Hodgen was professor of anatomy in 1853–54, but there is no record of Dr. W. W. Mayo's having been his assistant; that W. W. Mayo was not enrolled in the college in 1853–54 but did receive the *ad eundem* degree in 1854; and that the catalog of the college for 1854 carries the statement: "Application for the *ad eundem* degree must be accompanied by written evidence that the candidate is a graduate of an accredited School of Medicine; that he has been engaged, for the year preceding his application, in the practice of medicine; and, also, that he sustains a good moral character, and intends to devote his time wholly to the practice of his profession." Whatever written evidence of that sort Dr. Mayo presented has been lost (W. B. Parker, letter to HC, Jan. 19, 1939).

PAGE 32. So Mrs. Mayo was wont to tell the story of her husband's going, and, as she once added, "That was Dr. Mayo." (Meloney, "Mrs. Mayo, Wilderness Mother," *The Delineator*, Sept. 1914, p. 9; Leonard, *Olmsted County*, p. 303).

CHAPTER 2. ON THE MINNESOTA FRONTIER

PAGE 33, SECTION 1. *Wabash Atlas*, Feb. 12, 1850; *Lafayette Journal*, March 21, 1850, Aug. 7, 1851; *Daily Minnesota Pioneer* (St. Paul), May 5, Oct. 10 (citing *Pittsfield* [Illinois] *Union*), Oct. 31, 1854. See also Ralph H. Brown, "Fact and Fancy in Early Accounts of Minnesota's Climate," *Minnesota History*, 17:243–61 (Sept. 1936); Theodore C. Blegen, "Minnesota's Campaign for Immigrants," *Year-Book of the Swedish Historical Society of America*, 11:3–26 (1926).

PAGES 34–36, SECTIONS 2–3. I have here boldly departed from the traditional story, which is that Dr. Mayo turned back for his wife and daughter when he reached Galena. The problem is bound up with that of the date of the Mayos' removal to Minnesota, which has most often of late years been given as the spring of 1855. Wilson, "William Worrell Mayo," *Surg., Gynec. and Obst.*, 44:711 (May 1927), states that the Mayos were among the 814 passengers arriving in St. Paul on the *War Eagle* on April 17, 1855. But an advertisement for Mrs. Mayo's millinery appeared in the *Daily Democrat* (St. Paul) for April 17, 1855, phrased in a way that indicates the business had been going for some time previously. Since it stated that Mrs. Mayo was then in New York buying additions for her stock, perhaps it was she, returning to St. Paul, who arrived on the *War Eagle* that day.

*Winona and Olmsted Counties*, p. 1037, says Dr. Mayo moved to St. Paul in May 1854. That must have been when he left Indiana, for in testifying before a committee of the territorial legislature on Jan. 13, 1856, Dr. Mayo said, "I came to St. Paul last July, twelve months ago," which must mean July 1854 (*House Journal*, 1856, appendix, pp. 39–42). It is a certainty that he was in the Lake Superior region in Jan. 1855, and that not for the first time.

# Bibliographical Notes

Mrs. Berkman (to ROB) stated that her father went to Minnesota first and then came back for her and her mother, and that they moved to Minnesota on Oct. 6, 1854. However, entries in Mrs. Mayo's millinery stock book (CHM files) indicate that Dr. Mayo was in New York buying goods on Oct. 16, 1854. The fact that letters for W. W. Mayo were lying in the St. Paul post office in Aug. 1854 (*Daily Minnesota Pioneer*, Aug. 3, Sept. 4, 1854) certainly means that he had been there or intended to be there. Moreover, the cholera episode on the steamboat must have occurred before October, for the disease had gone from St. Paul and probably from the river districts generally by late Aug. 1854 (*Daily Democrat*, Aug. 9, 1854; *Daily Minnesota Pioneer*, Aug. 23, 1854).

It therefore seems most likely that Dr. Mayo left Indiana in May 1854, went all the way to St. Paul, reaching there sometime in July, left again before Aug. 1, and returned with his family late in October.

PAGES 34–35. For accounts of cholera along the river see the *Daily Minnesota Pioneer*, June 17, 20, 25, Aug. 3, 17, 1854; John M. Armstrong, M.D., "The Asiatic Cholera in St. Paul," *Minnesota History*, 14:288–302 (Sept. 1933); William Cairncross' story of "Death on the Water" in George B. Merrick, "Steamboats and Steamboatmen of the Upper Mississippi," *Saturday Evening Post* (Burlington, Iowa), Dec. 16, 1916.

PAGE 36. The newspaper quotation is given in Theodore C. Blegen, *Building Minnesota* (New York, 1938), p. 143.

PAGE 37. Entries in Mrs. Mayo's stock book (CHM files); *Daily Democrat*, April 17, 1855; *Daily Minnesotian* (St. Paul), July 23, Oct. 2, 1855. According to the stock book the value of the goods when invoiced in Chicago on Sept. 26, 1854 was $689.17. An invoice taken in Aug. 1855 shows that it had increased to $803.93, and the final entry, without date, is "Full amt of stock, $1750.02." Mrs. Berkman (to ROB) is the authority for the statement that the Mayos drove to St. Paul with a team and all the furniture they had.

For the medical story here: John M. Armstrong, M.D., "History of Medicine in Ramsey County," *Minnesota Medicine*, 21:698–703, 793–801, 850–55 (Oct., Nov., Dec., 1938); 22: 36–40 (Jan. 1939). For the activities of Dr. Kinney, see also the *Daily Democrat*, Aug. 3, Nov. 15, 1854; *Daily Minnesota Pioneer* (St. Paul), Jan. 1, 3, 4, 1855.

An interesting glimpse of the economics of medical practice in St. Paul from 1854 to 1856 is afforded by the ledger of Drs. Thomas R. Potts and William H. Morton, vol. 7 of the account books in the Potts Papers, Minnesota Historical Society. The two men were partners and were among St. Paul's leading practitioners, serving as physicians to such men as Alexander Ramsey. For "visits" in the daytime they charged a dollar, at night two dollars. The fee for an amputation was ten dollars, for a confinement twenty dollars, and for the treatment of syphilis twenty-five dollars. During 1854 collections were good and the sums substantial. Then the partnership was dissolved, Dr. Morton and another partner taking over Dr. Kinney's drug store (*Daily Minnesota Pioneer*, Feb. 6, March 8, 1855). After that, though not necessarily because of it, Dr. Potts did not do so well. His accounts mounted to sizeable sums, but those marked paid are appallingly few. Apparently the rule was, Call the doctor but don't pay him.

PAGE 38. Some penciled notes by Dr. W. W. Mayo (in the possession of the Mayo Clinic) express his pleasure in the new country. These notes were evidently the rough draft for an account of his pioneer experiences he intended to publish, probably in one of the Rochester papers, in which such letters from him frequently appeared. Nora H. Guthrey of the Clinic division of publications was kind enough to make a typescript copy for me, which is in the Press file. I have added punctuation and corrected an occasional misspelling.

PAGES 38–40, SECTION 5. Accounts of the early development at the head of Lake Superior may be found in John R. Carey, "History of Duluth, and of St. Louis County, to the Year 1870," *Minnesota Historical Collections*, 9:241–78 (1898); Walter Van Brunt, ed., *A History of Duluth and St. Louis County* (3 vols., American Historical Association, 1921); Frank A. Flower, *The Eye of the Northwest: First Annual Report of the Statistician of Superior, Wisconsin* (Milwaukee, 1890); Robert B. McLean, *Reminiscences of Early Days at the Head of the Lake* (no date or place of publication); Laurence Oliphant, *Minnesota and the Far West* (London, 1855); letter by "Mr. Scripps of the Chicago Democratic Press," in the *Daily Minnesotian*, Aug. 24, 1855.

PAGE 39. *Daily Minnesota Pioneer*, April 16–18, 1855, describes the routes to Superior. The quotation is from WWM, penciled notes.

PAGES 39–40. Dr. W. J. Mayo seemed to remember that his father had gone to Lake Superior originally as a member of the "territorial survey that laid out the northern counties." (WJM, "Medical Pioneers of Minnesota," *Minnesota Medicine*, 14:224–26 [March 1931]. See also, however, the report of his remarks to the state historical convention meeting in Rochester, June 13, 1930, in *Minnesota History*, 11:285 [Sept. 1930].) It is hard to guess what might have been the basis for that memory. The formal survey was a federal, not a territorial, project, and it did not get under way until late in 1855 or early in 1856.

Further details of the Doctor's third trip are given in the *Duluth News Tribune*, July 9, 1918; Van Brunt, *Duluth*, 1:112, 305; affidavit by Edwin H. Hall, Nov. 17, 1855, *Council Journal*, 1856, appendix, p. 44; Steward manuscript, p. 15; *Winona and Olmsted Counties*, p. 1037; letter by Edmund F. Ely, 1881, quoted in Carey, "Duluth," *Minn. Hist. Coll.*, 9:247.

In testifying before a committee of the territorial legislature on Jan. 14, 1856, Dr. Mayo outlined his journeyings between St. Paul and Lake Superior as follows: "I was at Lake Superior from about the 20th of July last, till the middle of March last. I returned there again in May, and remained there till the 24th of August last." The *July* is obviously a misprint, almost certainly for *Jany*, which was then the customary abbreviation for *January*. (*Council Journal*, 1856, appendix, p. 31.)

PAGE 40. For the confusion over the county names, see Van Brunt, *Duluth*, 1:99–101; *Session Laws*, 1856, pp. 63–64; note by Governor Gorman appended to his message to the legislature, *Council Journal*, 1856, appendix, p. 13.

The letters about appointees are on file in the Governors' Archives, Minnesota Historical Society. For the fact and date of W. W. Mayo's appointment, see the letter from Governor Gorman to William W. Kingsbury, published in the *House Journal*, 1856, appendix, p. 46; and for the census appointment, *Session Laws*, 1855, pp. 36–39, 53–55, and the testimony of WWM, *Council Journal*, 1856, appendix, p. 31, and *House Journal*, 1856, appendix, p. 39.

PAGES 41–42. The quotations are from WWM, penciled notes. One might think Dr. Mayo had confused his companions on this trip with Hall and Ely, who accompanied him in January, if it were not for the costumes he describes in such detail; they would have been impossible in a Minnesota January. Moreover, Ely was not of western birth; he came to Minnesota from Massachusetts in 1834. Hall, however, was apparently just such a dandy as Dr. Mayo pictures. Even in the Lake Superior wilderness he brightened the scene by wearing a red shirt with white bosom, red sash, broadcloth pants, and fine boots (Van Brunt, *Duluth*, 1:128–29, quoting manuscript autobiography of Alfred Merritt).

I may have assigned the forest fire incident to the wrong trip. It is worth noting that Dr. Mayo said nothing of taking a dog along when they started out. Often the story has been told as if Dr. Mayo were alone at the time and on the way back to St. Paul. CHM, "Early Days of the Mayo Clinic," states that there were five men in the party at the time, that one of them went insane, and that it was this fact which won the help of the superstitious Indians. It is W. W. Mayo's phrases about the "eventful journey" and the "foolhardy" route which lead me to think the episode most likely to have occurred on the trip he made to the lake in May 1855.

PAGES 42–45, SECTIONS 7–8. The story of Dr. W. W. Mayo's activities at the head of Lake Superior in the summer of 1855 is based on his testimony to the legislative committees as published in the *Council Journal*, 1856, appendix, pp. 31–33, and the *House Journal*, 1856, appendix, pp. 39–42.

PAGE 44. The census returns seem to have been lost, but on Jan. 17, 1856, the secretary of the territory certified a summary of the returns, then on file in his office, as follows: Doty County, 72 males and 45 females, total 117; Superior County, 74 males and 43 females, total 117 (*Council Journal*, 1856, appendix, p. 46).

PAGE 45. The activities of the county commissioners are described in Van Brunt, *Duluth*, 1:99–101; Carey, "Duluth," *Minn. Hist. Coll.*, 9:275–76; affidavit by R. H. Barrett, *Council Journal*, 1856, appendix, p. 41. The inability to find records verifying the tradition that Dr. Mayo established the county seat on the Nettleton claim has long been a source of vexation to local historians. Although under the circumstances any such action by Dr. Mayo and Mr. Burk was invalid, there can be little doubt that they did name a county seat. Dr. Mayo told the council committee he thought that as county commissioner he had the power to do so and that he had been urged several times to locate it on E. F. Ely's claim (*Council Journal*, 1856, appendix, pp. 31–33). Moreover, W. W. Kingsbury, the north-shore resident who was contesting the seat in the lower house, said in a "statement of facts" for the newspapers that "W. W. Mayo . . . in connection with Burke, located a county seat in said county." (*Daily Pioneer and Democrat*, Feb. 12, 1856.) *Winona and Olmsted Counties*, p. 1037, seems to me sufficiently reliable authority for the location on the Nettleton claim.

Dr. Mayo left Superior on Aug. 24. Entries in Mrs. Mayo's stock book show that Dr. Mayo purchased a lot of goods from one New York dealer on Sept. 14, and Mrs. Mayo one from another on Sept. 15. Their return and the arrival of the new stock was marked by a new advertisement in the *Daily Democrat*, Oct. 2, 1855.

PAGES 45–47, SECTION 9. Committee hearings and reports published in the *Council Journal*, 1856, pp. 100–2 and appendix, pp. 25–49, and the *House Journal*, 1856, pp. 143–44 and appendix, pp. 17–46; *Daily Minnesotian*, Oct. 15, 19, 22, 25, 1855, Feb. 1, 2, 7, 8, 1856; *Daily Democrat*, Oct. 22, 23, 1855; *Daily Pioneer and Democrat*, Nov. 19, 1855, Feb. 1, 12, 1856; *Daily Times* (St. Paul), Oct. 19, 25, 26, Dec. 28, 1855, Jan. 1, Feb. 4, 8, 1856. For Rice's attitude see William W. Folwell, *A History of Minnesota* (4 vols., Minnesota Historical Society, 1921–30), 1:340.

PAGE 48. The authority for Dr. Mayo's stay with the Dunhams was Mrs. Berkman (to ROB). See also the manuscript census schedules of 1857, Nicollet County, p. 46, and the *Plat Book of Nicollet County* (1899), both in the possession of the Minnesota Historical Society. Dr. Mayo was in St. Paul testifying before the territorial legislature on Jan. 13 and 14, 1856; he was elected a director of the Nicollet County Agricultural Society on March 1, 1856 (*St. Peter Courier*, Feb. 19, March 4, 1856). So his move to Cronan's Precinct occurred sometime between those two dates. The advertisement for Mrs. Mayo's millinery appeared for the last time in the *Daily Minnesotian* on May 7, 1856, and Phoebe Mayo was born on the Nicollet County farm on June 26, 1856. Presumably then Mrs. Mayo joined her husband in May or June 1856.

John Lang was the neighbor lad who worked for Dr. Mayo. He told the story of the Mayo farm in an interview reported in the *St. Paul Dispatch,* March 9, 1927.

PAGE 49. *The Mystery of Metropolisville* (New York, 1873), pp. 13–19. I have here put Eggleston's place of residence in 1856, and consequently the principal locale of the novel, at Traverse des Sioux on the authority of Thomas Hughes, *Old Traverse des Sioux* (St. Peter, 1929), p. 143. Another location is assigned, however, by John T. Flanagan, "The Hoosier Schoolmaster in Minnesota," *Minnesota History,* 18:347–70 (Dec. 1937).

PAGE 50. Notices of the activities of the agricultural society appeared in the *St. Peter Courier,* Feb. 19, March 4, April 22, June 11, Sept. 3, 1856; *Minnesota Free Press* (St. Peter), Feb. 17, March 3, 10, Sept. 29, Oct. 20, Nov. 3, 10, 1858; *Minnesota Statesman* (St. Peter), Jan. 14, 1859. Dr. Mayo's farming was described by Frank Smith in the *Chicago Daily Times* and also by Lang in the *St. Paul Dispatch.*

PAGES 50–52, SECTION 12. Newspapers often published items on the state of health in their communities, especially during an epidemic, and their obituary notices usually stated the cause of death and sometimes gave details about the illness. There was no systematic collection or compilation of vital statistics at this time, but the manuscript census schedules for 1860 (Minnesota Historical Society) include for each county a list of the deaths, with causes, during the preceding year. Among the most vivid manuscript sources on this matter of health are the letters that passed between Mary Aiton, living on a farm near St. Peter, and her husband, John Aiton, with the volunteer army at Judson, Minnesota, during the months of March and April 1863. These letters are among the Aiton Papers, Minnesota Historical Society.

PAGE 51. The advertisements quoted appeared in the *St. Peter Courier,* June 25, 1856 and the *St. Paul Pioneer,* Nov. 21, 1862.

PAGE 52. The description of Dr. Mayo's practice and other activities is drawn from Lang in the *St. Paul Dispatch*; Mrs. Berkman, Mrs. Richard Doran, C. N. Cosgrove (the last two of Le Sueur) to ROB; William G. Gresham, ed., *History of Nicollet and LeSueur Counties, Minnesota* (2 vols., Indianapolis, 1916), 1:490–91; *St. Peter Courier,* Oct. 2, 16, 1857; Edward D. Neill, *History of the Minnesota Valley* (Minneapolis, 1882), p. 669. Mrs. Doran remembered the ferry well, saying that it was the only way they had to get to town from Sibley County, but she did not remember Dr. Mayo's operating it. In this connection observe the birthplace of Sarah Frances Mayo as given by Mrs. Berkman, note to page 56 below.

PAGE 53. The full story of this frontier farce may be read in Folwell, *History of Minnesota,* 1:381–87.

PAGE 54. Republican relief legislation: *Daily Pioneer and Democrat,* Feb. 15, 22, 1860; *St. Peter Tribune,* Feb. 29, 1860; *Session Laws,* 1860, pp. 219–20; *Special Laws,* 1860, p. 18.

PAGES 54–55. The description of conditions following the panic is drawn from Minnesota Valley newspapers, 1857–60, especially the *Henderson Democrat, St. Peter Free Press,* and *Minnesota Statesman.* See also Gresham, *Nicollet and Le-Sueur Counties,* 1:343, 368–69; Hughes, *Old Traverse des Sioux,* pp. 143, 157; Flanagan, "The Hoosier Schoolmaster," *Minnesota History,* 18:348 (Dec. 1937); *Minnesota Free Press,* Dec. 16, 1857; and the cards of Dr. M. R. Wilcox in the *Henderson Democrat,* Nov. 9, 1858 and Dr. H. W. Catlin in the *Minnesota Statesman,* Nov. 25, 1859.

PAGE 56. Mrs. Berkman (to ROB) gave the birth records of the Mayo children as follows:

# Bibliographical Notes

| | | |
|---|---|---|
| Horace | Nov. 1851 (lived about six weeks) | LaPorte, Indiana (?) |
| Gertrude E. | July 18, 1853 | Lafayette, Indiana |
| Phoebe Louise | June 26, 1856 | Nicollet County, Minnesota |
| Sarah Frances | March 11, 1859 (died in the fall of 1860) | Sibley County, by ferry |
| William James | June 29, 1861 | Le Sueur, Minnesota |
| Charles Horace | July 19, 1865 | Rochester, Minnesota |

The manuscript census schedules of 1860 for Le Sueur County, p. 68, give data of birth dates and places that correspond with the above. However, the census of 1857 for Nicollet County, p. 48, lists two children as follows: Lucy, aged four, born in Indiana, and Mary, aged two, born in Indiana. Either the census taker was guessing, or he was hard of hearing. How else could he have made *Gertrude* into *Lucy* and *Phoebe* into *Mary*? He also listed Mrs. Mayo's birthplace as Indiana instead of New York.

For Dr. Mayo's first encounter with Cut Nose see WJM, "August, 1862," *Proceedings of the Mayo Clinic,* 7:463 (Aug. 3, 1932); Isaac V. Heard, *History of the Sioux War and Massacres of 1862 and 1863* (New York, 1864), p. 206.

Mrs. Mayo's life at this time is briefly described in Meloney, "Mrs. Mayo, Wilderness Mother," *The Delineator,* Sept. 1914, p. 9.

PAGE 57. A letter from Cronan's Precinct about the flood was published in the *Minnesota Statesman,* March 30, 1859.

PAGE 58. The date of the Mayos' removal to Le Sueur has been a disputed matter. Mrs. Berkman (to ROB) said it took place in the fall of 1859, and the evidence bears her out. In March 1859 the Mayos were marooned in Cronan's Precinct by the flood. James Mayo died in the Le Sueur house in Nov. 1859, after an illness of 35.6 days, according to the census schedules of 1860 for Le Sueur County, p. 193. If he helped to build the house (Lang in the *St. Paul Dispatch*) it must have been during the summer or early fall of 1859.

The Mayos sold the Le Sueur house when they moved to Rochester in 1864. Little is known of its history thereafter until 1932 when the Le Sueur paper featured a description of it and urged that steps be taken to preserve it. On November 23, 1932 the house was marked as a historic site by joint action of the Minnesota Historical Society and the Minnesota state highway department. In 1934 the Mayo brothers bought the house and turned it over to the city of Le Sueur for use as a library. (*Le Sueur Herald,* Sept. 7, 1932; *Rochester Times,* Nov. 25, 1932; *Minneapolis Tribune,* March 25, 1935.) Pictures of the Mayo family hang on the walls of the house and in the entryway stands the massive, rolltop desk with bookshelves above said to be the one Dr. W. W. Mayo used when he lived there.

W. J. Mayo (to HC) told the story of the first Le Sueur patient, and (to ROB) of the retort to Dr. Ayer, as he had heard the story from Fred Johnson of Mankato, a brother of Governor John A. Johnson and a local historian of the Mankato vicinity.

PAGES 59–60. *Winona and Olmsted Counties,* p. 1038; CHM, "Early Days of the Mayo Clinic"; CHM to ROB. A reasonably thorough survey of the literature on Upper Mississippi and Minnesota River steamboating as well as of the St. Paul, St. Peter, and Mankato newspapers for 1859 and 1860 has yielded no confirmation of W. W. Mayo's summer of steamboating. I have not even been able to identify the John Ransey who is said to have been the captain of the Davidson boat with which Dr. Mayo's steamer made connections downstream. According to an item in the *St. Peter Tribune,* June 27, 1860, a Mr. John Raney was clerk on the *Time and Tide* that season, but the *Time and Tide* was a Roberts, not a Davidson, boat. I have accepted the story nonetheless, because of its highly circumstantial character and the sequel with James J. Hill.

For the Hill anecdote see CHM to ROB; Steward manuscript, pp. 21–22. Hill appears in the accounts of steamboating as little as does Dr. Mayo, which is to say not at all, unless he was one of the "Messrs. Hills" listed as first and second clerks on the *Ocean Wave* in 1859 (*Daily Pioneer and Democrat*, Oct. 12, 1859). However, see Joseph G. Pyle, *The Life of James J. Hill* (2 vols., New York, 1917), 1:35, 50.

According to Thomas Hughes, "History of Steamboating on the Minnesota River," *Minn. Hist. Coll.*, 10 (part I) :147, the *Albany* was built by the Davidsons for the Minnesota trade in low water, but according to the newspapers she was built with capital furnished by Nathaniel Wright, after whose native city she was named, and was outfitted by subscriptions from the Valley merchants. For the *Albany* and *Little Dorrit* see the *St. Peter Tribune*, March 28, April 5, 18, May 9, 30, June 6, 13, Aug. 13, 1860; *Mankato Record*, April 3, 1860.

PAGES 60–61, SECTION 17. Letter from Le Sueur in the *Belle Plaine Enquirer*, Sept. 6, 1860; M. J. Severance, "The Expert Witness," *Trans. Minn. Med. Soc.*, 1897, pp. 144–46.

PAGES 61–62, SECTION 18. For Harry H. Young see the *Henderson Democrat*, Dec. 22, 1860; letter from Harry H. Young to Governor Alexander Ramsey, Sept. 20, 1861, Governors' Archives.

There is no file or copy of the *Le Sueur Courier* extant. Our knowledge of it comes from references to it and items reprinted from it in the other Valley newspapers: *Belle Plaine Enquirer*, Jan. 26, Feb. 9, 1861; *Henderson Democrat*, March 2, 1861; *Mankato Independent*, March 18, 1861.

PAGE 63. M. P. Hathaway's card appears in the *Mankato Independent*, March 18, 1861.

"The Views of the Publisher of the Le Sueur Courier," signed by William W. Mayo, were reprinted from the *Courier* in the *Henderson Democrat*, March 2, 1861.

PAGE 64. The *Mankato Independent*, Oct. 25, 1862, tells of Mayo's election to the district committee.

PAGE 65. Thomas Lang's daughter, Mrs. Richard Doran, told (to ROB) the anecdote of her father and Dr. Mayo.

### CHAPTER 3. CIVIL WAR DAYS

Preeminently valuable as a source of information about the events of this chapter are the hundreds of manuscript letters, petitions, and reports preserved in the Governors' Archives of Minnesota. Copies of some of the more important documents, particularly of letters sent from the governor's office, may be read in the ledger volumes commonly cited as the Governors' Archives, Records. There is much pertinent correspondence also among the personal papers of Alexander Ramsey, governor and United States senator, and Ignatius Donnelly, lieutenant governor and representative in Congress, during the years in question. All of these manuscript sources are in the possession of the Minnesota Historical Society.

Chief among the published sources is *Minnesota in the Civil and Indian Wars*, 1861–65 (2d ed., 2 vols., St. Paul, 1891, 1899). This is a collection of official reports, the rosters of the regiments, narratives by participants, and correspondence relating to the organization and engagements of the troops, published by the state as authorized by an act of the legislature in 1889. Some further information is contained in the *Report of the Adjutant General of Minnesota, 1862–65.* There is no specific study of the operation of the draft in Minnesota.

The national story is summarized in the *Final Report Made to the Secretary of War by the Provost Marshal General of the Operations of the Bureau of the Provost Marshal General of the U. S. from the Commencement of the Business of the Bureau, March 17, 1863, to March 17, 1866* (39 Congress, 1 session, House Executive Documents No. 1, 2 parts [serials 1251 and 1252], Washington, 1866). This is cited as the *Report of the Provost Marshal General, 1866.* See also Carl Russell Fish, "Conscription in the Civil War," *American Historical Review,* 21:100–3 (Oct. 1915).

The Sioux Outbreak has produced more literature of reminiscence and controversy than almost any other incident in Minnesota's history. Early general accounts are Heard, *History of the Sioux War,* and Charles S. Bryant, "History of the Sioux Massacre," in Neill, *History of the Minnesota Valley,* pp. 177–257. Largely superseding these by reason of greater accuracy and more critical judgment is the narrative in Folwell, *History of Minnesota,* 2:109–301, 361–74. To obtain more circumstantial details of the phases of the uprising in which Dr. and Mrs. Mayo participated I have reviewed the records of Dr. Folwell's interviews with surviving participants, his correspondence, and his notes, preserved in the Folwell Notebooks and the Folwell Papers, both in the possession of the Minnesota Historical Society. Especially valuable for my purpose were two special collections in the Folwell Papers: the New Ulm Notes and the Holbrook Notes.

The tradition surviving in the Mayo family concerning Dr. and Mrs. W. W. Mayo's experiences during the outbreak is well recounted in WJM, "August, 1862," *Proceedings of the Mayo Clinic,* 7:460–64 (Aug. 3, 1932). Asa W. Daniels, M.D., "Reminiscences of the Little Crow Uprising," *Minn. Hist. Coll.,* 15:323–36 (1915), is an account, principally of the events at New Ulm, by one of Dr. Mayo's medical associates. Helpful manuscript narratives in the possession of the Minnesota Historical Society are Samuel J. Brown's reminiscences, in the Samuel J. and Joseph R. Brown Papers; an account of the relief expedition sent from St. Peter to New Ulm and of the siege of New Ulm, written by William O. Hayden; W. H. Hazzard's autobiographical sketch, including an account of experiences in the uprising. The official report of Charles E. Flandrau, prepared on Aug. 27, 1862, and his reminiscent narrative written many years later are both published in *Minnesota in the Civil and Indian Wars,* 1:727–53 and 2:203–7. His reports and other letters written from New Ulm during the week of siege may be found in the Governors' Archives, principally file 116.

PAGE 66. Dr. Mayo's next-door neighbor was James B. Swan, his brother, Joseph H. Swan. See Alice Mendenhall George, *The Story of My Childhood* (Whittier, California, 1923), p. 36; Gresham, *Nicollet and LeSueur Counties,* 1:382–83, 449, 537; Warren Upham and Rose B. Dunlap, *Minnesota Biographies (Minn. Hist. Coll.,* vol. 14, 1912), p. 760; *Minnesota in the Civil and Indian Wars,* 1:147, 193.

PAGES 66–67. Dr. Mayo's two sets of letters requesting Governor Ramsey for an appointment and the accompanying letters of recommendation, Sept. 20–22, Oct. 21, 1861, are preserved in the Governors' Archives, file 111A. Henry A. Swift also wrote a letter to Donnelly, Oct. 21, 1861, Donnelly Papers.

The letters and petitions for Dr. Levi Butler and other applicants for the third regiment position are in the Governors' Archives, files 92 and 111A. There are biographical sketches of Butler in Upham and Dunlap, *Minnesota Biographies,* p. 97; *The Fifteenth Legislature of Minnesota: Biographical Sketches* (St. Paul, 1873), p. 7; C. L. Hall, *Memoirs of the State Officers, and of the Nineteenth Legislature of Minnesota* (St. Paul, 1877), pp. 12–13.

# The Doctors Mayo

PAGE 67. Dr. Mayo's letter to Donnelly, written from Shakopee, Oct. 25, 1861, is in the Governors' Archives, file 111A.

The report of the board of examiners may be found in the Governors' Archives, Records, A:455, 464, and also in the *Daily Pioneer and Democrat*, Nov. 9, 1861. General Orders No. 27 of the adjutant general of Minnesota, published in the *Daily Pioneer and Democrat*, Nov. 12, 1861, announced the appointment of Drs. Butler and Milligan. For the newspaper outcry about politics in appointments see the *Pioneer and Democrat*, June 25, Nov. 13–15, 1861, Aug. 2, 1862. It is hard to credit the governor's denials of political influence if one compares the appointments made with the correspondence about them in the Ramsey and Donnelly Papers, 1861–62.

PAGE 68. Concerning the appointment to fill Dr. Milligan's position, see H. C. Lester and WWM, letters to Ramsey, April 8, 22, 1862, Governors' Archives, file 115; telegrams between Ramsey and John N. Murdoch of Wabasha, April 15, 18, 19, 1862, Ramsey Papers.

On the draft see: Folwell, *History of Minnesota*, 2:102–5; *Report of the Provost Marshal General, 1866*, part 1 (serial 1251), pp. 10–12; General Orders Nos. 25 and 31, in the *Report of the Adjutant General of Minnesota, 1862*, pp. 219–20, 226; General Orders No. 36 in the *Pioneer and Democrat*, Aug. 17, 1862.

.File 119 of the Governors' Archives is full of letters asking concessions to permit the people to avoid the stigma of a draft. Such letters from Le Sueur County are George W. Stewart to Donnelly, Aug. 6, 1862, and Otis Ayer to Ramsey, Aug. 9, 1862.

PAGE 69. That the outbreak was not unexpected is apparent in the petitions and memorials warning of danger from the Indians and asking for help, Jan.–July 1862, Governors' Archives, file 116. See also Brown's reminiscences of the Sioux massacre; Folwell, *History of Minnesota*, 2:208; letter, Donnelly to Ramsey, April 13, 1861, Ramsey Papers; letters, Ramsey to Clark W. Thompson, Aug. 5, 1861, and to H. P. Van Cleve, Aug. 15, 1861, Governors' Archives, Records, A:389, 395; *Pioneer and Democrat*, Sept. 10, 13, 1862. It is interesting to note that the *Pioneer and Democrat* was skeptical about the reported uprising in the issues of Aug. 20 and 21, 1862, but on Aug. 22 it admitted that the Sioux were undoubtedly on the warpath, and thereafter its headlines and descriptions grew more lurid day by day.

PAGES 70–71, SECTION 4. Details of this phase of the outbreak are given in Daniels, "Reminiscences of the Little Crow Uprising," *Minn. Hist. Coll.*, 15:323–26; WJM, "August, 1862," *Proceedings of the Mayo Clinic*, 7:460–63 (Aug. 3, 1932); letters between Folwell and Daniels, Oct. 2, 9, 1917, Folwell Papers. Dr. Daniels claimed to be the "surgeon of the command" on this expedition, and it is more likely that he was unofficially in charge of the medical services than that Dr. Mayo was, as has also been claimed, because Daniels was surgeon at the Lower Sioux agency while Judge Flandrau was the Indian agent (Folwell, *History of Minnesota*, 2:135). However, there is no evidence in the various accounts of the battles of New Ulm to indicate that any one of the medical men was in charge.

All accounts agree that the news reached the citizens of the Valley in the night. Folwell (*ibid.*) accepts Agent Galbraith's statement that he got the news at sundown the evening before and spent the night collecting ammunition, but he admits that "Why the tidings were not spread through the place and the citizens roused that evening remains a matter for wonder." The explanation may perhaps be found in a statement in a letter that Henry A. Swift of St. Peter wrote to Governor Ramsey early in the morning of Aug. 19, 1862: "Last evening Maj. G. thought the stories a ruse to get him back to make the payment. This morning he has *no doubt* of the authenticity and truth of the reports, and has obtained arms for his men and returned to the scene of the troubles." (Governors' Archives, file 116.) Mrs. Berkman (to ROB), who was a child of nine at the time of the outbreak, remembered accurately that "Father went early in the morning to the Sioux Outbreak. He was gone when I wakened."

The *Pioneer and Democrat*, Aug. 26, 1862, quoting the *St. Peter Tribune*, whose reporter was present in New Ulm during this week, listed the wounded brought in from the country by scouting parties. Although it stated that the memorandum books of the doctors contained the names of eight hundred killed and wounded, its own list numbers barely one hundred, which is probably nearer the truth.

PAGES 71–73, SECTION 5. Daniels' "Reminiscences of the Little Crow Uprising," *Minn. Hist. Coll.*, 15:326–33; letters, Daniels to Folwell, Oct. 9, 23, 25, 1917, July 29, 1921; Hayden's reminiscences; Hazzard's autobiographical sketch; Folwell, *History of Minnesota*, 2:131–49.

PAGES 72–73. George, *The Story of My Childhood*, pp. 39–40, tells about Dr. Mayo's use of the pitchforks. The author was the daughter of H. W. Mendenhall and the niece of James B. Swan, both of whom were friends of Dr. Mayo's in Le Sueur and among the defenders of New Ulm.

PAGE 73. The incident of Dr. Mayo and the deserters from the guard is told in WJM, "August, 1862," *Proceedings of the Mayo Clinic*, 7:463 (Aug. 3, 1932).

Widely divergent accounts of Captain Dodd's sortie by survivors of the battle are recorded in the Holbrook Notes. I have followed the more complete and, it seems to me, more probable version given in Dr. Daniels' reminiscences and his letters to Folwell. Tradition has it that the defenders of New Ulm did not make Captain Dodd their commander because they feared he would be too reckless (Folwell, *History of Minnesota*, 2:138n).

According to Dr. Daniels, the minister who spoke in support of Dodd was "Father Sunrisen," which is approximately a phonetic spelling for *Sommereisen*. See *Mankato, Its First Fifty Years* (Mankato, 1903), pp. 22–23, 26–27; the *Mankato Record*, Aug. 30, 1862.

PAGES 74–75, SECTION 6. For the exodus from New Ulm and arrival at St. Peter, see Flandrau's report in *Minnesota in the Civil and Indian Wars*, 2:203–7; opinion of Jacob Nix, New Ulm Notes; letter, Daniels to Folwell, Oct. 9, 1917, and "Reminiscences of the Little Crow Uprising," *Minn. Hist. Coll.*, 15:333–34; the *Mankato Record*, Aug. 30, Sept. 6, 1862; Hayden's reminiscences; Holbrook Notes; the *Mankato Independent*, Aug. 29, 1862.

PAGE 75. Henry Scoville was the patient from Montana. See the *Malta* (Montana) *Enterprise*, March 18, 1920 (clipping in the HJH collection).

PAGES 75–77, SECTION 7. Mrs. Mayo's own story appears in Meloney, "Mrs. Mayo, Wilderness Mother," *The Delineator*, Sept. 1914, p. 9. The earliest version of the legend that I have found was in a feature article by Prescott Toomey in the *Dallas* (Texas) *Morning News*, Jan. 7, 1917. Since then it has become a staple item in the Mayo story. A good telling of it is WJM, "August, 1862," *Proceedings of the Mayo Clinic*, 7:463 (Aug. 3, 1932). Mrs. Berkman did not accept it. She insisted (to ROB) that though her mother might have put on men's clothing to scare away the Indians, she did not leave the house to lead, or march with, the women of Le Sueur.

Atrocity stories added to the terror of the women left at home. Dr. Mayo figured in one of these, which was told to a staff member of the Mayo Clinic in 1937 by a physician of Denver. "The Indians nailed to a tree a white, pregnant woman and opened her abdomen and uterus. Dr. W. W. Mayo, of the expeditionary force, repaired the uterus and abdomen. The woman lived to an old age; the child, of course, did not." When the story was told to Dr. W. J. Mayo, his comment was "This story about father may be true, but it is not one that I ever heard him tell." (R. M. Hewitt, letter to WJM, and reply, Jan. 4, 1937, Press file.) One may doubt its truth, especially in view of the state of abdominal surgery at the time.

PAGE 77. The story of the Le Sueur deserter is told in George, *The Story of My Childhood*, p. 44.

PAGES 77–78. For the fate of Cut Nose and his friends: *St. Peter Tribune*, Dec. 20, 1862, Jan. 30, 1863; *Mankato Daily Review*, Dec. 26, 1862; *Mankato Record*, Dec. 26, 1862, Jan. 3, 24 (citing *Le Sueur Herald*), 1863; Neill, *History of the Minnesota Valley*, p. 542; interview with Dr. A. W. Daniels, recorded in Folwell Notebooks, 4:91.

PAGES 78–79, SECTION 9. This section is based on *The War of the Rebellion: A Compilation of the Official Records of the Union and Confederate Armies* (130 vols., Washington, 1880–1902), series 3, vol. 5, p. 907; *Report of the Provost Marshal General, 1866*, part 1 (serial 1251), pp. 1–5, 12–13, 16–23, 32–35, and part 2 (serial 1252), pp. 182–88; "Report of the Enrolment Branch," *ibid.*, part 1, pp. 142–45; and a study of the local newspapers, especially the *Rochester City Post*, Aug. 1, Oct. 5, Nov. 28, Dec. 12, 1863; *Mankato Record*, May 16, 1863; *Rochester Republican*, July 1, 1863 (citing the *Saint Paul Press*).

The draft, scheduled to begin in July 1863, was so often postponed that it was never necessary in Minnesota. There was one drawing of names in the first district, however, before the notice of postponement arrived. See the *Republican*, Oct. 14, Nov. 12, 1863; *City Post*, Aug. 29, Nov. 14, 1863, Jan. 16, 1864.

PAGES 79–81, SECTION 10. Material was drawn from the "Report of the Medical Branch," *Report of the Provost Marshal General, 1866*, part 1 (serial 1251), pp. 240–45; paragraph 85 of the "Revised Regulations," *ibid.*, part 2 (serial 1252), pp. 285–87; *City Post*, June 18, July 2, 1864, Jan. 14, 1865; *Saint Paul Pioneer*, Jan. 28, 1865; *Chatfield Democrat*, Jan. 14, 1865; CHM, "Early Days of the Mayo Clinic."

For the scheduled dates of calls and drafts see "Report of the Medical Branch," *Report of the Provost Marshal General, 1866*, part 1 (serial 1251), pp. 29, 41–42, 43, 45, and "Report of the Enrolment Branch," *ibid.*, p. 145. Changes in the quotas, orders to proceed with the draft, then postponements and nullifications were so many that the editor of the *City Post*, weary of reporting them all, said he hoped that when the senator who had recently prayed the Lord to give the statesmen of America more brains next petitioned the Deity he would include Colonel Fry (the provost marshal general) and the War Department. The tale of the various quotas, drawings, and exemptions in the first district is recorded in the *City Post*, Feb. 27, April 23, May 28, June 4, 11, 18, 25, July 2, 23, Aug. 13, 20, Oct. 1, 1864, Jan. 7, 14, 21, Feb. 11, 1865.

PAGE 81. Mrs. Berkman well remembered the time the man came to offer her father a hundred dollars to be exempted from the draft. "We were all so frightened," she said. "He was so big and father was so little. But father stomped him right out of the house." (Steward manuscript, p. 53.)

PAGES 81–82, SECTION 11. See the *City Post*, Aug. 13, Dec. 10, 1864, Jan. 14, 1865; the *St. Peter Tribune*, Jan. 18, 25, 1865; Circular No. 46 issued by the acting assistant provost marshal general for Minnesota, published in the *Saint Paul Pioneer*, Dec. 17, 1864; "Report of the Enrolment Branch," *Report of the Provost Marshal General, 1866*, part 1 (serial 1251), p. 144; section 14 of the Act to amend the Enrolment Act of March 3, 1863, *ibid.*, part 2 (serial 1252), p. 192; *Mankato Union*, Jan. 20, 27, 1865; *Central Republican* (Faribault), Jan. 25, 1865.

PAGES 82–85, SECTIONS 12–13. The pros and cons of this affair emerge from various letters and editorials in the following: *Saint Paul Press*, Jan. 31, Feb. 4, 5, 1865; *Saint Paul Pioneer*, Feb. 2, 3, 5, 1865; *St. Peter Tribune*, Feb. 8, 1865; *Central Republican*, Feb. 1, 8, 15, 1865; *Chatfield Democrat*, Feb. 11, 1865; *Winona Democrat*, Feb. 18, 1865; *City Post*, Feb. 11, 1865 (quoting the *Winona Republican*). The most bitter denunciation of the enrolment board, attributing to it all the swindling that others blamed upon the outside operators, appeared in an article in the *Free Homestead* (Winnebago City) and was reprinted in the *Central Republican*, Feb. 15, 1865. One Reverend Stine, accused therein, made answer in a letter to the *Mankato Union*, Feb. 17, 1865.

PAGE 84. The names of the doctors and lawyers arrested are given in the *Saint Paul Press*, Feb. 28, 1865, and in a letter from H. L. Moss, United States district attorney, to Governor Stephen Miller, Governors' Archives, file 162A. See also the *Central Republican*, Feb. 8, 1865 and the *Saint Paul Press*, Feb. 9, 1865. As far as I have been able to discover, these cases never came to trial. For the organization of the Minnesota Valley Medical Association see the *Mankato Union*, Feb. 10, March 3, 1865 and the *St. Peter Tribune*, Feb. 15, 1865.

PAGES 84–85, SECTION 13. On Dr. Mayo's hearing and dismissal: *Saint Paul Press*, Feb. 10, 28, 1865; Special Orders No. 5 of the acting assistant provost marshal for Minnesota, published in the *Saint Paul Pioneer*, Feb. 12, 1865; reports of Dr. Wheelock and Captain Rossell, also published in the *Pioneer*, Feb. 22, 1865; *War of the Rebellion: Official Records*, series 3, vol. 5, p. 907. For the stories about Dr. Cross see the examples in the *Winona Democrat*, March 18, 1865 and the *Rochester Republican*, March 22, 1865 (quoting the *Wilton News*).

Dr. Mayo was mistaken in his contentions that the law allowed doctors to charge a five-dollar fee for preparing certificates of exemption. The law permitted such a fee to attorneys, but it expressly forbade doctors to make any charge whatever (section 22 of the act to amend the Enrolment Act of March 3, 1863, *Report of the Provost Marshal General, 1866*, part 2 [serial 1252], pp.193–94). However, Dr. Mayo's contention was made in good faith and was never questioned, because the general public shared his misconception. For some reason the unmistakable prohibition in the law was generally missed, even by attorneys.

The arbitrary action of the War Department, without waiting for the results of the investigation and on obviously insufficient evidence, caused some sarcastic comment (*Saint Paul Pioneer*, March 11, 1865). But quick action was necessary because the next draft was soon to commence, and feeling about conscription was bitter enough without its being aggravated by suspicions of dishonesty among the officials. To obviate charges of inequality in quotas owing to unjustified exemptions, all the certificates granted by the first district board at Preston, St. Peter, Mankato, and Faribault were nullified for the draft of March 1865 (*Pioneer*, Feb. 22, 1865).

PAGES 85–86, SECTION 14. My conclusions are based chiefly on the newspaper accounts cited for the preceding sections. The official documents in the case—Colonel Averill's report, any affidavits collected by his deputies, the correspondence with Washington, and the like—may be extant, but they were not available to me. They may lie among the records of the provost marshal general's bureau, which were not ready for study when I made inquiry (letters to HC from P. M. Hamer, chief of the division of reference of the National Archives, May 11, 1939, and Emory S. Adams, adjutant general of the United States army, March 24, 1941, Press file).

For one man's doubts, not without political bias, about Dr. Wheelock's ability, see Dr. J. H. Stewart, letter to Donnelly, May 28, 1863, Donnelly Papers. Differences of opinions among surgeons caused the War Department considerable trouble, and so did the detailed specifications of disqualifying diseases issued by the Wash-

# The Doctors Mayo

ington bureau. See "Report of the Medical Branch," *Report of the Provost Marshal General, 1866*, part 1 (serial 1251), p. 246; "Report of the Acting Assistant Provost Marshal General of Illinois," *ibid.*, part 2 (serial 1252), p. 35; *Central Republican*, Feb. 22, 1865.

PAGE 86. For the opinions of other surgeons, see *Report of the Provost Marshal General, 1866*, part 1 (serial 1251), pp. 243–44; "Report of the Enrolment Surgeon of the 12th District of Ohio," *ibid.*, part 2 (serial 1252), p. 91. Contemporary newspaper comments: *Mankato Union*, March 3, 1865; *Winona Democrat*, Feb. 18, 1865; *Chatfield Democrat*, Feb. 18, 1865 (quoting *Winona Republican*); *Rochester Republican*, Feb. 22, March 8, 15, 1865; *City Post*, Feb. 18, 1865. The *Mantorville Express*, March 3, 1865, was one paper that accepted the charges against Dr. Mayo as true, but even in its disillusionment, that "our model surgeon, Dr. Mayo," should have turned out to be a swindler, one may read an indirect tribute.

It is hard to tell from the newspapers just what the reaction of the Rochester folk was. The tone of one or two of the editorials suggests that there was a good bit of scandalized buzzing among them, but according to the *Republican* they were much dissatisfied with the exchange of Dr. Mayo for Dr. Cross.

CHAPTER 4. ROCHESTER THEN

This chapter and the local phases of those following are based principally on a reading of these Rochester newspapers in the files of the Minnesota Historical Society: *Democrat*, May–Oct. 1858; *Free Press*, March–June, Aug.–Dec. 1858; *Republican*, March–Dec. 1862, Jan. 1863–Aug. 1864; *City Post*, Nov. 1859–March 1862, April–Aug. 1863; *Post*, Feb.–Dec. 1866, Oct. 1867–Dec. 1870; *Federal Union*, 1868–73. The *City Post*, Nov. 1863–Jan. 1866, and the *Republican*, Feb.–March 1865, were read in the C. C. Willson newspaper file in the possession of the Olmsted County Historical Society, Rochester. For the period 1874–99 the *Record and Union* was used, with frequent supplementary use of the *Post* where the special importance or controversial nature of events required it. In Feb. 1899 the two papers merged to form the *Post and Record*, which was read through 1906.

Valuable additional information concerning Dr. Mayo's political activities is provided by the correspondence between him and Ignatius Donnelly in the Donnelly Papers, Minnesota Historical Society. Typescript copies of those letters and of pertinent entries in Donnelly's diaries, also in the possession of the society, were generously furnished for the Press file by the staff of the society's manuscript division.

PAGE 87. The quotation is from the *Chatfield Democrat*, Jan. 21, 1865.

During 1865, the first year after the railroad reached Rochester, the amount of wheat marketed there was 882,552 bushels. In June 1866 it was averaging ten thousand bushels a day, and for the last three months of 1867 it totaled just under half a million bushels. By the middle of 1868 Rochester was claiming to be the largest primary wheat market in the world. (*Post*, March 3, June 9, 1866, Dec. 21, 1867, Aug. 15, 1868.) See also the *City Post*, Dec. 16, 1865, and a letter signed "Farmer" (reprinted from the *Saint Paul Press* in the *Post*, June 2, 1866.)

PAGE 89. For the date of the family's removal to Rochester: Mrs. Berkman to ROB, and her letter to ROB, July 1, 1935, Press file.

The names of the principal Rochester streets have been changed: Main St. to 1st Ave., S.W. and N.W.; Franklin St. to 2d Ave., S.W. and N.W.; Prospect St. to 3d Ave., S.W. and N.W.; 4th St. to 1st Ave., S.E. and S.W.; Zumbro St. to 2d St., S.E. and S.W.; College St. to 4th St., S.E. and S.W.; Dubuque St. to 3d

740

Ave., S. E.; Cherry St. to 6th Ave., S.E. ; Oakwood St. to 7th Ave., S.E. and N.E.; Clark St. to 7th Ave., S.W. and N.W.; Cascade Road to 11th Ave., S.W. and N.W. (*History of the Rochester Old School Boys and Girls Association* [Rochester, 1927], p. 8).

For the story of the Third Street office: *Republican*, Oct. 28, 1863, Jan. 27, June 8, 1864; *City Post*, Oct. 31, 1863, Jan. 30, June 11, 1864, May 13, June 17, Dec. 30, 1865; *Post*, Feb. 3, 1866.

PAGES 89–90. The story of the library association and its lecture courses is told in *Winona and Olmsted Counties*, p. 819; Leonard, *Olmsted County*, p. 218; Eaton to ROB; *City Post*, Jan. 6, 20, 1866 ; *Post*, Dec. 7, 28, 1867, Jan. 18, Feb. 22, 1868, Jan. 16, 1869; *Federal Union*, Sept. 2, 23, Dec. 23, 1871, April 20, 27, 1872.

PAGES 90–91. For Rochester's school see the *Republican*, Aug. 3, 1864; *City Post*, Aug. 27, 1864, Sept. 9, 1865, Aug. 18, 1866; *Winona and Olmsted Counties*, pp. 725, 777–78; *Annual Report of the Superintendent of Public Instruction*, 1868, pp. 17, 155–56; *Post*, 1868 *passim*, May 22, July 3, 10 (citing the *St. Paul Dispatch*), 1869. For the personnel and report of the school committee, see the *Post*, Dec. 17, 1870; *Federal Union*, Jan. 28, 1871.

PAGES 91–93, SECTION 3. Dr. Mayo's attitude toward religion and morals is abundantly revealed in his published letters and speeches, which came to be a familiar feature of the Rochester newspapers. See especially "New York Letter," *Post*, Dec. 26, 1869, Jan. 1, 29, 1870 (in this last issue appeared an item naming Dr. Mayo as the author of the letters, which were published without signature) ; "Trip to the National Capital," *Post* and *Federal Union*, July 2, 9, 16, 23, Aug. 6, 1870 (these letters were not signed, but according to the *Post*, March 26, April 30, May 14, 1870, and the *Federal Union*, May 7, 1870, Dr. Mayo was in Washington at the time, and the style of the letters is indubitably his).

PAGE 91. On the 1870 election see the *Post*, April 9, 1870, and the *Federal Union*, Oct. 8, 1870.

The Friends of Progress and the furor they caused are described in the letter-reports, 1860–67, from the ministers of the Congregational Church of Rochester to the American Home Missionary Association, especially those by the Rev. Elias Clark, June 13, 1860, Rev. John S. Whitman, Sept. 6, 1865, and Rev. William R. Stevens, Nov. 1866 (no day date given). The Minnesota Historical Society has microfilm copies of these letters; the originals are in the possession of the Chicago Theological Seminary.

PAGE 92. The quotation from Thomas Huxley is from "On the Physical Basis of Life," *Essays* (New York, 1929), p. 158.

Dr. Mayo's copy of volume 1 of Spencer's *Principles of Biology* (New York, 1866) survives in the Mayo Clinic library. The other works of the Darwinists that William and Charles Mayo read from their father's library while they were boys have been scattered with the years. I am indebted to Thomas E. Keys of the Mayo Clinic library for the privilege of reading a paper he prepared on "The Medical Books of William Worrall Mayo," including a checklist of the books that are still available in the Clinic collection. An abstract of Mr. Keys's paper, together with Dr. W. J. Mayo's discussion of it, was published in the *Collected Papers*, 30:938–43, 946–50 (1938).

The quotations about Dr. Mayo's religion are from WJM to ROB; WWM, letter, *Post and Record*, June 3, 1904.

PAGE 93. Dr. Mayo was a good friend of Father Thomas O'Gorman, who served the Rochester parish from 1866 to 1877, and of Father William Riordan, whose incumbency began in 1881. He and the priest often answered calls together, the latter riding with the Old Doctor because he had the faster horses. (Remarks of Bishop O'Gorman at the unveiling of the statue to W. W. Mayo in Mayo Park, as reported in the *Olmsted County Democrat,* June 4, 1915; Leonard, *Olmsted County,* p. 216.)

PAGES 94–95, SECTION 4. This account is specific for Rochester and Olmsted County, as the conditions were reported in the newspapers, particularly in the *Post,* Nov.–Dec. 1869, and June–Aug. 1870, but the situation differed little from the general background of the agrarian crusade as described in detail in such works as Solon J. Buck, *The Agrarian Crusade: A Chronicle of the Farmer in Politics* (Yale University Press, 1921), and John D. Hicks, *The Populist Revolt: A History of the Farmers' Alliance and the People's Party* (University of Minnesota Press, 1931).

The most graphic description of economic conditions in the Rochester area is contained in the letters of John Edgar to C. H. McCormick, 1867–73. Edgar was the local district agent for the McCormick reapers, and his reports to his Chicago employer on business prospects in his district constitute an excellent summary and supplement for the items in the weekly papers. The Minnesota Historical Society has microfilm copies of these letters; the originals are in the possession of the McCormick Historical Association of Chicago.

Perhaps the best summary, replete with specific instances, of the grievances against the Winona and St. Peter Railroad is to be found in the report of the hearings held in Rochester by the legislative committee investigating the railroad situation *(Federal Union,* Feb. 11, 1871).

PAGE 95. The quotation is from Dr. Mayo's campaign letter in the *Record and Union,* Feb. 28, 1890.

PAGE 96. The quotation is from WWM, "The Bolting Movement. The Reasons Why It Was Begun," which appeared in the *Federal Union,* Aug. 27, 1870, and in the *Saint Paul Pioneer,* Aug. 26, 1870. The attack to which Dr. Mayo was replying was published in the *Republican Post,* Aug. 20, 1870.

From the time of the Republican convention in July until the election in November the papers were full of the bolt. The *Winona Republican* (daily) for August provides a sufficient sample of the attacks made on Dr. Mayo. See also excerpts from a number of papers as collected and reprinted in the *Saint Paul Press,* Aug. 14, 1870; *Winona Weekly Republican,* Aug. 24, 1870; *Mankato Weekly Record,* Aug. 16, 1870. For a glimpse behind the scenes see Dr. Mayo's letters to Donnelly, Aug. 9, 17, 26, Sept. 14, 1870.

PAGE 97. Dr. Mayo's opinion of Young was expressed in letters to Donnelly, April 5, 13, 1874. The story of Young's return to Minnesota and to health appears from items in the *Federal Union,* March 21, 1868, April 16, Sept. 24, 1870, Sept. 9, 1871. General biographical sketches of Young may be found in *History of Ramsey County and the City of Saint Paul* (Minneapolis, 1881), p. 632; *Northwest Magazine,* 3 (no. 6):16 (June 1885); *Post,* Feb. 14, 1896.

PAGES 97–98. Addresses by W. W. Mayo at the Olmsted County Democratic convention and at an anti-railroad indignation meeting were published in the *Federal Union,* Sept. 17 and 24, 1870, respectively. He spoke also at the last big Democratic rally of the campaign, called an "anti-monopoly mass meeting," but what he said on that occasion was not printed *(Union,* Nov. 5, 1870). For his speaking schedule and comments on his way with an audience, see the *Union,* Oct. 8, 15, 22, 1870. The *Post's* lament appeared in the issue for Nov. 12, 1870.

Dr. Mayo and his Democratic allies took the initiative in the anti-monopoly convention of 1870 and the passage of Minnesota's first law regulating railroads. See the *Post,* Nov. 12, 26, Dec. 3, 1870; *Federal Union,* Nov. 12, Dec. 3, 10, 1870, Jan. 7, 21, Feb. 4, 11, 18, 1871, Feb. 10, April 27, 1872, May 30, June 6, 30, 1873; *Saint Paul Press,* Dec. 10, 1870; *Mankato Weekly Record,* Dec. 10, 1870; WWM,

# Bibliographical Notes

letter to Donnelly, Aug. 9, 1870; Folwell, *History of Minnesota,* 3:33, 40–43, 55, 56–57; Leonard, *Olmsted County,* pp. 213–14.

PAGE 98. The epidemic of "western fever" was described in letters from Rochester in the *Saint Paul Press,* July 30, Aug. 10, 1870. A letter from a resident of Fergus Falls published in the *Federal Union,* June 10, 1871, stated that men from Rochester were arriving in that Dakota community daily. The Rochester colonization society, called the Minnesota Northwestern Association, set up its colony in the Cheyenne Valley. It prospered for a time but eventually ran into drouth and the grasshopper scourge. (*Federal Union,* March 1, 18, April 22, June 3, 17, July 22, 29, Aug. 5, 1871, April 6, 1872.) For the story of the Cook House see the *Post,* Feb. 1, Oct. 3, 1868, and 1869 *passim;* *Post and Record,* Sept. 11, 1903.

PAGE 99. Dr. Mayo's statement about Rochester appears in the *Federal Union,* July 8, 1871. For items describing the hard times and general pessimism see the *Union,* June 10, 17, Oct. 21, Dec. 30, 1871.

The Bear Creek project did not originate with Dr. Mayo, but he was named to the board of trade committee to investigate the possibilities of the idea and became the chief advocate of the plan (Leonard, *Olmsted County,* p. 227; *Federal Union,* June 17, July 8, 1871, March 9, June 8, July 13, 1872).

PAGES 99–102, SECTION 8. Probably nothing brings Dr. Mayo to life and reveals his ideas, ideals, and character so clearly as a reading of the Rochester newspapers for the year of April 1882 to April 1883, covering his term as mayor. All his speeches, the reports of the council proceedings each month, the editorial and epistolary debates about the ideas and policies of "His Honor the Mayor," make lively and often amusing reading, but they also make it easy to understand how infuriating Mayor Mayo must have been to those who did not agree with him.

PAGES 99–100. For Dr. Mayo's candidacies as school commissioner, see the *Record and Union,* April 7, 1876, April 6, 1877. The *Post,* March 31, April 7, May 5, 1882, tells of his campaign and election as mayor. His address and a report of the council proceedings were published in both the *Post* and the *Federal Union* for April 14, 1882. Eaton, who was city recorder, also recounted (to ROB) the story of the little farce of Dr. Mayo's first council meeting.

PAGE 101. Dr. Mayo served as alderman from the first ward from April 1886 until he resigned in April 1889 (*Record and Union,* March 12, 1886, April 5, 1889). W. J. Mayo told (to ROB) the story of the sunstroke, adding that he had often used oatmeal or rice for the same purpose, but apparently modern doctors can find no pharmaceutical justification for that remedy. The story of the waterworks is from Eaton (for many years the president of the Rochester Water Company), letter to ROB, Aug. 16, 1935, Press file; Leonard, *Olmsted County,* p. 234. In the rich newspaper record of the battle, see especially the *Record and Union,* June 19, July 10, 24, 1885, May 21, 1886.

PAGE 102. The quotation is from an address of April 4, 1894, at the dedication of an addition to St. Mary's Hospital (*Souvenir of Saint Mary's Hospital* [Rochester, 1922], p. 34).

PAGES 102–3, SECTION 9. Dr. Mayo practiced the political independence he was constantly preaching. In 1872 he joined the Liberal Republicans to work, finally in coalition with the Democrats, for the election of Horace Greeley. He was proposed for nomination to run for Congress against Mark H. Dunnell, who was up for reelection, and he spent two weeks canvassing the district to determine his chances. When Morton S. Wilkinson became available as the coalition candidate, Dr. Mayo recognized that the experienced and popular "Wilk" would be more likely to win than he and withdrew in his favor, seconding his nomination at the district convention. (*Federal Union,* Jan. 27, June 15, July 13, 20, Aug. 10, Sept.

21, Oct. 26, 1872; Donnelly diaries, Aug. 9, 1872; *Chatfield Democrat*, June 29, 1872.)

Dr. Mayo not only looked with sympathy upon the early attempts to form a third party but sometimes participated actively in them (*Record and Union*, June 4, 1886). Just once does the record show him to have been unsympathetic. He approved of the general purposes of the Greenback party, but he could not approve the coalition of the Democrats with that group, because he did not think a further issue of irredeemable paper currency was the right remedy for the debt-disease of western farmers (*Record and Union*, Oct. 27, 1876).

PAGE 102. For one of Dr. Mayo's pleasanter passages at arms with the woman suffragists, numerous and strong in Rochester, see his letters, "Trip to the National Capital," *Federal Union*, July 2, 23, 1870, and the replies by "One of the Weaker Sex," *ibid.*, July 9, 30, 1870.

For Dr. Mayo's attempts to get a competing railroad for Rochester and the bitter battle they involved him in, see the letter signed "Gulliver" in the *Record and Union*, Jan. 27, 1882, and Leonard, *Olmsted County*, pp. 94–99, which provides an excellent guide through the maze of newspaper wordage. Of chief importance in the latter are the *Record and Union*, Aug. 23, 30, Sept. 20, Oct. 4, 11, 1889, Jan.–March 1890, and the *Post*, Jan.–March 1890. Dr. Mayo's version was given in a letter to the editor of the *Record and Union*, Feb. 21, 1890. His activity in other railroad projects is described in the *Federal Union*, Jan. 21, Feb. 4, 1871, and the *Record and Union*, July 22, 1887, July 13, 20, 1888, Aug. 2, 1889.

PAGE 103. The Edgar controversy: *Record and Union*, Feb. 21, 28, March 28, 1890; *Post*, Feb. 28, April 4, 1890. For Dr. Mayo's reaction to the threatened libel suit, "I guess I can stand it," see his letters to Donnelly, April 10, 1890, Jan. 12, 1890.

PAGES 103–4. The German celebration was described in the *Post*, Sept. 10, 1870, the Irish mass meeting in the *Record and Union*, Jan. 9, 16, 1880. To the latter Dr. Mayo is said to have described "the wretchedness and utter want which he had observed in his visits to Ireland." When those visits occurred the record does not show; one was probably during his trip to Europe in 1876 (*Record and Union*, June 9, Aug. 25, 1876).

Dr. Mayo was the Democratic candidate for state senator in 1882 and 1890, for state representative in 1886 and 1888. The incidents of each campaign were reported in the newspapers (*Record and Union*, Oct. 15, Nov. 12, 1886, Sept. 7, Oct. 19, Nov. 9, 16, 1888).

PAGES 104–5. The description of Dr. Mayo's farm is from the *Post*, Aug. 10, 1877. See also the *Record and Union*, Dec. 3, 1875, June 2, 1876, July 25, 1879, Dec. 17, 1880.

PAGES 105–6. For the relations of Mayo and Donnelly during this period, see WWM, letters to Donnelly, March 8, 13, April 10, May 7, 20, 1890; Nov. 6, and reply Nov. 8, 1890; Donnelly diaries, June 21, 1890; *Post*, June 6, 1890, Jan. 9, 1891 (quoting the *St. Paul News*); *Record and Union*, June 27, 1890, Jan. 9, 1891. See also Folwell, *History of Minnesota*, 3:187–89. The *Record and Union*, Aug. 22, Oct. 17, 31, Nov. 7, 1890, tells of Mayo's campaign and election.

PAGES 106–7. Mayo's senatorial career: *Senate Journal*, 1891, 1893; *Record and Union*, Jan. 16, 30, Feb. 6, 13, 27, 1891; Folwell, *History of Minnesota*, 3:205–12.

## CHAPTER 5. HORSE-AND-BUGGY DOCTOR

Much of the opinion and characterization, as well as the incident, of this and the following chapter has been drawn from interviews with men and women who

# Bibliographical Notes

knew Rochester and Dr. and Mrs. Mayo in the period under consideration. Besides the three Mayo children, the following proved particularly helpful: Eaton, Granger, H. S. Plummer, Mrs. Plummer, Mrs. Stinchfield, Mrs. Nowell, Mrs. Witherstine, and Mrs. C. H. Mayo to ROB.

Some further anecdotal material is provided in "The Saga of a Country Doctor," by Dr. Charles T. Granger, brother of Judge Granger and long a rival of the Mayos in Rochester. His memoirs were published in installments in the *St. Paul Pioneer Press*, Jan. 13 to Feb. 3, 1935.

In addition to the published and manuscript papers of the Mayo brothers that have already been cited, two of their periodic addresses to the staff members of the Mayo Clinic have special bearing upon the subject of this chapter: WJM, "In My Father's Time," *Proceedings of the Mayo Clinic*, 4:349–50 (Dec. 4, 1929), a description of his father's methods of examination and treatment, and CHM, "The Transitional Age in Medicine," *Proceedings of the Mayo Clinic*, 7:584–87 (Oct. 13, 1932), a more general discussion of the old school of practice that includes some delightful details about his father and mother.

No history of medicine in Minnesota has yet been written, but the materials for one are being gathered under the auspices of the Minnesota State Medical Association and have been appearing in installments in *Minnesota Medicine* since Jan. 1938. Some phases of this chapter are treated in more detail in HC, "Health and Medicine in Rochester, 1855–70," *Minnesota History*, 20:221–42 (Sept. 1939).

The most fruitful sources have been, again, the indispensable newspapers and more especially here the *Transactions of the Minnesota State Medical Society*, of which I have read the volumes from 1870 to 1883 page by page.

PAGE 108. Quotation from Mayo, letter to Donnelly, April 17, 1890.

PAGES 108–9. For the story of the Rochester Infirmary: *Free Press*, Oct. 13, Nov. 18, 1858; *City Post*, Feb. 11, May 26, June 30, Dec. 22, 1860, Feb. 9, July 27, 1861, Jan. 11, Feb. 8, 1862. Biographical sketches and characterizations of the Drs. Cross appear in a letter from David Blakely of Rochester to Ramsey (no date, 1861?), Governors' Archives, file 93; Leonard, *Olmsted County*, p. 203; *Record and Union*, July 13, 1894; *Post and Record*, Nov. 24, 1899; Granger, "Saga of a Country Doctor," *St. Paul Pioneer Press*, Jan. 13, 1935; WJM, CHM, Mrs. Berkman, and Eaton to ROB.

PAGE 110. In announcing the continuance of the infirmary, Dr. E. C. Cross declared, "Homeopathic practice is commanding increased attention throughout civilized society. My own experience of nearly 20 years in the active practice of medicine confirms the favorable opinion in which this popular branch of science is justly regarded." See the *Post*, Feb. 3, 10, 1866.

WJM to ROB tells of Dr. Mayo's relationship with the Drs. Cross. The *Post*, Aug. 7, 1869, describes the incident of Cross and the widow.

PAGES 110–11. On Dr. Galloway see Granger, "Saga of a Country Doctor," *St. Paul Pioneer Press*, Jan. 13, 1935; Eaton to ROB. There are sketches of Dr. Galloway in Leonard, *Olmsted County*, p. 47; *City Post*, Oct. 8, 1864; *Post and Record*, March 10, 1899. He moved to Fargo, Dakota Territory, in 1879 (*Record and Union*, Oct. 17, 1879).

PAGE 111. Dr. Mayo's story of Dr. Allen's patient is in Mrs. Mayo's stock book, Jan. 17, 1866.

PAGES 111–13, SECTION 2. Dr. Duvall's career is sketched from the *Post*, Oct. 17 (supplement), Dec. 26, 1868, May 8, July 3, 1869; *Federal Union*, Oct. 17 (supplement), 1868, Jan. 2, 1869, July 23, 1870, July 22, 1871; *Saint Paul Press*, Nov. 27, 1870; *Mantorville Express*, Nov. 25, 1870. It is noteworthy that in Dr. E. C. Cross's first advertisements he "particularly solicits the patronage of those with *Chronic* diseases." (*Free Press*, Nov. 18, 1858.)

Later traveling healers included one Dr. Clark A. Miner, "unquestionably [he said] the most successful physician in the treatment of all *chronic* diseases." Dr. Miner made a tour of southern Minnesota towns every three months. In 1878, after four years of quarterly visits to Rochester, he moved there, rented a spacious suite of rooms, and announced the opening of the Rochester Medical Institute, which was to serve all the sick of southern Minnesota. Dr. Miner himself would be its resident physician, with the assistance of a staff of *ten* physicians and surgeons, the best available in the profession. In addition to the regular daily office hours, the institute staff would hold clinics for the worthy poor twice weekly, at which examinations and prescriptions would be given for one or two dollars. Unfortunately the records are silent as to the outcome of this institute. (*Record and Union*, Feb. 2, 1877, Oct. 11, 1878.)

Rochester was eager to be a resort for the sick, though it had in mind a somewhat different sort of resort than Dr. Miner planned. Minnesota had advertised itself into one of the nation's chief sanatoria for invalids, particularly for "consumptives," and Rochester made a special bid for the thousands who flocked to the state. The Rochester newspapers told the story of their coming—often in the obituary column, it must be admitted—and the city merchants addressed advertisements to them. All her life Gertrude Mayo remembered the thrill of her first train ride, to which she and little Will were treated by "a man from the East" who had come to Minnesota to be cured of his consumption and was living with the Mayos while the climate took effect (Mrs. Berkman to ROB).

Some major bits about the health business in Rochester are found in a letter signed "Traveler" in the *Springfield* (Massachusetts) *Weekly Republican*, June 27, 1868, of which the Minnesota Historical Society has a typescript copy; a letter from a visitor to Rochester reprinted from the *LaCrosse* (Wisconsin) *Republican and Leader*, May 31, 1873, in the *Federal Union*, June 6, 1873; a letter by T. H. Phillips reprinted from the *Cincinnati Gazette* in the *Post*, April 23, 1870; a letter to the *Cincinnati Commercial* quoted in the *Post*, June 27, 1868; descriptions of Rochester from the *Chicago Republican* and the *Milwaukee Sentinel* reprinted in the *Post*, Aug. 15 and Dec. 5, 1868, respectively; accounts of specific cases by E. C. Cross in Franklin Staples, "Report on the Influence of Climate on Pulmonary Diseases in Minnesota," *Trans. of the A. M. A.*, 27:381–417 (1876); E. D. Strang, comp., *Olmsted County, Minnesota, and Its Advantages of Soil, Climate, and Location* (Rochester, 1884), p. 60 *et passim*.

Clara Barton spent several months in Olmsted County in the fall of 1859 trying to nurse a nephew back to health from the verge of death from tuberculosis. The boy did improve remarkably, but died within a year of returning to his eastern home. (Marion L. Sloan, pioneer resident of Rochester in whose home Miss Barton and her nephew stayed for three weeks of their sojourn, to HC.)

PAGES 113–14. Mr. Eaton told this story for my benefit at a meeting of the Minnesota Historical Society held in Rochester, June 1939.

PAGE 114. The smashup is described in the *Record and Union*, March 25, 1881, and in Granger to ROB. CHM to ROB tells of Dr. Mayo's operation on his lip.

PAGES 114–15. For the tongue operation: Granger to ROB; Steward manuscript, p. 79.

PAGE 116. For the interval during which Dr. Mayo was the partner of O. W. Anderson the druggist, see the advertisements and news items in the Rochester newspapers, Nov. 1867 to Feb. 1869, especially the *Post*, Nov. 30, Dec. 14, 1867, Feb. 6, 1869, and the *Federal Union*, Jan. 4, Oct. 10, 1868. During the period of the partnership Dr. Mayo had his office at the drug store and dispensed his own medicines there. Mr. Anderson later built up a prosperous business manufacturing and peddling patent medicines (*Post*, Aug. 20, 1870; *Federal Union*, June 10, Dec. 9, 1871).

The *City Post*, Jan. 6, 1866, recounts the story of Ole Nelson.

PAGE 119. For Dr. Mayo's library: Keys, checklist of WWM's medical books.

PAGE 120. On the Olmsted County Medical Society and the Rochester *Conversazione*: *Post*, April 4, 25, 1868, Jan. 16, 30, Feb. 13, 27, March 13, 27, April 10, 24, June 5, 19, Sept. 18, 1869; *Federal Union*, winter of 1869-70 *passim*.

PAGES 121-22, SECTION 7. *Trans. Minn. Med. Soc.*, 1870 (which includes also the proceedings of the sessions of 1869) through 1880. See also the *Post*, Jan. 30, Feb. 6, 1869, and the *Saint Paul Dispatch*, Feb. 2, 1869. For biographies of the doctors mentioned: WJM, "Two Medical Pioneers," *Proceedings of the Mayo Clinic*, 12:535-37 (Aug. 25, 1937), and "Memoir of the Late J. B. McGaughey, An Appreciation," an address before the Southern Medical Association, published in the *Winona Daily Republican Herald*, Aug. 4, 1910; sketches of Drs. Staples, Stone, and Hewitt in Kelly, *American Medical Biographies*; "Dr. Franklin Staples," *St. Paul Medical Journal*, 6:292-94 (April 1904); J. J. Rothrock, M.D., "Dr. Alexander J. Stone—An Appreciation," *ibid.*, 12:432-44 (Sept. 1910); "Charles N. Hewitt, Apostle of Public Health," in Folwell, *History of Minnesota*, 4:413-25; Thomas E. Keys, "The Medical Books of Dr. Charles N. Hewitt," *Minnesota History*, 21:357-71 (Dec. 1940).

PAGE 122. Further details about the first medical practice law (1869) are given in HC, "Health and Medicine in Rochester," *Minnesota History*, 20:237-38 (Sept. 1939).

PAGE 123. Jacobs v. Cross, *Minnesota Reports*, 1873, pp. 524-27; *Cases and Briefs*, Minnesota State Supreme Court, April term, 1873, Cal. No. 62; Eaton to ROB. Mr. Eaton is the authority for the fact that Dr. W. W. Mayo suggested the theory on which the defense was based.

CHAPTER 6. PIONEER IN SURGERY

PAGE 124. Even in New York, surgery was only accessory to general practice, except in the case of Dr. James R. Wood, a man of independent means who could afford to give his time entirely to charity patients. There was not enough surgery as yet for others to support themselves on it alone. This was true until at least the late 1870's. (Arpad G. Gerster, *Recollections of a New York Surgeon* [New York, 1917], pp. 165-66, 191.)

For the farm-machine accidents see a letter from Rochester in the *Saint Paul Press*, Aug. 13, 1870. The tumbling rod between the horsepower and the separator in the threshing machine was responsible for so many accidents that the Minnesota legislature passed a law in 1868 requiring all owners and operators of threshing machines to enclose that part of the mechanism in a wooden case (*Session Laws*, 1868, p. 99; *Post*, Sept. 10, 1870).

PAGES 124-25. The skeleton of names and dates for this period of gynecology is provided by Garrison, *History of Medicine*, pp. 507-12, but there is more description and evaluation in Howard A. Kelly, "History of American Gynecology: A Brief Outline," in Arthur H. Curtis, ed., *Obstetrics and Gynecology* (4 vols., Philadelphia, 1933), 2:473-87, and in memoirs of the period such as Emilius C. Dudley, *The Medicine Man* (New York, 1927). Better than memories, however, are the revelations in such handbooks of practice as Paul F. Mundé, *Minor Surgical Gynecology* (New York, 1880) and D. Berry Hart and A. H. Barbour, *Manual of Gynecology* (Edinburgh, 1882). See also the comments and descriptions in Dr. W. J. Mayo's early papers on gynecological subjects, *Collection of Papers*

*Previous to 1909*, 2:164-250 *passim*. Lawson Tait of Birmingham, England, performed his first ovariotomy in 1868, and his widespread influence in this field did not appear until the 1870's. One Minnesota doctor of a later day, looking back at that period, remarked nostalgically, "A rich field it must have been!" (Rothrock, "Dr. Alexander J. Stone," *St. Paul Medical Journal*, 12:432 [Sept. 1910].)

On Sims see his autobiography, *The Story of My Life* (New York, 1884); Dudley, *Medicine Man*, pp. 216-19; Packard, *Medicine in the United States*, 2:1136-41; and a sketch by John A. Wyeth, M.D., in Kelly, *American Medical Biographies*.

PAGES 126-29, SECTION 2. The *Post*, Nov. 6, 1869, Jan. 29, 1870, records Mayo's departure and return. It has been said repeatedly that Dr. Mayo took an *ad eundem* degree on this occasion, usually at the Bellevue Hospital Medical College but sometimes at the Long Island College of Medicine or the College of Physicians and Surgeons (Columbia University). No corroboration of that assertion can be found in the records of any of those institutions (letters from their officials to Mrs. Mellish, Sept. 7, 1920, to ROB, Dec. 7, 1932, and to HC, Jan. 5, 12, 1938, Press file). The fact that memories preserved those several names suggests that Dr. Mayo did in fact attend lectures and clinics at more than one institution.

PAGES 126-27. Carlisle, *Account of Bellevue Hospital*, pp. 65-70, 72-76, describes the hospital at this time. Dr. Mayo's "New York Letter" in the *Post*, Jan. 29, 1870, describes the ambulance corps. His other letters from New York were published in the *Post*, Dec. 25, 1869, Jan. 1, 8, Feb. 5, 12, 1870.

PAGE 128. For the McDowell story see Sigerist, *American Medicine*, pp. 87-89; Simon Flexner, *Doctors on Horseback* (New York, 1937), pp. 121-31.

For the Atlees: sketches in Kelly, *American Medical Biographies*, and in Floyd E. Keene, M.D., ed., *Album of the Fellows of the American Gynecological Society, 1876-1930* (Philadelphia, 1930); Packard, *Medicine in the United States*, 2:1136; J. M. Toner, M.D., "Report on American Medical Necrology, 1879," *Trans. of the A. M. A.*, 30:794-805 (1879); Thomas M. Drysdale, "In Memoriam: Washington Lemuel Atlee," *American Journal of Obstetrics*, 12:148-59 (Jan. 1879); D. Hayes Agnew, "Memoir of John Light Atlee," *Trans. of the College of Physicians* (of Philadelphia), 3d series, vol. 8, pp. xxxv-xliii (1886). By the time of Dr. Atlee's death in 1878 the total number of his ovariotomies was 367 and the mortality just 30 per cent (Samuel D. Gross, *Memorial Oration in Honor of Ephraim McDowell* [Louisville, 1879]). WJM to ROB is the authority for the fact of his father's visit to the Atlees.

PAGES 128-29. The anecdote of the man from Jericho is told in Dudley, *Medicine Man*, pp. 211-12, 236.

PAGES 129-30, SECTION 3. WWM, "Rectocele," *Trans. Minn. Med. Soc.*, 1872, pp. 18-25. The report was read at the semiannual session in Minneapolis in June 1871 (*ibid.*, p. 6). Dr. Byford's visit to Rochester occurred in September 1870.

PAGES 131-32, SECTION 4. *Northwestern Med. and Surg. Jour.*, 1:51-52 (July 1870); *Trans. Minn. Med. Soc.*, 1871, pp. 13-14; 1874, pp. 12-14; 1880, pp. 4, 10, 13-14; *Federal Union*, June 18, 1870; *Saint Paul Press*, Feb. 8, 1871; *Saint Paul Pioneer*, Feb. 4, 1874; Dr. Robert Rosenthal of St. Paul, letter to HC, Oct. 30, 1939, Press file.

For the agitation over the admission of women students to the Philadelphia clinics see Francis R. Packard, *Some Account of the Pennsylvania Hospital, from Its Rise to the Beginning of the Year 1938* (Philadelphia, 1938), pp. 105-6; *Federal Union*, Feb. 19, 1870; *Lanesboro Herald*, Nov. 30, 1869 (quoting the *New York Tribune*).

PAGES 132-33, SECTION 5. Dr. Mayo had served as a vice-president of the state society in 1871, but his elevation to the presidency was not a matter of routine progression. In 1872 the society amended its constitution to read "the nominations . . . shall be made in open convention; and the election shall be by written ballot." Dr. Mayo's election followed. (*Trans. Minn. Med. Soc.*, 1872, pp. 31–32.) Dr. Mayo's presidential address and other brief remarks in his official capacity are given *ibid.*, 1872, pp. 33–35; 1873, pp. 13–15, 24–37.

PAGES 133–35, SECTION 6. For the St. Paul interlude: *Federal Union*, April 12, 19, 26, May 3, 1873; *Minnesota Record*, April 12, May 3, 1873; *Saint Paul Pioneer*, April 24, 1873, March 17, Jan. 28, 1874; *Record and Union*, March 20, 27, 1874; Dr. Armstrong, letter to ROB, Nov. 3, 1933, Press file, and "History of Medicine in Ramsey County," *Minnesota Medicine*, 22:409 (June 1939). Dr. Armstrong was mistaken in his assumption that Dr. Mayo took up residence and practice in St. Paul because he had been elected to the legislature. He served only one term in that body, from 1890 to 1894.

PAGE 135. WJM to ROB tells how scrupulously Dr. Mayo kept his office hours. They were usually from 11 to 12, 1:30 to 3, and 7 to 8 (Wilson, "William Worrell Mayo," *Surg., Gynec. and Obst.*, 44:715 [May 1927]). There is a sample announcement of his all-day hours in the *Post*, Dec. 4, 1867.

PAGE 136. For the stringing of the telephone line, see pages 160–61. The obvious advantage of the instrument led Dr. E. C. Cross to install one between his office and his home two months later (*Record and Union*, Feb. 20, 1880).

PAGES 136–37, SECTION 8. *Trans. Minn. Med. Soc.*, 1870, p. 17; 1881, p. 39; *Record and Union*, Feb. 12, 1875. I have collected a file of some two hundred newspaper reports of medical cases for the years from 1865 to 1883. Those in which Dr. Mayo figured make up about one third of the total. Very few appeared for him until after his return from St. Paul in 1874, but thereafter their number grew rapidly.

PAGES 137–38. The newspaper items are, respectively, from the *Record and Union*, March 24, 1876, Nov. 15, 1878, Jan. 14, 1876, Oct. 8, 1880, Oct. 13, 1876, May 26, 1876, Oct. 6, 1876.

PAGE 139. Graham, *Story of Surgery*, pp. 289, 293–94. The press accounts are from the *Record and Union*, May 17, 1876, Nov. 22, 1878.

PAGES 139–40. Mrs. Berkman to ROB recounts the incident of Dr. Mayo's saving the man's hand.

PAGE 140. The three newspaper items are, respectively, from the *Record and Union*, April 23, 1880, July 28, 1882, Oct. 27, 1882.

Drs. Staples and Stone were the other members of the committee on gynecology (*Trans. Minn. Med. Soc.*, 1874, p. 22). In 1878 Dr. Mayo was chairman of the committee on surgery, and in 1882 he served again on the committee on gynecology (*ibid.*, 1878, p. 12; 1882, p. 7). The rest of his service was on administrative committees, such as those on ethics, finance, and medical education.

PAGES 140–41. This account of early ovariotomies in Minnesota is based on Alexander J. Stone, M.D., "The Ovariotomy of Minnesota," *Trans. Minn. Med. Soc.*, 1874, pp. 83–86, which summarized the reports that had appeared up to that time; *ibid.*, 1875, pp. 48–52; 1876, pp. 124–28, 128–32; 1877, pp. 69–74; Thomas M. Drysdale, M.D., "In Memoriam: Washington Lemuel Atlee," *Trans. Amer. Gynec. Soc.*, 3:391–92 (1878). Dr. Hewitt is said to have performed two successful ovariotomies before 1878 (William B. Atkinson, M.D., ed., *The Physicians and Surgeons of the United States* [Philadelphia, 1878], p. 566), but no report of them appears in the state society *Transactions*.

PAGES 141–42. For the Waggoner case: *Record and Union*, Dec. 17, 24, 1880; WWM and WJM, "Reports of Cases," *Trans. Minn. Med. Soc.*, 1885, pp. 45–46 (of which a re-edited version is given in the *Collection of Papers Previous to 1909*,

2:549); Mrs. Berkman to ROB; CHM, "Early Days of the Mayo Clinic"; Mrs. C. H. Mayo to HC. The story of the operation on Mrs. Waggoner was a favorite one with the Mayos, whose memories placed it in 1870 or 1871, perhaps through confusing it with the one for the removal of the rectocele. In the report of the state society, which must have been written from memory, the year of the operation is given as 1882, but there is no doubt that it was the one reported in the news-papers of 1880.

PAGE 144. The description of Dr. Bigelow is from Dudley, *Medicine Man*, pp. 227–28. The quotation from Dr. Mayo is in *Trans. Minn. Med. Soc.*, 1872, p. 20.

About the Campions: Granger, "Saga of a Country Doctor," *St. Paul Pioneer Press*, Feb. 3, 1935, and frequent items in the Rochester newspapers.

PAGE 145. WWM, "Report of a Case of Purpura Hemorrhagica," *Trans. Minn. Med. Soc.*, 1878, pp. 170–74; *Record and Union*, May 14, 1875. See also the reports of similar cases by Drs. Murphy and Millard in *Trans. Minn. Med. Soc.*, 1878, pp. 13, 23. For Mayo's and Cross's partnership see the *Record and Union*, Dec. 29, 1876, June 14, 1878. H. S. Plummer to ROB describes the extent of Dr. Mayo's practice and his habits of consultation.

PAGES 146–47. For Dr. Mayo as a member of the Rochester board of health, see the *City Post*, Nov. 11, 1865; *Post*, June 2, 1866, April 16, 1870; *Record and Union*, Nov. 19, Dec. 3, 10, 1880, Feb. 24, May 12, June 16, 1882; Eaton to ROB, and his letter to ROB, Aug. 16, 1935, Press file. According to Keys, checklist of WWM's medical books, the manual Dr. Mayo bought was C. B. Fox, *Sanitary Examinations of Water, Air, and Food: A Handbook for the Medical Officer of Health . . .* (London, 1878).

PAGE 147. For the dentist's office boy: *Federal Union*, June 11, 1870; *Record and Union*, March 19, 1886. Dr. Mayo used to assist "Dr. Williams," the dentist, by administering the laughing gas for him and by certifying its harmlessness to nervous patients (*Post*, June 13, 1868; *Mantorville Express*, Dec. 18, 1868).

PAGES 147–48. On Henry S. Wellcome: *Who's Who*, 1933; "Sir Henry Well-come," *American Journal of Tropical Medicine*, 16:647–51 (Nov. 1936); remarks by WJM, *Minnesota Medicine*, 19:383 (June 1936); CHM, "Early Days of the Mayo Clinic"; Eaton to HC; *Record and Union*, Sept. 19, 1884, Dec. 25, 1885, Aug. 4, 1893.

PAGE 148. The tribute by Wellcome is from "Presentation of Replicas of the Lister Exhibition," *Surg., Gynec. and Obst.*, 45:857 (Dec. 1927).

The quotation about Mrs. Mayo is from CHM, "Transitional Age in Medicine," *Proceedings of the Mayo Clinic*, 7:586–87 (Oct. 13, 1932). See also WJM to ROB; Steward manuscript, pp. 77–78. The characterization of Mrs. Mayo given here is a summary of Dr. Beard's interviews with persons who knew her; without exception they seem to have had the deepest admiration for her qualities of mind and heart.

PAGE 149. The church story is told in Granger, "Saga of a Country Doctor," *St. Paul Pioneer Press*, Jan. 13, 1935. Relations between Dr. Mayo and his wife are described in CHM, Mrs. Stinchfield, Mrs. Berkman, and H. S. Plummer to ROB; Donnelly diaries, Jan. 17, Aug. 9, 1872. For the Totten suit: WJM to ROB; "The Mayo Family," unsigned manuscript in the Press file; WJM, Story to Mrs. Mellish, pp. 3–4.

PAGE 150. For the orphans and the English colony: CHM to ROB.

PAGE 151. The *Record and Union*, June 9, Aug. 11, 25, 1876, records the fact of Dr. Mayo's trip to Europe. For some of the more extensive property improve-ment projects, see the *Post*, Dec. 12, 1868, Jan. 8, 1870, Jan. 4, 1878.

PAGE 152. Granger to ROB tells of the settlement of the Grangers' bill. All who knew Dr. Mayo were agreed as to his utter lack of business sense and his extreme kindheartedness.

PAGES 153–55, SECTION 16. The *Post* and the *Federal Union,* June 3, 1881, tell the story of the birthday celebration.

## CHAPTER 7. WILL AND CHARLIE

For this chapter the major sources are the transcripts of interviews that Drs. W. J. and C. H. Mayo gave to Dr. Beard and the statements scattered through the brothers' papers, especially: CHM, "Early Days of the Mayo Clinic"; CHM, "The Transitional Age in Medicine," *Proceedings of the Mayo Clinic,* 7:584–87 (Oct. 13, 1932); CHM, Discussion, *ibid.,* 3:72–74 (March 7, 1928); WJM, "Libraries Useful in Their Day," *Bulletin of the Medical Library Association,* 25:70–72 (Sept. 1936); WJM, Discussion, *Collected Papers,* 30:938–43 (1938); WJM, "Nu Sigma Nu," a paper read before the Los Angeles chapter of Nu Sigma Nu fraternity, May 4, 1929, typescript copy in the Press file. Helpful too are the reminiscences of the brothers and their friends recorded in *The Reunion [of the Old School Boys] at Rochester, Minnesota, October 14–15, 1916* and *History of the Old School Boys and Girls Association.*

PAGE 159. The quotation is from WJM to ROB. Albert N. Younglove of Riverside, California, who was an inseparable companion of Charles Mayo as a boy, does not remember that Will was with them much. "Dr. Will, being older, did not have much in common with us younger fellows," he writes. (Letter to HC, April 30, 1940, Press file.)

Mrs. W. W. Mayo is the authority for the statement that Charlie was not strong as a child (Meloney, "Mrs. Mayo, Wilderness Mother," *The Delineator,* Sept. 1914, p. 46).

For the story of the "pigeon days" see Thomas S. Roberts, *The Birds of Minnesota* (2d ed., 2 vols., University of Minnesota Press, 1936), 1:576–87, including on p. 583 a letter from Dr. W. J. Mayo describing a boyhood trip to a pigeon roost.

PAGES 159–60. Frank Smith in the *Chicago Daily Times* records the circus story as told to him by Judge Charles Ellison of Rochester, the "playmate" of the incident.

PAGE 160. Mrs. Berkman told the story of Will at the parade (to ROB) and described Charlie as a boy at home (Frank Smith in the *Chicago Daily Times*). The incident of the steam engine is given as told by Dr. W. W. Mayo (E. H. Hall, "Echoes from St. Mary's Clinic," *Canada Lancet,* Dec. 1906, p. 4 of reprint in Press file), but Dr. Will told it a little differently, saying that he and Charlie earned the twenty-five dollars for the engine by hoeing corn (*Daily Post and Record,* June 23, 1916; WJM to ROB). Mrs. Trenholme to HC repeats the family tradition about the telephone. For the newspaper account see page 136.

PAGE 161. For the reforms in the Rochester Central School see the reports from Rochester and Olmsted County in *Annual Report of Superintendent of Public Instruction,* 1870–75, especially 1871, pp. 158–62. See also the note to pages 90–91. The story of the rotten eggs as Dr. Will told it is in *History of the Old School Boys and Girls Association.*

PAGE 162. Frank Smith in the *Chicago Daily Times* reports the story of the grocer's wagon as it was told him by Mark Holmes of Rochester, the driver. For Will as a horseman: *Reunion of the Old School Boys*; *Post,* Sept. 18, 1869, Sept. 17, 1870; Leonard, *Olmsted County,* p. 54; Granger to ROB.

PAGE 163. For Charlie's school days: CHM to ROB; CHM's reminiscences reported in the *Rochester Bulletin*, Oct. 15, 1927; Carol Wolfe, "Rochester—Then, Now and Always," *Rochester Post-Bulletin*, June 7, 1929; Albert N. Younglove, letters to HC, April 9, 30, 1940.

PAGES 163–64. For the Rochester high school see the reports from Rochester and Olmsted County in *Annual Report of Superintendent of Public Instruction*, 1871–75, 1877; *Winona and Olmsted Counties*, pp. 737–39. Dr. Mayo's attitude toward the high school is described in WJM, Story to Mrs. Mellish, p. 4. Will Mayo did not graduate from the Rochester high school (Eaton to HC; WJM, Story to Mrs. Mellish, p. 4; lists of the graduating classes in the *Post*, 1875–85).

PAGE 164. WJM, Story to Mrs. Mellish, p. 4, identifies the teacher of the private school he attended as "Mrs. Finch." Announcements of the select school conducted by Miss Mary Finch appeared in the *Post*, July 1, Sept. 9, 1876, Feb. 9, 1877, and not thereafter. Although Dr. Mayo usually said he spent one year in the Finch school, he also said that Horace Witherstine was one of his teachers at the Niles school (Story to Mrs. Mellish, p. 19), and Witherstine was with the Niles school only during the spring of 1877 (*Winona and Olmsted Counties*, p. 729; *Post*, Jan. 5, June 8, 1877). Therefore it seems most likely that Will was a student at Miss Finch's school during the fall term of 1876 and transferred to Niles's academy when it opened in Jan. 1877.

PAGES 164–65. For Sanford Niles and his Rochester Training School: Maria L. Sanford, "Sanford Niles," *School Education*, 24:6 (Sept. 1905); *Annual Report of Superintendent of Public Instruction*, 1868–78 *passim*; *Post*, Jan. 5, 12, Feb. 9, May 11, June 8, July 27, Aug. 10, 17, 24 (citing *Dodge County Republican*), 31, Sept. 7, 14, Nov. 23, 1877, Jan. 4, March 29, June 7, 1878. The quarters of the Niles school are described in Eaton to HC. A partial list of those who attended the school is given in *History of the Old School Boys and Girls Association*, p. 26. Mrs. Mayo's advertisement for boarders appeared in the *Post*, Aug. 10, 1877.

PAGE 165. The item on Farrell is from *Reunion of the Old School Boys*, p. 15. For the Rochester Gymnasium: *Post*, March 16, 1877, April 19, 1878; *Record and Union*, March 16, Dec. 21, 1877, April 19, 1878.

In a brief account of his schooling (to ROB) Dr. Charlie said, "I went through to the last year of the high school," an ambiguous statement. However, he was never listed among the graduates of the high school in the newspapers, and the following letter is preserved in the CHM files:

"Rochester, Minn. 4 Mo., 15 day, 1884

"Charles H. Mayo has been for more than two years a member of our high school and has given attention to Arithmetic, Algebra, Latin, Physical Geography, Natural Philosophy and Civil Government.

"He is a young man of *good character* and *good abilities*, is *ambitious* and *capable* of doing *excellent work* upon any subject he will be likely to undertake.

H. O. DURKEE
Supt. of schools and Prin. High School"

PAGE 166. Dr. Mayo made the comment on his knowledge of French and German in his story to Mrs. Mellish, p. 15.

The Old Doctor's remark to the railroad man is quoted from B. B. Scripture in H. C. Garvin, letter to W. J. Mayo, May 31, 1939, WJM files. The story of Will's attempt at smoking is from WJM to ROB. Mrs. Mayo's comment on the Doctor's susceptibility to book agents is reported in Meloney, "Mrs. Mayo, Wilderness Mother," *The Delineator*, Sept. 1914, p. 46. The picture of the Old Doctor among his books is from WJM, "Libraries Useful in Their Day," *Bulletin of the Medical Library Association*, 25:70 (Sept. 1936).

# Bibliographical Notes

PAGE 167. That the boys learned their osteology from the skeleton of Cut Nose is a staple item in their story. The details about the size of the skull and the length of the femur come from CHM, "Early Days of the Mayo Clinic." The quotations about John Dalton are from WJM, "Advancement of Learning in Medicine," *Collected Papers*, 20:968 (1928); CHM to ROB.

PAGE 168. The quotation about Dr. Charlie as a boy on the farm is from CHM, "Early Days in the Mayo Clinic."

PAGE 169. Dr. Will's analogy is quoted from his "Personal Reminiscences of Great Surgeons," a paper he read before the fellows of the Mayo Foundation, Dec. 9, 1921, typescript copy in the WJM files. Powderly to ROB repeats the story of Will's leaving the farm as she heard Jay Neville tell it. WJM to HC gives the story of Charlie's first "store suit."

PAGE 170. Mrs. Berkman showed Dr. Beard the record of the horses in the family Bible.

PAGES 170–71. The quotations are from CHM, "Transitional Age in Medicine," *Proceedings of the Mayo Clinic*, 7:584–87 (Oct. 13, 1932). See also CHM, Discussion, *Proceedings of the Mayo Clinic*, 3:72–74 (March 7, 1928).

PAGE 171. For the boil on Bill's neck: Steward manuscript, p. 79.

PAGE 172. The story of the New York clinic is from WJM, Discussion, *Proceedings of the Mayo Clinic*, 9:243–44 (April 18, 1934).

PAGES 172–73. How Dr. Mayo came to buy his second microscope was one of the stories the brothers told over and over again. Dr. Will always said it happened when his father returned from the trip to New York in 1869–70 (he usually said 1871), but Dr. Charlie said the trip was the one to Europe in 1876. The new books on the use of the microscope he subsequently bought are listed in Keys, checklist of WWM's medical books. Dr. Will described his boyhood attendance at postmortems in "Nu Sigma Nu."

PAGE 174. The quotation is from WJM, Discussion, *Collected Papers*, 30:940 (1938). This story too is one that Dr. Will often told. He thought he was about sixteen when it occurred, but (to ROB) he identified the patient as a man named Collins, and the *Post*, July 30, 1880, reported Dr. Mayo's attendance on Mr. Collins of the Bradley House. It seems queer that Dr. Mayo's two students of the moment, Dr. Vilas and Dr. Gould, were not present.

PAGES 174–75. For W. J. Mayo's observation on Paget's book, see "In the Time of Henry Jacob Bigelow," *Journal of the A. M. A.*, 77:597–603 (Aug. 20, 1921); "Libraries Useful in Their Day," *Bulletin of the Medical Library Association*, 25:71 (Sept. 1936). Dr. Will's admiration for John Hunter is attested by his personal secretary (Guthrey to HC).

PAGES 175–76. As early as 1906 Dr. W. W. Mayo was telling visitors how Charlie first gave the anesthetic when he was nine years old (Hall in the *Canada Lancet*), and the brothers continued to tell the story. But the doctor they always named as the anesthetist was F. R. Mosse, whose card did not appear in the *Post* until April 1877, when Charlie was twelve. Moreover, WJM to ROB says the incident occurred at the "Voltz place," and two operations, both for ovarian tumors, on patients named Voltz were reported in the *Post*, Feb. 24, 1882, and Jan. 5, 1883. For the second of these Dr. Mosse is named as Dr. Mayo's assistant, as is W. J. Mayo, who was home on vacation from Ann Arbor at the time. But Dr. Bowers, superintendent of the hospital for the insane, was also present to assist, which would seem to have made Charlie's help unnecessary. Besides, Dr. Mayo's first ovariotomy did not occur until 1880.

However, the Mayos were so insistent on Charlie's being a small boy when the incident occurred and remembered such circumstantial details—like Charlie's "peeking through the door" and "wearing knee breeches"—that it is hard to believe their memories were so completely at fault. The story made the rounds in Rochester and there is a good version of it in Granger, "Saga of a Country Doctor," *St. Paul Pioneer Press*, Jan. 13, 1935.

PAGE 178. WJM, "Medical Pioneers of Minnesota," *Minnesota Medicine*, 14:224–226 (March 1931). For Dr. Daniels see pages 70–75. For Dr. Tefft see *History of Wabasha County* . . . also *A History of Winona County* (Chicago, 1884), pp. 982–84; *Plainview News*, Jan. 27, 1905.

PAGES 178–79. L. B. Wilson to HC tells the story on Jay Neville. CHM to ROB repeats his father's remark about not charging poor folk.

PAGE 179. Dr. Will's statement of his father's principle of *noblesse oblige* was reported in the *Minneapolis Journal*, March 23, 1917.

PAGES 179–80. For Mrs. Mayo's influence on her sons: Eaton, Mrs. Plummer (quoting H. S. Plummer), and WJM to ROB. The remark by Dr. Charlie was reported in the *Daily Post and Record*, June 23, 1916.

### CHAPTER 8. AT MEDICAL SCHOOL

PAGES 181–83, SECTION 1. Comments on the state of medical education appear in every book of medical memoirs, biography, and history of these years as well as in such official records as the *Transactions of the American Medical Association*. Among the contemporary descriptions used for the text account are William Pepper, M.D., *Higher Medical Education: The True Interest of the Public and of the Profession* (Philadelphia, 1894); E. C. Seguin, "Higher Medical Education in New York: The System of Clinical Teaching in College," *Archives of Medicine*, 6:57–65 (Aug. 1881); *Report of the United States Commissioner of Education*, 1870–84, especially 1870, pp. 384–96, 1879, pp. cxliv–cl, 1882–83, pp. clxii–clxxix; Illinois State Board of Health, *Medical Education and Medical Colleges in the United States and Canada*, 1765–1886 (Springfield, Illinois, 1886).

PAGES 183–84. By 1880 the medical departments of the University of Syracuse, Boston University, Yale College, and the University of Michigan had followed Harvard's example. Chicago Medical College, the medical school of Northwestern University, had been the first to institute a three-year graded course, but its annual session was still only six months long and the third year was optional.

For the situation in Minnesota: C. Eugene Riggs, "Minnesota Medicine in the Making," *Minnesota Medicine*, 4:579 (Oct. 1921); Arthur S. Hamilton, "The Early History of Medicine in Minneapolis," *Journal-Lancet*, new series 38:123–31, 163–67 (March 1, 15, 1918); Illinois State Board of Health, *Conspectus of the Medical Colleges of America* (Springfield, Illinois, 1884), pp. 50–51, and *Medical Education and Medical Colleges*, pp. 98–101. See also "Report of the Committee on Medical Education," *Trans. Minn. Med. Soc.*, 1874, pp. 74–79, which was the report Dr. Mayo helped to prepare.

PAGES 184–86. The account of the Michigan medical school is taken principally from "The University of Michigan Medical School," in Vaughan, *A Doctor's Memories*, pp. 184–212; sketches of Moses Gunn, Corydon L. Ford, and Douglass Houghton in Kelly, *Amer. Med. Biog.*; *Calendar of the University of Michigan*, 1880–83. See also WJM, "Victor C. Vaughan: Standard Bearer," *Journal of Laboratory and Clinical Medicine*, 15:827–28 (June 1930), the entire issue of which is given over to sketches and tributes to Dr. Vaughan, the founder and first editor of the magazine.

Dr. Mayo must almost certainly have considered sending Will to the Chicago Medical College. His friend Dr. Byford was a professor there, and many of its teachers were the accepted specialists called in consultation by Minnesota doctors.

# Bibliographical Notes

He had himself consulted with Byford and with Dr. Nathan Smith Davis, the nationally celebrated dean of the school, on some of his more difficult cases in Rochester. But so long as the third year was optional at Chicago Medical College, who could know whether a doctor holding its degree was a two-year or a three-year man? And perhaps Dr. Mayo had visited the college and found its amphitheaters dusty and dark, the microscopes few and "ludicrously antiquated," the dispensary "horribly dirty and inadequate," and its service to patients a matter of "careless and trifling attention by the hurried clinical teachers." (Bayard Holmes, "Medical Education in Chicago in 1882 and after," *Medical Life*, 28:8–12, 57–62 [Jan., Feb., 1921].)

PAGE 185. The quotation is from the *Calendar of the University of Michigan,* 1880, p. 75.

PAGES 186–87. The *Post*, Sept. 17, 1880, announced Will's departure. It was Donald Maclean who called young Mayo "a green Western boy." (*Journal of the A.M.A.*, 25:1103 [June 6, 1896].)

PAGE 187. Vera M. Cummings, recorder of the University of Michigan Medical School, letter to HC, April 12, 1940, Press file, reports that "Will James Mayo" was enrolled in the school from 1881 to 1883, naming Dr. W. W. Mayo as his preceptor, but that all other records concerning him are lost. WJM to ROB is the authority for the boxing championship.

PAGES 187–88. For Dr. Will's memories of his classmates see "The Social Training of the Surgeon and Physician," *Proceedings of the Mayo Clinic*, 7:193–97 (March 30, 1932). See also Sabin, *Franklin Paine Mall.*

PAGES 188–89. For Palmer and Frothingham: WJM, "Nu Sigma Nu," pp. 4–5; Vaughan, *A Doctor's Memories*, pp. 198–202; sketch of Frothingham in Kelly, *Amer. Med. Biog.*

PAGES 189–91, SECTION 4. WJM, "Nu Sigma Nu"; Francis W. Shepardson, ed., *Baird's Manual of American College Fraternities* (13th ed., Menasha, Wisconsin, 1935), pp. 538–39; *Nu Sigma Nu in 1907* (published by the Grand Council of the fraternity), *passim*, especially the reminiscences of Frederick C. Bailey, pp. 559–62.

PAGE 191. The quotation is from WJM, "Medical Education for the General Practitioner," *Journal of the A.M.A.*, 88:1377–79 (April 30, 1927). See also WJM, "Nu Sigma Nu," p. 5, and "Recollections of the Medical School of the University of Michigan in 1880–1883," typescript paper in the Press file, p. 3.

PAGE 192. For Dr. Maclean: Vaughan, *A Doctor's Memories*, p. 202; WJM, "Nu Sigma Nu," p. 4, and "Recollections of the Medical School . . ." pp. 2, 4; William W. Potter, "Donald Maclean, M.D., LL.D.," *Trans. Amer. Assoc. Obst. and Gynec.*, 16:476–78 (1903).

PAGES 192–93. The remark of the old woman in London is quoted from Graham, *Story of Surgery*, p. 336. For Listerism: *ibid.*, pp. 332–60; William Watson Cheyne, *Lister and His Achievement* (London, 1925).

PAGES 194–97, SECTION 7. This general story emerges from a reading of pertinent articles and discussions in the *Trans. Amer. Surg. Assoc.*, 1880–85; *Trans. of the A.M.A.*, 1882–83; and *Trans. Minn. Med. Soc.*, 1875–85. Further details appear in almost every biography or book of memoirs from the period, for example: Gerster, *Recollections*, pp. 192–94; Franklin Martin, *Fifty Years of Medicine and Surgery: An Autobiographical Sketch* (Chicago, 1934), pp. 96–102; Dudley, *Medicine Man*, pp. 230–36; Robert T. Morris, *Fifty Years a Surgeon* (New York, 1935), pp. 30, 57–61; John M. T. Finney, *A Surgeon's Life* (New York, 1940), pp. 74–76; *The Life of Chevalier Jackson: An Autobiography* (New York, 1938), pp. 60–61; Lewis S. McMurtry, "Joseph Price, M.D.," *Trans. Southern Surg. and Gynec. Assoc.*, 24:609–11 (1911); Horace M. Brown, ". . . An

755

Anecdotal Sketch of Professor Doctor Nicholas Senn," *Military Surgeon,* 46:554 (May 1920) ; Lewis L. McArthur, "Christian Fenger As I Knew Him," *Bulletin of the Society of Medical History of Chicago,* 3:55 (Jan. 1923); Coleman G. Buford, "Christian Fenger—A Biographical Sketch," *ibid.,* 1:199 (March 1913).

PAGE 196. The quotation in the footnote is from Charles H. Hunter, "The Treatment of Wounds, with Especial Reference to the Aseptic Method of Mr. Lister," *Trans. Minn. Med. Soc.,* 1883, pp. 93–103. See also Arpad Gerster, *The Rules of Aseptic and Antiseptic Surgery* (New York, 1888), p. 27.

PAGE 197. For Maclean's Listerism: Vaughan, *A Doctor's Memories,* p. 143; WJM, "Recollections of the Medical School . . ." p. 2.

PAGES 198–200, SECTION 9. For Dr. W. J. Mayo on Ford: "The Relation of Anatomy to Present-Day Surgery," *Journal of the A.M.A.,* 74:367–68 (Feb. 7, 1920) ; "Nu Sigma Nu," p. 4; "Recollections of the Medical School . . ." p. 1. See also Vaughan, *A Doctor's Memories,* pp. 193–94; Dudley, *Medicine Man,* pp. 158, 160 (where the name is given as Gordon Ford, but the man is Corydon L., according to Gerster, *Recollections,* pp. 163–64) ; Sabin, *Franklin Paine Mall,* pp. 23, 28–30, 127–33.

PAGE 199. The quotation is from WJM, "Relation of Anatomy to Present-Day Surgery," *Journal of the A.M.A.,* 74:367–72 (Feb. 7, 1920).

PAGES 200–1. For the Sewall incident: Vaughan, *A Doctor's Memories,* pp. 209–12; remarks by WJM and Dr. Sewall, *Proceedings of the Mayo Clinic,* 6:311–12 (May 20, 1931) ; Sabin, *Franklin Paine Mall,* pp. 26–28. Walter Courtney became the chief surgeon for the Northern Pacific Railroad and the chief of staff in the Northern Pacific Beneficial Association hospital at Brainerd, Minnesota (A. W. Ide, "Dr. Walter Courtney," *Minnesota Medicine,* 7:617 [Sept. 1924]).

PAGE 201. WJM, Story to Mrs. Mellish, p. 4, reports his courses with Alexander Winchell. A certificate now in the possession of the Mayo Clinic shows that Dr. Will successfully completed an optional course in electrotherapeutics, a frill attached to the curriculum in 1882–83.

PAGE 202. The *Rochester Post,* July 6, 1883, announced that "Will Mayo graduated with honor. . . ." There is no evidence that this "honor" was anything more than the editor's embellishment.

PAGES 202–3. For the Atlee episode see *Trans. of the A.M.A.,* 33:33, 56, 176–208 (1882). For Dr. Will's memory of the occasion: WJM to ROB, and "The Congress of American Physicians and Surgeons," remarks to the Mayo Clinic staff, Jan. 28, 1925, typescript copy in the Press file.

PAGE 203. WJM, Story to Mrs. Mellish, p. 4, reports the Mayo family council. For Dr. Will's stopovers in Chicago: WJM, "Masters of Surgery in the Early Years of the Annals of Surgery," *Annals of Surgery,* 81:3–8 (Jan. 1925) ; "Two Medical Pioneers," *Proceedings of the Mayo Clinic,* 12:536 (Aug. 25, 1937); Story to Mrs. Mellish, p. 12. The *Rochester Record and Union,* Sept. 25, 1885, reported the Mayos' departure for Chicago.

PAGES 203–7, SECTIONS 12–13. About the only bit of personal reminiscence by Dr. Charlie about his medical student days is in "Problems of Medical Education," in CHM, Reprints, vol. 4. So the story has been filled in from Arthur H. Wilde, *Northwestern University: A History, 1855–1905* (4 vols., New York, 1905), 3:293–331; *History of Medicine and Surgery and Physicians and Surgeons of Chicago, 1803–1922* (Chicago, 1922), pp. 205–11; historical and reminiscent addresses in *Dedication of the Montgomery Ward Memorial Building—Northwestern University Medical School . . .* (Chicago, 1929) ; *Annual Catalog of Northwestern University,* 1885–86 to 1889–90; transcript of CHM's college record furnished for the Press file by C. W. Patterson, registrar, Northwestern University Medical School; letters from CHM's classmates to HC, Press file, as follows: Dr. Harry C. Whiting, Fairfield, Iowa, March 18, April 8, 1940; Dr. William R. Fringer, Rockford, Illinois, April 4, 1940; Dr. W. L. Warriner, Topeka, Kansas, March 20, 1940; Dr. H. B. Carriel, Elgin, Illinois, May 1, 1940; Dr. C. W. More, Eveleth, Minnesota, April 10, 1940; Dr. Samuel C. Plummer, Chicago, March 25, 1940. To them I here give my thanks for their cordial responses to my requests for information.

PAGE 207. The certificate of character is quoted from C. W. Patterson, registrar, Northwestern University Medical School, letter to HC, April 20, 1940, Press file. The *Record and Union*, March 23, 1888, reported Dr. Mayo's departure for Chicago to attend his son's graduation.

### CHAPTER 9. FROM FATHER TO SONS

PAGE 208. The quotation is from the *Record and Union*, May 11, 1883.

PAGE 209. Dr. Will's remark to Judge Start is reported in Martin, *Fifty Years of Medicine and Surgery*, pp. 282–83. The story has an apocryphal tone, but I have accepted it because it is in keeping with Dr. Will's character as it appears from other evidence.

PAGES 209–10. For the law regulating medical practice: "Report of the Committee on Medical Education," *Trans. Minn. Med. Soc.*, 1883, pp. 238–53; *Session Laws*, 1883, pp. 167–69.

In the *Official Register of Physicians, 1883–1890* (published by the State Medical Examining Board of Minnesota, St. Paul, 1890), p. 46, Dr. W. W. Mayo was listed as a graduate of the University of Michigan in 1854. Obviously *Michigan* was a mistake and it was changed to Missouri in later lists (Polk's *Medical and Surgical Register of the United States* [Chicago, 1896], p. 797). But why not the Indiana Medical College, 1850? The fact that Dr. Mayo's certificate from Missouri is extant, whereas his diploma from Indiana is not, suggests the possible explanation that the latter had been lost, but it is equally plausible that the Mayos had made a calculated choice. The Indiana Medical College was dead and unremembered; a degree from the University of Missouri would be more impressive.

PAGE 210. The instance of the Old Doctor's persistence is taken from the Steward manuscript, p. 106.

PAGES 210–11. Mrs. C. H. Mayo to HC tells the complete story of the confinement.

PAGE 211. For Mrs. Eaton's illness: Eaton to HC; *Post*, May 2, 9, 23, 1884. Though I have given the story as Mr. Eaton told it to me, I wonder whether actually this might not have been the occasion Dr. Will had in mind when he said, "I had a bad row with Dr. E. C. Cross when I first came on, and after that he respected me and depended on me for everything." (WJM to ROB.)

PAGES 211–12. The story of the old Irishman is from WJM, Little Anecdotes of Early Practice, dictated memorandum, Press file.

PAGE 212. The *Record and Union*, Jan. 16, 1885, reported the incident of the wolves. See also *ibid.*, March 28, 1884, and Jan. 23, 1885.

PAGES 213–14. The newspaper items are from, respectively, the *Record and Union*, July 4, 1884 (Mr. Cooper did not recover. See "Report of Drs. W. W. and W. J. Mayo," *Trans. Minn. Med. Soc.*, 1885, pp. 43–51), Sept. 28, 1883; *Post*, May 2, June 13, 1884; *Record and Union*, Jan. 30, 1885; *Post*, June 26, 1885; *Record and Union*, June 11, 1886, April 10, 1885.

PAGE 214. The statistics are from James L. Cabell, "On Sanitary Conditions in Relation to the Treatment of Surgical Operations and Injuries," *Trans. Amer. Surg. Assoc.*, 1:55, 64–68 (1881–83).

PAGE 216. The newspaper items are from, respectively, the *Record and Union,* Nov. 21, Dec. 19, 1884, April 17, 1885, Aug. 16, 1889.

PAGE 217. The remark of the Rochester merchant is reported in the *Record and Union,* Nov. 20, 1885. Minnesota was listed fourth among the states of former residence for settlers going to Dakota in 1885 (*First Biennial Report of the Commissioner of Immigration and Statistician to the Governor,* 1885–86 [Bismarck, 1886], p. 48).

PAGES 217–18. For Mrs. Vail, see the *Post,* June 13, 1884; for David Dyson, the *Record and Union,* April 24, 1885.

PAGE 218. For the Libby case: *Post* and *Record and Union,* May 23, 1884; "Report of Drs. W. W. and W. J. Mayo," *Trans. Minn. Med. Soc.,* 1885, pp. 47–48. WJM to ROB, and Story to Mrs. Mellish, p. 6, and CHM, "Early Days of the Mayo Clinic," p. 8, describe Mrs. Carpenter's nursing home.

PAGE 219. Father Lawler's account of the Old Doctor's enthusiasm was published in the *History of the Old School Boys and Girls Association,* p. 11. Dr. Charlie made the comment on his brother in "Early Days of the Mayo Clinic," p. 12.

PAGE 220. The case story is from the *Record and Union,* Sept. 14, 1888. See also *ibid.,* July 13, Sept. 7, Dec. 7, 1883, Feb. 4, 1887.

PAGES 220–21, SECTION 8. WJM, "Masters of Surgery in the Early Days of the Annals of Surgery," *Annals of Surgery,* 81:3–8 (Jan. 1925); WJM, "Early Days of the New York Surgical Society," *ibid.,* Jan. 1930 (p. 15 of reprint in the Press file); WJM, Story to Mrs. Mellish, p. 15.

Full references for the books mentioned: Charles Hilton Fagge, *The Principles and Practice of Medicine* (2 vols., London, 1886); William Osler, *The Principles and Practice of Medicine* (New York, 1892); James Grieg Smith, *Abdominal Surgery* (4th ed., London, 1891); Walter H. A. Jacobson, *The Operations of Surgery, Intended Especially for the Use of Those Recently Appointed on a Hospital Staff and for Those Preparing for the Higher Examinations* (London, 1889).

PAGES 221–22. The story of Dr. Will's attendance at the American Surgical Association meeting is from WJM, "Masters of Surgery in the Early Years of the Annals of Surgery," *Annals of Surgery,* 81:3–8 (Jan. 1925).

PAGES 222–23. For the account of the postgraduate schools: D. B. St. John Roosa, "The Opportunities for the Study of Medicine in New York City after Graduation," *New York Medical Journal,* 37:200–1 (Feb. 24, 1883); Thomas E. Satterthwaite, "Postgraduate Beginnings in This Country," *ibid.,* 113:755–57 (May 18, 1921); E. C. Seguin, "Post-graduate Instruction," *Archives of Medicine,* 8:158–68 (Oct. 1882); John A. Wyeth, *With Sabre and Scalpel: The Autobiography of a Soldier and Surgeon* (New York, 1914), pp. 461–66; Flexner, *Medical Education,* pp. 174–77; Illinois Board of Health, *Medical Education and Medical Colleges,* pp. 153–54.

PAGES 223–26. For Sands: "Henry Berton Sands, M.D.," *Medical News,* 53:599–600 (Nov. 24, 1888); John C. Peters, "Dr. Sands and the New York Pathological Society," *Medical Record,* 34:673–74 (Dec. 8, 1888); "Henry B. Sands, M.D.," *Journal of the A.M.A.,* 11:755 (Nov. 24, 1888).

For the history of appendicitis: Donald C. Collins, "Historic Phases of Appendicitis," *Annals of Surgery,* 94:178–88 (Aug. 1931); W. J. Cruikshank, "Historical Sidelights on Appendicitis," *Medical Life,* 29:315–61 (June 1922); John B. Deaver, *Appendicitis* (4th ed., Philadelphia, 1913), pp. 1–40.

For Dr. Will's experience with Sands: WJM, "Early Days of the New York Surgical Society," *Annals of Surgery,* Jan. 1930 (pp. 16–17 of reprint in the Press file), and Story to Mrs. Mellish, pp. 10–11. The two versions differ in some minor details, the latter saying, for instance, that the man was taken to the operating room instead of the work's being done in the ward. The quotations are from the former.

PAGE 226. The story of the young Swede is from WJM, Story to Mrs. Mellish, p. 11.

PAGES 226–27. Eaton to HC tells the story of the schoolteacher. Mr. Eaton remembered the case as one in which he and the fiancé of the deceased girl's sister sat up with the corpse. The story on the Mayos' side he had got from Mrs. Berkman, and he was able to fix the date beyond question by the records of the Rochester cemetery. I have assumed this to be the case of the girl whose parents refused an operation (Steward manuscript, p. 109).

PAGE 227. Reginald H. Fitz, "Perforating Inflammation of the Vermiform Appendix, with Special Reference to Its Early Diagnosis and Treatment," *Trans. of the Assoc. of Amer. Phys.*, 1:107–35 (1886); Charles H. Peck, "Charles McBurney, 1854–1913," *Surg., Gynec. and Obst.*, 36:430–32 (March, 1923). Dr. Will's copy of Fitz's article in book form with his name on the flyleaf is in the Mayo Clinic library.

PAGES 227–28. The Press accounts are, in order of appearance, from the *Record and Union*, Aug. 19, Sept. 9, 1887, July 26, 1889. Unless Dr. W. J. Mayo's memory was at fault, Mr. McCormick was at least the third person to have the operation.

PAGES 228–29, SECTION 12. Dr. Mayo's paper was published in the *Trans. Minn. Med. Soc.*, 1888, pp. 63–72. The previous reports were F. A. Dunsmoor, "Suppurative Perityphlitis," *ibid.*, 1885, pp. 38–42; J. H. Stuart [Stewart], "Perityphlitic Abscess," *ibid.*, 1886, pp. 113–15.

The *Trans.*, 188, p. 5, list Dr. W. W. Mayo as the chairman elected, but the *Record and Union*, June 29, 1888, makes it Dr. W. J. Mayo, and the *Trans.*, 1889, pp. 38–48, show that the newspaper was correct.

PAGES 230–31. WJM to ROB; WJM, Story to Mrs. Mellish, p. 3; dictated memorandum in the Press file; *Record and Union*, Nov. 16, 23, 1888. Dr. Will's memory placed the incident in 1884 or 1885, but in spite of differing details it seems certain that the case reported in the paper in 1888 was the one to which he referred.

PAGE 232. For the rebirth of the Olmsted County Medical Society, see Leonard, *Olmsted County*, p. 152; *Record and Union*, May 21, 1886, Jan. 7, 1887.

Biographical material on the men mentioned: WJM, "Memoir of the Late J. B. McGaughey of Winona, An Appreciation," an address to the Southern Minnesota Medical Association, reported in the *Winona Daily Republican Herald*, Aug. 4, 1910; WJM, "Two Medical Pioneers," *Proceedings of the Mayo Clinic*, 12:535–36 (Aug. 25, 1937); WJM, "Medical Pioneers of Minnesota," *Minnesota Medicine*, 14:224–26 (March 1931); sketches of Wheaton and Millard in Kelly, *Amer. Med. Biog.*; John T. Rogers, "Charles W. Wheaton," *Surg., Gynec. and Obst.*, 37:699–700 (Nov. 1923).

PAGE 233. The papers of the Drs. Mayo are listed under their names in *Physicians of the Mayo Clinic*.

PAGES 233–34, SECTION 16. "James Henry Dunn, M.D.," *Journal of the A.M.A.*, 42:1692 (June 25, 1904); "Dr. James Henry Dunn," *Northwestern Lancet*, 24:252 (July 1, 1904). Dr. Will paid tribute to the Minnesota physicians of foreign birth and training in "An Appreciation of Dr. Arnold Schwyzer," *Proceedings of the Mayo Clinic*, 9:162–65 (March 14, 1934).

PAGES 234–35. On Listerism in Minnesota: "Report of Drs. W. W. and W. J. Mayo," *Trans. Minn. Med. Soc.*, 1885, pp. 43–51; "Report of the Committee on Surgery," *ibid.*, 1880, pp. 22–24; "Report of the Committee on Gynecology," *ibid.*, pp. 47–51; Perry H. Millard, "President's Address," *ibid.*, 1883, p. 23; Charles H.

Hunter, "The Treatment of Wounds, with Especial Reference to the Aseptic Method of Mr. Lister," *ibid.*, pp. 93–103 (see also p. 10); James H. Dunn, "A Decade of Observation and Experience in Antiseptic Surgery," *ibid.*, 1887, pp. 56–67.

PAGES 236–37. Dr. Will's trip to New York was announced in the *Record and Union*, Sept. 25, Nov. 20, 1885. On the occasion of their father's death, Dr. J. A. Wyeth wrote to Dr. Will and Dr. Charlie: "When you both were younger than you are now your father paid me a great compliment in asking me to look after you. . . . I feel a just pride in the fact that I had something to do with starting you on the upward way." (March 13, 1911, CHM files.) It is not clear whether that was merely Dr. Wyeth's way of referring to their attendance at the Polyclinic or whether Dr. Mayo as a solicitous father actually wrote to ask Dr. Wyeth to keep an eye on the boys when they braved the big city.

For the Gerster story: WJM, "Early Days of the New York Surgical Society," *Annals of Surgery*, Jan. 1930 (pp. 17–18 of reprint in the Press file); WJM, "Arpad Geza Charles Gerster," *Surg., Gynec. and Obst.*, 40:582–84 (April 1925); WJM, "Masters of Surgery in the Early Years of the Annals of Surgery," *Annals of Surgery*, 81:3–8 (Jan. 1925); WJM, Story to Mrs. Mellish, p. 11; Gerster, *Recollections*, pp. 219–22 (reference to WJM on p. 221), 237–38. Though the publisher dated *The Rules of Aseptic and Antiseptic Surgery* 1888, it actually came out in 1887 (Gerster, *Recollections*, pp. 237–38).

PAGE 239. The *Record and Union*, April 13, 1888, reported Dr. Charlie's successful examination with pride.

PAGE 240. The quotations are from CHM, Discussion, *Proceedings of the Mayo Clinic*, 3:72–74 (March 7, 1928), which describes Dr. Charlie's toe-in-the-door days. WJM to HC is the source for the story of Mike's mistake.

PAGES 240–41. Dr. Charlie described this trip and his attendance at Pasteur's lecture in "Forty-Five Years," an address at a banquet of the Northwestern University Medical School Alumni, June 2, 1933, typescript copy in the Press file. See also the *Record and Union*, Jan. 4, April 19, 26, May 3, 1889.


CHAPTER 10. BY ACT OF GOD AND THE SISTERS OF ST. FRANCIS

I am greatly indebted to Sister Domitilla, superintendent of St. Mary's Hospital, for permission to read the Annals of St. Mary's Hospital, a manuscript record made by Sister Cyril. It is in two volumes: one marked II, which chronicles the events year by year through 1923, and another without numeral telling the story from 1930 to 1935, the date of Sister Cyril's death. The gap between the two was caused by the sister's illness. Preceding the dated entries in the volume marked II is a running narrative of the founding of the hospital and a description of conditions in its early years. Some of this material was published in the *Souvenir of Saint Mary's Hospital*. These, together with the Rochester newspapers, and the various accounts by the Drs. Mayo and Mrs. C. H. Mayo (the Edith Graham of this period) are the principal sources for this chapter.

PAGES 242–45, SECTION 1. The story of the "cyclone" has been told so often that there is an embarrassing abundance of material on it and as many versions as tellers. I have used principally WJM, CHM, and Mrs. Berkman to ROB; WJM, Story to Mrs. Mellish, pp. 5–6; CHM, "Early Days of the Mayo Clinic," pp. 5–6; *Post* and *Record and Union*, especially for Aug. 24, 1883; *Winona and Olmsted Counties*, pp. 757–68, which is practically a contemporary account; Annals of St. Mary's, II, pp. 11–15. I make no apology for selecting the version arbitrarily, for there is no way to establish the correct details—for instance, whether Dr. Will and

Dr. Charlie turned back before they got to the slaughterhouse, when they got there, or after they had worked a while.

PAGE 244. Mrs. Berkman to ROB is the authority for how Dr. Mayo came to be put in charge. Dr. Mayo's appointment is nowhere mentioned in the newspaper accounts of the time, but see his own statement that he was in charge of the hospital, in the *Record and Union*, March 14, 1884, and in his speech at the dedication of 1894 as published in *Souvenir of Saint Mary's Hospital*, p. 33.

This account of how the sisters came to supervise the nursing is from the Annals of St. Mary's, II, pp. 14–15. For Dr. Mayo's version see *Souvenir of Saint Mary's Hospital*, p. 33.

PAGES 245–47, SECTION 2. Annals of St. Mary's, II, pp. 5–10; *Souvenir of Saint Mary's Hospital*, pp. 33–34; *Post*, May 25, June 1, 1877, April 6, 1894; *Post and Record*, June 3, 1904.

PAGE 246. Bishop Ireland's suggestion is reported in the Annals of St. Mary's, II, p. 15.

PAGES 247–48, SECTION 3. Riggs, "Minnesota Medicine in the Making," *Minnesota Medicine*, 4:579–87 (Oct. 1921); Hamilton, "The Early History of Medicine in Minneapolis," *Journal-Lancet*, new series 38:197–98 (April 1, 1918); Armstrong, "History of Medicine in Ramsey County," *Minnesota Medicine*, 22:36–40 (Jan. 1939); James Clark Fifield, ed., *American and Canadian Hospitals* (prepared in cooperation with American Hospital Association, Minneapolis, 1933), pp. 606–46, which gives the history of only those hospitals that have survived but which must suffice in the absence of any more complete source.

A fourth hospital, Bethesda, was started in St. Paul in 1883 but had to close its doors in 1884, not to reopen them again till 1891. In Minneapolis the Cottage Hospital enlarged its quarters and became St. Barnabas Hospital in 1884. Dr. Charles N. Hewitt of Red Wing was reporting to the state medical society certain cases that he had "ordered to the hospital" (*Trans. Minn. Med. Soc.*, 1878, pp. 152, 153), but the chances are that his "hospital" was a nursing home like Mrs. Carpenter's in Rochester. Other hospitals were to appear in Minnesota within a few years, some before Mother Alfred's proposed hospital became a fact, but those listed were all there were in 1883.

PAGE 248. The quotation on the Winona hospital is from the *St. Paul and Minneapolis Pioneer Press*, Nov. 28, 1888.

PAGE 249. Annals of St. Mary's, II, p. 16, says the site was purchased Oct. 17, 1887, but the *Record and Union* of Oct. 7, 1887, announced that the purchase had been made. The statement in the *Sketch of the Mayo Clinic*, p. 12, and elsewhere that the original site was fourteen acres and the cost of the first building $75,000 is evidently based on the statement in the *Report of St. Mary's Hospital*, 1895, p. 6, without regard to the qualifying phrase "as it now stands," which was after the addition of 1893–94 and the purchase of additional acreage.

PAGE 250. The letter from Dr. de Forest, Aug. 1, 1932, is in the WJM files. For this trip see also the *Souvenir of Saint Mary's Hospital*, pp. 33–34.

The building did not proceed without impediment, for the contractor proved to be incompetent and inexperienced, and he wasted time and materials at a disastrous rate. Finally he went bankrupt, and his bondsmen, Mr. George Weber and Mr. Granville Woodworth, Rochester businessmen, faced the prospect of considerable loss. "Many a night's sleep I lost over it," said Weber. "Every dollar I had in the world was at stake." But fortunately Woodworth was himself a contractor and his experience saved the day. The hospital was completed within two months of the date originally scheduled, without any loss to the Sisters of St. Francis and at no more cost to the bondsmen than their time. (Annals of St. Mary's, II, pp. 16–18; *Souvenir of Saint Mary's Hospital*, p. 21.)

PAGES 250–51. For the newspaper descriptions, see especially the *Record and Union,* July 19, 1889, and the *Post,* Oct. 4, 1889; also the *Record and Union,* Oct. 12, 1888, May 3, 1889, and the *Post,* Jan. 18, April 12, May 24, July 5, 1889. Sister Joseph's comment is from vol. II of the Annals, p. 27.

PAGE 252. Mother Alfred's request and Editor Blakeley's gift were announced in the *Record and Union,* Aug. 2, Oct. 25, 1889. Sept. 30 has always been named as the day for the first operation, but the *Post,* Sept. 27, 1889, reported that the hospital was open and had eleven patients. On the other hand, the *Record and Union* of Oct. 4, 1889, stated that the hospital had opened "on Monday last," Oct. 1. For the blessing of the hospital, see the *Post,* Oct. 18, 1889, and the *Record and Union,* Oct. 25, 1889.

PAGES 252–54. For announcements about the intended nature of the hospital, see the *Post,* July 5, 1889; *Record and Union,* Oct. 12, 1888, July 19, 1889. The Olmsted County Medical Society adopted resolutions of thanks to the Sisters of St. Francis and Dr. Mayo for erecting the hospital and resolved that "it is worthy of the support of the medical fraternity of this vicinity." (*Post,* Oct. 11, 1889.)

Authorities for the opposition to the hospital are WJM, Story to Mrs. Mellish, pp. 17–18 (partially published in the *Sketch of the Mayo Clinic,* p. 14); CHM to ROB; CHM, "Early Days of the Mayo Clinic," p. 6. It is curious that no one else seems to have remembered this opposition, and there is no clear evidence of it in the newspapers of the time. However, the story of John Willis Baer is of his own telling (*Souvenir of Saint Mary's Hospital,* pp. 15–16).

For the A.P.A.: Humphrey J. Desmond, "American Protective Association," *The Catholic Encyclopedia,* 1:426–28; Albert C. Stevens, ed., *The Cyclopaedia of Fraternities* (2d ed., New York, 1907), pp. 293–98; John M. Mecklin, *The Ku Klux Klan: A Study of the American Mind* (New York, 1924), pp. 131–32, 138–39, 166–68.

PAGES 254–55. The young Catholic doctor was P. N. Kelly. For his activities and his relations with the Mayos, see the *Record and Union,* Nov. 21, 1884, Aug. 5, Oct. 29, 1886, Oct. 10, 1890; *Trans. Minn. Med. Soc.,* 1886, pp. 148–52.

PAGE 255. Some have doubted this story of disagreement within the sisterhood, but it is fully told in the Annals of St. Mary's, II, pp. 19–25. After her retirement Mother Alfred went to live quietly at the mission in St. Paul, where she died on Dec. 19, 1899. Although with Christian charity she spent many hours of her last years in prayer for the "enemies," unknown by name to her, who had accomplished her removal as mother superior, she must have rejoiced to see her judgment vindicated by the tremendous success and expansion that St. Mary's Hospital had achieved even before her death.

PAGE 256. The story of the young Sister Joseph is from Mrs. C. H. Mayo to HC.

PAGES 257–61, SECTION 9. CHM, "Early Days of the Mayo Clinic," pp. 7, 11; Annals of St. Mary's, II, pp. 26–30; Mrs. C. H. Mayo to HC.

PAGE 260. The editor's comment is in the *Record and Union,* Jan. 8, 1892.

PAGES 260–61. The story of the candles and Dr. Will's remark are given in the Annals of St. Mary's, II, 1890.

PAGE 261. The authority for the reluctance of patients to enter the hospital is Mrs. C. H. Mayo to HC.

PAGES 262–63. The improvements are described in the *Record and Union,* Jan. 16, 1891; Annals of St. Mary's, II, 1889–92 (see also *Souvenir of Saint Mary's Hospital,* p. 15). The story of the electric annunciator is from the Annals, II, 1892 and 1922, and the *Record and Union,* Jan. 16, 1891.

PAGES 263–64, SECTION 12. WJM, Story to Mrs. Mellish, p. 18; Annals of

St. Mary's, II, 1891–93; *Record and Union*, Feb. 21, 1890, Jan. 13, 1893; *Post,* Jan. 15, 1892.

PAGE 264. For the opening of the Riverside: *Record and Union*, April 15, Sept. 30, Oct. 14, Nov. 18, 1892; *Post*, Oct. 7, Nov. 11, 1892.

PAGES 264–65. For the renewed activity of the A.P.A., see the note to pages 252–54; for the Faribault plan, see the account in Folwell, *History of Minnesota,* 4:174–83.

PAGES 266–67, SECTION 14. As Dr. Will remembered the story of the Riverside, a homeopathic surgeon was imported from Minneapolis to operate on the Presbyterians when he and Dr. Charlie refused. Both patients required abdominal operations and both died. Whereupon the citizens of Rochester backed off, aghast, and the Riverside faded quietly into oblivion. (WJM, Story to Mrs. Mellish, p. 19; WJM to Thomas E. Steward, Dec. 9, 1936, notes in the Press file; also CHM to ROB.) But the newspapers, which reported the activities and patients of the Riverside fully, tell no such story. And there was no reason for Dr. Allen to call in an outside operator. He was himself a surgeon who had done abdominal operations on a number of occasions. During the two years of the Riverside's existence, patients came from Dakota, Iowa, Illinois, and Tennessee to be treated by Drs. Allen and Granger, and a number of them published cards of gratitude and recommendation for the hospital. Yet something queer must have happened to send Dr. Allen away in such a hurry when he was at a peak of prosperity and popularity. He was even mayor of Rochester at the time. He returned to Rochester the following spring (*Post,* Feb. 14, March 13, 1896) and carried on a large practice there for many years. He did not, however, renew his partnership with Dr. Granger or reopen the Riverside Hospital. The newspaper item quoted is from the *Record and Union*, Sept. 13, 1895.

CHAPTER 11. YOUNG DOCTORS FROM THE WEST

The principal sources of this chapter are the following accounts by Dr. W. J. Mayo: "Early Days of the New York Surgical Society," *Annals of Surgery*, Jan. 1930, reprint in the Press file; "Masters of Surgery in the Early Years of the Annals of Surgery," *Annals of Surgery*, 81:3–8 (Jan. 1925) ; "An Appreciation of the Leadership of the Southern Surgical Association," *Trans. Southern Surg. Assoc.*, 44:546–53 (1931); "An Appreciation of Dr. Arnold Schwyzer," *Proceedings of the Mayo Clinic*, 9:162–65 (March 14, 1934) ; "Personal Reminiscences of Great Surgeons," Mayo Foundation lecture, Dec. 1921, typescript copy in the Press file; Story to Mrs. Mellish, pp. 11–15. Most of the trips described can be dated from the newspaper reports of the Mayos' comings and goings. The citations that follow are *in addition* to these.

PAGE 270. The quotation is from WJM, dictated memorandum, Jan. 5, 1937, Press file.

PAGES 271–72. The episode and quotations are from the *Trans. Minn. Med. Soc.*, 1891, pp. 81–95.

PAGE 273. The usual statement that the brothers *never* left Rochester at the same time is demonstrably inaccurate. The *Transactions* of both the American Medical Association and the American Surgical Association show that on occasion both brothers were present to read papers and participate in discussions. See also the *Record and Union*, June 20, 1890, June 19, 1891.

PAGES 274–75. Charles L. Gibson, "Robert Abbe, 1851–1928," *Annals of Surgery*, 88:794–97 (Oct. 1928) ; J. B. Walker, "William Tillinghast Bull (1849–1909)," *Surg., Gynec. and Obst.*, 39:515–17 (Oct. 1924); Charles H. Peck, "Frank Hartley, 1856–1913," *ibid.*, 41:117–18 (July 1925); Charles H.

Peck, "Charles McBurney, 1845–1913," *ibid.*, 36:430–32 (March 1923); John H. Bradshaw, "Robert F. Weir, 1838–1927," *ibid.*, 50:506–9 (Feb. 1930); and sketches in Kelly, *Amer. Med. Biog.*

PAGES 275–79, SECTION 5. J. W. Kennedy, "Lest We Forget—Memorial to the Late Joseph Price," *Virginia Medical Monthly*, 48:409–13 (Oct. 1921); A. P. Butt, "Joseph Price," *Surg., Gynec. and Obst.*, 55:788–91 (Dec. 1932); sketch in Kelly, *Amer. Med. Biog.* The story of the electrotherapist is from the sketch in Kelly, *Amer. Med Biog.* The others are from various papers by Dr. W. J. Mayo.

PAGE 279. The Old Doctor's precept is quoted in Hall, "Echoes of St. Mary's Clinic," *Canada Lancet*, Dec. 1906 (p. 4. of reprint in the Press file).

PAGES 279–82, SECTION 6. Frank Billings, "Christian Fenger, 1840–1902," *Surg., Gynec. and Obst.*, 35:365–69 (Sept. 1922); Coleman G. Buford, "Christian Fenger—A Biographical Sketch," *Bulletin of the Society of Medical History of Chicago*, 1:196–204 (March 1913); Lewis L. McArthur, "Christian Fenger As I Knew Him," *ibid.*, 3:51–57 (Jan. 1923); Nicholas Senn, "Life and Work of the Late Professor Christian Fenger . . ." *Journal of the A.M.A.*, 39:4–8 (July 5, 1902); Bayard Holmes, "Medical Education in Chicago in 1882 and After," *Medical Life*, 28:572 (Nov. 1921); biographical sketch in Kelly, *Amer. Med. Biog.*

PAGE 279. Frederic A. Fenger, letter to WJM, May 28, 1939, WJM files, recalled that "I was only a boy when, in the middle 90's you and your brother used to come down for father's Thursday clinics and the evenings over the microscope in our home on La Salle Avenue."

PAGE 282. L. B. Wilson to HC is the authority for the story of Dr. Will and the picture of Fenger.

PAGES 282–84, SECTION 7. John B. Murphy, "Nicholas Senn, Ph.D. M.R., LL.D.," *Surg., Gynec. and Obst.*, vol. 6, insert between pp. 114 and 115 (Jan. 1908); Carl Beck, "Nicholas Senn, 1844–1908," *ibid.*, 37:398–400 (Sept. 1923); Rudolph Matas, "In Memoriam: Nicholas Senn . . ." *Journal of the A.M.A.*, 51:961–62 (Sept. 19, 1908); Horace M. Brown, ". . . An Anecdotal Sketch of Professor Doctor Nicholas Senn," *Military Surgeon*, 46:549–63 (May 1920); Holmes, "Medical Education in Chicago in 1882 and After," *Medical Life*, 28:570–71 (Nov. 1921); sketch in Kelly, *Amer. Med. Biog.*

PAGES 284–85. E. H. O., "Albert John Ochsner," *Trans. Southern Surg. Assoc.*, 38:491–94 (1925); Allen B. Kanavel, "Albert J. Ochsner, 1858–1925," *Proceedings of the Institute of Medicine of Chicago*, 6:48–50 (1926); WJM, "Memoir—Albert J. Ochsner," *Surg., Gynec. and Obst.*, 41:255–58 (Sept. 1925).

PAGES 285–87, SECTION 9. Loyal Davis, *J. B. Murphy, Stormy Petrel of Surgery* (New York, 1933); WJM, "Dr. John B. Murphy—An Appreciation," *Surg., Gynec. and Obst.*, 23:234–35 (Oct. 1916); sketch of Murphy by WJM in Kelly, *Amer. Med. Biog.*

PAGES 287–92, SECTIONS 10–11. WJM, "What We Owe to Johns Hopkins University," *Proceedings of the Mayo Clinic*, 7:32–34 (Jan. 20, 1932); Harvey Cushing, *The Life of Sir William Osler* (2 vols., Oxford, 1925), 1:311–43 *passim*; William S. Thayer, "The Osler Clinic," *Johns Hopkins Hospital Bulletin*, 52:101–6 (Jan. 1933); John M. T. Finney, "The Halsted Surgical Clinic," *ibid.*, 52:106–13 (Jan. 1933); W. G. MacCallum, *William Stewart Halsted—Surgeon* (Johns Hopkins Press, 1930); Sigerist, *American Medicine*, pp. 127–30, 138.

PAGE 291. The story of the origin of rubber gloves is told best in Finney, *A Surgeon's Life*, pp. 89–90.

PAGE 292. Dr. Finney describes his European experience in *A Surgeon's Life*, pp. 126–27. See also John C. Hemmeter, "The German Clinics of Today," *Philadelphia Medical Journal*, 7:862–63 (May 4, 1901).

# Bibliographical Notes

PAGES 292–93. This story, given here according to WJM, Story to Mrs. Mellish, pp. 13–14, is apparently something of a legend in Boston, for Clinic men still hear it when they are visiting medical men there (L. B. Wilson to HC). It is more than a little curious that Dr. Will should have been so unknown to the Boston men, for he was chairman of the surgical section of the American Medical Association at the time (see page 409).

PAGE 294. The quotation is from WJM, "The Advantages of Postgraduate Work in Boston," *Collection of Papers Previous to 1909*, 2:500.

PAGES 294–95, SECTION 13. WJM, "Notes on A Visit to the Surgical Clinics of Germany and France," *Collection of Papers Previous to 1909*, 2:503–14.

PAGES 295–96, SECTION 14. "The Society of Clinical Surgery," for 1906 and 1913, booklets in the WJM files; Davis, *J. B. Murphy*, p. 201; Finney, *A Surgeon's Life*, pp. 129–30.

## CHAPTER 12. APPLYING THE NEW SURGERY

This account is based in large part on the early papers of the Mayo brothers as brought together in the two volumes of *A Collection of Papers Published Previous to 1909*, supplemented by the statistics given in the *Report of St. Mary's Hospital*, 1889–93, 1895–1905. In attempting to set the Mayos' early surgery against the background of its times, I have made use of various medical textbooks from that period—especially William Osler's *Principles and Practice of Medicine*, which represents the best medical opinion at the time of its publication in 1892— and even more the papers and discussions published in the medical society transactions listed in the introductory note, page 720.

PAGE 297. For the flu epidemic, see the *Record and Union*, Jan. 10, 17, 24, 31, 1890. See also Osler, *Principles of Medicine*, pp. 87–88.

PAGES 297–98. Authorities for the brothers' work at the hospitals for the insane are WJM, Story to Mrs. Mellish, pp. 6–7, and WJM and CHM to ROB. See also WJM, "Limitations of Surgical Work for the Insane," *Collection of Papers Previous to 1909*, 2:459–65.

PAGE 299. For the change in the preparation of the operation site, see the *Collection of Papers Previous to 1909*, 2:141.

PAGES 300–2, SECTION 3. See the note to pages 124–25.

PAGE 302. Dr. Will's admission is quoted from *Collection of Papers Previous to 1909*, 2:209.

PAGES 302–4, SECTION 4. WJM, "Caesarean Section and Puerperal Hysterectomy for Pregnancy Complicating Myofibroma; Porro's Method; Recovery of Mother and Child," reprinted from the *American Journal of Obstetrics*, 1896, in *Collection of Papers Previous to 1909*, 2:199–202.

PAGES 304–7, SECTION 5. See the note to pages 223–26. The principal source, however, is the various papers and discussions in the medical society transactions, which on this subject at least are now amusing reading.

PAGES 305–6. For pertinent material on the Ochsner starvation treatment: Discussion of a paper by Robert T. Morris, *Trans. Sect. on Surg. and Anat. of the A.M.A.*, 1908, pp. 190–201; WJM in discussion, *ibid.*, 1902, pp. 243–44; report of a meeting of the Chicago Medical Society in which WJM participated, *Chicago Medical Recorder*, 22:62–81 (Jan. 1902).

PAGE 307. The Old Doctor's remark is from a discussion reported in the *Trans. Minn. Med. Soc.*, 1892, pp. 61–70. The speaker is identified only as "Dr. Mayo," but the context points to W. W. Mayo, who often engaged in arguments with this same "Dr. Phillips."

PAGE 308. For the case of the man from Sleepy Eye: *Trans. Minn. Med. Soc.*,

1891, pp. 47–48; *Collection of Papers Previous to 1909*, 1:327, 335. This was the first operation on the gallbladder to be reported to the state medical society. However, WJM, "An Appreciation of Dr. Arnold Schwyzer," *Proceedings of the Mayo Clinic*, 9:162–65, states that Dr. Justus Ohage of St. Paul "was the first in this country to plan and carry out the operation of cholecystectomy, in St. Joseph's Hospital, St. Paul, September 24, 1888."

PAGES 309–10. For the case of the old man from Racine: *Collection of Papers Previous to 1909*, 1:330, 335. See also above, page 286.

PAGE 310. The case account is from the *Post*, Feb. 18, 1898.

PAGE 312. The Old Doctor's way of treating strangulated hernia is described in WJM, "In My Father's Time," *Proceedings of the Mayo Clinic*, 4:349–50 (Dec. 4, 1929).

PAGES 313–14. For the story of umbilical hernia, in addition to the articles in *Collection of Papers Previous to 1909*, 2:146–47, 150–53, see WJM, "Radical Cure of Umbilical Hernia," *Journal of the A.M.A.*, 48:1842–44 (June 1, 1907), reprinted in *Collected Papers, 1905–09*, pp. 321–27.

PAGES 315–16. The case history is given in *Collection of Papers Previous to 1909*, 1:22–24.

PAGES 317–18. The case history is quoted from *ibid.*, 1:58.

PAGE 322. The quotation on Dr. Weir's address is from WJM, "Early Days of the New York Surgical Society," *Annals of Surgery*, Jan. 1930, p. 19 of reprint in the Press file. Dr. Will's warning about the neurasthenics is from the *Collection of Papers Previous to 1909*, 1:272–73.

PAGE 323. For Dr. Will's position in stomach surgery by 1905, see pages 434–35.

PAGE 324. For the unfortunate experience with the Murphy button, see the *Collection of Papers Previous to 1909*, 1:152.

PAGE 326. *Ibid.*, 1:260–61, 294–96. See also above, pages 411–12, 414.

PAGES 327–28, SECTION 15. D. B. Delavan, "A Sketch of the History of Tonsillotomy," *Medical Record*, 89:89–90 (Jan. 15, 1916); Joseph C. Beck, "The Evolution of the Tonsil and Adenoid Operation . . ." *Surg., Gynec. and Obst.*, 19:98–109 (July 1914); Osler, *Principles of Medicine*, pp. 332–39; papers and discussions, *Trans. Minn. Med. Soc.*, 1898, pp. 38–41; 1902, pp. 107–13.

PAGE 328. Mrs. C. H. Mayo to HC makes the comment on Dr. Charlie's instruments and methods for removing tonsils and adenoids.

PAGES 329–30. For the argument over the removal of scrofulous glands: Papers and discussions, *Trans. Minn. Med. Soc.*, 1897, pp. 108–11, 133–42; 1900, pp. 141–52, 1904, pp. 288–95.

PAGE 331. For the knee-joint operation, see the *Collection of Papers Previous to 1909*, 2:408–13, 425–26, 557–59. See also above, pages 404–5, 435.

PAGE 332. The newspaper report is from the *Post and Record*, May 26, 1899.

PAGES 332–33. Dr. Charlie told how these patients came to him in a paper on "The Cause and Treatment of Ulcer," *Proceedings of the Inter-State Post-Graduate Medical Assembly of North America*, 1928, pp. 538–41.

PAGE 333. Dr. MacLaren's comment is quoted from the discussion reported in the *Trans. Minn. Med. Soc.*, 1904, pp. 331–37. See also the paper and discussion in the *Trans. Southern Surg. Assoc.*, 1905, pp. 246–52.

PAGE 334. MacCallum, *William Stewart Halsted*, pp. 91–92.

PAGES 335–36. The Mayos told this story often. There is a good version of it in WJM, "The Work of Henry S. Plummer," *Proceedings of the Mayo Clinic*, 13:418–19 (July 6, 1938). In some versions it is Dr. Charlie who did the operating, in others Dr. Will.

PAGES 336–38. For the story of goiter, in addition to the papers by C. H.

# Bibliographical Notes

Mayo in *Collection of Papers Previous to 1909*, 2:357–71, see Walter M. Boothby, "Diseases of the Thyroid Gland," *Archives of Internal Medicine*, 56:136–206 (July 1935); John de J. Pemberton, "The Development of Surgery of the Thyroid Gland," *Northwestern University Bulletin*, Feb. 24, 1936 (reprint in the Press file); Osler, *Principles of Medicine*, pp. 711–16.

PAGE 337. Christopher Graham, "Cretinism with Report of a Case of the Sporadic Variety," *Trans. Minn. Med. Soc.*, 1898, pp. 138–42. It was Dr. Graham who handled the case. For his partnership with the Mayos, see above, pages 362–64.

## CHAPTER 13. THE RADIUS LENGTHENS

PAGE 339. The story of Pat Glynn comes from Dr. Charles G. McMahon, letter to Dr. H. C. Habein, May 1939, WJM files.

PAGES 339–40. The attitude of the older doctors is reported in Granger, "Saga of a Country Doctor," *St. Paul Pioneer Press*, Feb. 17, 1935.

PAGE 340. The story of Mrs. Robertson is from her son, Dr. H. E. Robertson, to HC.

PAGES 340–41. For the organization of the local medical societies, see WJM, "Medical Pioneers of Minnesota," *Minnesota Medicine*, 14:224–26 (March 1931). The meetings of the various groups were all reported in the Rochester newspapers.

PAGE 341. For the comment of Dr. J. W. Andrews, see the *Trans. Minn. Med. Soc.*, 1896, pp. 145–46.

PAGES 341–42. Edgar B. Wesley, *Owatonna: The Social Development of a Minnesota Community* (University of Minnesota Press, 1938), pp. 121–22.

PAGE 342. Dr. R. N. Jackson, the Faribault physician, made his statement in the discussion reported in the *Trans. Minn. Med. Soc.*, 1893, pp. 45–50.

PAGES 342–44. WJM to ROB recounts the incidents of this day.

PAGE 344. The quotation is from WJM, Little Anecdotes of Early Practice, dictated memorandum, Press file.

PAGES 344–45. The tale of "Dr. Smith" is quoted from WJM in the Steward manuscript, pp. 142–44.

PAGES 345–46, SECTION 5. Davis, *J. B. Murphy*, pp. 212–20; *Trans. Minn. Med. Soc.*, 1900, pp. 114–23; WJM, Story to Mrs. Mellish, p. 29.

PAGE 347. The two press items quoted are from the *Post*, May 20, 1892, July 27, 1894. They are typical of dozens.

PAGES 347–48. The Hunt letter, from the WJM files, is quoted in the Steward manuscript, pp. 144–45.

PAGE 349. The story of Carrie Brown is from the *Post*, July 15, 1898.

PAGES 349–50. R. A. Patchin, "President's Address" (of Iowa Assoc. of Railway Surgeons), *Railway Surgeon*, 5:563–69 (1898–99); C. B. Herrick, "The Railway Surgeon and His Work," *Trans. of the Med. Soc. of the State of New York*, 1898, pp. 214–19; W. H. Elliott, "The Organization of a Railway Surgical Department," *Trans. of the National Assoc. of Railway Surgeons*, 5:31–36 (1892); R. C. Richards, "Why a Surgical Department is Necessary," *Railway Surgical Journal*, 13:94–97 (Nov. 1906).

PAGES 350–51. For the Bennett case: *Post*, Sept. 9, 30, 1892; *Collection of Papers Previous to 1909*, 2:323. Other minor railroad cases were reported in the papers from time to time.

PAGE 351. For Dakota hard times, see Harold E. Briggs, "The Settlement and Economic Development of the Territory of Dakota," *Abstracts in History . . . of the State University of Iowa* (Iowa City, 1932), no. 7, pp. 89–104; Commissioner of Immigration for South Dakota, *Facts about South Dakota: An Official*

# The Doctors Mayo

*Encyclopedia* (Aberdeen, 1890), pp. 7–11; *Rochester Post,* Dec. 20, 1889; *Minneapolis Tribune,* June 21, 1893.

PAGES 351–52. WJM, Story to Mrs. Mellish, p. 8, tells the story of the returning Dakotans. For Johnson, see *Who's Who,* vol. 20, 1938–39.

PAGE 352. For the Dakota cases mentioned, see the *Post and Record,* Jan. 23, Feb. 6, 1903, Feb. 19, 1904. Dr. Will's promotions were reported in the *Post,* Feb. 23, 1894, Feb. 28, 1896. Major calls that came for Dr. Will are reported in the *Post,* Jan. 10, 1896; *Post and Record,* Oct. 6, 1899, May 11, 1900, Sept. 5, 1902.

PAGE 353. For Dr. Will's call to Mrs. Johnson, see the *Post and Record,* May 18, 1900; for the attempted suicide, the *Post,* June 18, 1897; for Sister Martha, *ibid.,* July 2, 9, 1897.

PAGES 353–54. The newspaper items are from, in the order of their appearance, the *Post,* Dec. 30, 1898; *Post and Record,* July 12, 1901; *Post,* Nov. 18, 1898; *Post and Record,* May 21, 1899.

PAGE 354. The story of the blind boy from Mountain Lake is told in the *Post and Record,* Aug. 16, 1901, and in WJM, Story to Mrs. Mellish, pp. 8–9. The extent of the practice in 1893 is given in the Annals of St. Mary's, II, 1893.

PAGE 355. The quotation is from the *Post and Record,* March 16, 1900. Some of the major accounts of the boom in horse-raising are: *Record and Union,* May 15, 22, 1891, March 11, April 8, May 13, 1892; *Post,* April 2, 1897, Sept. 2, 1898, March 17, 1899; *Post and Record,* Dec. 12, 1902 (quoting the *Horse Review,* Dec. 2, 1902). The Rochester papers always said the census showed Olmsted to be the "richest county," as does WJM, Story to Mrs. Mellish, p. 8, but allowance for exaggeration of local pride is necessary.

PAGE 358. For Dr. Moore's statement, see the *Trans. Amer. Surg. Assoc.,* 1905, pp. 185–86; for Dr. Dunsmoor's statement, the *Trans. Minn. Med. Soc.,* 1903, pp. 172–73.

CHAPTER 14. . . . AND COMPANY

Biographies and bibliographies for the various persons who joined the Mayos' professional staff are given in the directory, *Physicians of the Mayo Clinic and the Mayo Foundation* (University of Minnesota Press, 1937), and the positions they held, with dates, may be determined from the list of the staff included in each annual *Report of St. Mary's Hospital.*

PAGE 359. No statistics on the number of office examinations are available, but ten thousand is a conservative estimate. Dr. Will said that one fourth of their patients came to operation in those years. In 1903 he stated that of 1,200 persons who were given the test meal, about 400 came to surgery, and in 1904 that of over 1,500 such persons 478 came to operation. (*Collection of Papers Previous to 1909,* 1:200, 208, 225.)

PAGE 360. For Dr. Stinchfield: WJM, Story to Mrs. Mellish, p. 20; CHM to ROB; CHM, "Early Days of the Mayo Clinic," p. 9; Mrs. Stinchfield to ROB; Mrs. C. H. Mayo to HC; Leonard, *Olmsted County,* pp. 311–12; and newspaper items, especially the *Record and Union,* Feb. 5, 19, 26, 1892, and the *Post,* Feb. 5, 1892. Leonard states that Stinchfield had built up quite a practice in surgery and had even established a hospital in Eyota, which if true would suggest that the Mayos might have been trying to remove competition by a merger. But no other source corroborates this, and Mrs. Stinchfield stated positively that her husband had never done any surgery except when he was faced with an emergency in the country.

In 1897 Dr. Charles N. Hewitt was dropped from his position as executive secretary of the state board of health. In an interview with Dr. Folwell, Mrs.

Hewitt said the Mayos had remarked to Dr. Hewitt then that if he had joined them as they wanted him to he would not have suffered this injustice (Folwell Notebooks, 8:126 [Oct. 19, 1920], Minnesota Historical Society). So perhaps the Mayos tried to secure Hewitt as their partner in 1892.

PAGE 361. Mrs. C. H. Mayo and Mrs. Trenholme to HC; *Record and Union*, April 7, 1893; *Post*, April 6, 1893. Many of the bicycle trips were also reported in the newspapers.

PAGE 362. About the plans for the joint library: *Post*, June 16, 1893; Mrs. C. H. Mayo to HC.

Miss Magaw took the position in March 1893 (*Post*, March 10, 1893). But she had assisted the Mayos before that (*ibid.*, Sept. 9, 1892). For her course in the use of the microscope, see *ibid.*, June 16, July 28, 1893.

PAGES 362–64. Graham and Eaton to HC; Eaton, Hines, and WJM to ROB; WJM, Story to Mrs. Mellish, p. 20; *Post*, July 21, Sept. 22, 1893, June 22, 1894; *Record and Union*, July 13, 1894.

PAGE 363. The laboratory in Red Wing, established in 1889 after Dr. Hewitt returned from studying bacteriology with Pasteur in Paris, was the first bacteriology laboratory for the study of human infections to be established west of the Allegheny Mountains (Keys, "The Medical Books of Dr. Charles N. Hewitt," *Minnesota History*, 21:361 [Dec. 1940]).

PAGES 364–65, SECTION 4. Graham to HC; *Post*, Aug. 16, 1895; and scattered statements in the Mayos' papers, e. g., *Collection of Papers Previous to 1909*, 1:52, 64, 73–74, 123, 163, 172, 208, 225; 2:490–91.

PAGE 366. For the public response to the x-ray, see Graham, *Story of Surgery*, p. 368, and the *Post*, March 13, 1896.

PAGES 366–67. For Dr. Cross's x-ray machine: *Post*, Feb. 21, Aug. 14, 1896, Jan. 15, 1897; CHM, "Removal of An Open Buckle Impacted in the Esophagus (with X-ray Skiagraph)," reprinted from the *Northwestern Lancet*, 1897, in *Collection of Papers Previous to 1909*, 1:10. Curiously, Dr. W. J. Mayo could remember nothing about Dr. Cross's work and insisted that Henry Plummer was the first to use an x-ray machine in Rochester (WJM to ROB). Dr. Plummer, however, did remember that Cross had had the first machine and had done diagnostic work for the Mayos with it (H. S. Plummer to ROB).

PAGE 367. The story of the damage suit against Dr. Cross is from Eaton to ROB, and the *Post and Record*, Dec. 8, 15, 1899. For other cases that Dr. Cross handled for the Mayos, see the *Post*, Aug. 27, 1897, July 15, Aug. 26, 1898; *Post and Record*, March 10, 17, 1899.

PAGES 367–68. For the Mayos' first x-ray machine: WJM and H. S. Plummer to ROB; WJM, "The Work of Dr. Henry S. Plummer," *Proceedings of the Mayo Clinic*, 13:418 (July 6, 1938); CHM, "Forty-Five Years," typescript paper in the Press file, Dr. Charlie said he had brought the Wagner machine home with him when he graduated from medical school, which was impossible, since Roentgen did not make his discovery until 1895. For the Wagners and their machine, see Percy Brown, *American Martyrs to Science through the Roentgen Rays* (Springfield, Illinois, 1936), pp. 77–85, and for the general status of x-ray at the time, *ibid.*, pp. 3–31.

PAGE 368. The reports of Dr. Graham's x-ray results are in the old record books, Graham No. 4, 1901. See also *Post and Record*, Nov. 29, 1901.

PAGES 368–69. For the first addition to St. Mary's: *Record and Union*, Jan. 13, June 16, Aug. 18, Dec. 1, 1893, April 6, Sept. 14, 1894; *Post*, April 28, 1893, Jan. 19, April 6, 1894. Speeches at the dedicatory banquet are published in the *Souvenir of Saint Mary's Hospital*, pp. 32–49. See also the remarks of A. T. Stebbins, Annals of St. Mary's, II, 1922.

PAGE 369. The newspaper item is from the *Post*, Aug. 5, 1898. The attempt to form a school for nurses was reported in the *Record and Union* and the *Post*, Sept. 14, 1894. The episode over the loan is recorded in the Annals of St. Mary's, II, 1894 (see also *Record and Union*, July 27, 1894).

PAGE 371. For the hiring of Spillane, see the *Post*, July 9, 1897. He later became one of Rochester's leading lawyers and one of the Mayos' most enthusiastic friends. For Dr. Booker: CHM to ROB; *Post*, Jan. 14, 1898. For the second addition to St. Mary's: *Post*, Jan. 14, Feb. 11, 25, March 4, 18, May 13, Aug. 26, Dec. 23, 1898; *Post and Record*, Feb. 3, March 31, 1899; *Sketch of the Mayo Clinic*, p. 22.

PAGES 371–72. For Dr. Millet: sketches in the *Report of St. Mary's*, 1907, following p. 29, and the *Post and Record*, May 10, 1907; *Post*, Nov. 8, 1895, Jan. 10, 1896, Jan. 8, 1897, Nov. 4, 18, 1898; WJM, Story to Mrs. Mellish, p. 22, which is wrong in implying that Millet joined the group after Plummer; CHM to ROB; *Sketch of the Mayo Clinic*, pp. 39–40. See also James H. Dunn, "Cystotomy —Its Modern Objects and Methods," with discussion by WJM, *Trans. Minn. Med. Soc.*, 1892, pp. 168–78, 204–9.

PAGES 372–73. For Dr. Herb: *Post and Record*, Nov. 10, 1899; Annals of St. Mary's, II, 1899. *Sketch of the Mayo Clinic*, p. 51, says Dr. Herb started the clinical laboratories and was in charge of them part time. She did not start them, but she may have taken over the supervision of them, though only until Plummer's coming a year later.

PAGES 373–75. Eaton to ROB, Mrs. C. H. Mayo to HC, and scores of items from the Rochester newspapers, 1890–1905.

PAGE 374. The story of the fancy carriage lamps is from the Steward manuscript, p. 221.

PAGE 375. Dr. Mayo's many trips and his speech-accounts of them were all reported in the newspapers. For his political activities, see the *Post and Record*, Aug. 28, 1903, July 8 (citing in part the *Wabasha Herald*), Nov. 18, 1904.

PAGES 375–76. For Mayo and Willson: Mrs. Stinchfield to ROB; Mrs. Bunn T. Willson of Rochester to HC; *Post and Record*, Aug. 8, 15, 22, 29, Sept. 5, 1902, March 25, April 29, 1904, March 17, 1905.

PAGE 376. Dr. Mayo's letters were published in the *Post*, April 30, May 28, June 4, 11, 1897; *Post and Record*, Aug. 23, 30, Sept. 6 (three), 13, 1901.

PAGES 376–77. The birthday banquet was fully reported in the *Post and Record*, June 3, 1904. The loving cup is now on display in the Mayo Foundation Museum of Hygiene and Medicine.

PAGES 377–79, SECTION 9. Dr. Will referred often to this great decision, sometimes placing it in 1894 but more often in 1898. This account of what it entailed is based mainly on WJM to ROB, and Story to Mrs. Mellish, pp. 9, 23.

PAGE 379. The bank-stock incident is from WJM to Thomas E. Steward, Dec. 9, 1936, notes in the Press file.

PAGES 379–80. Eaton and Harwick to ROB; Eaton to HC; WJM, Story to Mrs. Mellish, p. 23. Mr. Eaton said and Dr. Will implied that Eaton took over the financial affairs in 1898. But Mr. Harwick said he could recall when the Mayos turned matters over to Eaton, and Mr. Harwick did not join the group until 1908.

PAGES 380–81, SECTION 11. Eaton and WJM to ROB; Eaton to HC; WJM, Story to Mrs. Mellish, pp. 20–21. This whole matter is a tangle of conflicting and incomplete statements. The above seems the most likely sequence of events, though when it occurred is uncertain. Certain indications from personal and family events suggest that it happened about 1900–1.

PAGE 382. For the new offices: WJM, Story to Mrs. Mellish, p. 28; *Post*, March 18, 1898; *Post and Record*, April 27, May 11, 18, 1900, Jan. 11, 25, 1901.

# Bibliographical Notes

For the story of the druggist: WJM to Thomas E. Steward, Dec. 9, 1936, notes in the Press file; Guthrey to HC, Nov. 18, 1940.

PAGES 383–84. The account of Jay Neville is from WJM, L. B. Wilson, and Hines to ROB.

PAGE 384. There is a brief sketch of William Graham in Leonard, *Olmsted County*, p. 242.

PAGES 385–86. The old case books are preserved in the record room of the Mayo Clinic.

PAGES 386–87. The story of Dr. Charlie's handling of the neurotic girl is from Mrs. Stinchfield to ROB.

PAGE 387. The time that Dr. Will and Dr. Charlie gave up general examining may be fixed roughly from the case books. The last one in Dr. W. J. Mayo's series, for instance, covers the years from 1899 to 1903; yet it is only partly filled. There are just a few cases, with great gaps of time between, for 1902, and only one, in February, for 1903.

PAGES 387–88. Dr. Graham and his son to HC.

PAGES 389–90. WJM to ROB; WJM, Story to Mrs. Mellish, pp. 21–22; WJM, "The Work of Dr. Henry S. Plummer," *Proceedings of the Mayo Clinic*, 13:417–22 (July 6, 1938); *Post*, Aug. 6, 1897; *Post and Record*, July 6, 1906.

PAGES 390–91. The characterization of Plummer is based on many appraisals of the man, but mainly on Lobb to HC and Plummer's own statements to ROB.

PAGE 391. For the "later telling" of Plummer's work with esophageal stricture, see above, pages 462–64.

PAGES 391–92. For Dr. Judd: WJM, CHM, and Sloan to ROB; *Sketch of the Mayo Clinic*, pp. 19–20; *Souvenir of Saint Mary's Hospital*, p. 71; *Post and Record*, May 19, 1899, May 25, 1900, Oct. 4, 1901, June 13, 1902, July 3, 1903.

PAGES 392–93. For the addition to St. Mary's: Annals of St. Mary's, II, 1903, 1904; *Sketch of the Mayo Clinic*, p. 22; *Post and Record*, Oct. 31, 1902, March 27, 1903, Feb. 12, 1904.

PAGE 393. For the details on transportation, see the *Post and Record*, March 16, 1900, Sept. 16, 1904, March 24, 1905, Sept. 21, 1906; *Post*, May 13, 1892, July 2, 30, 1897; *Record and Union*, May 13, 20, 1892.

PAGES 393–94. The story of the Cook House appears from the *Post*, Feb. 28, April 3, 1896, Feb. 5, 1897; *Post and Record*, Sept. 28, 1900, April 24, Sept. 11, Dec. 11, 1903, April 29, 1904.

PAGE 394. WJM, Story to Mrs. Mellish, p. 28, gives the Mayos' decision.

PAGE 395. The full story of the rest room is a long and interesting one. The Rochester women had started something. Before long the businessmen's associations of Mankato and Winona paid them the compliment of imitation and the women's clubs of other towns followed suit. The movement spread until an eastern news organ called this establishing of rest rooms a characteristic activity of women's clubs in the West and gave the credit for starting it to the energetic and public-spirited club of Rochester, Minn. (*Record and Union*, Oct. 11, 1895; *Post*, Feb. 14, June 26, Sept. 25, Dec. 4, 18, 25, 1896, April 16, June 4, July 2, 16, Sept. 10, Oct. 15, Nov. 5, 1897, Jan. 7, March 4, Sept. 9, 1898; *Post and Record*, March 3, May 26, Nov. 17, 24, Dec. 15, 1899, Nov. 30, Dec. 14, 1900, Oct. 10, 1902, April 24 [citing the Rochester, N. Y., *Democrat and Chronicle*], June 19, 1903, Jan. 22, 1904; *Rochester Bulletin*, June 6, 1928 [clipping in the Press file].)

The pros and cons on street-paving fill many columns in the newspapers. The excerpt given is from the *Post and Record*, April 6, 1906.

PAGE 396. The quotation is from the *Post and Record*, Oct. 10, 1902. See also the *Record and Union*, July 1, 1892; *Post*, July 23, Aug. 27, 1897.

PAGES 396–98, SECTION 20. WJM, Story to Mrs. Mellish, pp. 23–25; *Post and*

*Record,* July 1, 15, 1904, April 14, 1905, March 2, 16, June 29, 1906; Eaton, letter to ROB, Aug. 16, 1935, Press file. For a summary of the parks. story, see Leonard, *Olmsted County,* pp. 227–29.

PAGE 397. The quotation is from WJM, Story to Mrs. Mellish, pp. 23–24.

### CHAPTER 15. RECOGNITION WON

Bibliographies of the Mayos' papers may be found under their names in the *Physicians of the Mayo Clinic,* and many of them were reprinted in the *Collection of Papers Previous to 1909,* but in large measure the sources for this chapter are the discussions published in the various medical society transactions listed in the introductory note, pages 717–19.

PAGE 399. Dr. W. J. Mayo was already a member of the Minnesota Academy of Medicine in 1890. Dr. C. H. Mayo was one of two successful applicants out of a field of twenty when he was elected in 1893. His inaugural thesis, on "Skin-Grafting," had to be postponed a month because on the evening for which it was scheduled he was blockaded en route to St. Paul by a snowstorm. (*Post,* Jan. 13, Feb. 3, 1893; *Northwestern Lancet,* 13:134, 148–51 [April 1, 1893].)

Dr. W. J. Mayo was a member of the state board of health and vital statistics from 1892 to 1900 and Dr. C. H. Mayo in his turn from 1900 to 1905. When the latter had to resign the office because of heavy duties in Rochester, Dr. Christopher Graham took his place. (*Record and Union,* Jan. 22, 1892, Jan. 5, 1894, Jan. 17, 1896, Jan. 22, 1897; *Post and Record,* Jan. 12, 1900, Jan. 10, 1902, March 16, 1903, Jan. 20, 1905.)

PAGES 399–400. *Minneapolis Tribune,* June 23, 24, 1893; *Trans. Minn. Med. Soc.,* 1893, pp. 4, 18–51, 115–19. Dr. Will's presidential address the next year (*ibid.,* 1894, pp. 6, 8–9) was chiefly a résumé of the problems confronting the profession, including the prevalence of malpractice suits. He had himself been named defendant in a malpractice suit in 1891, but the plaintiff failed to appear when the case came to trial (*Post,* May 29, June 5, Dec. 11, 1891). In an attempt to solve this problem, which was becoming more and more of a plague, several of the leaders of the state profession, including Dr. W. J. Mayo, in 1900 organized the Medical Defense Association of Minnesota, a sort of mutual insurance society to fight the case of any doctor whom his fellows judged to be unjustly charged with malpractice (*Northwestern Lancet,* 20:368–70 [Sept. 15, 1900]. See also Donald B. Pritchard, "Malpractice Suits, How Best to Protect Ourselves Against Them," *Trans. Minn. Med. Soc.,* 1900, pp. 84–88).

PAGE 401. For Dr. Will's denial that he was a gynecologist, see the *Trans. Minn. Med. Soc.,* 1897, pp. 50–51; For Dr. Dunsmoor's comment on pyloric surgery, the *Northwestern Lancet,* 18:136 (April 1, 1898).

PAGE 402. For the doctor's comment on C. H. Mayo's paper, see *ibid.,* 12:275, 289–92 (Sept. 1, 1892); for Dr. Will's formula for speeches, Guthrey to HC; for instances of the newspaper reports, *Record and Union,* Feb. 8, May 17, June 7, July 19, 1895.

PAGES 402–3. For the commencement address: *Post,* Aug. 24, 1894; *Record and Union,* Jan. 25, May 17, 1895; *Collection of Papers Previous to 1909,* 2:522–31.

PAGES 403–4. Martin, *Fifty Years of Medicine and Surgery,* pp. 280–81. Dr. Martin thought the incident occurred about 1893, but the first notice of his presence at a meeting of the Minnesota state society appears in the *Trans.,* 1899, pp. 159–63. The experiences in Boston which he says occurred "soon after my visit to the Twin Cities" make the latter date seem more likely; yet in 1899 Martin would surely have recognized the name of W. J. Mayo at least.

# Bibliographical Notes

PAGES 404-5. WJM, "Masters of Surgery in the Early Years of the Annals of Surgery," *Annals of Surgery*, 81:3-8 (Jan. 1925) ; *Collection of Papers Previous to 1909*, 2:104-5, 337-38, 556-66; Arpad Gerster, "Open Treatment of Acute Phlegmonous Inflammation of the Knee-Joint by a Free Transverse Incision," *Annals of Surgery*, 22:503-6 (1895) ; *Post*, April 13, 1894, Oct. 18, 1895; *Record and Union*, Jan. 18, 1895. The story of the knee-joint operation is told above, pages 330-31.

PAGES 405-6. The story and the quotation are from WJM, dictated memorandum in the Press file. A reasonably thorough search of the "Proceedings of the American Medical Association" from 1890 to 1900 has not turned up any record of this incident. The decade brought forth a number of studies based upon the statistics collected under the supervision of John Shaw Billings in the census of 1880, but none of them fits the circumstances either in author or subject. Dr. Mayo expressed the idea that the statistics were being incorrectly interpreted in regard to cancer in a paper on "Cancer and Its Surgical Treatment," which he read before the Minnesota Academy of Medicine on February 3, 1892 (*Collection of Papers Previous to 1909*, 2:433), but there is no way of knowing whether his experience with the surgeon general led to the paper or vice versa. No attempt has been made to locate the episode in the transactions of any other society.

PAGE 406. The biographical dictionary referred to is Irving A. Watson, ed. and comp., *Physicians and Surgeons of America: A Collection of Biographical Sketches of the Regular Medical Profession* (Concord, New Hampshire, 1896).

PAGES 406-7. For Will's paper and Ferguson's comment, see the *Journal of the A.M.A.*, 26:1101-3 (June 6, 1896). For the amazement of those who listened to that and succeeding papers, see John H. Bradshaw, "The Mayo Clinic," *Journal of the Medical Society of New Jersey*, 24:285 (May 1927).

PAGES 407-8. The authority for the story of the rejected manuscript is Dr. Mazyck P. Ravenel (editor-in-chief of the *American Journal of Public Health*, Columbia, Missouri), letter to HC, Aug. 2, 1939, Press file. Dr. Ravenel heard the story directly from Dr. Stengel on two occasions. A letter from Lea and Febiger, the present publishers of the *American Journal of the Medical Sciences*, to HC, Aug. 7, 1939, Press file, states that Dr. Stengel was editor of the journal from 1898 to 1901. Within that period Dr. W. J. Mayo published two reports of his gallbladder surgery, one of a hundred and five cases and one of a hundred and thirty-two cases. Since the second was given before the surgical section of the American Medical Association and was promptly published in the journal of the association, the paper submitted to Dr. Stengel was probably the first, "Some Observations on the Surgery of the Gall-Bladder and the Bile-Ducts," which was published in the *Annals of Surgery*, 30:452-58 (1899)—after it had been rejected by Dr. Stengel, one may reasonably suppose. One wonders whether Dr. Stengel was unaware that Dr. W. J. Mayo was chairman of the surgical section of the A.M.A. that year, or just did not consider the position sufficient guarantee of his veracity.

For the survey of gallbladder surgery in Louisville, see William L. Rodman, "The Influence of Age, Sex, and Race in Surgical Affections," *Journal of the A.M.A.*, 31:495-96 (Sept. 3, 1898).

PAGES 408-9, SECTION 5. Dr. Carl Beck, letters to HC, April 2, 1940, Press file, and Mrs. C. H. Mayo, June 5, 1939, CHM files. Dr. Beck remembered the incident as occurring "in about 1894" and thought Dr. Senn had returned from hearing W. J. Mayo speak on gallbladder surgery at an A.M.A. meeting in Atlanta. The meeting of the A.M.A. was held in Atlanta in 1896 and Nicholas Senn was president, but that was Dr. Will's first appearance before the national society and he spoke on stomach surgery. If that was the occasion, then Dr. Mayo's first paper must have made even more of an impression than appears from the record. One would be tempted to believe the incident occurred in 1900 just after Drs. Senn and Mayo crossed swords on gallbladder surgery at the session in Atlantic City (see pages 422–23), but that was a little late for wonder at the use of the Murphy button. There is a brief biographical sketch of Dr. Carl Beck in James C. Fifield, *American Physicians and Surgeons* (Minneapolis, 1931), p. 234.

PAGE 410. WJM, Story to Mrs. Mellish, p. 14, testifies to his pride in the election to fellowship in the American Surgical Association. At that time the group numbered one hundred and twenty-five, three of whom were from Minnesota. Dr. James E. Moore of Minneapolis had been a member for several years and Dr. James H. Dunn was elected along with Dr. Mayo in 1899 (*Post and Record*, June 9, 1899, quoting the *Minneapolis Journal*). The membership list with the dates of election was published in the *Trans. Amer. Surg. Assoc.*, 21:xi–xvi (1903).

For Maclean's comment and the Michigan degree: *Journal of the A.M.A.*, 29:781 (Oct. 16, 1897); *Post and Record*, June 29, 1900; *Calendar of the University of Michigan*, 1900–1, p. 279.

PAGES 410–11. The Boston episode comes from Martin, *Fifty Years of Medicine and Surgery*, p. 281; *Boston Medical and Surgical Journal*, 146:451–56, 467–69 (May 1, 1902).

PAGE 411. The newspaper item is from the *Post and Record*, June 14, 1901.

PAGES 411–12. For the visits of Robson and Mikulicz, see the *Post and Record*, May 17, 1901, May 8, 1903. See also "Sir Arthur Mayo-Robson," *British Medical Journal*, 2:761–62 (Oct. 21, 1933); "Arthur William Mayo Robson," *Lancet*, 225:948–49 (Oct. 21, 1933); Garrison, *History of Medicine*, pp. 637–38. "Prof. Munch of Paris, France, editor of the *French Surgical Journal*" was another visitor from overseas at this time (*Post and Record*, March 20, 1903).

PAGES 412–13, SECTION 8. *Trans. Sect. Anat. and Surg. of the A.M.A.*, 1903, pp. 178–86. See also the *Trans. Amer. Surg. Assoc.*, 19:296–306 (1901), and the *Collection of Papers Previous to 1909*, 2:141–49, 151.

PAGES 413–14. The authority for the banquet incident is Dr. William Niles Wishard, Sr., of Indianapolis, to HC. Dr. Wishard was present at the speakers' table when this occurred. He was sure it was at the A.M.A. meeting of 1903 but thought it took place in Chicago.

PAGE 414. For Moynihan and the Philadelphia meeting: *Collection of Papers Previous to 1909*, 1:178–93; Donald Bateman, *Berkeley Moynihan—Surgeon* (New York, 1940), pp. 125–26; Finney, *A Surgeon's Life*, pp. 131–32. Other sketches of Lord Moynihan are by W. J. Mayo in *Surg., Gynec. and Obst.*, 63:684–87 (Nov. 1936); by George Crile in the *Bulletin of the American College of Surgeons*, 22:24–25 (Jan. 1937); by Donald C. Balfour in the *Trans. Amer. Surg. Assoc.*, 54:441–43 (1936); by Rutherford Morison in the *British Journal of Surgery*, 24:4–6 (July 1936); and by G. Grey Turner in the *British Medical Journal*, 2:653–54 (Sept. 26, 1936).

PAGES 414–16. WJM, dictated memorandum in the Press file; *Trans. of the Congress of Amer. Phys. and Surg.*, 6:195–227 (1903); E. Payr, "Hans Kehr," *Muenchener Medizinsche Wochenschrift*, 63:1046–47 (July 18, 1916). It is difficult to make a comparison between the reports of Drs. Kehr and Mayo. The former's paper was a general discussion of the principles in surgery of the common duct, with only incidental references to the statistics given in his last published report, whereas Dr. Mayo talked about several types of gallbladder and duct surgery with careful statistics for each.

PAGE 416. See page 481 for the "first layman's article"; *Journal of the A.M.A.*, 43:721 (Sept. 10, 1904), for Bloodgood's remark; *Trans. Minn. Med. Soc.*, 1899, pp. 113–15, for Dunsmoor's retort.

# Bibliographical Notes

PAGE 417. *Ibid.*, 1903, pp. 14, 24–25, 102–5.

PAGES 417–19, SECTION 11. Mrs. C. H. Mayo and Mrs. Trenholme to HC.

PAGE 420. The remarks by Dr. Dudley Tait are given in the *Trans. Amer. Surg. Assoc.*, 23:190 (1905).

PAGE 421. For the discussions summarized see the *Trans. Southern Surg. Assoc.*, 18:64, 67, 246–52 (1905); 20:60–67, 300 (1907); *Trans. Western Surg. Assoc.*, 12:37–39 (1903); 18:159–61, 165–66 (1908). The oration on surgery was "The Association of Surgical Lesions in the Upper Abdomen," *Collection of Papers Previous to 1909*, 1:231–43.

PAGE 422. For Dr. Charlie's advising removal of the gallbladder, see the *Trans. Southern Surg. Assoc.*, 20:206 (1907).

PAGES 422–23. For the Senn episode, see the *Journal of the A.M.A.*, 35:1396–97, 1401–3 (Dec. 1, 1900); for Dr. Moore's remark, *Trans. Sect. Surg. and Anat. of the A.M.A.*, 1902, p. 151; for Dr. Mayo's warning, *ibid.*, 1905, p. 384.

PAGE 424. The quotations are from, in order of appearance, the *Collection of Papers Previous to 1909*, 1:168, 170–71, 275, 279.

PAGES 424–25. Dr. Charlie's explanation of preventive surgery is given in *ibid.*, 2:490.

PAGES 425–26. *Collection of Papers Previous to 1909*, 1:123, 163, 231–33; 2:451–53, 490–91; *Trans. Minn. Med. Soc.*, 1902, pp. 81–86; Louis B. Wilson, "Elements of Error in Interpreting the Widal Reaction in Typhoid Fever," *ibid.*, 1898, pp. 43–49. Statements of the kind quoted are to be found in most of the Mayo papers from this period.

PAGE 427. The quotation is from the discussion of M. C. Millet, "The Diagnostic Significance of Pus in the Urine," *St. Paul Medical Journal*, 6:833–39 (Nov. 1904). The papers of the Mayos' associates before 1905 have not been gathered into any volume of collected papers, but most of them will be found listed in the bibliographies in *Physicians of the Mayo Clinic*.

PAGES 427–31, SECTIONS 16–17. Statements by Alice Magaw and Dr. James E. Moore, *Trans. Minn. Med. Assoc.*, 1904, pp. 98–102; observations of Dr. George N. P. Mead, Winchester, Mass., as reported in the *Boston Transcript*, April 21, 1906, and reprinted in the *St. Paul Dispatch*, April 28, 1906; Finney, *A Surgeon's Life*, p. 78; Hugh Young, *A Surgeon's Autobiography* (New York, 1940), pp. 58–59, 68; *Trans. Southern Surg. Assoc.*, 18:282–91 (1905); 22:307–19 (1909); *Trans. Western Surg. Assoc.*, 17:133–59 (1907); 19:333, 341–43 (1909); *Collection of Papers Previous to 1909*, 1:83–84, 117, 287; 2:368–69, 377–78, 382–83, 448–49.

I have been unable to find any secondary account of these early developments in anesthesia. Between the dramatic period of discovery and the later coming of local and regional anesthesia the story is blank. Miss Magaw and Dr. Moore certainly seemed to give the latter the credit for introducing the drop method of administration into the United States, but it seems hard to believe that among all the Americans visiting and observing in German clinics Dr. Moore should have been first and alone in adopting the new method.

Miss Magaw's papers, which are not listed in the *Physicians of the Mayo Clinic*, were these: "Observations in Anesthesia," *Northwestern Lancet*, 19:207–10 (May 15, 1899); "Observations on 1092 Cases of Anesthesia from January 1, 1899, to January 1, 1900," *St. Paul Medical Journal*, 2:306–11 (May 1900); "A Report of 245 Cases of Anesthesia by Nitrous Oxide Gas and Ether," *ibid.*, 3:231–33 (April 1901); "Observations Drawn from an Experience of Eleven Thousand Anesthesias," *Trans. Minn. Med. Assoc.*, 1904, pp. 91–99; "A Review of Over Fourteen Thousand Surgical Anesthesias," *Surg., Gynec. and Obst.*, 3:795–99 (Dec. 1906).

775

# The Doctors Mayo

PAGE 431. For the statement of the Iowa doctor, see the *Trans. Western Surg. Assoc.*, 17:158 (1907); for that of the German surgeon, Wilhelm Nagel, "*Aertzliche Reisebilder aus America*," *Berliner Klinische Wochenschrift*, 48:223–24 (Jan. 30, 1911).

PAGES 432–33. *Trans. Southern Surg. Assoc.*, 17:30–41 (1904).

PAGE 433. The Murphy story appears in the *Trans. Minn. Med. Soc.*, 1894, pp. 119–20. For Dr. W. J. Mayo's report of failures, see "Complications Following Gastroenterostomy," *Trans. Amer. Surg. Assoc.*, 21:151–64 (1902).

PAGES 434–35. *Trans. Amer. Surg. Assoc.*, 21:151–64, 178–88 (1902); 23:168–93 (1905); *Trans. Sect. Surg. and Anat. of the A.M.A.*, 1906, p. 210.

PAGE 435. For the dispute over priority in the knee-joint operation, see the *Trans. Western Surg. Assoc.*, 17:87–91 (1907).

PAGE 436. *Journal of the A.M.A.*, 45:281 (July 22, 1905). Dr. Rodman's nominating speech was reprinted in the *Post and Record*, July 28, 1905.

PAGES 436–38. *Post and Record*, July 28, 1905.

PAGE 438. *Journal of the Minn. Med. Assoc.* and the *Northwestern Lancet*, 25: 284–85 (Aug. 1, 1905); 26:410–11 (Sept. 15, 1906).

PAGES 438–40. *Ibid.*, 26:253–54 (June 15, 1906); *Journal of the A.M.A.*, 46:1737–40, 1884 (June 16, 1906).

## CHAPTER 16. THE SURGEONS CLUB

With this chapter descriptions of Rochester and the work of the Mayos by professional visitors become a valuable source of information. Among them I have used the following: Ernest Hall, "Echoes from St. Mary's Clinic," *Canada Lancet*, Dec. 1906, reprint in the Press file; George N. P. Mead in the *Boston Transcript*, April 21, 1906, as reprinted in the *St. Paul Dispatch*, April 28, 1906; A. C. Bernays, "A Visit to the Mayos at Rochester, Minnesota," *New York Medical Journal*, 83:808–10 (April 21, 1906); C. Hamilton Whiteford, *Glimpses of American Surgery in 1906* (London, 1906), pp. 18–20 *et passim*; P. G. Skillern, Jr., "A Visit to the Mayo Clinic in Rochester, Minnesota . . ." *International Clinics*, series 24, vol. 4, pp. 200–24 (1914); A. Laphorn Smith, "Notes on the Mayos' Surgical Clinic," *Montreal Medical Journal*, 37:323–33 (May 1908), reprint in the Press file; R. B. H. Gradwohl, "The Mayo Surgical Clinic at Rochester," *Medical Brief* (St. Louis), 36:478 (Sept. 1908), reprint in the Press file; Wilhelm Nagel, "*Aertzliche Reisebilder aus America*," *Berliner Klinische Wochenschrift*, 48:223–24 (Jan. 30, 1911); Steer Bowker, *Some Notes on Surgical Clinics* (Sydney, Australia, 1915), pp. 49–64; Kenelm Winslow, *A Life Against Death* (Lowman and Hanford, n.p., 1933), pp. 178–93.

PAGES 441–44, SECTIONS 1–2. L. B. Wilson to HC; WJM, Story to Mrs. Mellish, p. 28; biography and bibliography of L. B. Wilson in *Physicians of the Mayo Clinic*; *Post and Record*, Feb. 3, 1905; L. B. Wilson, "The Early Development of the Mayo Foundation," an address given at the annual meeting of the staff of the Mayo Clinic, Nov. 21, 1938, which Dr. Wilson kindly allowed me to read in typescript.

PAGE 441. Ochsner's comment is quoted from the *Journal of the A.M.A.*, 29:782 (Oct. 16, 1897).

PAGE 442. Lobb to HC is the authority for Plummer's attitude and remark. For Dr. Stewart, see L. B. Wilson, "Pioneers in Research," *Minnesota Alumni Weekly*, 39:481–82 (May 4, 1940).

PAGE 443. Robertson to HC gives Dean Wesbrook's opinion.

PAGE 444. For a description of the apparatus and methods for specimen photo-

graphy, see

graphy developed by the Rochester men see L. B. Wilson and Henry G. Andrews, "Stereo-Photography of Pathologic Specimens," *Collected Papers*, 1:579–97 (1905–9).

PAGES 444–46, SECTION 3. L. B. Wilson to HC; Wilson, "A Method for the Rapid Preparation of Fresh Tissue for the Microscope," *Collected Papers*, 1:579–80 (1905–9); WJM, "The Diagnostic Value of Microscopic Examination of Frozen Fresh Tissue," *Surg., Gynec. and Obst.*, 49:859–60 (Dec. 1929), and "In the Time of Henry Jacob Bigelow," *Journal of the A.M.A.*, 77:597–603 (Aug. 20, 1921).

PAGES 446–47, SECTION 4. MacCarty to HC.

PAGE 448. Murphy's letter to Moynihan is quoted in Bateman, *Berkeley Moynihan*, p. 131.

PAGES 448–49. Mead, in the *Boston Transcript*.

PAGE 449. Bernays in the *New York Medical Journal*, 83:808–10 (April 21, 1906); *Post and Record*, April 27, 1906.

PAGES 450–53, SECTION 6. Minutes of the Surgeons Club, June 7 to Oct. 10, 1906, preserved in the office of the Mayo Foundation in Rochester; *Post and Record*, May 18, June 22, Aug. 17, Sept. 28, Nov. 16, 1906; *Sketch of the Mayo Clinic*, pp. 138–40.

PAGE 451. Dr. Carrel had agreed (letter to HC, Feb. 1, 1939, Press file) to write an account of his visit to Rochester for use in this volume, but the march of Hitler's armies interfered.

PAGE 452. The quotation is from Hall in the *Canada Lancet*, pp. 14–15 of reprint.

PAGES 452–53. CHM, "Early Days of the Mayo Clinic," pp. 12–13, is the authority for the brothers' vow based on their own experience.

PAGES 453–54. The illustration is drawn from the discussion reported in the *Trans. Southern Surg. Assoc.*, 23:422–25 (1910).

PAGE 454. The quotation is from Hall in the *Canada Lancet*, p. 15 of reprint.

PAGES 454–55. Dr. Andrews' comment is recorded in the minutes of the Surgeons Club, June 14, 1906.

PAGE 455. The description of Dr. Charlie as a clinical speaker is from A. H. McIndoe, "Charles Horace Mayo," *British Medical Journal*, No. 4092:1207–8 (June 10, 1939). The illustrative maxims are quoted from Hall in the *Canada Lancet*, pp. 11–13, 15 of reprint, and Hewitt to HC.

PAGE 456. Such a verbatim report is given by Gradwohl in the *Medical Brief*, pp. 489–503. The Binnie story is from Winslow, *Life Against Death*, pp. 178–93. Binnie's book, *Manual of Operative Surgery* (Philadelphia, 1905), ran through eight huge editions and as late as 1937 was called "the best single volume on operative surgery that has ever been written." Binnie was a great friend of Will Mayo's and for many years went to Rochester each Christmas to act as Santa Claus for Carrie and Phoebe. (Emmet Rixford, "John Fairbairn Binnie, 1863–1936," *Annals of Surgery*, 106:157–60 [July 1937]; Thomas G. Orr, "John Fairbairn Binnie," *Trans. Western Surg. Assoc.*, 1936, pp. 446–48.)

PAGE 458. The story is from Winslow, *Life Against Death*, pp. 178–93. Dr. Haggard's neatly evasive comparison is from his "Doctors W. J. and C. H. Mayo —An Appreciation," a paper read before the Inter-State Post-Graduate Medical Association of North America, Nov. 1939, typescript copy in the Press file.

PAGE 459. The story on Dr. Charlie's talent in action is from WJM, dictated memorandum in the Press file. Henderson to HC is the authority for Sister Joseph's remark. The statement of St. Mary's central aim is from Dr. Emil Beckman (*Saint Mary's School of Nursing* [Rochester, 1924], p. 20).

PAGES 459–60. The quotation is from Gradwohl in the *Medical Brief*, p. 478.

PAGE 460. See Smith, "Notes on the Mayos' Surgical Clinics," p. 7 of reprint, for the comment of the Montreal surgeon.

PAGES 460–61. For the Halsted episode: L. B. Wilson to HC; *Post and Record,* March 8, 1907; WJM, "What We Owe to the Johns Hopkins Hospital," *Proceedings of the Mayo Clinic,* 7:33 (Jan. 20, 1932).

PAGE 461. For the presence of the Foss poem on the wall, see the *History of the Old Boys and Girls Association,* p. 20.

PAGES 462–64. Reports by H. S. Plummer in the *Collected Papers,* 1:11–49 (1905–9); Winslow, *Life Against Death,* pp. 178–93; L. B. Wilson to HC; WJM, "The Work of Dr. Henry S. Plummer," *Proceedings of the Mayo Clinic,* 13:417–22 (July 6, 1938).

PAGES 464–65. This version of the anecdote is from Samuel Hopkins Adams, "Modern Surgery," *McClure's Magazine,* 24:484–85 (March 1905).

PAGES 465–66, SECTION 13. L. B. Wilson to HC; *Trans. Amer. Surg. Assoc.,* 25:237–54, 271 (1907); *Northwestern Lancet,* 26:308 (July 15, 1906); minutes of the Surgeons Club, June 21, July 2, 1906; Mayo, Wilson, and Giffin, "Acquired Diverticulitis of the Large Intestine," *Collected Papers,* 1:294–317 (1905–9).

PAGE 466. Dr. J. E. Crewe, tribute to C. H. Mayo, read before the Olmsted-Houston-Fillmore-Dodge County Medical Society, May 1939, typescript copy in WJM files.

PAGE 467. Guthrey to HC tells the story of the fallen duck.

PAGES 467–69, SECTION 15. Mrs. C. H. Mayo and Mrs. Trenholme to HC.

PAGE 469. *Post and Record,* April 27, 1906; Dr. Carl Beck, letter to HC, April 2, 1940, Press file; minutes of the Surgeons Club, summer months of 1906; Hall in the *Canada Lancet,* p. 3 of reprint; Olson to HC.

PAGE 470. Lobb to HC for the story; *Annals of St. Mary's,* II, p. 33, for the note of thanks.

PAGES 470–71. The semicentennial and Dr. Mayo's address are reported in the *Post and Record,* Sept. 21, 1906. For the Salt Lake incident: Mrs. Bunn T. Willson to HC, and the *Post and Record,* Jan. 18 (quoting the *Salt Lake Herald*), Feb. 22, 1907; for the Old Doctor's trip around the world: WJM and CHM to ROB; *Post and Record,* April 19, 1907.

PAGE 471. Mrs. Plummer, one of Mrs. Mayo's companions at the time, to ROB is the authority for the pumpkin-stealing; WJM to ROB for the office occurrence.

PAGES 472–73, SECTION 17. *Daily Post and Record,* March 6, 7, 1911, June 1, July 15, 1915; *St. Paul Dispatch,* March 6, 1911; *Olmsted County Democrat,* March 10, 1911; *St. Paul Pioneer Press,* May 30, 1915; CHM, WJM, Mrs. Berkman, Sister Joseph, and Eaton to ROB. Notice of Dr. Mayo's death with accompanying sketches of his life appeared in most of the newspapers of the state; for instance, in the *Duluth Herald,* March 6, 1911; *Sleepy Eye Herald-Dispatch,* March 10, 1911; *Moorhead Citizen,* March 15, 1911. The last was an item two thirds of a column in length, in "boiler type" furnished by a syndicate.

PAGES 473–74. There is a description of Lake Allis in Leonard, *Olmsted County,* p. 285. Caryl B. Storrs, *Visitin' Round in Minnesota* (a series of sketches reprinted from the *Minneapolis Tribune,* 1916), pp. 87–89, records an interview with Captain Cassidy.

PAGES 474–75. Mrs. C. H. Mayo and Mrs. Trenholme to HC, and the Steward manuscript, pp. 412–13, describe Mayowood and Dr. Charlie at home.

PAGE 475. The story of the x-ray plates in the greenhouse is from Winslow, *Life Against Death,* pp. 178–93.

PAGES 475–76. The quotation is from Bowker, *Some Notes on Surgical Clinics,* pp. 54–56.

# Bibliographical Notes

PAGE 477. The *Post and Record*, March 8, 1908, reports the proposal of Mayo for mayor.

PAGES 477–80, SECTIONS 19–20. CHM and Eaton to ROB; WJM to HC; accounts of Dr. C. H. Mayo's work as health officer prepared by Dr. D. C. Lochead, typescript copies in the Press file; *Daily Post and Record*, Jan. 25, 1907, April 1, 2, 6, 9, 22, 26, May 2, 4, 1912, Dec. 4, 1918; "Rochester Milkmen Must Wash Their Hands with Antiseptic Soap," *Minneapolis Morning Tribune*, April 23, 1925; "Mayo Picks Foe of Law to Inspect Milk," *Minneapolis Evening Tribune* and *St. Paul Dispatch*, April 28, 1925; CHM, "The Health Problems of a Small City," *Journal of the A.M.A.*, 74:1187 (April 24, 1920); CHM, "Milk: The Cheapest Food Available," *Everybody's Health*, 19 (no. 11): 2–3, 28 (Nov. 1934); Marguerite Breen, "Dr. Charles H. Mayo Made Great Contribution to Minnesota's Fight Against Tuberculosis," *ibid.*, 24 (no. 6): 2–3, 10, 14 (June–July 1939). The items from the Twin City papers are clippings in the Press file.

## CHAPTER 17. TARGET AND MAGNET

PAGES 481–82, SECTION 1. "Such is Fame!" *Northwestern Lancet*, 25:233 (June 15, 1905); Samuel Hopkins Adams, "Modern Surgery," *McClure's Magazine*, 24:482–92 (March 1905); *Boston Transcript*, April 21, 1906, as reprinted in the *St. Paul Dispatch*, April 28, 1906; W. J. and C. H. Mayo, "A Protest Against Compulsory Publicity," *Journal of the A.M.A.*, 48:626 (Feb. 16, 1907), and *Northwestern Lancet*, 27:84 (Feb. 15, 1907); "A Disclaimer from the Mayo Brothers," *Journal of the A.M.A.*, 52:1596 (May 15, 1909); *Post and Record*, Feb. 24, Sept. 1, 1905.

PAGES 482–83. Wilfred T. Grenfell, "Two Leaders in Surgery," *Outlook*, 86: 404–9 (June 22, 1907); *Post and Record*, Feb. 22, 1907.

PAGES 483–85. Thomas D. Richter, "The Mayos, Father and Sons," *Human Life*, 6 (no. 1): 8, 36, 41 (April 1909); "A Disclaimer from the Mayo Brothers," *Journal of the A.M.A.*, 52:1596 (May 15, 1909).

PAGES 485–87, SECTION 3. I have gathered the details of this controversy between friends and foes of the Mayos chiefly from interviews with men who participated in it, but indications of it are to be found in many of the contemporary articles about them. In addition to those cited in the introductory note to chapter 16, see the editorial in the *Northwestern Lancet*, 26:454 (Oct. 1, 1906), and the unsigned article, "Visits to Surgical Clinics at Home and Abroad," *British Journal of Surgery*, 2 (no. 5): 114–18 (Oct. 2, 1914).

PAGE 485. Dr. Richardson's gesture was recorded by Mrs. Mellish in the original draft for the *Sketch of the Mayo Clinic*, parts of which are in the Press file.

PAGE 486. Dr. Haggard told this story often, once in "Doctors W. J. and C. H. Mayo—An Appreciation."

PAGE 487. For the Mayos' decision, WJM, Story to Mrs. Mellish, pp. 8–9. The quotation is from WJM, letter to Walter J. Kohler, governor of Wisconsin, Jan. 15, 1930, WJM files.

PAGES 487–89, SECTION 4. *Daily Pioneer Press* (St. Paul), *Minneapolis Tribune*, *Daily Post and Record* (Rochester), *Chicago Daily Tribune*, *New York Tribune*, Sept. 14–22, 1909; Frank A. Day and Theodore Knappen, *Life of John Albert Johnson* (St. Paul, 1910), pp. 85, 125, 248–58; Mrs. C. H. Mayo to HC.

PAGES 489–91, SECTION 5. Scores of newspaper clippings, Dec. 16, 1911, to Jan. 17, 1912, in the CHM collection; *St. Paul Pioneer Press*, Jan. 2, 1912, quoting the *Washington Post*, a clipping in the Minnesota Historical Society Scrapbooks, 66:60; Laura L. McDonald of New York City, letter to WJM, July 8, 1939, WJM files.

PAGES 491–92. For the Clinical Congress and the college: Martin, *Fifty Years of Medicine and Surgery*, pp. 292–330; Finney, *A Surgeon's Life*, pp. 132–36.

PAGES 492–93. William Allen White, letter to HC, April 10, 1940, in the Press file.

PAGES 493–96, SECTIONS 7–8. H. S. Plummer, "The Function of the Thyroid Gland," *Collected Papers*, 17:473–99 (1925); Walter M. Boothby, "Disease of the Thyroid Gland," *Archives of Internal Medicine*, 56:136–206 (July 1935); John de J. Pemberton, "The Development of Surgery of the Thyroid Gland," *Northwestern University Bulletin*, Feb. 24, 1936, reprint in the Press file; Boothby, W. A. Plummer, and L. B. Wilson to HC. The primary sources are of course the many contemporary papers on the subject, the most important of which may be found in the annual volumes of the *Collected Papers*.

PAGES 496–97. The incident is from my own childhood experience.

PAGE 497. Mrs. C. H. Mayo to HC is the authority for the feeling among Rochester women.

PAGE 498. The story of Jay Neville is from Mrs. Mellish's first draft for the *Sketch of the Mayo Clinic*; that of the kitty, which appeared again and again in newspaper items on the Mayos, is here taken from a letter written home by Mrs. Lola O. Coffey, a Mayo patient, and published in the local paper of Wellman, Iowa, Oct. 18, 1917 (clipping in HJH collection).

PAGES 498–99, SECTION 11. "Data for a History of the School of Nursing," and other manuscript papers loaned me by Sister Domitilla from the archives of St. Mary's Hospital; *Souvenir of Saint Mary's Hospital*, pp. 28–31; *Saint Mary's School of Nursing*; Cecilia Mary Young, "Anna C. Jammé: Director California State Nurses Association," *Catholic News*, 18:1–2 (Nov. 8, 1930); WJM, "St. Mary's Commencement Address," *Proceedings of the Mayo Clinic*, 7:301 (May 25, 1932); WJM, Story to Mrs. Mellish, p. 16; Sisters Joseph and Domitilla to ROB.

PAGE 499. Dr. Judd paid tribute to Sister Fabian's ability in an address at the opening of the St. Mary's surgical pavilion (Annals of St. Mary's, II, 1922); Mrs. C. H. Mayo to HC quotes Dr. Charlie's tribute.

PAGE 500. The sisters' suggestion is reported in the Steward manuscript, pp. 216–17.

PAGES 500–1. Lobb to HC is the authority for the emergency use of the Cook House and its effect on the Mayos' thinking.

PAGES 501–2. For the Chute Sanatorium and the building of the Kahler House: WJM, Story to Mrs. Mellish, pp. 28, 34; Harwick to HC; *Post and Record*, Feb. 2, 23, April 6, May 18, July 27, Aug. 17, Oct. 5, 1906, March 22, 29, April 26, May 10, 1907.

CHAPTER 18. THE CLINIC TAKES SHAPE

This account is a composite of information from the following sources, which will not be cited further: biographical sketches in the *Physicians of the Mayo Clinic*; *Sketch of the Mayo Clinic, passim*; staff lists in the *Report of St. Mary's Hospital*, 1906–14; and interviews with staff members of the Mayo Clinic as listed in the introductory note, pages 717–19. The first two are to be used with care in this connection because they often apply for the earlier years the division and section terminology in use when they were written. Wherever possible the facts from interviews have been checked with documentary sources and, in matters of interpretation, against each other.

PAGE 503. Dr. Stinchfield's retirement and the change in the partnership attending it were reported in the *Post and Record*, July 6, 1906, and the *North-*

*western Lancet,* 26:308 (July 15, 1906). For Dr. Millet's death, see the *Post and Record,* May 10, 1907, and the *Report of St. Mary's Hospital,* 1907, following p. 29.

PAGE 506. The story of the South American potentate is told in Winslow, *Life Against Death,* pp. 178–93.

PAGE 507. Dr. Beckman's resignation from his Minneapolis position was reported in the *Post and Record,* March 8, 1907 (quoting the *St. Paul Pioneer Press*). The quotation is from the *Sketch of the Mayo Clinic,* p. 20.

PAGES 508–9. WJM, "Present-Day Surgery in England and Scotland," *Collected Papers,* 1:608–10 (1905–9); G. Grey Turner, "The Late Sir Robert Jones of Liverpool," *British Medical Journal,* Jan. 28, 1933, pp. 170–71.

PAGE 510. The quotation from Dr. Will and the item about the knife-throwing surgeon are from "Personal Reminiscences of Great Surgeons," p. 14. The two quotations from assistants are from, respectively, McIndoe, "Charles Horace Mayo," *British Medical Journal,* No. 4092:1207–8 (June 10, 1939), and Harold L. Foss, "An Appreciation of the Life and Work of Dr. W. J. and Dr. C. H. Mayo," an address to the North Central Clinical Society, Pittsburgh, Pennsylvania, April 29, 1939, typescript copy in WJM files.

PAGE 511. The Sunday morning rounds with the children are recalled in Mrs. Trenholme to HC, and Dr. Donald V. Baker, letter to Mrs. C. H. Mayo [May 1939], CHM files. There are dozens of reminiscent letters from the patients of these years among those sent during the last illnesses of the two brothers. These are in the files at the Mayo Clinic. The quotation is from Dr. Harold L. Foss, Danville, Pennsylvania, letter to WJM, June 29, 1939, WJM files.

PAGE 512. Dr. Eusterman's experience and remark are from the Steward manuscript, p. 228. Dr. Carman's laboratory and work are described in Bowker, *Some Notes on Surgical Clinics,* pp. 57, 62.

PAGE 514. For Dr. Will's attitude toward research, see WJM, Story to Mrs. Mellish, p. 32, and to HC. See also above, page 200.

PAGES 515–17, SECTION 7. Kendall, "Recent Advances in Our Knowledge of the Active Constituent in the Thyroid: Its Chemical Nature and Function," *Boston Medical and Surgical Journal,* 175:557–62 (Oct. 19, 1916); Kendall, letter to Dr. Harvey Cushing, Feb. 25, 1937, copy in the Press file; Steward manuscript, p. 283.

PAGES 518–21. WJM, "Maud H. Mellish Wilson and the Mayo Clinic," *Proceedings of the Mayo Clinic,* unpaged supplement to vol. 8, no. 51 (Dec. 20, 1933); L. B. Wilson, "A Woman Pioneer in a New Profession, Medical Editing," *ibid.;* Maud Mellish Wilson, original draft of chapter 10 of the *Sketch of the Mayo Clinic.*

PAGES 521–22, SECTION 9. The incident is from L. B. Wilson to HC. There is some confusion about the date for this development. In *Physicians of the Mayo Clinic and Mayo Foundation* (2 vols., Philadelphia, 1927), 1:v, Mrs. Mellish Wilson wrote that the name *fellow* was applied in 1908. However, in a "Historical Sketch of the Mayo Foundation," written in 1937 (typescript copy in the Press file), Dr. Wilson said that by 1912 the three-year rotation was being followed by thirty-six men "who at that time were first designated fellows of the Mayo Clinic." And this later date seems more likely in view of other episodes in the evolution of the term *Mayo Clinic.* But neither the new terminology nor any clear evidence of the rotation appears in the staff lists of the *Report of St. Mary's Hospital.* There the terms "surgical assistants," "clinical assistants," and "assistants in pathology" were still in use in 1914. Dr. Wilson's tours were made in 1911 and 1912.

PAGE 524. Apparently Mr. Harwick as purchasing agent did not get far in persuading the group to economize, for when the depression of the early 1930's came, the staff is said to have been urged for the *first* time to get along with a little less than they thought they might want (Farr to ROB).

PAGE 525. For Jay Neville's illness and death: *Mankato Review*, July 13, 1914 (citing the *Winona Independent*), clipping in the Press file.

PAGE 530. The ceremony and words of dedication are reported in the *Rochester Daily Bulletin*, Oct. 11, 1912.

PAGES 530–31. Typescript of the Rush commencement address, Press file.

PAGES 531–33, SECTION 15. *Post and Record*, March 7, 1914; ROB, "The Mayo Clinic Building at Rochester," *Journal-Lancet*, 34:425–34 (Aug. 15, 1914); description of the building by W. J. Whipple in the *Winona Republican Herald*, Oct. 12, 1917.

PAGE 531. Although ostensibly Dr. W. J. Mayo's Clinic colleagues disagree on the question of his ability as an organizer, they really differ more on the meaning of the term than on the thing itself. Two typical statements, both from close and long-term associates, are worth quoting:

"Dr. Will was not a great organizer. He detested organization and would have none of it. It was Dr. Plummer who did the organizing. He was all wrapped up in rules and details and schemes for organization. Dr. Will knew the greater drive that comes from freedom and responsibility. He gave the men he chose the opportunity and the inspiration to do their best, and when you did good work he left you unbound so you were somebody and grew in stature as a result."

"I wouldn't say Dr. Will lacked organizing ability and Plummer had it. What Plummer had was the idea and ability to devise method; his was the idea, the vision, and the philosophy of the integrated practice, group practice, or whatever you want to call it. But he was not a good judge of men. Dr. Will was a superlative judge of men, and he took Plummer's ideas and worked them into an organization. He selected the men and built up the organization along the line of Plummer's idea."

To which may properly be added a few of Dr. Will's own words, from one of the last bits of advice he gave to the Clinic staff:

"Admitting that rules and regulations may be necessary to conduct the affairs of the Clinic, we hope that too many rules and regulations will not be instituted. Our organization concerns sick people, and it is necessary to have a liberal attitude toward those who are responsible for the care of the patient, and to see that necessary rules and regulations do not needlessly interfere with the initiative of members of the staff. We know only too well the necessity for efficient management, but there is a spiritual as well as a material quality in the care of sick people, and too great efficiency in material details may hamper progress." (WJM, talk to the staff, Nov. 21, 1932, typescript copy in WJM files.)

PAGE 534. The memorial tributes to the Mayo brothers (see page 711) and the many letters that came to the family and Clinic after their death made the point over and over again that group practice was the brothers' great achievement and one of the most important in modern medicine. Dr. Hugh Cabot, whose experience and integrity no one questions, however much the majority may disagree with his opinion, calls the Clinic "the most important single influence in the improvement of the practice of medicine in my lifetime." (Letter to Donald C. Balfour, Jan. 23, 1940, Mayo Foundation files.) On the history of cooperative group practice, see the note to pages 575–76.

Dr. Will's remark, "We did not know it" was made at the dedication of his friend Crile's Cleveland Clinic in 1925 (P. E. Truesdale, "Group Practice," *Boston Med. and Surg. Journal*, 196:977 [June 16, 1927]).

The summary by a Minnesota doctor is from Owen H. Wangensteen, "Dr. William J. Mayo As I Knew Him," *Surg., Gynec. and Obst.*, 69:534–38 (Oct. 1939).

# Bibliographical Notes

CHAPTER 19. TO THE PEOPLE, FROM WHOM IT CAME

Materials for this phase of the story are abundant. Foremost among them are the voluminous newspaper and magazine records preserved as clippings in the HJH collection and the Press file. Perhaps the most complete coverage of the story, with a candid bias against the affiliation, is afforded by the numerous articles in the *Minnesota Alumni Weekly*, 1915–17. Many details of the early history of the affiliation and the opposition are given in *The Medical School of the University of Minnesota and the Mayo Foundation for the Promotion of Medical Education and Research*, a booklet issued by the Committee on the Relations of the Medical School with the Mayo Foundation [1915]. The various articles, agreements, and contracts may be found in the *Sketch of the Mayo Clinic*, pp. 158–77, and also, many of them, in the *Official Statements Concerning the Graduate Work in Medicine and Surgery Done by the University of Minnesota in Cooperation with the Mayo Foundation* (undated, 1917?). There is a miscellany of documents and pamphlets on the subject among the Folwell Papers at the Minnesota Historical Society, and, especially important, the notes from a number of interviews with participants in the controversy in the Folwell Notebooks. These were the basis for the sketch of the Foundation in Folwell, *History of Minnesota*, 4:115–18.

Among the valuable personal accounts of the "fight" are WJM, Story to Mrs. Mcllish, pp. 32–33; WJM and CHM, "A Private Statement in Regard to the Mayo Foundation (Not for publication or general distribution)," typescript in WJM files; WJM, Wilson, Eaton, and Granger to ROB; Ford, Wangensteen, Wright, and Guthrey to HC; George E. Vincent, letter to Thomas E. Steward, Jan. 18, 1937, Press file. See also Ford, "An Experiment in Graduate Medical Work," reprinted from the Association of American Universities, *Journal of Proceedings and Addresses*, 1929, in Ford, *On and Off the Campus* (University of Minnesota Press, 1938), pp. 324–36; Wilson, "Historical Sketch of the Mayo Foundation."

PAGES 539–41, SECTION 1. Abraham Flexner, *Medical Education in the United States and Canada*; George E. Vincent, "The University of Higher Degrees in Medicine," *Journal of the A.M.A.*, 64:790–94 (March 6, 1915); L. B. Wilson, "Graduate Instruction in Medicine," *St. Paul Medical Journal*, 14:287–95 (June 1912); Guy Stanton Ford, "An Experiment in Graduate Medical Work," in *On and Off the Campus*, pp. 324–36; Donald C. Balfour, "Graduate Medical Education," *Minnesota Alumni Weekly*, 39:298–300 (Jan. 27, 1940).

PAGE 539. Lobb to Thomas E. Steward, notes in the Press file, is the authority for Vincent's surprise over Wilson's action; Wilson to HC for Vincent's Rochester visit and remark.

PAGE 541. The best expression of the reasoning that led the Mayo brothers to choose the regents of the university as their trustees is in WJM, "A Letter to the University of Minnesota," *Proceedings of the Mayo Clinic*, 9:116–19 (Feb. 21, 1934), also printed in a separate pamphlet, of which there is a copy in the Press file.

PAGES 541–43. Dr. Richard O. Beard, "The Past of the Medical School of the University of Minnesota," *Journal-Lancet*, 41:155–63 (March 15, 1921); George E. Vincent, letter to Thomas E. Steward, Jan. 18, 1937, Press file; "Medical School Observes Anniversary," *Minnesota Alumni Weekly*, 39:69–70 (Oct. 7, 1939); Wilson, "Graduate Instruction in Medicine," *St. Paul Medical Journal*, 14:294–95 (June 1912); Flexner, *Medical Education*, pp. 43, 51, 112, 247–48.

PAGES 543–44. Ford, "The Mayo Foundation from the Standpoint of the Graduate School," in *The Medical School and the Mayo Foundation* [pp. 8–9]; "The Formal Statement of the Committee," *ibid*. [pp. 2–3].

PAGE 545. The terms of the first proposal for affiliation are given in "The Formal Statement of the Committee," in *The Medical School and the Foundation* [pp. 4–5].

PAGE 546. For the medical societies' resolutions, see the *Minneapolis Journal*, March 23, 1915, and the *Journal-Lancet*, 35:275 (May 15, 1915); for the bill introduced into the legislature, the *Senate Journal*, 1915, p. 874. Simultaneously a similar bill was introduced in the lower house by Paul W. Guilford, coeditor of the *Twin City Reporter*, but it soon dropped from sight (*House Journal*, 1915, pp. 1060, 1316).

PAGES 546–47. This account of the objections is a summary of what, along with the answers by advocates of the affiliation, made up many columns in the newspapers and many pages of pamphlet material. All the Twin City papers carried the pros and cons throughout the months of March to June 1915, the *Minneapolis Journal, Minneapolis Tribune, St. Paul Dispatch,* and *St. Paul Pioneer Press* being for the affiliation and the *Minneapolis Mirror* and *St. Paul Daily News* against it. Some of the pamphlets are in the Press file, others among the Folwell Papers in the Minnesota Historical Society, and still others in the various files at the Mayo Clinic. A good summary of the objections is provided by the statements of Drs. Charles L. Greene and George D. Head, both members of the medical school faculty, in the *Minnesota Alumni Weekly*, 14 (no. 25):13–16 (March 22, 1915). The objections and answers to them are brought together in *The Medical School and the Foundation* [pp. 4–6, 10–11].

PAGE 547. The visit of the four men to Rochester is recorded in WJM, Story to Mrs. Mellish, pp. 32–33. Dr. Will thought these men ceased their opposition after their talk with him, but Dr. J. Warren Little and Dr. John W. Bell, the two he remembered (note to Thomas E. Steward, Press file), remained among the opponents to the end.

PAGES 547–48. Dr. Richard O. Beard, who was on the medical faculty at the time and who in general approved of cooperation with the Foundation, still referred to the affiliation with the graduate school as a "misfortune" twenty years later. Also, in a letter to W. J. Mayo on July 6, 1934, Press file, he suggested that a percentage of the earnings of the additional half a million the Mayos had just given to the Foundation be used to provide more fellowships at the university instead of in Rochester.

PAGES 548–49. The quoted matter is from the *Twin City Reporter*, March 19, 26, April 9, 16, May 7, June 11, 1915.

PAGE 550. The quotation from the *St. Paul Pioneer Press* was in the issue for April 6, 1915; the item from downstate is from the *Spring Valley Mer Vid*, March 26, 1915.

PAGES 550–51. The objections and answers are from the Fergus Falls *Wheelock's Weekly*, March 11, 1915.

PAGE 551. *Pontiac* (Michigan) *Press*, May 29, 1915; *Boston Herald*, May 28, 1915; *Commerce and Finance*, June 2, 1915; *St. Paul Dispatch*, June 2, 1915.

PAGE 552. For the bill: *Minneapolis Tribune*, April 6, 1915; *Senate Journal*, 1915, pp. 874, 1245, 1252, 1276, 1352, 1406; *House Journal*, 1915, p. 1769; Eaton to ROB. The vote of Senator Carley of Plainview, Olmsted County, for the anti-affiliation bill is recorded in the *Senate Journal*, 1915, p. 1406, and for the boxing bill, *ibid.*, p. 1356. The latter had a stormy course in both house and senate. The hearing before the regents was reported in the *St. Paul Pioneer Press*, June 1, 1915.

PAGE 553. The resolutions of the Hennepin County society were printed in the *Minneapolis Journal*, June 8, 1915. The report of the executive committee was published as a separate pamphlet, of which there is a copy in the Press file. It was also included in the *Official Statements*, pp. 31–39. The unfortunate resolution appears in the Minutes of the Regents, June 9, 1915, and the official explanation in the *Minnesota Alumni Weekly*, 15 (no. 1):2 (Sept. 20, 1915). The action of the American Surgical Association was reported in the *Journal-Lancet*, 35:361 (July 1, 1915), and the *St. Paul Pioneer Press*, June 10, 1915.

PAGES 553–54. The early successes were attested in a joint statement by Dean Ford and Dean Lyon, *Minneapolis Journal*, March 26, 1917; also in the *Official Statements*, pp. 6–12.

PAGES 554–55. For the renewed fight see, in addition to the *Minnesota Alumni Weekly*, the *Minneapolis Tribune*, March 9, 1917, and "Dr. Sweeney Flays False Reports by Foes of Drs. Mayo," *St. Paul Pioneer Press*, March 25, 1917.

PAGE 555. The new agreement was set forth in a letter from the Drs. Mayo to the board of regents, March 19, 1917, published in *Official Statements*, pp. 4–5. The letters of protest appeared in the *St. Paul Pioneer Press*, April 5, 1917. Among those writing were: William Welch, Stuart McGuire, Nicholas Murray Butler, Abraham Flexner, Walter B. Cannon, Theodore C. Janeway, Alfred Stengel, and John B. Deaver.

PAGES 555–57, SECTION 8. The hearings, including Dr. Mayo's talk, were reported in all the major Twin City newspapers on March 23, 1917, and there was a feature article by Thomas Malone, entitled "Dr. Mayo's Stirring Address," in the *Minneapolis Evening Tribune*, March 24, 1917. See also G. S. Ford, "The Story of the Lost Oration," in *The Making of the University* (president's biennial report, University of Minnesota Press, 1940), pp. 17–19.

PAGE 557. For the life history of the bill: *Senate Journal*, 1917, pp. 563, 1184, 1189. There was much about the new proposal and the reasons for the Mayos' making it in Twin City newspapers during June and July and again in September 1917. See also the *Minnesota Alumni Weekly*, 17 (no. 1):5–8; (no. 4):5 (Oct. 8, 29, 1917).

PAGES 557–58. The statement by Dr. Will is quoted from the *Minneapolis Tribune*, Sept. 14, 1917. Substantially the same statement appeared in the *St. Paul Dispatch*, Sept. 13, and the *Rochester Bulletin*, Sept. 14.

PAGES 558–59. For the continued opposition: *St. Paul Daily News*, Sept. 13, 1917; *Minneapolis Mirror*, Sept. 5, 15, 1917; *Minnesota Alumni Weekly*, 13:7 (Oct. 13, 1919); Leo M. Crafts, "With the Brutal Frankness of a Blood Relative," *Minnesota Alumni Weekly*, 17:5–6 (Jan. 28, 1918); *Minneapolis Journal*, March 12, 1918.

PAGE 559. The Burton incident was reported in the *Minneapolis Tribune*, Dec. 12, 25, 1920. Wangensteen to HC is the authority for the banquet incident. The press comments are from the *New York Post*, Sept. 14, 1917; *New York Sun* quoted in the *Minneapolis Journal*, Sept. 18, 1917; *Kansas City Journal*, Sept. 20, 1917; *Daily Camera* of Boulder, Colorado, clipping in the HJH collection, undated but filed with those from mid-September 1917.


## CHAPTER 20. THE CLINIC AND THE FIRST WORLD WAR

Much of the earlier part of this chapter is based on the reports and letters in the section of Military Papers and Correspondence in the WJM files (cited as the WJM World War file). For background details, Martin, *Fifty Years of Medicine and Surgery*, pp. 368–93, is helpful, Dr. Martin having served in Washington throughout the war. Interviews and the HJH and CHM collections remain invaluable sources for this period, although a reading of the *Rochester Post and Record*, April 1917 through Dec. 1918, yielded little except the activities of the Clinic staff members in Liberty Loan drives, Red Cross fairs and auctions, and the campaign for food conservation.

PAGES 560–61, SECTION 1. *New York Times*, Aug. 7, 1914, p. 3; Mrs. C. H. Mayo to HC.

PAGES 561–62. Martin, *Fifty Years of Medicine and Surgery*, pp. 368–73; Arthur A. Law, "History of the University Base Hospital No. 26," *Journal-Lancet*, 38:16–18 (Jan. 1, 1918), and "History of Base Hospital No. 26," *Minnesota Medicine*, 2:201–5 (June 1919).

PAGES 562–63. For the rumors and questions, see Wayne Bissell, letter to WJM, Aug. 4, 1918, and reply, Sept. 2, 1918, both in the WJM World War file.

PAGE 563. The statement by Dr. Will when the Foundation affiliation was made permanent—and there seems no reason to doubt his sincerity in the belief that either he or Charlie would accompany the troops overseas—occasioned a great deal of comment in the newspapers, some of which played up the patriotism of men who would give up a potential income of a million dollars a year to work for the government at three thousand; others used such headlines as "Sammies on the French Battle Front Will Have Two of the World's Best Surgeons to Take Care of Them." The announcement was soon denied, with the statement that the Mayos would not go to France immediately but would perform their service as advisers to the surgeon general. Neither of the brothers accepted any salary from the government (WJM to ROB).

PAGES 565–66. "Refusal to Serve on the General Staff," *Army and Navy Register*, June 8, 1918, clipping enclosed in a letter from Major W. O. Owen, office of the surgeon general, to W. J. Mayo, June 10, 1918 (the letter and Dr. Will's reply, June 14, 1918, are both in the WJM World War file); "The Passing of the General Staff," *Military Surgeon*, 43:74–76 (July 1918); and the story of Colonel Hoff's resignation, *ibid.*, 43:215 (Aug. 1918); WJM to ROB.

In reply to Major Owen's letter of inquiry about the circumstances, Dr. Will said he and Charlie had been appointed to the general staff to assist in hospital construction but that they found the duties required a special knowledge of building which they did not have. He concluded with a sentence that suggests this explanation was face-saving rather than strict truth: "My brother and I would be very glad to serve if we were given a position that would be commensurate with the responsibilities and have wide enough scope to make us really useful."

WJM briefly discussed the relations between medical officers and the regular corps in his article, "Observations on South America," *Journal of the A.M.A.*, vol. 75 (July 31, 1920), pp. 8–9 of reprint in the Press file.

PAGE 566. There is a full-page account of the banquet in honor of Dr. Charlie, quoting from the many toasts, including one from Dr. Will, in the *Daily Post and Record*, June 23, 1916.

PAGES 566–67. For the alcohol question and Dr. Charlie's presidential speech: Vaughan, *A Doctor's Memories*, pp. 418–21; *Journal of the A.M.A.*, 68:1721, 1768 (June 9, 1917); 69:226–27 (July 21, 1917); CHM, "War's Influence on Medicine," *ibid.*, 68:1673–77 (June 9, 1917); *New York Times*, June 5 (p. 9), 6 (p. 9), 8 (p. 5), 1917; and many clippings in the HJH and CHM collections. See also CHM, "Medical Service in the U. S. Army," *St. Paul Medical Journal*, 19:351–53 (Dec. 1917); "War Problems," *Medical Record*, 96:172–73 (July 26, 1919); "A Cabinet Officer for Supervision of National Health and Educational Problems," *Journal of the A.M.A.*, 74:691 (March 6, 1920); and his address to the Clinical Congress of the American College of Surgeons as reported in many newspapers, e.g., the *St. Paul Pioneer Press*, Oct. 28, 1917.

PAGE 567. For the brothers' illnesses: Harwick to HC; WJM, letter to CHM, Sept. 27, 1918, and to Major V. P. Blair, Baltimore, Jan. 25, 1919; telegrams, two a day, from the doctors in Washington to WJM reporting Dr. Charlie's condition, Dec. 1918. The letters and telegrams are all in the WJM World War file.

PAGE 568. For the training program at Rochester: WJM, dictated memorandum in the Press file; descriptions of specific courses in the WJM World War file; Annals of St. Mary's, II, 1918. The picture of Dr. Graham is from the *Souvenir of Saint Mary's Hospital*, p. 59.

PAGES 568–69. The wartime crisis in the surgical pathology laboratory is described in Broders and Guthrey to HC, and Farr to ROB.

PAGES 569–71, SECTION 7. Annals of St. Mary's, II, 1918; Farr and others of the nonprofessional staff to HC; *Chicago Daily Tribune*, Oct. 17, 1918; *Waterloo (Iowa) Times*, Oct. 20, 1918; and dozens of clippings from other Minnesota, Wisconsin, Iowa, and Dakota newspapers from early November to late December 1918, all in the HJH and CHM collections.

PAGE 570. For the circumstances of Dr. Rosenow's joining the Mayos, see Rosenow to HC; WJM, letter to E. C. Rosenow, April 25, 1915, copy in the WJM files. The italics are mine.

PAGE 572. For the Mayos' attitude toward the "enemy": WJM, "Some of the Old Hospitals of London with Special Reference to the Treatment of Fistula in Ano with Hemorrhoids," *Minnesota Medicine*, 2:197–201 (June 1919); WJM, letter to Dr. Alexis Moschcowitz of New York, Feb. 8, 1926, copy in the Press file; report of American Surgical Association meeting in the *Journal of the A.M.A.*, 73:47 (July 5, 1919).

PAGES 572–73. This story of the efforts toward reinstatement emerges from the documents and resolutions and Dr. Will's correspondence on the matter, of which there are copies in the Press file.

PAGES 573–74, SECTION 9. William M. German, *Doctors Anonymous: the Story of Laboratory Medicine* (New York, 1941), pp. 43–52; L. B. Wilson, "The Pathologic Service of the American Expeditionary Force," *Military Surgeon*, 45: 692–705 (Dec. 1919); "Museum and Art Service of the American Expeditionary Force," *ibid.*, 46:165–72 (Feb. 1920); "The Autopsy Service of the American Expeditionary Forces," *Trans. Assoc. of Amer. Phys.*, 34:291–97 (1919). See also CHM, "Educational Possibilities in the National Medical Museum," *Journal of the A.M.A.*, 74:691 (March 6, 1920); Percy N. Stone, "World War Gave More Lives Than It Took, Declares Dr. Mayo," *New York Herald Tribune*, Feb. 28, 1926, II, 4; WJM, "Modifications of Some Civil Surgical Practices Suggested by the Surgery of the War," *Southern Medical Journal*, 12:31–35 (Jan. 1919).

Presentation of the distinguished service medal to Dr. Wilson was made June 26, 1922, with the following citation: "For exceedingly meritorious and distinguished services as the assistant to the director of laboratories and infectious diseases . . . ; he organized most efficiently a pathological service throughout the American Expeditionary Forces in France that was of inestimable value to the medical and surgical service." (Steward manuscript, p. 279.)

PAGES 574–75. Dr. Lockwood, letter to HC, April 11, 1940, Press file.

PAGES 575–76. "Group Practice," *Journal of the A.M.A.*, 117:122–24 (July 12, 1941); "Private Group Practice," report by the Bureau of Medical Economics in the *Journal of the A.M.A.*, 100:1695 (May 27, 1933); CHM, "The Nature, Value, and Necessity of Team-Work in a Hospital," *Modern Hospital*, 12 (no. 1): 1–3 (July 1916), quoting Dr. Goldwater; M. Schulman, letter advocating pay clinics and protesting against a New York medical society's resolutions against them, *New York Times*, April 5, 1916, 12:7; Michael M. Davis and Andrew R. Warner, "Pay Clinics—A Step toward Democratic Medical Service," *Survey*, 40:334–36 (June 22, 1918); Michael M. Davis, "Group Medicine," *American Journal of Public Health*, 9:358–62 (May 1919); Donald J. Frick, "Group Medicine—a Discussion of Its Value to the Profession and the Public," *California State Journal of Medicine*, 20:234–37 (July 1922). According to the A.M.A. studies, particularly the one in 1933, eighteen of the groups reporting in 1933 had been founded before 1912 and nine more were founded in 1912.

The early development of group practice is badly in need of historical study. The surveys made by committees and bureaus of the American Medical Association were properly concerned with the present extent of group practice and but incidentally with its history. Consequently, precisely where and why the early clinics were organized is still lost in the records.

The earliest instance of imitation of the Mayo Clinic I have come across is the formation in Winona in 1901 of a partnership by Dr. James B. McGaughey and his son with five other Winona physicians. Each man in the group retained his individual general practice but they set up joint offices for specialty work in one building equipped with laboratories, "for the purpose of giving as good or better service than in the past at an economy of management." (*Winona Republican and Herald*, Oct. 31, 1901.) In view of the fact that Dr. McGaughey had long been a close friend of the Mayos, visited them frequently, and had often referred patients to them, there is every reason to see in this an imitation of Mayo methods. This group eventually became the Winona Clinic and was still functioning in 1930 (Fifield, *American and Canadian Hospitals*, p. 634).

The Guthrie Clinic in Sayre, Pennsylvania, was founded about 1910 by Dr. Donald Guthrie, who was a junior assistant at the Mayo Clinic from 1906 to 1909. The Jackson Clinic of Madison, Wisconsin, was founded in 1911 by Dr. Reginald H. Jackson and his two sons, one of whom took his graduate training at the Mayo Clinic. (Carlyle N. Haines, "Urology in the Robert Packer Hospital," *Guthrie Clinic Bulletin*, 9:11 [July 1939]; *Jackson Clinic Bulletin*, 1:86–90 [Oct. 1939]; Guthrie and Jackson in *Physicians of the Mayo Clinic*.)

Dr. K. S. Menninger of the Menninger Clinic (Psychiatric), Topeka, Kansas, in a letter to WJM, May 29, 1939, WJM files, said that on his first visit to the Mayo Clinic, some thirty years before, he got a vision of what he would like his sons to aspire to when they became physicians and that subsequently he had helped them to build in psychiatry an institution based on the same high ideals as those of Dr. Will and Dr. Charlie. Dr. Menninger concluded, "I have always been devoutly thankful that I had that experience in my early medical life, and I owe you many thanks."

In a letter to Dr. Will on July 12, 1939, WJM files, Mr. L. J. Jarvis Nye of Brisbane, Australia, remarked that one bit of evidence of the Mayos' influence on medical science was to be found in Brisbane, because on his first visit to the Clinic many years before he was so struck with the team spirit of the Mayo Clinic that a "Mayo seed" was planted in that outpost of the empire when he returned home. It had grown until "today we have a very happy and efficient team of six medical men working harmoniously with a lay staff of twelve in this British Colony and we feel there is no organization in the country which gives better medical service." In his consulting room above his desk, said Mr. Nye, hung the pictures of Dr. Will and Dr. Charlie, "an inspiration in our enterprise and an ever-present stimulus to more earnest and efficient work."

The HJH and CHM collections are full of the kind of newspaper items mentioned. Feature articles on the Mayos from this period are: "The Mayo Brothers, Masters of Efficiency," *The Independent*, 88:92–93 (Oct. 16, 1916); Prescott Toomey, "Pioneer, Physician, Citizen," *Dallas* (Texas) *Morning News*, Jan. 7, 1917; W. J. Whipple, "Drs. Mayo, Public Philanthropists," *Winona Herald*, Oct. 20, 1917; Mary B. Mullett, " 'Dr. Will' and 'Dr. Charlie,' " *American Magazine*, 85 (no. 2):11–12, 67–70 (Feb. 1918); "Two Brothers Who Have Performed a

788

# Bibliographical Notes

Wonder of the Medical World," *Current Opinion*, 64:177–78 (March 1918); Alvin J. Steinkopf, "We are Selected as Trustees of Sickmen's Dollars," *St. Paul Pioneer Press*, June 12, 1921; Frances Boardman, "Rochester, A City on Wheelchairs," *St. Paul News*, Aug. 28, 1921; James O. Bennett, "Superlative Americans," *Chicago Tribune*, March 20, 1923.

PAGES 576–77. The three stories summarized are from, respectively, the *St. Paul Dispatch*, Oct. 9, 1917; *Minneapolis Tribune*, Jan. 22, 1918; *Marinette* (Wisconsin) *Eagle-Star*, June 14, 1921.

PAGE 577. One version of the "business tycoon" story, the only one that names James J. Hill as the man in question, is given in Whipple, "Drs. Mayo . . ." *Winona Herald*, Oct. 20, 1917. The details varied from version to version, especially as to the amounts involved. In some cases the businessman's check was said to have been for $5,000 and the Clinic's bill for $25,000. The earliest telling of the "head doctor" story I have found is by James O. Bennett in the *Chicago Tribune*, March 20, 1923.

For the illness of Hill: *New York Times*, May 27 (9:2), May 28 (I, 1:2), May 29 (1:4), May 30 (1:1), 1916. For the Harding episode: *New York Times*, Sept. 11 (1:6), 13 (1:2), 1922; Finney, *A Surgeon's Life*, pp. 265–66. For Taft's tribute: "Taft Praises Work of Mayos," *Spokane* (Washington) *Spokesman*, May 30, 1920, quoting "his copyrighted article" in the *Philadelphia Ledger*; W. H. Taft, "Work of the Mayo Brothers," *Science*, n.s. 51:569–70 (June 4, 1920).

PAGES 577–78. For Lane's story: Anne W. Lane and Louise H. Wall, eds., *The Letters of Franklin K. Lane* (New York, 1922), pp. 398–465; *Rochester Post and Record*, May 18, 1921; *New York Times*, May 19, 29, 1921; Lawrence F. Abbott, "A Passionate American," *Outlook*, 128:205–8 (June 1, 1921); Franklin H. Giddings, "From This Side of Death," *Independent*, 105:585 (June 4, 1921); editorials in the *New York World, New York Globe, Brooklyn Eagle*, and various religious papers cited in *Current Opinion*, 71:756 (July 1921).

PAGES 578–79. *Pasadena Star-News* (Feb. 11, 1922); *Los Angeles Examiner* (Jan. and Feb. *passim*, 1922). Many papers in the Northwest carried the story of the Mayos' going to California and the *Marshalltown* (Iowa) *Times-Republican*, March 1, 1922, denied it, printing in full Dr. Will's letter to John Willis Baer. The HJH collection is full of clippings carrying similar reports, and Harwick to HC says he still squelches them at the rate of about one a month.

PAGE 579. The stories of the impostors come from clippings in the HJH collection. There was annoyingly little the Clinic could do to prevent such misrepresentation. They did print on the back of their registration card the following notice: "Any person traveling about the country representing himself as in any way connected with this institution or using our name to secure public confidence should be looked on as a swindler. Testimonials or recommendations in which our name is used in advertisements are not genuine. We are not responsible for unsigned statements or articles concerning us appearing in public print."

PAGES 579–80. A statement that the many clinics sprouting all over the country were imitating the Mayo Clinic was attributed to Dr. W. E. Ground of Duluth in the *Duluth News-Tribune*, May 9, 1920. For an example, see the statements by Dr. Thomas H. Halsted, fellow of the American College of Surgeons and president of the New York State Medical Society, about a clinic he and several associates were starting in the old home of Andrew D. White in Syracuse, New York, as reported in the *Syracuse Herald*, Feb. 22, 1920. Another example is the Cleveland Clinic of Dr. George W. Crile, long a close friend of the Drs. Mayo. F. H. Ellerbe of St. Paul was the architect for Crile's building and Dr. Will was the principal speaker at the dedication ceremonies. (*St. Paul Pioneer Press*, Feb. 9, 1920; an unidentified clipping [May 1921] in the HJH collection; WJM, "The Medical Profession and the Public," *Journal of the A.M.A.*, 76:921–25 [April 2, 1921].)

## CHAPTER 21. TOWARD THE FUTURE

The basic sources here are the *Sketch of the Mayo Clinic, passim,* and the transcripts of personal interviews listed in the introductory note, pages 717-19. In the spirit of the pledge of the Clinic (footnote, page 589) I have included no more about the clinical phases of the modern organization than seemed necessary to suggest the general development. For a good description of the patient in the Clinic, see Lucy Wilder, *The Mayo Clinic* (New York, 1939), pp. 58-75, and, from one patient's point of view, Henry H. Harper, *Merely the Patient* (New York, 1930).

Among later articles describing the Clinic and its work I have been able to obtain the following: Matthew O. Foley, "The Mayo Clinic and Its Work," *Hospital Management,* 16 (no. 3): 28-40 (Sept. 1923); A. Norman Leeming, "American Notes after a Visit to the Mayo Clinic," *Guy's Hospital Gazette,* 38:403-7 (Sept. 13, 1924); J. B. Parfitt, "A Glimpse of the Mayo Clinic and Its Dental Department," *British Dental Journal,* 46:786-89 (July 1, 1925); James A. Mattison, "Some Observations on Eastern Clinics," *Medical Journal and Record,* 122:522-24 (Nov. 4, 1925); George B. Lake, "The Mayo Clinic," *Clinical Medicine,* 32:675-80 (Oct. 1925); John H. Bradshaw, "The Mayo Clinic," *Journal of the Medical Society of New Jersey,* 24:284-89 (May 1927); Brown S. McClintie, "Notes of a Visit to the Mayo Clinic," *Military Surgeon,* 65:705-8 (Nov. 1929); W. L. Brown, "A Visit to the Mayo Clinic," *Southwestern Medicine,* 15:518-20 (Nov. 1931); Murray A. Falconer, "The Work of the Mayo Clinic," *New Zealand Medical Journal,* 37:316-27 (Dec. 1938).

PAGES 581-84. WJM, "Observations on South America," *Journal of the A.M.A.,* 75:311-15, 377-78, 475-77, 540-41, 606-7, 672-73 (July 31, Aug. 7, 14, 21, 28, Sept. 4, 1920); WJM, "South American Surgeons," *Surg., Gynec. and Obst.,* 30:534 (May 1920); Franklin H. Martin, "South American Surgeons," *ibid.,* 30:427-35, 535-41 (April, May 1920), 31:209-18 (Aug. 1920); *Post and Record,* March 15, 1920.

PAGE 582. The interpolation is on p. 28 of WJM, Story to Mrs. Mellish.

PAGES 584-85. Guillermo Colunge, translator and editor, *Record of Proceedings [sic] and Papers: Second Congress, Pan-American Association* (Panama, 1931), pp. v, vi, 187-91. The quotation is from *Surg., Gynec. and Obst.,* 37:406 (Sept. 1923). See also *ibid.,* p. 412. For accounts of trips by other individuals: *ibid.,* 32:573-93 (June 1921), 34:826-33 (June 1922), 35:381-96 (Sept. 1922). For notices of cruises and the Mayos' participation: *Journal of the A.M.A.,* 91:330, 1558 (Aug. 4, Nov. 17, 1928), 92:241 (Jan. 19, 1929), 93:1819 (Dec. 7, 1929), 102:382, 1239 (Feb. 3, April 14, 1934); "Floating Congress of the Pan-American Medical Association," *Bulletin of the Pan-American Union,* 68:342-44 (May 1934); *New York Times,* March 31, 1934, p. 13; *Science,* n.s. 79:312 (April 6, 1934).

PAGES 585-86, SECTION 3. Lockwood and Hartman, "A Trip to Mexico," *Clinic Bulletin,* vol. 2, no. 210, April 5, 1921; Hartman to HC; *Post and Record,* April 13, 1921, p. 3; news item in *Minnesota Medicine,* 4:269 (April 1921). The last item says it was "General Hill of the U. S. Army" who was ill, but the man was undoubtedly Benjamin Hill, one of Obregón's able lieutenants during the attempt to overthrow Huerta in 1912 and his companion in his dramatic flight from Mexico City in April 1920 (Henry B. Parks, *A History of Mexico* [Boston, 1938], p. 337; Herbert I. Priestly, *The Mexican Nation: A History* [New York, 1923], pp. 421, 447; *New York Times* [April 15, 1920, p. 1]). Obregón took office as president Dec. 1, 1920, and the railroad strike, fomented by a member of his own government staff, was merely one of many disturbances he had to deal with during his early months in office. The United States did not recognize the Obregón government until Sept. 23, 1923.

PAGES 587–88, SECTION 4. According to some of Dr. Will's friends, among whom this is a much-loved tale, he split the skin with a little folding scalpel he carried in his pocket, but the scissors version is the one given by Dr. Will in a typescript memorandum in the Press file. See also the Associated Press item in the *Minneapolis Journal*, March 10, 1922, p. 1; *Post and Record*, March 11, 1922, p. 1; *New York Times*, March 11, 1922, p. 6; and WJM, "Mexico," *Surg., Gynec. and Obst.*, 35:376–80 (Sept. 1922).

PAGE 590. The announcement to the alumni was reported in the *Post and Record*, Oct. 9, 1919. Dozens of clippings in the HJH collection describe the organization of the Mayo Properties Association as a means of perpetuating the Clinic.

PAGES 591–93. There is an account of the organization of the Properties Association, including the articles of incorporation, in the *Sketch of the Mayo Clinic*, pp. 117–32. H. J. Harwick also outlined it in a talk to the Clinic staff, Nov. 20, 1939, copy in the Press file.

PAGE 593. Harwick to HC is the authority for Mellon's comment.

PAGE 595. For the Graham story: Harwick and WJM to ROB; Graham and Guthrey to HC; WJM Story to Mrs. Mellish, p. 20.

PAGE 597. For the opening of the new Kahler, see the *Post and Record*, Sept. 28, 1921.

PAGES 598–99, SECTION 9. *Souvenir of Saint Mary's Hospital; Saint Mary's School of Nursing*; Annals of St. Mary's, II, 1918–23; "Saint Mary's Hospital," *St. Paul Pioneer Press*, May 7, 1922, sixteen-page supplement to celebrate the opening of the pavilion.

PAGE 605. The story of Dr. Carman is from the Steward manuscript, p. 270.

PAGES 606–7. For Dr. Billings' remark, see the *Journal of the A.M.A.*, 95:646–47 (Aug. 30, 1930). For the early work in clinical investigation, see *The Rockefeller Institute for Medical Research—History, Organization, and Equipment* (published by the Institute, New York, 1936).

PAGES 608–9. Mary A. Foley, "The Work of the Rochester Diet Kitchen," *Proceedings of the Mayo Clinic*, 6:459–61 (Aug. 5, 1931).

PAGE 610. The quotation is from a letter by Osler published in the *Journal of the Tennessee State Medical Association*, Oct. 1919, p. 222, clipping enclosed in a letter from Harvey Cushing to W. J. Mayo, May 25, 1939, WJM files.

PAGE 611. The Adson episode is from the Steward manuscript, p. 262.

PAGE 614. For Dr. Lundy's coming: WJM, Discussion, *Proceedings of the Mayo Clinic*, 9:244 (April 18, 1934); Lundy to HC.


CHAPTER 22. ON THE FRONTIERS OF MEDICINE

Even a brief survey of the research work at the Clinic would be impossible here—if it were desirable—and I have attempted only to outline the setup and suggest how it works. For this I have relied chiefly on personal interviews with members of the Clinic staff, as listed in the introductory note, pages 717–19, supplementing them with published papers where more than a general description is given. The references to such papers may be found in the bibliographies in the *Physicians of the Mayo Clinic*, and many of them are abstracted or printed in full in the annual volumes of the *Collected Papers*. The events of the story before 1926 are included in the *Sketch of the Mayo Clinic*, and there are many descriptive details in O. N. Andersen, "Report to the Council on Medical Education and

Hospitals of the American Medical Association: The Mayo Foundation," type-script copy, dated Jan. 20, 1939, in the Foundation files.

PAGE 616. L. B. Wilson to HC is the source of the Chapman story.

PAGE 618. The *Post and Record,* May 8, 1923, reports the burning of the "research station" but makes no mention of a possible incendiary origin. The National Board of Fire Underwriters, letter to HC, Aug. 1, 1941, Press file, says the fire was officially attributed to careless smoking.

PAGE 623. Dr. Broders worked out the principle and his classification from a study of microscopic slides, and learned only after publishing it that it was a refinement of an old German idea that called tumors "not quite ripe," "ripe," and "overripe." (Broders to HC.)

PAGES 624–25. Clinic members still differ sharply about the justice of the criticisms of the old medical unit, and this story is a reconciliation of many conflicting statements. Who was right and who was wrong is, after all, of less importance than what was thought and done about it.

PAGE 626. For the life and work of Dr. Brown, see Norman Keith, William S. Middleton, and Leonard G. Rowntree, *George Elgie Brown, M.D., F.A.C.P.,* 1885–1935 (Rochester, n.d.).

PAGE 633. The quotation is from the Steward manuscript, p. 288. For an outside opinion see Eugene F. Du Bois, *Basal Metabolism in Health and Disease* (Philadelphia, 1936), pp. 158–59.

PAGES 634–36, SECTION 11. H. S. Plummer, "The Function of the Thyroid Gland," *Collected Papers,* 17:473–99 (1925); Boothby, "Disease of the Thyroid Gland," *Archives of Internal Medicine,* 56:136–206 (July 1935); Pemberton, "The Development of Surgery of the Thyroid Gland," *Northwestern University Bulletin,* Feb. 24, 1936, reprint in the Press file. For some of the appraisals of Plummer's iodine treatment, see the *Journal of the A.M.A.,* 95:646 (Aug. 30, 1930); Leeming, "American Notes after a Visit to the Mayo Clinic," *Guy's Hospital Gazette,* 38:403–7 (Sept. 13, 1924); Mattison, "Some Observations on Eastern Clinics," *Medical Journal and Record,* 122:522–24 (Nov. 4, 1925).

PAGES 637–38. W. M. Boothby, "Oxygen Administration . . . " *Proceedings of the Mayo Clinic,* 13:641–46 (Oct. 12, 1938); W. R. Lovelace, II, "Oxygen for Therapy and Aviation . . ." *ibid.,* pp. 646–54; A. H. Bulbulian, "Design and Construction of the Masks for the Oxygen Inhalation Apparatus," *ibid.,* pp. 654–56.

PAGES 639–40. WJM, "New Zealand and Australia," *Surg., Gynec. and Obst.,* 38:833–35 (June 1924); Franklin H. Martin, "Australia and New Zealand," *ibid.,* 38:846–56 (June 1924); WJM, dictated memorandum in the Press file; clippings in the WJM collection.

CHAPTER 23. TRAINING YOUNG DOCTORS

General sources: Wilson, "Historical Sketch of the Mayo Foundation," and "Mayo Foundation," remarks to the Clinic staff, n.d., typescript copy in the Press file; Donald C. Balfour, "The Mayo Foundation," *Proceedings of the Mayo Clinic,* 12:59–61 (Jan. 27, 1937), and "The Mayo Foundation . . . 1915–40," in *Twenty-fifth Anniversary of the Mayo Foundation for Medical Education and Research* (Rochester, 1941), pp. 4–11; Ford, "An Experiment in Graduate Medical Work," in *On and Off the Campus,* pp. 324–36; Andersen, "Report to the Council on Medical Education and Hospitals of the American Medical Association: The Mayo Foundation," typescript copy, Jan. 20, 1939, in the Foundation files; "Graduate Training for General Surgery and the Surgical Specialties: Mayo

# Bibliographical Notes

Foundation for Medical Education and Research," *Bulletin of the American College of Surgeons*, April 1939, reprint in the Press file; *Graduate Medical Education* (Report of the Commission on Graduate Medical Education, Chicago, 1940), especially chapter 3, "The Residency," pp. 96–166; and interviews with members of the Foundation and university staffs, especially Wilson and Farr to ROB, and Ford, Balfour, and Farr to HC.

PAGES 643–44. The quotation is from Ford in *On and Off the Campus*, pp. 326–27.

PAGE 644. The "few annual volumes" stopped with two: *Papers from the Mayo Foundation . . . and the Graduate School of Medicine of the University of Minnesota, 1915–20* (Philadelphia, 1921), and *ibid., 1921–22* (published in 1923).

PAGE 646. Statements on the subject of medical education appear in many of Dr. Will's later papers; see especially "Presidential Address" (Clinical Congress of American College of Surgeons), *Surg., Gynec. and Obst.*, 30:97–99 (Jan. 1920); "Specialization in Surgery," *Archives of Surgery*, 10:264–66 (Jan. 1925); "Medical Education," *Trans. Resident and Ex-Resident Phys. of the Mayo Clinic*, 6:285–87 (1925); "Medical Education for the General Practitioner," *Journal of the A.M.A.*, 88:1377–79 (April 30, 1927); "Function of the Medical Schools is to Turn Out Medical Practitioners," *School Life*, 13:41–43 (Nov. 1927); dedicatory address, Temple University medical school, published in full in the *Rochester Bulletin*, Oct. 15, 1930, clipping in the Press file; "The Preliminary Education of the Clinical Specialist," *Proceedings of the Congress on Medical Education, Medical Licensure, and Hospitals*, 16:17–18 (1931).

PAGE 651. The story of the mud bath is from WJM, dictated memorandum in the Press file.

PAGES 654–55. For the library: WJM, "Maud H. Mellish Wilson and the Mayo Clinic," *Proceedings of the Mayo Clinic*, 8:[3] (Dec. 1933), and Arthur H. Sanford, "The Mayo Clinic Library," *Bulletin of the Medical Library Association*, 25:141–43 (Sept. 1936).

PAGE 656. The man who reorganized the Clinic work in statistics was Halbert L. Dunn (*Physicians of the Mayo Clinic*).

PAGE 657. For the work of the editors, see Richard M. Hewitt, "The Division of Publications of the Mayo Clinic," *Bulletin of the Medical Library Association*, 25:133–38 (Sept. 1936).

PAGES 658–59. The account is of an actual seminar, Dec. 5, 1939, which I was permitted to attend.

PAGE 662. Pierre Depage founded the Clinique Antoine Depage in Brussels, Belgium. J. Fletcher Robinson heads the Mysore University Medical College, Mysore, India. (*Physicians of the Mayo Clinic.*)

PAGE 663. *The Advisory Board of Medical Specialties* (prepared by Paul Titus, secretary, 5th ed., Pittsburgh, 1939); "The Specialty Boards," chapter 5 in *Medical Education*, pp. 203–23.

PAGE 664. The episode of the school building is from Harwick to ROB and Lobb to HC.

PAGES 664–65. A. H. Bulbulian, "Annual Report of the Activities of the Mayo Foundation Museum of Hygiene and Medicine," 1935–39, typescript copies loaned me by Dr. Bulbulian.


CHAPTER 24. MY BROTHER AND I

The characterization of the brothers is necessarily a composite from many sources, to which no further references are given: the interviews listed on pages

793

717–19; the memorial tributes listed in the note to page 711; and scores of letters from friends, fellow doctors, and former patients, preserved in the WJM and CHM files.

PAGE 666. See WJM, "The Value of the Weekly General Staff Meeting," *Proceedings of the Mayo Clinic*, 10:70–72 (Jan. 30, 1935).

PAGE 668. Harry J. Harwick, "How the Mayo Clinic Protects Personnel with Group Insurance," *Hospital Management*, 32:56–62 (Nov. 1931).

PAGES 668–69. Priscilla Keeley, "Annual Report of the Section on Medical Social Service," 1931–36, typescript copies loaned me by Miss Keeley; Blanche Peterson, "Medical Social Work with Tuberculous Patients at the Mayo Clinic," *Hospital Social Service*, 18:29–35 (July 1928). Mrs. James R. Learmonth of Aberdeen, Scotland, the Charlotte Bundy who inaugurated the section, agreed to write an account of its beginnings for this volume, but the hazards and demands of war service prevented her doing so.

PAGES 669–70. The story of the high school boy is from an unidentified clipping in the HJH collection.

PAGE 670. The story of the millionaire is from Winslow, *Life Against Death*, pp. 178–93. I have been amazed by the number of instances of Clinic generosity I have encountered since I began work on this story. And if the motive is as practical as the Clinic men say, the method leaves no such impression.

PAGES 672–73. F. B. Lund, New Center, Mass., letter to WJM, May 25, 1939, and W. D. Haggard, Nashville, Tenn., telegram to WJM, May 26, 1939, both in the WJM files.

PAGE 673. Dr. Charlie's credo about the treatment of incurable cases has been described by one of his assistants: "The treatment should be homely and simple, understood fully by the patient, and he must be allowed to go home with a ray of hope in his heart. A patient coming in January, and found to have a progressive disease that would certainly terminate his life by spring, might be advised by Dr. Charlie that a diet of watermelons, which only come in late summer, would be a distinct help. One can visualize a poor wretch living in hope of this, and in his last days happy, for within a few weeks the panacea was at hand." (Harry L. Parker, "Charles Horace Mayo, An Appreciation," *Irish Journal of Medical Science*, series 6, no. 164, pp. 614–17 [Aug. 1939].)

There is a description of Dr. Will's visits in Harper, *Merely the Patient*.

PAGE 675. The classmate was Dr. William R. Fringer (letter to HC, April 4, 1940, Press file).

PAGE 676. The story of the muskeg experiment is from "Dr. Will and Dr. Charlie," a sketch by Fred B. Snyder, regent of the University of Minnesota, typescript copy in the Press file. The remark by an Australian doctor is from Bowker, *Some Notes on Surgical Clinics*, p. 50.

PAGES 676–77. For one expression of this astonishment, see Elmer T. Peterson, "Doctor Mayo Tells How to Live," *Better Homes and Gardens*, 12 (no. 8):16–17, 64 (April 1934).

PAGE 680. Dr. Joseph B. DeLee, letter to WJM, July 18, 1939, WJM files, is the authority for the story of the young Chicago surgeon.

PAGES 681–83, SECTION 8. For the origins and name changes of the interstate association, see Edwin Hines, Jr., "Foreword," *Proceedings of the Inter-State Post-Graduate Medical Assembly of North America*, 1925 [pp. 3–5]; *Journal of the A.M.A.*, 81:1030, 1702, 1888 (Sept. 22, Nov. 17, Dec. 1, 1923), 85:1409 (Oct. 31, 1925). For the European sessions: *ibid.*, 85:47–49 (July 4, 1925), 86:126 (Jan. 29, 1926), 87:185, 257, 260, 955 (July 17, 24, Sept. 18, 1926); *New York Times*, June 3 (p. 25), 4 (p. 18), 5 (p. 17), 7 (p. 24), 12 (p. 18), 14 (p. 25), 19 (p. 19), 24 (p. 20), 27 (p. 20), 30 (p. 6); Mrs. Trenholme to HC.

# Bibliographical Notes

PAGES 683–84. For the Mayos' papers, see their bibliographies in the *Physicians of the Mayo Clinic.*

PAGES 684–85. There are a dozen or more letters that passed between Dean Owre and Dr. Will and Dr. Charlie in the Owre Papers, Minnesota Historical Society. The banquet story is from Ford to HC.

PAGES 685–86. *The Custodianship of the Rush-Jenner-Pasteur-Lister-Curie Mementos in the Cabinet of the College of Physicians of Philadelphia,* undated pamphlet in the Press file.

PAGES 686–87. Day's suggestion appeared in the *Fairmont Daily Sentinel,* Feb. 13, 1920; Dr. Will's refusal in the *Rochester Post and Record,* March 15, 1920. The boom in between is revealed in the clippings of the HJH collection. See also the *Minneapolis Journal,* May 31, 1920, for a proposal from S. D. Van Meter of Denver that W. J. Mayo be the Democratic candidate for president.

PAGE 687. About C. H. Mayo for president: *Minneapolis Tribune,* Feb. 5, 1924; *Rochester Post and Record,* March 3, 1924; *New York Times,* Feb. 13, 1924, p. 18; clippings in the CHM collection; letters in the CHM files.

The brothers' decision on the question of interviews is given in WJM, Story to Mrs. Mellish, p. 27, and letter to Dr. William O. Sweek, Jan. 24, 1930, WJM files.

PAGES 687–88. The newspaper accounts of this incident, which occurred in Sept. 1928, are in the HJH collection; the letter, and others like it, in the WJM files.

PAGES 688–89. Only after the account in the text, written from the newspaper reports in the HJH collection (see especially the *New York Telegram,* Dec. 15, 1921), was set in type, was I able to obtain a copy of Lorenz, *My Life and Work* (New York, 1936). His interesting account of the episode appears on pp. 281–90. The name should be spelled Adolf Lorenz.

PAGES 689–90. For the argument over the "white-cap famine," see the *Pictorial Review,* 23 (no. 1):15, 82 (Oct. 1921); (no. 3):28, 79, 80 (Dec. 1921); (no. 5):28, 94, 95 (Feb. 1922); *New York Times,* Sept. 21 (p. 14), 26 (p. 14), 1921. See also WJM on the nurse question in "Observations on South America," *Journal of the A.M.A.,* 75:314–15 (July 31, 1920).

PAGE 690. WJM, "Nursing and Hospital Costs for Individuals in Moderate Circumstances," *Proceedings of the Mayo Clinic,* 4:307–8 (Oct. 16, 1929), and newspaper reports in the HJH collection. The "first page" quotation is from the *Minneapolis Tribune,* Oct. 17, 1929.

PAGES 690–91. Whether or not one believes the Mayos', and now the Clinic's, disclaimers depends on one's slant of mind. The doubting doctors say the principle is "Apologize and deny when you have to but go ahead just the same." Through a study of the articles, the charges about them, and the disclaimers in Dr. Will's letters I have decided that he could have been telling the truth, and my own experience during the preparation of this volume convinced me that he was.

For the record, one example may be given of how nasty some of the criticism can be. The following is from an editorial published in a western journal, clipping in the HJH collection:

"(You fellows get your local papers to publish this editorial. Our message goes to the profession and we are the only medical journal in the country with guts enough to print it. You get it before the public. If you don't know the editor of your local paper by his first name and well enough to ask a favor of him, you haven't got brains enough to be practicing medicine.)

"A few years ago wealthy people from all parts of the country flocked to Rochester, Minnesota, to have one or the other of the famous Mayo brothers operate on them. Nowadays, people in all walks of life go to Rochester for all manner of ailments. Farms and horses are mortgaged, little businesses sacrificed and life-time savings frittered away in the vain hope that the Mayos can cure anything.

"The Mayo Brothers used to do slick surgery; probably they can do it yet, but they do not operate on one hundredth part of the cases that come to their institution, and as long as they allow the impression to grow among the lay people all over the country that a trip to Rochester will result in personal contact with one of the brothers, they are committing a grievous wrong.

"The Northwest has numerous examples as to the utter incompetence of the staff who diagnose, treat or operate at the Rochester institution. Almost any surgeon of repute anywhere in the United States can tell you names and dates of the most obvious and dumb-headed blunders made by the understrappers at this institution. And sad to say, lots of these people who have been blundered over by the Mayo staff are people who used their last dollar to get to this fake haven of relief. Of course, hundreds of incurables strike out for the Mayos after being told that their cases are hopeless. Thousands of cases go there because they think the Mayo Brothers infallible, yet how many even get a glimpse of them, let alone get anything slit by them except their pocketbooks.

" . . . Their credit man is a bird, and before the average patient goes through the routine examination, his financial rating back home is better known in the clinic that his physical condition. This is found out through affiliation with many large banks in which the ethical brothers are stockholders.

" . . . One or the other of the brothers seems always out drumming up trade for their hired help, and the ape-neck local surgeons turn out agape to see the master slicker—they know it's precious little of surgery they will learn from their visit and chat—maybe they have a vain hope that one of the brothers might impart a little business knowledge to them. After all is said, the local surgeon has his silly ego tickled in being seen or heard with one of the great, and for months afterward he rolls the choice morsels about 'what he said to Charley Mayo and what Charley said to him' to every patient that comes in his office, and then he is mortified to death because some of his listeners slip off to Rochester and get operated.

" . . . The grand glorious bunk goes on and all the local simp surgeons in the country feed it and lose cases themselves in so doing. Go to the Mayos! Where will you find them? Out drumming up trade from sucker surgeons. Bah! If a local physician would advertise on a half page in a local paper and tell the truth in the advertisement we would honor him more than a thousand slickers like the 'Gold Dust Twins of Rochester.' "

For later articles and what evidence there is in print of the trouble they caused, see Paul De Kruif, "A News Reel of Death Fighting," *Ladies Home Journal*, Sept. 1930, p. 16; Roy B. McKnight, "Are Any Too Big to Be Answerable to the Terms on Which We Hold Membership in the A.M.A.?" *Southern Medicine and Surgery*, 92:667–69 (Sept. 1930), and editorial "Are Any Too Big?" *ibid.*, p. 699; Frank Smith in the *Chicago Daily Times*, July 21, 1937, p. 14; "Mayo Clinic Publicity," *Time*, 30:32–34 (Aug. 16, 1937); "Mayo Clinic," *Life*, 7 (no. 10):37–41 (Sept. 4, 1939); report of the house of delegates of the Minn. State Med. Assoc., *Minnesota Medicine*, 23:528–31 (July 1940).

PAGE 691. For the later articles written by visiting doctors, see the general note to chapter 21.

PAGE 692. The story of the dutiable coffee is from Carl Beck, letter to HC, April 2, 1940, Press file; that of the strawberry gallbladder from Finney, *A Surgeon's Life*, p. 302.

PAGE 695. Dr. Charlie's record as a member of the school board is reported in the newspapers and summarized in a typescript paper in the CHM files. For this later public health work, see the general references listed in the note to pages 477–80.

## CHAPTER 25. A LIVING MEMORIAL

The personal interviews, listed on pages 717–19, remain the principal source. Where letters in the WJM files have been used, the writers or receivers are not identified, because they are still living and their permission to quote has not been asked.

PAGE 697. The dedication of the carillon was reported in the *Rochester Post-Bulletin*, Sept. 17, 1928, and the *Proceedings of the Mayo Clinic*, 3:284–85 (Sept. 26, 1928). The building was not yet finished, but Dr. Charlie told the audience that "because of the necessity of using the new Clinic building as rapidly as the floors are completed there will be no formal opening, and this day of dedication must serve. The Clinic is declared open."

Wilder, *Mayo Clinic*, p. 59, tells of two patients who did not recognize the Clinic building, one of them, in 1938 or thereabouts, asking the way to the building where the "Mayo boys" had their offices.

PAGES 697–98. WJM, "The Work of Dr. Henry S. Plummer," *Proceedings of the Mayo Clinic*, 13:418 (July 6, 1938) ; Magath to HC.

PAGE 699. The two paragraphs of the quotation are from two papers: seventieth birthday remarks in the *Annals of Surgery*, 94:799–800 (Oct. 1931), reprinted in the *Proceedings of the Mayo Clinic*, 6:617–19 (Oct. 21, 1931), and "The Establishment of Mayo Foundation House and Its Purpose," *ibid.*, 13:553–54 (Aug. 31, 1938). The circumstances of Dr. Charlie's retirement are described in Mrs. C. H. Mayo to HC, and McIndoe, "Charles Horace Mayo," *British Medical Journal*, no. 4092: 1207–8 (June 10, 1939). When Dr. C. W. Mayo was asked to corroborate Dr. McIndoe's account, he answered, "He's nearly enough right."

For evaluations of the Mayos as surgeons see the articles cited in the note to page 711. About 1911, in conversation with August Bier of Berlin, "recognized head of surgery in Germany" at the time, Dr. Truman W. Brophy remarked that he considered Nicholas Senn the greatest of America's surgeons past or present. Bier disagreed. "In my opinion he was not the greatest surgeon America has produced."

"Who in your opinion was?" asked Brophy.

"Unquestionably William Mayo," answered Bier. (G. B. Eusterman, letter to WJM, Sept. 4, 1916, in the WJM files, reporting the story that was told him by Dr. Brophy.)

In "An Appreciation of the Mayos," printed in the *Yorkshire Post* on July 22, 1929, when the brothers were in England, Lord Moynihan of Leeds wrote, "They have shown a technical ability for surgical work of all kinds that is, I believe, unsurpassed by any surgeons in the world today. I have intimately known only one surgeon who in his day was a finer technical surgeon even than they." (Steward manuscript, p. 237.)

PAGE 700. The quotation from Dr. Will is from his remarks to the staff reported in the *Proceedings of the Mayo Clinic*, 3:284 (Sept. 26, 1928). The story of the trip to Manchester, including descriptions of the memorial window and reports of the various social and civic functions in the brothers' honor, is told in clippings from English papers in the WJM collection. "Tay Pay" O'Connor, the London journalist, in reporting the Pilgrim Society banquet, wrote of Dr. Charlie, "I could scarcely believe that one of the founders of this mighty revolution in the medical history of the world was the very quiet, rather small man at my side. . . . The chief suggestions of his face are benignity and modesty. He has no sense whatever of his own remarkable character and career." (Steward manuscript, pp. 385–86.)

PAGES 700–1. The story of Dr. Will's visit to the Tucson hospital is from the ROB notes on the WJM collection.

PAGE 701. WJM to HC is the source for Dr. Charlie's comment on the first report.

PAGES 701–2. The quotation is from WJM's remarks reported in the *Annals of Surgery*, 94:799–800 (Oct. 1931).

PAGE 702. The quotation is from WJM, "The Establishment of Mayo Foundation House and Its Purpose," *Proceedings of the Mayo Clinic*, 13:553–54 (Aug. 31, 1938). There is a typescript copy of Dr. Will's announcement to the staff on Nov. 21, 1932, in the WJM files.

PAGE 703. It took constant admonition to keep the ideals active. When the panic of 1929 and the depression of the early 1930's came along, there was little drop in registrations at the Clinic but a marked increase in the proportion of non-paying patients. The overhead was high, and to preserve the financial stability of the group Dr. Will as early as 1930 proposed a pro rata salary cut, the money saved to be kept in a separate fund as a guarantee of future salaries and operating expenses should conditions get worse. Time proved the wisdom of the step, but it was hard for the men to take at the time, and apparently some of them urged that instead fees be raised and more pressure be used to collect accounts. For on Aug. 1931 Dr. Will spoke to the staff about it, saying in part: "The common man is now retrenching, trying by frugal living to establish a new basis of living. The Clinic must in its business relations follow him in his retrenchment and scale down its charges. We must meet him halfway, and not by more severe methods of collection add to his already great distress. We must adjust the accounts, both past and present, to his ability to pay, and give him such time as is necessary for adjustments. We must send out, not collectors, but adjusters. We must not sacrifice the ideals of the Clinic because of temporary inconvenience to ourselves." (Typescript copy of the talk in the WJM files.)

PAGE 704. The elaborate ceremonies attending the Legion citation are reported fully in the Rochester papers, especially in the *Post-Bulletin*, Aug. 8, 1934. Rochester was disappointed that Mrs. Roosevelt could not come with her husband, but it made her acquaintance a few years later when her son was a patient at the Clinic. On that occasion Dr. Will, letter to Harvey Cushing, WJM files, said she was the most intelligent woman he had ever met.

PAGES 704–5. Guthrey to HC describes the long-distance calls, mostly from Franklin H. Martin, that supplemented the letters and telegrams in the WJM files urging Dr. Will to reconsider his decision.

There is discernible in Dr. Will's words and actions during the 1930's a note of uncertainty and bewilderment about social and political developments—a wavering between approval of theory and disapproval of practice in efforts for the social welfare of the common man. Perhaps the trouble was a conflict between the progressive ideals and ideas surviving from his youth under the influence of his "radical" father and the political conservatism of most of his associates and advisers. And perhaps this uncertainty about social trends was partly responsible for his determination to leave decisions in the hands of younger men.

PAGES 706–7. The literature of the controversy over group practice is abundant. Some major items in it are WJM, "The Right to Health," *North American Review*, 211:194–202 (Feb. 1920); Stuart McGuire, "The Modern Medical Clinic," *Virginia Medical Monthly*, 53:465–70 (Oct. 1926); P. E. Truesdale, "Group Practice," *Boston Medical and Surgical Journal*, 196:973–83 (June 16, 1927); Rufus C. Rorem, *Private Group Clinics* (publication No. 8 of the Committee on

# Bibliographical Notes

the Costs of Medical Care, Washington, D.C., 1931), and "Private Group Clinics: Where, How, and Whom They Serve," *Modern Hospital*, 37:134, 136, 138 (July 1931); "Private Group Practice," *Journal of the A.M.A.*, 100:1693–99, 1773–78 (May 27, June 3, 1933); "Group Practice," *ibid.*, 117:122–24 (July 12, 1941); William Gaver, "Group Medicine and the Doctors," *Scribner's Magazine*, 98:46–48 (July 1935); Hugh Cabot, *The Doctor's Bill* (Columbia University Press, 1935), *The Patient's Dilemma* (New York, 1940), and "Give the Patient a Break," *American Magazine*, 129 (no. 4):32–33, 101–4 (April 1940); James Rorty, "Attack on Group Medicine," *Nation*, 143:15–17 (July 4, 1936), and "Toward a Socialized Medicine," *ibid.*, 143:127–29 (Aug. 1, 1936).

The statement by Dr. Will is quoted from "The Medical Profession and the Public," *Journal of the A.M.A.*, 76:921–25 (April 2, 1921). The same idea is to be found in many of his and Dr. Charlie's later papers. They took every opportunity that offered for emphasizing the fact that the development of medicine had made imperative close cooperation between general practitioner and specialist and among specialists if the patient was to be given proper care. Their conviction was undoubtedly strengthened by such experiences as this: A woman came to the Clinic from the West Coast. She had been ailing for some time and had made the rounds of a dozen specialists, each of whom had treated her at length and in vain for his own brand of disease. But no one of them had thought to trouble with so simple a thing as urinalysis. The Clinic internist ordered it first thing and it showed the patient to be suffering from Bright's disease, now so far advanced that there was nothing to do but put the woman on the train so she could at least die among her family and friends. (Ford, who was present when the case was reported to Dr. Will, to HC.)

PAGE 707. The quotation on "the most amazing thing" about the Mayo Clinic is from McIndoe, "Charles Horace Mayo," *British Medical Journal*, no. 4092: 1207–8 (June 10, 1939). The elimination of the direct financial relationship between doctor and patient is one of the distinguishing and fundamental features of the Clinic setup. It is said of group practice in general and of the Mayo Clinic in particular that it has commercialized medical practice. The basis for that charge is hard to see. It would seem that removing the doctor's direct dependence on the fee of the patient before him would have nearly the opposite effect.

PAGES 708–9. For another matter Dr. Will considered important to the Clinic's existence—maintaining proper balance between individual initiative and regulations for the sake of efficiency—see the note to page 531.

PAGE 711. The list of these tributes is too long for complete inclusion here. Chief among them are those by Irving Abell in the *Bulletin of the American College of Surgeons*, 24:249, 251 (Sept. 1939); George Crile, *ibid.*, 24:155–56 (June 1939); T. E. Crewe in *Minnesota Medicine*, 22:558 (Aug. 1939); Harvey Cushing in *Science*, n.s. 90:225–26 (Sept. 8, 1939); Donald Guthrie in *Surg., Gynec. and Obst.*, 69:118–19 (July 1939); Owen H. Wangensteen, *ibid.*, 69:534–38 (Oct. 1939); James R. Learmonth in *Nature*, 144:274–75 (Aug. 12, 1939), and in the *British Medical Journal*, no. 4091:1159–60 (June 3, 1939); McIndoe, *ibid.*, no. 4092:1207–8 (June 10, 1939); Parker in the *Irish Journal of Medical Science*, series 6 (no. 164):614–17 (Aug. 1939); Thurston S. Welton in the *American Journal of Surgery*, 44:417–18 (Sept. 1939); Horace G. Wetherill in the *Western Journal of Surg., Gynec. and Obst.*, 47:558 (Sept. 1939); and unsigned articles in the *Journal of the A.M.A.*, 112:2342 (June 3, 1939), and 113:524–25 (Aug. 5, 1939); *Medical Journal of Australia*, July 29, 1939, pp. 185–86, and Aug. 19, 1939, pp. 299–301; *Journal-Lancet*, 59:408 (Sept. 1939).

PAGE 712. This eloquent statement is by Dr. Richard M. Hewitt, successor to Mrs. Mellish Wilson as director of the division of publications.

# Index

opposed, 269, 682; at St. Mary's, 514. *See also* Institute of Experimental Medicine

*Annals of Surgery,* 404

Antisepsis, beginnings, 193, 197; in America, 194, 207; in Europe, 194, 234, 235, 241; opposed, 195, 196, 234; distinguished from asepsis, 196n, 291; adopted by WJM, 235–37; influence of Gerster, 236; methods, 237, 257, 299; aid to surgical technique, 268, 307, 334; use by Halsted, 290. *See also* Asepsis, Listerism

A.P.A., *see* American Protective Association

Appendectomy, 305, 610; accepted, 227; mortality, 304; in chronic cases, 306; by Mayos, 352, 353, 454, 497

Appendicitis, identified, 227, 285, 466; treatment, 228, 304, 305; chronic, 306, 307; relation to stomach disorders, 316; diagnosis, 365. *See also* Perityphlitis

Archibald, Alexander, joins Mayo staff, 505

Argentina, 582

*Army and Navy Register,* 565

Asepsis, distinguished from antisepsis, 196n, 291; beginnings, 241; methods, 291, 299; adopted by Mayos, 299. *See also* Antisepsis

Association of American Physicians, 636

Association of Military Surgeons, 616

Atlee, John, gynecologist, 128; president of A.M.A., 202

Atlee, Washington L., gynecologist, 128, 141, 145, 202

Augustana Hospital (Chicago), 284, 518

Automobiles, 497; use by Mayos, 468–70

Autopsies, *see* Postmortems

Averill, Colonel John T., 84

Aviation and medical research, 637–39

Ayer, Otis, LeSueur physician, 58; malpractice suit, 60; in Sioux Outbreak, 70, 71, 75

Bacteriology, clinical, 363, 364, 513, 602; experimental, 570, 617, 619, 620

Baer, John Willis, 254, 579

Bailey, Frederick C., charter member of Nu Sigma Nu, 190

Balfour, Donald C., surgeon, 592; sketch, 508; marriage, 527; Clinic partner, 545, 546; trip to Mexico, 587

Balfour, Mrs. Donald C., 239, 527. *See also* Mayo, Carrie

Base Hospital No. *26,* history, 562

Basedow's disease, 338, 635

Bastianelli, Raffaele, physician to king of Italy, 488, 489

Beard, Richard O., Minneapolis physician, 400

Beck, Carl, Chicago surgeon, 408, 692; visits to Rochester, 409, 451, 469

Beckman, Emil H., surgeon, 502, 508, 521, 522, 527, 610, 611

Bell, Sir Charles, 10

Belle Plaine (Minn.), 59

Bellevue Hospital (New York), in *1845,* 14; in *1870,* 126; ambulance corps, 127

Berkman, Daisy, *see* Plummer, Mrs. Henry

Berkman, David, 140, 152, 243, 244; marriage, 142

Berkman, Mrs. David, 142, 155, 375, 529. *See also* Mayo, Gertrude

Berkman, Helen, laboratory assistant, 441; marriage, 527

Bernays, A. C., St. Louis surgeon, 421, 449

Bevan, Arthur D., surgeon, 411; World War service, 563

Bigelow, Henry J., Boston surgeon, 144

Billings, Frank, Chicago internist, 206, 282, 413, 541, 570, 606

Billings, John Shaw, planner of Johns Hopkins Hospital, 252, 290

Billroth, Theodor, German surgeon, 200, 294, 316, 336, 412

Binnie, J. Fairbairn, manual of surgery, 456; World War service, 563, 564

Biochemistry, 496, 683; research, 516; experimental, 532, 617, 619

Biometry, 655, 656

Biophysics, 617, 619, 621

Blackburn, M. H., Princeton (Ill.) surgeon, 450

Blake, Joseph, surgeon, appendectomy on CHM, 489

# Index

# Index

# Index

# Index

Iron mining, in Minnesota, 356
Isham, Ralph N., teacher at Chicago Medical College, 206

Jacobson, Walter H. A., author of surgery manual, 221
Jail fever, 15
Jammé, Anna C., head of St. Mary's nursing school, 499
Jaundice, 610
Johns Hopkins Hospital, charity aspect, 252; reputation, 287; Mayos' visits, 288–92; staff, 289, 414, 416, 421, 432; demonstration clinics, 290–92, 449, 460; anesthesia at, 428; nurses' school, 499
Johns Hopkins Medical School, 21, 198, 508; entrance requirements, 288; graduate system, 289, 540; research at, 290; teaching policy, 541
Johnson, Alexander C., railroad agent, 352
Johnson, John A., governor of Minnesota, 375, 487, 686; operations at Rochester, 437, 488; death, 489
Johnson, Mrs. John A., 488
Jones, Robert, orthopedist, 508
Judd, Edward Starr, surgeon, 391, 392, 489, 499, 501, 502, 508, 592, 596, 699; Mayo partner, 503, 545, 546; orthopedist, 509; marriage, 527; director of war training school, 568; death, 710
Judd, Mrs. Edward Starr, 527

Kahler, John, hotel man, 394, 437, 500, 501, 528, 596, 639
Kahler, Mrs. John, 639
Kahler Corporation, 596, 597, 599, 608
Kahler Hospitals School of Nursing, 596
Kahler Hotel, 599; built, 596; capacity, 597; tunnel to Clinic, 597; hospital section, 636
Kahler House (Rochester), 597; opening, 501; enlargement, 502; hospital facilities, 502, 528
Keen, William W., Philadelphia surgeon, 433, 465, 481, 518, 555
Kehr, Hans, German surgeon, 415, 481
Kellogg, Frank B., 164, 437
Kelly, Howard A., surgeon, 279, 289, 291, 301, 302, 422, 481

Kendall, Edward C., research chemist, 515, 532, 602, 619; isolates thyroxin, 516, 620, 633
Kidney disease, 372, 493. *See also* Urology
King George V, 682
Kinney, L. C., drug store proprietor, 37
Kirklin, Byrl R., radiologist, 605
Knee-joint infection, 331, 404, 405, 435
Knowlton, E. A., Rochester merchant, 501
Know-Nothing movement, 253
Koch, Robert, bacteriologist, 329
Kocher, Theodor, goiter surgeon, 336, 455, 493, 494, 634, 635
Ku Klux Klan, 253

Labat, Gaston, anesthesia expert, 614
Laboratory medicine, *see* Clinical pathology
Lafayette (Ind.), sketch, 15; cholera, 18, 27; economic conditions, 30
Lake Superior, 38, 39, 43, 44, 45
Lanc, Arbuthnot, orthopedist, 509
Lane, Franklin K., at Mayo Clinic, 577
Langenbeck, Bernhard von, performing of cholecystectomy, 309
LaPorte (Ind.), medical college, 16, 20
Laryngology, 612
Law, Arthur A., surgeon, 561
Lawler, John J., 165, 219
Leeds General Infirmary, 411, 414
Le Sueur (Minn.), 48, 52, 57, 64, 65; Baptist church, 61; site, 62; in Sioux Outbreak, 75
Le Sueur County, in Civil War, 68
*Le Sueur Courier*, 65; history, 61–64; politics, 62, 63
Leukemia, 389
Lincoln, Abraham, 68, 77, 78
Lister, Joseph, 143, 197; antiseptic surgery, 192–94. *See also* Listerism
Listerism, 127, 196, 207, 234, 235, 268, 299; development, 192–94. *See also* Antisepsis
Liston, Robert, surgeon, 192
Little, J. Warren, surgeon, 417
Little Crow, Sioux chief, 69
*Little Dorritt*, steamboat, 59
Liver, pathology, 619
Lockwood, A. L., surgeon, 575, 585, 612; World War service, 574; trip to Mexico, 586

28, 32; character, 29, 65, 113, 119, 150, 166, 470; teacher, 30, 147, 177; birth of children, 31, 56, 58, 89; study trips, 31, 126–28, 151, 172, 286, 290, 310; departure for Minnesota, 32, 34–38; Lake Superior trips, 39, 40–42, 44; census project, 40, 43, 44, 46, 47; in politics, 46, 52, 62, 63, 64, 90, 91, 95–107, 375; in Minnesota Valley, 47–78; homes, 48, 58, 89, 104, 151, 375, 529; farmer, 50, 168; medical practice, 50, 51, 65, 108, 111–18, 122, 208, 212–18; veterinarian, 52, 58; ferry operator, 52, 65; encounter with Indians, 56; removal to Le Sueur, 57; on steamboat, 58–60; witness in malpractice suits, 60, 123; newspaper publisher, 61–64; Civil War activities, 66–86; in Sioux Outbreak, 70–78; reputation, 86, 144–46, 340, 399; move to Rochester, 88; offices, 89, 135, 208, 237; civic interests, 89, 99, 101, 146, 395, 396, 470; addresses, 90, 103; interest in evolution, 92, 120, 168; ideals and opinions, 93, 132, 145, 177, 179, 279, 319, 345; attitude toward women, 102, 131; cases, 115–18, 136; drug business, 116; surgeon, 116, 117, 137–44, 212–15, 226, 230; society officerships, 121, 132, 134, 140, 232, 233; gynecologist, 124, 126, 129, 132, 142, 175, 214, 218, 219, 230, 301; interlude in St. Paul, 133–35; office hours, 135; first telephone, 135, 160; public health work, 146; birthday celebrations, 153, 376; views on medical education, 164, 183, 186, 222; licensed, 210; sponsor of WJM, 210, 219; demonstration clinics, 219, 347; attitude toward antisepsis, 234, 299; travels, 238, 375, 471; in tornado of *1883*, 243, 244; affiliation with St. Mary's, 246, 247, 248, 249, 253, 254; anesthetist, 252, 260; at seventy, 256; attitude toward exploratory surgery, 307; treatment of strangulated hernia, 312; withdrawal from practice, 359; leaves partnership, 380; death, 472; funeral, 473

Mayo, Mrs. William Worrall, 36, 57, 134, 153, 155, 164, 165, 166, 169, 173, 375, 409, 437; marriage, 25; character, 25, 55, 148–51, 471; housekeeping difficulties, 30, 55, 168; birth of children, 31, 56, 58, 89; millinery business, 31, 37, 45, 48; illnesses, 32, 56, 110; interest in natural science, 56, 167, 476; during the Sioux Outbreak, 75–77; doctor's assistant, 142, 148, 171; influence on children, 179; travels, 238; death, 473

Mayo brothers, 539, 544, 547, 552, 555, 594, 607, 611, 664, 697, 710; honorary degrees, 4, 410, 431, 438–40, 492, 582, 682, 685, 700; contribution to medicine, 4, 699; boyhood, 142, 159–63, 166; mutual devotion, 159, 169, 202, 300, 418, 671–73; early schooling, 161, 162, 164, 165; family chores, 165, 168; interest in reading, 166–68, 270, 694; medical apprenticeship, 170–72, 173, 174, 175–80; study trips, 203, 223, 225, 236, 241, 272–95, 452, 584, 681; progressiveness, 228, 270, 304, 459; writings, 231, 233, 340, 399, 400, 404, 405, 407, 414, 422, 426, 432, 434, 518, 683; activities in medical societies, 231–33, 296, 340, 399, 400, 402, 403–7, 409, 410, 412–27, 431–35, 491, 493, 518, 560, 561, 681, 683; office facilities, 237, 360, *see also* Mayo Clinic, buildings; surgical competence, 240, 256, 300, 334, 338, 347, 456; in tornado of *1883*, 242, 243; affiliation with St. Mary's Hospital, 249, 253, 254, 257, 258, 260, 261, 262, 264, 265, 266, 267, 268, 298, 341, 369, 498, 502, 598; use of anesthesia, 259, 362, 428, 429, 430, 431; conservatism, 292, 425, 529; development of surgical specialization, 297, 346, 505, 532, 534; work at state insane hospitals, 298; adoption of antisepsis, 299; surgical team, 299; division of labor, 300, 370, 526, 667; appendectomies, 305, 307; gallbladder surgery, 307–11, 422, 432; spread of reputation, 307, 339–58, 399–421, 407–9, 431–40, 481, 493, 497, 585, 685; hernia surgery, 312, 313; stomach surgery, 314–26; development of diagnosis, 318–23, 364,

# Index

"Milk sickness," 28

Millard, Perry H., 145, 232, 233; support of Listerism, 234

Millet, Melvin C., 426, 441, 513; sketch, 371; study of urinary disease, 372, 393, 427; partnership with Mayos, 503; death, 503

Milligan, Francis, army surgeon, 67

Minneapolis, 35, 561; growth, 356. *See also* Twin Cities

Minnehaha Falls, 35

Minnesota, health conditions, 33, 49; in *1854*, 35, 36; north shore, 38, 43, 44, 45; railroads, 38, 45, 46, 217, 348, 357; county organization, 40, 43; politics, 45, 62, 96–98, 102, 105–7; panic of *1857*, 54; Civil War, 66–68, 78–86; medical licenses, 177, 209, 239, 539; early medical schools, 183; hospitals in *1883*, 247; in *1900*, 356

*Minnesota*, river boat, 692

Minnesota Academy of Medicine, 399, 401

Minnesota legislature, WWM in, 105–7; Foundation struggle, 546, 552, 554, 555

Minnesota River, navigation, 49, 59, 64; floods, 57

Minnesota State Board of Health, 133, 146, 339, 442

Minnesota State Medical Society, 183, 232, 399, 433, 438, 691; organized, 121; action against quackery, 122; meetings, 131, 132, 136, 228, 231, 271, 403, 416; sponsor of board of health, 133; committee on gynecology, 140; investigation of fee-splitting, 346

Minnesota State Nurses Association, 498

Minnesota Valley, Mayos in, 47–78; described, 49; health conditions, 51; economic conditions, 53, 54; title defined, 64; during Sioux Outbreak, 70–77

Minnesota Valley Medical Society, 84, 178; merged with Southern Minnesota Medical Society, 341

Mississippi River, steamboating, 34

Mixter, Samuel, Boston surgeon, 292, 293; World War service, 563

Moes, Josephine, *see* Mother Alfred

Monk, George, Boston surgeon, 457

Montes, Beatriz, 588; Clinic secretary and librarian, 589

Moore, James E., Minneapolis surgeon, 271, 330, 358, 423, 428, 434, 544

More, Charles W., classmate of CHM, 204

Morgan, James, classmate of CHM, 204

Morton, Edward C., classmate of CHM, 204

Mosse, F. R., Rochester physician, 140, 214

Mother Alfred, 244, 245, 252, 253, 255, 258; hospital plan, 246, 248, 249, 250; retirement, 255

Mother Matilda, 255, 256

Mt. Sinai Hospital (New York), 236, 576

Moynihan, Berkeley, English surgeon, 175, 326, 414, 435, 448, 457, 574, 611

Mumford, James, Boston surgeon, 296, 448

Munro, John C., Boston surgeon, 410, 434, 435

Murphy, John B., Chicago surgeon, 282, 283, 285, 287, 291, 307, 321, 329, 400, 410, 411, 413, 414, 422, 433, 448, 457, 481, 560; attitude on fee-splitting, 346. *See also* Murphy button

Murphy, Mrs. John B., 286, 560

Murphy, John H., St. Paul surgeon, 121, 140, 145

Murphy button, 285, 286, 287, 295, 310, 317, 323, 408, 433

Mussey, Robert D., member of Mayo staff, 505

Myrick, Andrew J., Indian trader, 69, 70

Myxedema, 336, 337, 493, 496

Nativism, 253, 264

Nelson, Knute, Minnesota governor, 359

Nelson, Ole, 116, 228

Neurasthenia, 322, 386

Neurology, 506

Neurosurgery, 269, 274, 287, 332, 610, 639, 640; early, 331, 350

Neville, Jay, Mayo caretaker, 168, 169, 178, 181, 259, 383, 498, 520, 524, 525

New, Gordon B., member of Mayo

815

# Index

# Index

St. Mary's Hospital (Rochester), 450, 475, 514, 533, 540, 635, 710; planned, 246, 249; relations with Mayos, 249, 253, 254, 257, 258, 260, 261, 262, 264, 265, 266, 267, 268, 298, 341, 369, 498, 502, 598; built, 250–52; admission policy, 252, 253, 264; nursing sisters, 252, 255, 256, 257, 258, 259, 260, 263, 369; attitude of community, 253, 254, 263, 265, 267; supervisors, 255; furnishings, 257, 261, 368; operating rooms, 257, 262, 392, 453, 528; location and communication problems, 258, 259, 262, 393, 395; mortality record, 260, 261, 264; number of patients, 261, 262, 264, 370, 481, 595; finances, 261, 263; elevator, 262; surgical cases, 297, 301, 305, 310, 323, 324, 332, 335, 350, 351, 353, 387, 500; antisepsis at, 299; enlarged, 368, 371, 392, 441, 502, 528, 569, 598, 607, 608; nursing school, 369, 498, 568; staff, 370, 371, 373, 521, 569; laboratories, 371, 372, 441, 513, 602, 608, 624; autopsies, 444; progressiveness, 459; isolation unit, 569. See also Demonstration clinics, Sisters of St. Francis

St. Mary's Park (Rochester), 397, 697

St. Paul, 59, 693; in 1854, 35, 36, 37, 38; capital controversy, 53; hospitals, 247. See also Twin Cities

St. Paul Civic and Commerce Association, 550

St. Paul Medical College, 183

*St. Paul Pioneer Press,* 550

St. Peter, 48, 49, 52, 59, 64; proposed state capital, 53; county seat, 54; in Sioux Outbreak, 70; draft board session, 81, 82, 84

St. Peter Company, 53, 54

St. Peter State Hospital, 298

Salford (England), 10

Samaritan Hospital (Montreal), 460

Sampson, G., case, 138

Sands, Henry B., New York surgeon, 224, 225, 226, 274

Sanford, Arthur H., pathologist, 513, 522, 528, 532, 602, 621

Sanford-Sheard photolometer, 621

Santiago (Chile) dental school, 583, 584

Scandinavia, medical center, 234

Scarlet fever, 28, 51, 477

Schede, Max, German surgeon, 294, 315, 333, 435

Scrofula, 328, 329

Semmelweis, Ignaz P., Hungarian obstetrician, 195

Senn, Nicholas, surgeon, 203, 282, 283, 286, 291, 292, 399, 422

Serology, 513, 602

Sewall, Henry, physiologist, 200

Sheard, Charles, physicist, 621, 622, 630, 641

Shelden, Walter D., diagnostician, 504, 506

Ship fever, 15

Shock, surgical, 291, 619

Sibley, Henry H., 46, 77

Sigma Xi, 683

Siler, Col. Joseph F., U. S. Medical Corps, 574

Sims, James M., Alabama physician, 125

Sioux Indians, 36, 48. See also Sioux Outbreak

Sioux Outbreak, 68–78; causes, 69; first raids, 69; New Ulm battle, 72; hanging of condemned Indians, 77

Sister Constantine, 252

Sister Fabian, 256, 499

Sister Fidelia, 252

Sister Hyacinth, 252, 255, 263

Sister Joseph, 246, 251, 255, 256, 261, 459, 473, 499; assistant to WJM, 370, 373, 460; retirement, 508; sketch, 710

Sister Sienna, 252

Sisters of St. Benedict (Bismarck, N. D.), 248

Sisters of St. Francis, 470, 590; in tornado of 1883, 243, 244; history, 245, 246, 263, 369; hospital, 249, 250, 252, 253, 254, 255, 264, 266, 267, 298, 368, 392, 452, 569, 596, 598. See also St. Mary's Hospital

Sisters of the Holy Cross, 245

Sister Sylvester, 256

Skin-grafting, 334

Slavery question, 63

Smallpox, 51, 478

Smith, Andrew, A.M.A. vice-president, 454

Smithies, Frank, pathologist, 513

# Index